Systems Behaviour
Third Edition

Edited by **Open Systems G**

Harper and Row, Publishers
in association with
The Open University Press

Harper & Row, Publishers
London

Cambridge
Hagerstown
Philadelphia
New York

San Francisco
Mexico City
Sao Paulo
Sydney

Acknowledgements

I would like to thank those inside the Open University Systems Group and outside who have made valuable contributions to the contents of this and earlier editions. To name them all would be impossible. However, I must acknowledge the contribution made by John Beishon who was joint editor of the first two editions and founder of the Open University Systems Group, and without whom this and many other things would never have happened. In compiling this edition I have had the invaluable assistance of our course manager Rita Daggett who has also compiled both glossaries. Finally Harper and Row in the form of Michael Forster and Marianne Lagrange have been their normal efficient selves.

Geoff Peters

This selection and editorial matter copyright © 1972, and 1976, 1981 The Open University

First published 1972
2nd edition 1976
3rd edition 1981

British Library Cataloguing in Publication Data
Systems behaviour. – 3rd ed.
  1. Systems theory – Addresses, essays, lectures
  I. Open Systems Group
003'.08   Q295

ISBN 0-06-318211-4
ISBN 0-06-318212-2 Pbk

Printed and bound in Great Britain
at The Pitman Press, Bath

Preface to the First Edition

This book is a collection of papers and articles on systems. It arose out of the development of a course at the Open University on systems behaviour. In common with most Open University courses, the Systems Behaviour course adopts a multidisciplinary and interdisciplinary approach and it covers a range of topics not normally dealt with in a conventional university course. One of the problems in developing new courses is that suitable reference and back-up material is difficult to find and is usually spread across a wide variety of sources. This is particularly true of new areas such as systems where there are few, if any, "standard" texts and most of the books available cover specific subject or technique areas. The Systems Behaviour course does not, for example, have any text books set as "required reading", for the reason that no book dealing with more than a few parts of the course can be found. So one of our main reasons for producing a book of readings is to gather together material on systems which is scattered far and wide in the literature, often in journal articles or reports which are difficult to obtain.

Collections of readings suffer from a number of disadvantages: they are uneven in style and level, gaps in arguments and in the development of ideas occur, the coverage of a field is sometimes very patchy, and it is always possible to criticize the selection of material on one ground or another. Editors make valiant attempts to overcome these problems by providing linking passages and by careful editing where possible, but the results are not always satisfactory. However, one of the great advantages of readings from our point of view is that students can consult original sources and can compare and evaluate the different ideas and concepts presented. This is an essential part of our systems courses.

It is worth pointing out, however, that the final choice of articles is not always what one would like. Material which would logically appear at a certain point is sometimes left out because it is readily available elsewhere, or because it would make the book unduly long, or more simply because permission to reprint it is not forthcoming. We have selected articles which seem to us to be of general interest as well as of direct relevance to the Systems Behaviour course, and we have inserted recommendations for other reading at appropriate places in the linking texts between sections.

A final point – the articles we have selected supply essential background reading for students taking the Systems Behaviour course, hence the title of this reader. The articles do not, however, deal exclusively with systems behaviour but cover a wider field of systems topics.

The Open University

John Beishon
Geoff Peters

Preface to the Third Edition

In compiling this selection of articles, we have tried to bring together our experience of the earlier editions, the views and needs expressed by the many academics in other institutions who have adopted this book, and our own needs for a reader to match a new and thoroughly revised course on systems behaviour.

The resulting compromise is a reorganized collection which, we hope, retains and builds on the strengths of the earlier editions. It is thus not simply a book about systems behaviour, it is more than that. It is intended to be the beginnings of a systems library, incorporating a range of views, references and cross-references, which allow the reader to go on to explore further aspects of the subject.

Perhaps the most compelling strand in our thinking in planning this revision has been the need to design a book which matched the requirements specified by the Systems Behaviour course team to those of readers and users outside the Open University. In this context it is necessary to point out that the Open Systems Group has come to view the Systems Behaviour course as a first systems course. This course deliberately sets out to explore the application of systems concepts to a range of different fields, and in this way raises to a new prominence the debate about the subjectivity of a systems view. This debate about the role of the interpreter of a system is mirrored in the readings in this edition.

It is this appreciation of the importance of values in determining what system an observer or interpreter perceives, and the appreciation that so-called "hard" systems cannot be effectively studied in isolation from the "soft" human systems through which they are designed and controlled, which characterizes the contribution to the systems approach by the Open Systems Group. It is this change in emphasis which distinguishes the present edition from its predecessors, and of itself marks out some of the ground covered by the British Systems Movement over the last decade.

The Open University Systems Group

Victor Bignell
Margaret Blunden
Sheila Cameron
Ruth Carter
Peter Checkland (visiting professor)
Gordon Dyer
Rob Forrester-Paton
John Hamwee
John Martin
William Mayon-White
Richard Morris
John Naughton
Geoff Peters
Roger Spear
Joyce Tait
Alan Thomas
Peter Walters
Tony Wright

Research and course support staff
Clive Agnew
Suzanne Brown
Chris Cornforth
Rita Daggett
Liz Grier
Julie Joyce
Christina Lay
Gary Mantle
June McGowan
Michel Mouthon
Doreen Pendlebury
Viv Risby
Sue Snelling
Robin Stenham
Tunja Stone
Jenny Thornley
Claire Willemstyn

The Open University Systems Courses

The Systems Group have produced six half-credit systems courses, each of which entails sixteen weeks' study totalling about 160–200 hours of study time. As well as comprehensive course texts and set books like this, the courses have radio and television programmes as integral parts of the teaching material, and two of them have home kits for experiments and practical activities, all of which students use and study at home. Students on all but the food course attend a one-week residential summer school and two of the courses involve computing.

Systems Behaviour (T241)

This is a second-level course designed as an introduction to the concept of "system" and its associated ideas, and their use in understanding entities in the "real world". The course is directed at students from many backgrounds which might include science, technology and the social sciences, and approximates to a second-year undergraduate course at a British university. There are six major case studies in the course, involving the study of correspondence text together with audio cassettes, television programmes and a limited range of "user-friendly" computer exercises and home experiments.

Throughout the course there is an emphasis, not on "problem solving" but on understanding and describing the behaviour of systems. This is developed progressively through the case studies which cover aspects of:

Air traffic control
Industrial social systems
Planning systems
Telecommunications
An ecological system
Physiological systems.

These case studies also allow the introduction of a limited range of techniques for data collection, statistical analysis and simulation modelling.

Systems Management (T242)

This is also a second-level course which concentrates on the organization as a system. It examines how such systems come to behave as they do and it draws on a number of case studies to illustrate its points. The course looks at the conventional management divisions of operations, man-management and socioeconomic aspects from a systems viewpoint, studying the goal setting and goal conflicts, information and decision making, and the overall behaviour of these. It then integrates these views into systems views of organizations and their behaviours. The course has eleven radio and TV programmes which develop case studies on the organizational aspects of such topics as British Rail's operations, kidney machines, blood analysis, coal mining and common ownership firms.

In 1980 this course was replaced by the course entitled *Systems Organisation*. The course materials are, however, still available.

Systems Organization: The Management of Complexity (T243)

This second-level course was written primarily for people with a technical (or professional) background who are moving into more administrative or managerial jobs. Apart from discussing important organizational practices (both "in principle" and in terms of sometimes unintended effects), the course is an introduction to systems ideas; it emphasizes the fact that organizational problems do not respect the boundaries of academic disciplines, and that a wider, more "holistic" (but practical) understanding of organizations and their difficulties requires the ability to adopt different frameworks and move between different levels of analysis. To this end the course is explicitly structured in terms of subsystem, organizational and multi-organizational levels; and the principle frameworks taught are associated with the recurrent themes of control, change and conflict. Apart from course units the teaching material includes TV programmes, audio cassettes, case studies, activities and also a range of optional exercises and discussion topics suitable for use by groups of students taking the course.

Food Production Systems (T273)

This is a second-level course which can be regarded as a case study in the application of a systems approach to a major area of international concern, namely, the provision of food for the world's population. This is not merely a technical problem of increasing agricultural production, but involves an understanding of the economics of agriculture, the technology and economics of food processing and the social and political factors which influence matters of production and consumption. The first half of the course concentrates on the science of crop and animal production, crop protection, food processing and human nutrition, and looks at the ways in which the efficiency of the human food chains can be increased. The second half of the course concentrates more on the economic, social and political factors which affect decisions about food production methods, and contrasts the experience of various countries. Television and radio are used to illustrate and explore some of the areas of controversy in the course, such as the use of novel proteins and different strategies for rural development.

Systems Modelling (T341)

This is a third-level course which, as the title implies, deals with the modelling of systems. The aim is to break down the mystique that surrounds the use of quantitative models and computer methods in the making of major decisions.

The course concentrates on the problems of formulating models of complex systems and of interpreting the results they give. It draws on a range of case studies to illustrate the use of linear models and simulation modelling. Two units deal with modelling community decisions and large-scale economic modelling (including world modelling).

Systems Performance: Human Factors and Systems Failures (TD342)

This is also a third-level course and it deals comprehensively with analyses of the performance of systems, concentrating particularly on the human element in systems and the problems of failures. It develops techniques for the analysis of failures such as failure modes and effects analysis and it critically deals with a wide range of systems failures. These cover catastrophic failures such as the Aberfan tip disaster, the Summerland fire and the Hixon level-crossing train smash; and organizational studies in the field of science policy, mental health provisions and a major case study of the Bay Area Rapid Transit system in California. There are sixteen TV programmes and four radio cassettes which deal with those and other case studies, including earthquakes and air crashes, in depth. The course also studies concepts of reliability and safety in relation to the design of safe and effective systems. A unique home kit included with the course illustrates the range of problems which can arise in systems and shows how many of them can be avoided.

In 1984 it is hoped to replace both the Systems Modelling and Systems Performance courses by a full credit course on how to conduct systemic analyses of complex situations.

Contents

Difficult but worth reading. (e.g. definitions).

Introduction

Systems and systems behaviour

The concepts of systems have slowly emerged in the present century to assume a central importance in the thinking and approach of many scientists and technologists. The ideas are now having an increasing impact on the approach of social and political scientists and economists. In the slow development of knowledge about the physical and biological world the most significant advances have generally come from painstaking, detailed study and analysis of ever smaller areas of knowledge and application. The natural philosophy of earlier scientists gradually developed into the major natural sciences, physics, chemistry and biology; these in turn have been increasingly subdivided into subjects such as nuclear physics, polymer chemistry, molecular biology, and so on. By the middle of the twentieth century this subdivision process had chopped reality and the phenomena of the real world into hundreds of individual subjects and areas of professional expertise. Knowledge was compartmentalized and departmentalized into small and seemingly more manageable "chunks".

The success of analytical techniques, and in particular structural analysis, tended to concentrate attention on static and structural properties, and some writers have seen this as a reflection of the desire of people to live in well-ordered, static, social and political environments. Victorians might have fitted this picture but not our contemporaries. At least two groups found this approach both limiting and unhelpful: the mechanical, and later the electrical engineer who wanted to build and run mechanisms and devices which *worked*, and the psychologist or ethologist who was interested less in the anatomy of the human or animal system than in the *behaviour* of the complete organism. The full history of the emergence and effects of the systems thinking "revolution" has yet to be written although some of the ground has been covered ably by one of the pioneers in the field, L. von Bertalanffy* and, more recently, by Peter Checkland.‡

* See Article 4.
‡ See Article 2.

The impetus towards systems thinking and the systems approach has come partly from a recognition (some would say a belated recognition) of the complexity of behaviour which arises in both natural and man-made systems, and partly from the need to gain control over the more threatening outcomes of their behaviour. So one powerful stimulus to adopt a systems approach arises from our attempts to predict and control the *behaviour* of systems instead of passively suffering from, or just reacting to, the often mysterious changes which occur in the surrounding physical, biological, social, economic and political climates. Attempts to exercise control over systems, whether human or economic, have not been notably successful and, for example, there are real fears being expressed that control is no longer even possible over some of the ecosystems which we have constructed or interfered with.

Problems which we consider as system problems are intractable since we know so little about systems, about systems analysis, about control over systems behaviour or about system design. Even identifying the system we are trying to deal with by drawing its boundaries can present formidable difficulties. Most scientific disciplines have a large body of facts and knowledge to draw on which has been accumulated over years of testing and experimenting. Theories can be tested against this body of knowledge and gaps identified. When it comes to the behaviour of systems we have surprisingly little in the way of studies or documented experience. The formal structure of a system is often known but its behaviour is another matter. It is unfortunate that we often have to wait for a system to fail before its possible behaviours are revealed and there are many vested interests engaged in seeing that full records of what happened are not readily available! There are other difficulties, of course; system malfunctioning often occurs suddenly and catastrophically and it is unreasonable to expect people to start making detailed observations when all is falling about their ears. This is one reason why black box flight recorders are used on aircraft, so that a disaster can be analyzed in detail after the event. The cost, a relatively small one, is that thousands of perfectly normal operations are recorded.

Systems thinking and the systems approach are now growth areas. Systems ideas appear in different guises in cybernetics, systems engineering, general system theory, operations research, systems analysis, computer systems, and also in fields like geography, planning, accountancy, social work and psychology. New jargon abounds – open and closed systems, human activity systems, appreciative systems; the ideas are new and exciting and innovators rush to apply them to different problem areas. There must be many a bewildered manager, administrator or scientist gazing at the brand-new, shiny, systems approach and wondering quite what hit him. Yet a systems approach is essential if we are to have any hope of coping with the complexity of modern life with its multinational organizations, space modules, international monetary policies, high-speed transport systems, and so on.

This book of readings contains twenty different articles or extracts, all concerned with systems. They have been chosen to illustrate something of the systems approach itself and the way it can be applied to different subjects or activities. The articles are grouped into a number of sections to give some organization to the book, but it is a feature of system design that it is always difficult to bring the components of a system into a relationship which is useful and yet can serve a number of different purposes. In a sense this book is a multipurpose system. People will read separate articles for one purpose, a combination of articles for another, and some will want to read progressively through the book. An order of presentation which might suit a social science student might be inappropriate for a biology student, so our order is only one arrangement designed to serve one, fairly general, purpose. One of the messages of the systems approach is that very simple systems can nevertheless show remarkable complexity of behaviours. Our twenty articles could be arranged in twenty different ways, which is about 2.4×10^{18} ways! Enough for a different order for every person on Earth with a good few left over, and this of course implies that they read each article only once!

Perhaps the book should have been produced in loose-leaf form so that each reader could assemble, and reassemble, the articles into any desired order, and also reject or add material to suit individual need.

In this edition we have strengthened the basic systems introductory material and concentrated a little less on the technical work in any one specific area. The result is a new structure which is as follows:

Section I
Broad systems material describing the history and content of systems thinking and its general relationship to science and social science.

Section II
On the relevance of systems concepts and the methods of systems engineering applied to human factors and engineering.

Section III
On social and sociotechnical systems.

Section IV
On the development and application of systems ideas in biological and ecological contexts.

Section V
On systems in geography, planning and political science.

Section VI
On the application of systems thinking in large-scale or complex contexts and the implications of such applications.

We have provided linking passages where appropriate and references to other books or papers which could usefully be read at certain points or which complement the existing material. Since the articles cover such a wide range of scientific and organizational matters we have provided a technical glossary to assist people who are not familiar with all the different areas.

It is worth emphasizing two further points. This collection of articles reveals the way in which different people coming from different backgrounds and different base disciplines have interpreted and attempted to apply systems ideas. Not surprisingly there are often differences in the interpretation of the concepts or contradictory applications of the ideas. Sometimes these are unimportant and arise from different usage of terms. On other occasions, however, the differences are more fundamental and reveal misunderstandings of the nature of basic ideas or deficiencies in the basic concepts themselves, which limit their general application. The application of the ideas of open and closed systems in the organizational field is an example of an area where many kinds of confusion can arise. Reference to Bertalanffy (Article 4) reveals that the distinction is a fundamental one based on thermodynamical considerations. An organization could *never* have existed as a closed system; they have always been open systems. But the *idea* of closed and open systems encouraged sociologists to *think* of organizations, and to treat them, as open systems which altered the way they analyzed organizational behaviour. One valuable function of this book is to help students make contrasts amongst different usages and to try to distil the common or core concept. The presentation of original material also enables students to realize the extent to which common systems ideas crop up in different guises and under different names in the various discipline areas covered.

A second point which arises from the first one, is that the language used in some fields is very difficult to understand by people from different backgrounds. The language of the sociologists, for example, as can be seen in the article by Buckley (Article 10), is particularly specialized and we have found that it presents serious difficulties to people with a technological or scientific background. Nevertheless it is important that students are encouraged to grapple with these different presentations because they will, we hope, want to extend their reading on systems topics beyond the range of this book, and they will then have to consult articles and books from the full range of disciplines as systems ideas spread and are incorporated into different theoretical and practical approaches.

At the end of the book is a glossary of technical terms which Rita Daggett has compiled. Clearly, it cannot be a complete dictionary but, taken together with the systems glossary at the beginning of Section I, it should counteract some of the jargon.

One final point: this book has been produced in connection with an Open University course on systems, but it does not in any sense represent either the views adopted in that course or by the Systems Group at the university. The book is an attempt to bring together the minimal library that a student should have available in studying courses in systems which cover a wide range of applications in the hard and soft systems areas. So, just as any good library should, the book reflects a broad range of approaches and attitudes to systems, and readers must be prepared to use their own critical judgement in assessing the material.

Section I

Introduction

These first four articles indicate the basic features, history and development of systems ideas and systems thinking. In the previous two editions it had always been our intention to include "something by Sir Geoffrey Vickers" but we never quite found the right piece. Because he is such a prolific writer one article could never do justice to the impact he has made on the systems movement. In this edition we have settled for an article which sets the tone for systems thinking as we view it, the emphasis being on what is at the heart of the systems movement.

The diversity of interest reflected by those involved in the development of the subject of systems must inevitably mean that the ideas and concepts which they all share are few. The remaining three articles in this section all undertake the task of specifying systems as they see it and its relationship to science and/or social science.

Peter Checkland's article, which is abstracted from his excellent book *Systems Theory and Systems Practice*, is a most thorough exploration of the relationship between science, social science and systems. The article spells out the need for a systems approach as a complement to that of science, and shows the basis for current systems activity.

Kast and Rosenzweig present their own view of systems and its application to the social sciences, particularly the world of organizations. They give a broad general introduction to a number of basic systems concepts, such as open and closed systems, holism and hierarchy, and show how the systems approach can be applied to organizations. However, the claims which are made for General Systems Theory (GST) – that it has provided a basis for the integration of scientific knowledge across a broad spectrum – are highly controversial. A critical view of GST is given in the preceding article, *Science and the systems movement*, by P. B. Checkland. It is also important to make clear that the relevance of a systems approach in the social sciences extends well beyond functionalism.

The next article, by Ludwig von Bertalanffy, is a review of general systems theory conducted by one of its pioneers. The motives of the GST wing of the systems movement are enumerated in a way which makes clear the distinction from the applied soft-systems wing which Checkland eventually identifies. Taken together, the articles by Checkland and von Bertalanffy cover much of the core of systems history. Neither of these articles is easy reading; they are both written by insiders who are aware of the dangers of brevity and unwarranted generalization. Probably more than any other articles it is these two which we would expect new readers to refer to and reread when more familiar with the subject area.

In any new and growing subject area problems of terminology and definition often predominate in the early stages of development, and much time may be taken up in what, with hindsight, may turn out to be sterile or trivial debates on the meaning or status of concepts and terms. The establishment of an agreed vocabulary is, however, an essential step if effective communication is to be possible. Systems as a subject has been particularly prone to controversy and confusion about the meaning of its words. The emergence of systems thinking in various forms at different centres and arising from different base disciplines has been one of the main causes for the proliferation of terms, and this has hindered the setting up of an agreed vocabulary. People starting from engineering, sociology or geography backgrounds are bound to draw on different terminology. The particular phenomenon or process being discussed may turn out to be a common, systems-based one but this may be obscured by these differences. Other problems arise when the terms from one discipline are uncritically transferred to another and applied inappropriately.

One of the most difficult problems for the newcomer to systems ideas is in understanding what systems thinking and the systems approach are actually all about. It is worth first making a distinction between being *systematic* and being *systemic*. The former is used to describe the use of a plan or an explicit method or procedure. It can be a useful way of achieving results efficiently in a wide range of activities. *Systemic*, however, is rather different. It is a term which has been coined to refer to the activity of using systems ideas, especially in tackling problems. It can be defined strictly as "pertaining to system" but it is generally used to refer to the process or activity of treating things as systems or from a systems viewpoint. This, loosely speaking, means looking at situations, topics, problems, etc., as a complex of interacting parts which can be divided into specific systems and within these, subsystems, and if necessary into sub-subsystems, and so on. Identification of these various systems is followed by an examination of the relationships among them, including the flows of influences, materials and energy and the routes these take among and within the systems involved. There is much more to it than this of course, as will become clear as readers work through the articles in this book, but this is the basic starting point involved in systems thinking. It is important to emphasize that this process of identifying systems is not (entirely) an objective process since the purposes and interests of the person doing the identification will enter into the choice and identification of the systems concerned.

The idea of a (or the) systems approach is a development of the use of systems thinking: a series of steps or guidelines are followed which assist with this conceptualization of things as systems and in identifying their properties and behaviours. At present, there is no single, all-embracing systems approach which is applicable to all classes and types of systems thinking. Research workers have developed individual versions for specific purposes and then extended their range where possible. Although there are several forms of systems approach they have much in common. In their simplest form, systems approaches consist of lists of questions which the would-be systems thinker can follow and apply to the system concerned. In their more sophisticated forms, the approaches embody more structuring and include iterative routes allowing more penetration and extension of the thinking. They may also include systems design or redesign sections.

System

After the idea of systems thinking and the more formalized concept of a systems approach, the question of what is a *system* arises; in spite of the widespread use of the term there is as yet no generally agreed definition. An extensive analysis of the word has been carried out by Nehemiah Jordan in his article "Some thinking about 'system' " in his book *Themes in Speculative Psychology* (Tavistock, 1970) which revealed a very confused state of affairs. A major cause of difficulty is due to a distinction between a system

as it exists "objectively" out there in the real world, for example, the solar system, and the idea of the system in a person's mind, for example, a seventeenth-century astronomer's concept of the solar system. The point is perhaps clearer if we compare the seventeenth-century astronomer's view with that of a present-day astronomer. The solar system has not changed essentially over the last few hundred years but the two astronomers had different systems in mind. Clearly the two ideas had much in common but they were not the same.

One of the more dangerous consequences of the scientific approach is a tendency to encourage people to think that their perceptions of reality are real and that there is indeed an objective reality "out there". We are not denying objectivity or reality but drawing attention to the subjective aspect of our perceptions of reality. A large number of objects and processes in the real world are so similarly perceived or experienced that there is no disagreement about their objective existence. But there are many other things in which subjective aspects are more important and which give rise to confusion. Systems concepts are particularly prone to these confusions because they tend to have strong objective and subjective parts; but regrettably the subjective aspects are often unrecognized.

Most writers who have attempted to define "system" have ignored this subjective element, or at least not explicitly recognized it. A widely quoted definition of "system", for example, is:

A set of objects together with relationships between the objects and between their attributes connected or related to each other and to their environment in such a manner as to form an entirety or whole.

We have used a definition developed in our courses which has four parts:

A system is an assembly of parts where:

1 The parts or components are connected together in an organized way.
2 The parts or components are affected by being in the system (and are changed by leaving it).
3 The assembly does something.
4 The assembly has been identified by a person as being of special interest.

This definition has advantages and disadvantages. It does exclude some things, by emphasizing the behavioural aspect. It does distinguish between an assembly and a system and it explicitly includes the subjective aspect which we regard as particularly important. Although the definition is not rigorous, we have found that it is helpful in drawing attention to the important features of systems thinking for newcomers to the subject. The definition helps us to check that what we have is a system rather than just an unorganized collection.

In the glossary which starts this section we have tried to steer a path between the precise nature of a rigorous definition and the greater explanatory value that can sometimes be derived from a looser or, in some cases, an alternative form. The words in the glossary are all mentioned several times in the articles and, where appropriate, reference to the text is given. There is also a glossary of technical terms at the end of the book and an index in which all the systems words reappear.

When compiling a list of terms there is inevitably a conflict between the apparent logical order implied by the conceptual relationship which exists amongst them and the need for quick and easy reference. We have plumped for an alphabetical listing but there is one area where this choice does not seem appropriate.

Currently there is a set of words like *aim, goal, objective* and *ideal* which are used quite differently by different authors. The easiest way to consider these terms is to think of them all as a *preferred outcome in a particular situation.* The distinctions which authors try to achieve are between outcomes which are actually achievable and those which are not, and between short-term, immediate, complete achievement and longer-term, perhaps limited, achievement. Unfortunately, because some of these words are used interchangeably in everyday conversation they have been defined differently by authors. For example, goal is taken to mean *a specified outcome which can be achieved in a specified time* in one place, which contrasts with the Report of the (United States) President's Commission on National Goals which starts:

The paramount goal of the United States was set long ago. It is to guard the rights of the individual, to ensure his development, and to enlarge his opportunity.

It is perhaps easiest to consider a *hierarchy of objectives* which range from the long-term distant intentions down to the short-term, clearly achievable, and by implication, checkable tasks.

Associated reading

There are many general introductions to system concepts and most books with the term "systems" in the title include an opening section dealing with broadly similar ground.

Peter Checkland's *Systems Thinking, Systems Practice* (Wiley, 1981) is a thorough overview of the area, particularly of the British developments in soft systems.

A good straightforward coverage is given by C. W. Churchman in *The Systems Approach* (Dell Publishing Co, 1968). Another useful general introduction is by Jenkins and Youle, *Systems Engineering: A unifying approach in industry and society* (C. A. Watts, 1971), which interprets systems engineering in broader terms. General concepts are dealt with in several books on cybernetics, e.g., Ross Ashby, *Introduction to Cybernetics* (Chapman and Hall, 1956); Stafford Beer, *Decision and Control* (Wiley, 1966). Van Court Hare Jr in *Systems Analysis: A diagnostic approach* (Harcourt Brace Jovanovich, 1967) gives a more detailed introduction to the whole field of systems definition, analysis and treatment.

A full account of general systems theory is given in a book by von Bertalanffy, *General Systems Theory: Essay on its foundation and development* (Braziller, 1969). Other articles in this area can be found in the *General Systems Yearbooks* (1956 –) published by the Society for General Systems Research and originally edited by L. von Bertalanffy and A. Rapoport. Some relevant extracts from several of the above books, together with other more specialized material, can be found in *Systems Thinking, Vols. I and II* edited by F. E. Emery (Penguin Books, 1981). A further collection of basic articles can be found in G. J. Klir, *Trends in General Systems Theory* (Wiley, New York, 1972).

Several books by Geoffrey Vickers explore the implications of systems ideas. See G. Vickers, *Value Systems and Social Process* (Basic Books, New York, 1968) and *Freedom in a Rocking Boat; Changing values in an unstable society* (Penguin Books, 1970).

An introduction to systems ideas and their application to management can be found in *Management Systems: Conceptual considerations,* by P. P. Schoderbek, A. G. Kefalas and C. G. Schoderbek (Business Publications Inc., Dallas, Texas, 1975). Several Open University units cover introductory systems material: *Systems* (Unit 1, The Man-made World T100), *Human Activity Systems* (Unit 3, Systems Management T242), *Systems and Failures* (Unit 1, Systems Performance: Human Factors and Systems Failures TD342), *Introduction to Systems Thinking and Organisation* (Block 1, Systems Organisation T243), all published by the Open University Press.

Glossary of systems concepts

Adaptive system   A system with the capacity to modify its internal state or structure in response to changes in environmental demands or opportunities.

Appreciative system   The system which interprets observations of the outside world into mental images, in accordance with the observer's *Weltanschauung* (q.v.).

Vickers says of appreciative systems that they are "carved out by our expectations and evaluated by our standards of judgement". *(interests, s tructured by ow)*

Behaviour (of a system)   The time course of a system's state variables (q.v.).

Black box   A (component of a) system that is only considered in terms of its inputs and outputs. Its internal mechanisms are unknown or ignored.

Boundary   The conceptual division between a system and its environment; it may or may not correspond to recognized geographical, physical, legal or cultural divisions and will be drawn according to the observer's purpose.

Closed system   A system which does not take in from, or give out anything to, its environment. In practice such systems cannot exist; however, for certain purposes it may be reasonable to view a system as closed.

Closed loop   A system where part of the output, or information about it, is fed back to the input so that the system's output can affect its input or some of its operating characteristics.

Constraint   A restricting condition.

Cybernetics   The study of control and communication in living beings and machines, often involving the application of information theory to the comparison of mechanical or electrical controls with the biological equivalents. (See Article 2.)

Environment (of a system)   The totality of external conditions and concrete or abstract items which affect the behaviour of a system.

Feedback   The modification of a variable, process or system resulting from its own effects or outputs. In the strict sense the modification depends on the difference between the actual state and a reference state, but the term is also used more loosely to refer to any relationship involving a causal loop (cf. closed loop).

Positive feedback increases the discrepancy between the actual state and the reference state.

Negative feedback decreases the discrepancy between the actual state and the reference state.

Feedforward   Response in anticipation of a discrepancy between a future actual state and the reference state (cf. Article 12).

Flow-block diagram   One which displays the subsystems as blocks and the flows between them as arrows. Flows may be of money, material, energy, information or decisions.

General systems theory (GST)   A (potentially) all-embracing theory of systems. Boulding states: "GST aims to provide a framework or structure of systems on which to hang the flesh and blood of particular disciplines and particular subject matters, in an orderly and coherent corpus of knowledge." The aims of the Society for General Systems Research are:

To encourage the development of theoretical systems which are applicable to more than one of the traditional departments of knowledge; to develop theoretical systems of concepts, relationships and models and to investigate the isomorphy of concepts, laws, and models in various fields, and to help in useful transfers from one field to another; to encourage the development of adequate theoretical models in the fields which lack them; to minimize the duplication of theoretical effort in different fields; to promote the unity of science through improving and breaking down the barriers of communication among the specialists in various scientific fields.

Goal-seeking system   A system that can respond differently to events until it produces a particular state (outcome). The system has a choice of behaviour.

Holism   Theory or doctrine according to which a whole cannot be analyzed without residue into the sum of its parts, or reduced to discrete elements.

Holistic   Emphasizing the functional relation between parts and wholes; pertaining to totality, or to the whole. Used more loosely to imply a complete or overall analysis, etc., as opposed to a specific or reductionist one.

Homeostasis   The maintenance of a system in a relatively constant state in a changing environment. (See Article 12.)

Human activity system   A system in which human beings could be considered, from a particular viewpoint, to interact with each other in an organized way, e.g., in traditional organizations and institutions or socially.

Interface   The area between interacting systems or subsystems and the components which overlap.

Open loop   A control system in which corrective action depends on external intervention without reference to the present output of the system. The action is often taken in accordance with pre-set rules, or algorithms.

Open system   A system that is connected to, and interacts with, its environment.

Process(es)   The activities which are undertaken by a system or subsystem.

Regulation   Preservation of form. (See Article 1.)

State (of a system)   Describes a set of relevant properties (state variables) which the system has at a particular moment in time.

Structure   The components of a system or subsystem and the relationships between them.

Synergy   The phenomenon that an assembly of parts is both more and less than the sum of its parts. Its performance cannot be predicted from the fullest knowledge of each part's performance in isolation. (See Article 1.)

System   Four-part definition from the course: A system is an assembly of components, connected together in an organized way. The components are affected by being in the system and the behaviour of the system is changed if they leave it. This organized assembly does something and has been identified as a particular interest.

OR

An assembly of parts connected in an organized way that has been identified by someone as a special interest and that behaves in some way (i.e., does more than just exist).

OR

A structured set of objects and/or attributes, together with the relationships between them.

Systematic   Using a method, or following a plan or an explicit and rational procedure.

Systemic   Using systems ideas; treating things as systems or from a systems viewpoint; pertaining to a system or systems.

Weltanschauung   Literally "world view". An individual (or collective) viewpoint, which is conditioned by environment, background, beliefs, upbringing, etc. It is not itself a set of beliefs, but a framework which underlies one's beliefs.

1 Some implications of systems thinking

by Sir Geoffrey Vickers

Systems is a word of very wide application. It is used amongst other fields in astronomy, physics, biology, ecology, political science, economics and sociology. It can even be applied to those systems of concepts and values through which we see all the others. Recent developments have given such prominence to man-made technological systems that they are in danger of obscuring all those which cannot be technologically modelled. Although all systems have in common some important characteristics, there are equally important differences between them, as there are, for instance, between biological and social evolution. My own interest lies chiefly in social and institutional relations and in what I have called the ecology of ideas. So I shall use this occasion to talk about the effect of systems thinking on our outlook on life and our philosophy of life. This seems to me especially important because it tends to correct some of the grosser ideological errors with which we have saddled ourselves by the illicit extension of ideas and habits of thought derived from the natural sciences. These are so deeply entrenched that we cannot be sure that the new insights will prevail against them. It should, I think, be a major purpose of all of us to help them to do so.

I shall start from the briefest summary of the world view which seems to me appropriate to 1978. An educated child today should have a picture of the world and of his own place in the world and even of his own nature different from those which were current in my youth or even in my children's youth. The world about him, and he himself, are a complex of interrelated systems. Some are related hierarchically like the levels of organization in an organism. Some are related laterally and functionally like the organs of the body or the departments of a business. Some are related by that strange mixture of competition and cooperation which an ecologist sees when he looks under a paving stone or into the Amazon jungle. Nearly all systems which include human beings are unstable and their instability is nearly always the unwilled result of man's actions, monstrously multiplied in power by technology but not correspondingly informed by increased understanding. So

the order of which we are part is of infinite complexity from the biosphere to the cell and far beyond. The extent to which we can redesign any part of it without disastrous impact on other parts is very limited and we do not know and probably cannot fully know its limitations. Moreover, the limitation which we now know best is the one most in conflict with our recent faith in linear progress. For the linear development of any element in any system is bound in time to be self-limiting or self-reversing or lethal to the stability of the system as a whole. Man the master of nature is a false myth. Man the steward has an unbearable responsibility.

This is a different picture from that entertained by many systems technologists, but I think it is a more valid one. It is the explanation and the justification for the mistrust of science and technology which is becoming endemic in the Western world today. Moreover, it applies not only to the ecological relationship between our species and the planet. It also enlarges and changes our ideas of every human relationship and even our ideas of those internal relationships which give each of us individually whatever character and coherence we may possess.

This, in barest outline, is the conceptual revolution which I associate with systems thinking. I can do no more than mention those of its implications which seem most important to me.

Entities and relations

Regulation

Newton's world was a world of inert objects which stayed put unless they were moved by some "force". Explanations of change postulated a mover and ultimately a prime mover, even for entities so manifestly active as living creatures. The word "motivation" records this way of thinking. Our world, by contrast, is a world of active relations in which stability, not change, requires explanation. Most things which are important enough to us to deserve a name would not remain constant enough to earn one unless some mechanism were constantly at work to regulate them, that is, to preserve their form.

A familiar example was described by Claude Bernard 150 years ago, when he pointed out the advantages gained by the so-called warm-blooded animals in developing a regulator to maintain a constant internal body temperature. This "stability of the internal milieu" was, he declared, "the condition of free and independent life". Few statements, true in their own contexts, have been true also in so many other contexts as that famous generalization of Claude Bernard. Probably everyone who reads these words will remember occasions when a threat to his internal milieu has also threatened his capacity for free and independent response, whether the internal threat were to his digestion or to his self-confidence or whatever.

Of course the warm-blooded animals are not fully "free and independent". They depend on their external milieu for countless exchanges of matter, energy and information. Nonetheless their range of response is larger than that of creatures which do not maintain a stable internal climate. So there arises even at that level the paradox that these more free and independent creatures are also more bound by ties of interdependence.

Inner and outer relations

Hence the importance of the interface between a system and its surround which distinguishes inner from outer relations. The inner relations hold the system together and enable it to act as a whole on its surround. And as Bernard had observed so long ago, the scope of its external relations depends on the coherence which its inner relations secure. But this interface between inner and outer is elusive. Subsystems may be parts of more than one whole and so may fall within more than one *system boundary*. The boundary itself may be differently perceived and defined by different elements in the system. Elements in it, themselves subsystems, may disclaim their membership, as cells do when they become cancerous and disregard the in-built instructions which regulate their multiplication and function. Human subsystems may claim and disclaim membership to an extent which makes impossible demands both on themselves and on the systems concerned. This, I think, explains the impasse into which both political government and business management are sliding in so many Western democratic countries. Equally, these human subsystems may set – and manifestly have set – multiple and inconsistent regulative norms on which they rely but which they cannot support. Such, I believe, is the persistent notion that full employment, rising living standards for all, free collective bargaining and stable money are mutually consistent and attainable norms in a Western society today.

I do not think it too much to hope that an understanding of systemic relations may bring us a better understanding of our limitations and even of our possibilities.

Perhaps the situation should be expressed more radically. We are accustomed to regard "relating" as something which entities do, rather than as something which they are. Should we not rather regard entities as systems created by the relations which sustain them? A nation state, a business corporation, a trade union, act for some purposes as a whole in relation to their milieu, and the extent to which they can do so depends on the extent to which their internal relations give them enough coherence. Are they any more – or any less – than names for these complementary sets of relations? If not, what of human individuals, of you and me?

Identity and continuity

This view of entities as both systems and constituents of systems raises intriguing questions about identity and continuity. When does something, or somebody, retain its identity and continuity through change? When by contrast does it cease to be its old self and either vanish or become something new and different? The question is not frivolous or merely metaphysical but may be of great practical concern. For it determines whether people within the system or outside it continue to accord it their loyalty or perhaps their hatred.

The answer depends on what aspect of a system interests or concerns us. My home town remains for me its old self though it has vastly grown and changed, and I have long since ceased to live there. But if some other old inhabitant said that for him it was no longer the same place, I should not assume that he or I must be wrong. I should only assume that some relationships now lacking were for him essential to the system called by that city's name, whilst for me they were not.

Individuality and responsibility

This change of view about entities and relations must, I think, change our attitude towards human responsibility. The West used to attach high value to the ideal of the responsible person but during the last 200 years this has, in my view, been overlaid by the ideal of the autonomous individual. The change is very important and it can easily be expressed in systemic terms. The responsible person recognizes his obligations as part of a larger system or of two or more perhaps conflicting systems. He does not necessarily conform to the cultural norms of all or any of these systems. Western history honours innovators as well as conservators, reformers, revolutionaries as well as defenders of ancient faiths. The honour is accorded .to them because of their loyalty to their self-chosen commitments. And these commitments are to change or preserve some relationship, not merely between themselves and their surround but within some system of which they accept membership or between that system and its surround, be that system a nation state, a religious community or an aspect of the culture which they share. The reformers of all ages have been concerned either to bring societal behaviour into line with norms which were acknowledged in principle but ignored in practice (like the abuse of wealth by the mediaeval church) or to replace an existing norm by one which did more justice to the demands of the systemic situation (like the changes in norms of personal responsibility which have marked the last hundred years and the corresponding changes in criminal law and punishment).

The autonomous individual is not so judged and is not so honoured. His external relations are viewed as far less essential to what he is. Any overt attempt to manipulate them (except of course for the stunning exception of commercial advertising) is viewed as a threat to individual freedom. He is accorded a right though not usually a duty to "actualize himself" but it is seldom admitted that this involves what Erikson (1964) calls fidelity to his self-chosen commitments and acceptance of the constraints which these involve.

Yet we could scarcely find, outside a psychotic ward, an individual who did not to some extent accept the constraints and commitments attaching to his membership of at least one, probably more than one system. And his performance as a member of these systems constitutes a large part of what he is – or at least of what he is perceived to be by others and by himself.

Commitments and constraints are not popular words today, but they are conditions of being human; and they are more so when they are self-chosen rather than imposed. The concept of responsibility is badly shaken today and badly needed. I believe that systemic thinking can make it again both powerful and acceptable.

Organizations as designed systems
New levels, new laws
A further effect of the conceptual revolution has been to legitimize and clarify the concept of organization. Only a few decades ago the influence of reductionism was so strong that informed people could debate whether an organization can possibly be more than the sum of its parts. Today every schoolchild should know, though few do, that every organization must be both more and less than the sum of its parts. It is less, because organization constrains. Elements in a system are not free to do all the things which, unorganized, they might do. It is more because, when organized, they are enabled to do together what none of them could do alone, or, if unorganized, even together. Nor could their performance when organized be predicted even in theory from the fullest knowledge of their performance in isolation. This is true at all levels from the subatomic to the social. That dreaded heresy, "vitalism", can at last be acknowledged to be a special case of a general and acceptable principle. Every new step in organization exhibits laws and principles not to be found at the level below, though bounded by limits which lower-level laws impose. This makes is possible to study the human social field with sufficient acknowledgement of its peculiarity.

Stability and success
One of these peculiarities is described in memorable language by the Open University (1976) in a preliminary note to its course on the performance of human systems. Human systems, it asserts, are the only kind of systems which can be said to succeed or fail. It boggles at defining success, but it produces what I find a persuasive definition of failure. A human system fails if it does not succeed in doing what it was designed to do; or if it succeeds but leaves everyone wishing it had never tried. The St Lawrence Seaway, I am told, may well exemplify the first; DDT clearly exemplifies the second.

Whether you accept the definition or not, it clearly stresses an aspect of human organizations which is often overlooked. They are governed both by the demands of stability and by criteria of success. I find it ridiculous to try to reduce the second to the first as so many people try to do. Of course, whatever a human system's function may be, it cannot fulfil its function unless it continues to exist. Stability therefore, at least in this limited sense, is an essential *condition* of success. It is not, however, a *criterion* of success. A local authority, for example, like any other organization, must ensure that the inflow of money is sufficient to balance the outflow of money; that employees, when they die, retire or are promoted, are replaced by others who are at least equally competent; and so on. But the townspeople judge the local authority not by its performance as financial controller or an employer but by the quality of the services which it provides in many diverse and disparate fields, such as education, transportation, sewage disposal and a dozen others. Stability is a necessary but not sufficient condition of success.

What then is sufficient? If we look at the services now being provided by some local authority, whether in America or Europe, we shall almost certainly find that they are far superior to those which it was providing a century ago. Many were not even expected of it a century ago. Yet it may be judged by its electorate today as far less successful than it was a century ago. Something has changed, beside its performance. That something is the standard by which its performance is judged.

The cybernetic signal

This brings me back to Wiener's concept of the cybernetic signal. The cybernetic signal is generated by the regulator by comparing some aspect of what is or of what is likely to be with some standard of what ought to be. Any disparity between the two is supposed to alert the regulator to the fact that it is "off course" and to generate action appropriate to bring it back "on course".

This model is clear enough, in the simple context in which it was originally stated, namely, the helmsman steering a course. It is fruitful in wider contexts. But it is a poor simulation of human reality so long as it assumes that the course is unitary, given and attainable. In nearly all the important situations of human life, the relations to be attained are multiple and conflicting; they are not all fully attainable; and they are set by a process which we do not understand. But at least we can no longer ignore the importance of norms as generators of cybernetic signals on which we constantly act, both individually and collectively. The revolution in personal expectations which took place in the West between 1948 and 1970 is a constant reminder of the power of rising norms to overwhelm regulators.

The great ideological cleavage of our day concerns the extent to which governments may legitimately mould the expectations of their citizens rather than merely responding to them. And the West's concept of freedom in this regard is manifestly too simplistic to be viable, although the alternatives practised in the greater part of the world do not yet widely commend themselves to us. The process by which norms are set and changed is still by far the most important and the most neglected area of study in both social and individual psychology. But we can no longer explain this by ignoring them. They are essential to every cybernetic signal.

A new epistemology
Intersubjectivity

The recovery of norms re-establishes the credibility of ethics, but it is not confined to the province of ethics. It is necessary also to understanding the process we call judgement in the factual and the aesthetic as well as the ethical field. We know only by arranging experience by reference to our existing constructs,* a process which often changes the constructs as well as defining how we interpret experience and even what we notice. These constructs determine our view of factual reality no less than of ethical obligation. Our personal representations of what is, no less than of what ought to be, are designs of our own minds, collective works of art, created within the varying constraints which experience imposes to meet needs dictated by our concerns, our situations and our culture.

Clearly the categories "objective" and "subjective" are inadequate to comprehend the combined process of design and discovery which goes into human knowing – and that for reasons wider even than those expressed by Michael Polanyi (1958) in his seminal books. With these categories is failing the whole structure of positivism and especially its extension to human and social systems. A system made up of subsystems capable of representing to themselves (whether rightly or wrongly) their own position in a system, their own power to change it and their own norms of what it should be will surely behave differently from one not so composed. It will, I think, become logically impossible for it to predict its own behaviour or its own future state.

Parallel with this change has gone a revolutionary change in the concept of intersubjectivity. For centuries it has been a central faith of science that a belief, however widely held, may be wrong and may be shown to be wrong by a single dissentient who appeals successfully to "facts". The earlier history of science records many such successful challenges to accepted beliefs, of which the theory of biological evolution is a relatively recent one. Yet philosophers of science today are increasingly driven to the conclusion that the current view of what "is" derives what validity it has from the consensus of informed minds in their agreement to treat it so. The consensus may be mis-

* The word "constructs" is extensively used in this sense by George A. Kelly (1963) in *A Theory of Personality*, Norton, New York. But the concept of knowledge and indeed of nearly all ways of perceiving and responding as cultural artifacts is becoming increasingly widespread. cf. Berger, P.L. and Luckman, T. (1967) *The Social Construction of Reality*, Allen Lane, London.

taken, so the commitment to it is always "hazardous", as Polanyi observes. But consensus there must be, to create it, to legitimize and sustain it, and ultimately to change and perhaps abandon it. To survive possibilities of disproof, however often, can never amount to logical validation.

Recognition and identification

This is the process by which norms or standards come into existence to guide human judgement, whether factual or ethical or aesthetic. It cannot be explored without accepting a view of human judgement which, though old, has been long denied. This is the view that judgement is more and other than calculation, just as recognition is more and other than identification and synthesis more and other than analysis (Vickers, 1978). This acknowledgement is another of those changes which I recognize as part of the current conceptual revolution, and another of those human facts which science has long stifled, although science is our best attested evidence of it.

Evolutionary biology is a good example. The continuity of the change which has turned Eohippus into a modern racehorse is recognized by a sense of similarity which is generated by looking at successive stages but which cannot be fully defined by a checklist of characteristics.

A brave effort to win acknowledgement for this human capacity to recognize and create form was made in the 1920s by gestalt psychologists like Koehler and holistic philosophers like Smuts. But the forces of inertia were too strong for them and their weapons too weak. Today significant research in various fields, including brain science, supports the view that we are equipped with two distinct cerebral mechanisms, one apt for analysis and the logical handling of causal sequences, the other apt for synthesis, for the manipulation of figure and ground and the recognition of form and context. One can hope, but by no means be sure, that we shall soon be allowed to admit the existence of the second faculty and its relation with the other which is usually the relation of creator to critic.

Agent and observer

These changes, if fully realized, would give us an epistemology at least better than that which we are commonly allowed to use. It will, I think, be qualified by an insight which has found expression during the same period and which is, I believe, at least indirectly related to systems thinking. This insight concerns the relation of agent and observer. In the natural sciences the stance of the observer has always been cherished, and has been carried over confidently from the natural sciences to the psychosocial field. Grotesque efforts have been made by scientists in the psychosocial field to maintain the same independence of their subject matter, ignoring the fact that most of their vocabulary as regards their fellow human beings would have no meaning at all if they had not filled it with their own experience before applying it tentatively to others. (For example, behaviour indicative of pain would be meaningless to an observer who had not, as a sentient being, experienced pain.) It is therefore a radical change of stance to see human beings, even scientists, like other live agents, primarily as agent-experients in situations of which they are themselves a part rather than as observers or manipulators outside the system.

This is not to deny the importance to men of their capacity to withdraw and become observers even of themselves. But it does require us to recognize the converse, our capacity and inescapable need to engage as agent-experients with the course of events and even to use our experience as agents to illuminate our understanding of our fellow agents and to give insight into their incommunicable experience. This dialogue between the self as agent and the self as observer is, I believe, essential to our understanding of ourselves and others and also to our acceptance of the partial blindness which is inherent in both stances.

The gulfs between self and other and between agent and observer cannot be wholly bridged. But they can be bridged to a far greater extent than many scientists are yet willing to admit. For the concept of the individual has gone the way of the atom. A comparison of the two is suggestive.

Belief in the atomic theory was sustained for more than two thousand years before anyone actually demonstrated the existence of an atom. Within a few years after that recent event, atoms were found to lack the only two qualities with which they had ever been credited. They were neither indestructible nor indivisible. Yet atomic theory, far from receiving its death blow, took off into the study of the subatomic world, enriched by a concept without which the earlier theory hardly made sense. It now had a clue to the key question why these supposedly separate indivisible little billiard balls cohered so firmly in structures visible to the eye.

Similarly, in the human field we are enriched by the concept of each individual as a process extended in time, vastly complex in both its eternal and its external relations and dependent on both for its quality and its very existence, as well as for its constancy or inconstancy.

The one and the many

Some of you may detect ambiguity, even paradox, in what I

have said. I hope you do, for I believe that to accept ambiguity and paradox is necessary to the understanding of human life. I am sure that systems thinking makes it easier to accept the most basic of all the paradoxes, the paradox of "the one and the many".

To our Western minds discrimination seems to be the basis of all knowledge. The language we learn from birth is structured with nouns, adjectives and verbs, distinguishing objects, qualities and activities from each other. It seems that it is a necessary function, even though it almost prevents us from drawing any distinction which our language has not learned to recognize. We have another capacity for discrimination, the discrimination between figure and ground. It is more flexible. Merely by shifting our attention we can dissolve one figure and substitute another with a correspondingly changed ground. It is also more meaningful for it enables us to take account of context in interpreting the figure. But both these capacities tend to isolate us from the objects we are observing and thus to cast us in the role of observer or manipulator, rather than participant. Remember how many psychologists have propounded supposedly comprehensive theories of human nature and behaviour which manifestly failed to explain their authors.

The opposite view is possible. It stresses the interconnectedness of things and the inescapable interrelation between knower and known. It is no accident that in the last two decades the Western mind has developed so great an interest in Eastern thought, which in so many forms stresses the unity of life and the twofold danger of the analytical approach, prone to exclude both the experient and the context from the reality which the experient as observer is seeking to understand.

Systemic thinking removes the apparent antithesis between these approaches. As observers we are also creators building complementary pictures of inexhaustible reality. As agents our simplest behaviour will have repercussions, probably unsuspected, in many systems which concern us. And above all, whether as observers or agents, we are ourselves part of the systems which we seek to understand and to change or sustain.

This approach has already begun to affect our concepts of policy making, of organization and of personal responsibility. It is greatly to be welcomed.

Technological threats

I have drawn a picture which, however summary, may seem to you to be at least hopeful. In fact it includes dangers as well as hopes and I will identify two which seem to me to be justly feared.

One is the growth of what I will call digital thinking. I can best describe this by an illustration drawn from a situation at which I was present. A computer scientist was describing to a possible supporter of his work the result of teaching young children to programme a computer to make drawings. They had learned how to programme an approximate circle, and they were heard later in earnest metaphysical debate about whether there was or could be a real circle. Was not every circle a more or less refined polyhedron?

It seems to me that the concept of circularity is simple and important, easy to teach and rich in implications. No child with a lathe or a compass could conceive itself to be producing polyhedrons. To this computer scientist, however, it evidently seemed an expendable concept. Why bother children in a computer age with concepts foreign to computers? The same argument would justify an effort to persuade children that time is best conceived for all purposes (not merely for mathematical convenience) as a series of moments of no duration. Perhaps this helps to explain today's disastrous contempt for history.

Hence my anxiety that the concept of gestalt recognition may again be stifled and with it our belief in an essential part of our own mental capacity for judgement. For this, I believe, depends essentially on our ability to combine our two mental capacities.

Hypnosis by models

My second and allied anxiety is that the new conceptual revolution, by multiplying our power to make models and our habit of using them, may also magnify our confidence in the models we make and may equally reduce our confidence in our power to know any reality we cannot explicitly model. The clear message of systems thinking is that human scope is limited and that we cannot use even what scope we have except in a situation in which we are sensitively and intimately engaged. We have been offered both this insight and the temptation to ignore it, and vested interests powerfully favour the second. This we should avoid both as a duty and as a vital interest of our society. For if I am right, we can know more, as well as less than we can model and we shall be doubly hampered, even by comparison with our present plight, if we overrate our models and underrate ourselves.

References

Erikson, E. (1964) *Insight and Responsibility,* W. W. Norton & Co., New York.

Open University (1976) *Systems Performance: Human Factors and Systems Failures,* Open University Press,

Milton Keynes.

Polanyi, M. (1958) *Personal Knowledge,* Kegan Paul, London.

Vickers, G. (1978) "Rationality and intuition", in Wechsler, J. (ed.), *Aesthetics in Science,* MIT Press, Cambridge, Mass.

2 Science and the systems movement
by P. B. Checkland

1 The method of science

If systems thinking and "a systems approach" are serious, if they are more than a temporarily fashionable piece of claptrap – and I believe they are – then it is necessary to establish what exactly systems thinking is, and what it means to adopt a systems approach to a problem. It is in order to do this that I have found it necessary to outline the development of science, the human activity which is "the origin of the modern world and the modern mentality" (Butterfield, 1949) and within which the systems movement has emerged during the last thirty to forty years. In order to see systems thinking as a complement to the main mode of thinking in science, it is necessary to summarize the essential elements in the activity of science and then to see where systems thinking includes or excludes them; hence we arrive at a view of the systems movement in relation to the science movement which spawned it.

Science has emerged as a consciously recognized, organized human activity. As such it is itself "a system". It is an institutionalized set of activities which embody a particular purpose, namely, the acquiring of a particular kind of knowledge (Bernal, 1939; Ravetz, 1971; Skair, 1973). Science is an *enquiring* or *learning* system, a system to find things out about the mysterious world we find ourselves inhabiting. The crucial characteristics of this learning system derive from its history. The Greeks contributed the invention of rational thought, breaking with the idea of the irrational authority who is not to be questioned; the mediaeval clerics started the conscious development of methodology and provided the beginnings of the experimental approach; and the age of Newton united empiricism and theoretical explanation in a way which "dealt with necessity and contingency at the same time", which "made the real world comprehensible through ideas" (Hall, 1963). The twentieth century has reminded us that the knowledge gained is always provisional. These are the strands which unite in science as we now perceive it, and our account of that activity as a whole would be in some such terms as these:

Science is a way of acquiring publicly testable knowledge of the world; it is characterized by the application of rational thinking to experience, such as is derived from observation and from deliberately designed experiments, the aim being the concise expression of the laws which govern the regularities of the universe, these laws being expressed mathematically if possible.

In making this outlook a reality, a particular pattern of human activity has evolved and been institutionalized. We may *reduce* the complexity of the variety of the real world in experiments whose results are validated by their *repeatability*, and we may build knowledge by the *refutation* of hypotheses. The three characteristics which define this pattern are, therefore, reductionism, repeatability and refutation.

We may describe in the following (slightly idealized) terms what happens when a piece of scientific work is planned and carried out – or rather this is the logic of what should happen; a real instance may not follow the logic! The scientist, as a result of his choice of problem, decides what section of the world's variety to examine. He makes his reduction, designing an artificial situation within which he can examine the workings of a few variables while others are held constant. His experimental design will "make sense" in terms of some particular view of, or theory about, that part of the world's variety which he is investigating, and his particular experiment will constitute the testing of a hypothesis within that theory. The question the experiment poses is: will it pass the test? And the artificiality of the experimental situation is such that, when the results are carefully described, analyzed and interpreted, well-defined critical discussion among interested scientists can take place. Human thought is polemic; new thoughts are necessarily the foes of those they replace, and the experimental approach of science generates, contains and orchestrates critical debate.

When a hypothesis is subjected to test in the way

(Polemic :–
Controversial, disputatious)

described, it must in logic be the case that we are more interested in a refutation than a corroboration. The experimentalist ought to be trying to test his hypothesis to destruction, setting it the most severe test he can think of.

We have a picture of science, then, as a method of enquiring, or learning, which offers us, at any moment of time, a picture of our understanding of the world's reality which consists of certain conjectures, established in reductionist repeatable experiments, which have not yet been demolished. The most pleasing image of this activity comes not from a scientist or a philosopher of science but from a novelist, Vladimir Nabokov. In his story *Ultima Thule*, he writes:

> When a hypothesis enters a scientist's mind, he checks it by calculation and experiment, that is by the mimicry and pantomime of truth. Its plausibility affects others, and the hypothesis is accepted as the true explanation for the given phenomenon, until someone finds its faults. I believe the whole of science consists of such exiled or retired ideas; and yet at one time each of them boasted high rank: now only a name or a pension is left.

The method of science has turned out to be powerful enough to create the modern outlook, and the exploitation of science in Western technology has largely created the modern world in a physical sense. This ascendancy is due to the fact that the potent combination of rational thinking and experimentation demonstrably works. It provides knowledge different in kind from that derived from consulting the oracle at Delphi, reading the entrails of slaughtered goats, casting horoscopes or turning up the Tarot cards.

But the method of science is not all-powerful, even at a material level, and there is much to be learned by examining the limitations of the scientific method, not least because an examination of the bounds of science, carried out in the rational, enquiring spirit of science itself, might provide a more civilized base for cultural change than 'that likely to be provided by a mindless cult of unreason'.

The crucial problem which science faces is its ability to cope with complexity. Descartes' second rule for "properly conducting one's reason", i.e., divide up the problems being examined into separate parts – the principle most central to scientific practice, assumes that this division will not distort the phenomenon being studied. It assumes that the components of the whole are the same when examined singly as when they are playing their part in the whole, or that the principles governing the assembling of the components into the whole are themselves straightforward. We

now know, on the basis of the success of physical science so far, that these seem to be reasonable assumptions, at least for many of the physical regularities of the universe.

The interesting question is: To what extent can the method of science cope with complexity? Where does it fall down, and why? This article examines some of the limitations of the method of science as the complexity of the subject matter examined increases. After examining some of the problems of complexity within the physical sciences, attention is drawn to the problems of two other areas rich in complexity: the social sciences and "problems in the real world", the latter being viewed as problems of "management", defining that term very broadly. It is as a response to these problems of complexity that systems thinking develops.

2 Problems for science
2.1 Complexity

Cursory inspection of the world suggests that it is a giant complex with dense connections among its parts. We cannot cope with it in that form and are forced to reduce it to some separate areas which we can examine separately. Our knowledge of the world is thus necessarily divided into different "subjects" or "disciplines", and in the course of history these change as our knowledge changes. Because our education is from the start conducted in terms of this division into distinct subjects, it is not easy to remember that the divisions are man-made and are arbitrary. It is not nature which divides itself up into physics, biology, psychology, sociology, etc.; it is we who impose these divisions on nature, and they become so ingrained in our thinking that we find it hard to see the unity which underlies the divisions. But given that our knowledge has to be arranged in this way – and it is inevitable given our limited ability to take in the whole – then it is useful in the interests of coherence to arrange the classification of knowledge according to some rational principle.

It is useful to recall the classification of the sciences proposed by Comte in the nineteenth century. The principles behind the classification are: the historical order of the emergence of the sciences, the increasing degrees of complexity of subject matter, and the increasing ease with which the facts studied by a particular science may change. The classification remains, with a few modifications, a useful framework for the examination of some of the difficulties and limitations of the scientific method. The modifications concern the inclusion of psychology (which Comte omitted) as a science linking biology and the social sciences, and the exclusion of mathematics, regarding it not as a science in its own right but as a language which any science may use, and which is more used the lower down the hierarchy we travel. This gives us a classification of the experimental sciences into, in sequence, physics, chemistry, biology, psychology and the social sciences. In this sequence physics is the most basic science, being concerned with the most general concepts, such as mass, motion, force and energy. Chemical reactions obviously entail these phenomena, and are increasingly explained in terms of them, but when hydrochloric acid gas and ammonia mix, and a white solid not previously present settles out, we have a phenomenon which intuitively is more complex than those of physics. And though a biological phenomenon such as the growth of a plant from a seed entails much chemistry (as well as physics), the reproductive ability of the plant again brings in a new level of complexity. Psychology, and the concept of consciousness, bring in a higher level still and social life exhibits yet higher levels.

It is physics which is most clearly successful as a science. It exemplifies most clearly the characteristics of the scientific method, and examination of the main difficulties for this particular method of gaining knowledge becomes an examination of the degree to which reductionism, repeatability and refutation can characterize the study of increasingly complex phenomena as we ascend the hierarchy. Can the scientific method cope with phenomena more complex than those of physics? Where does it break down?

Physics can provide an account of the mechanism of some chemical phenomena, but cannot explain the existence of problems of chemistry as such. The puzzle is that of the apparent existence of a hierarchy of levels of complexity which we find it convenient to tackle through a hierarchy of separate sciences. Again, at a level above chemistry, the problems of the development of embryos and of heredity are problems of biology. Explanations in terms of chemistry, though welcome, do not explain away biology; we are left with a level of complexity which is characterized by its own autonomous problems. Popper (1974), in a section called "Darwinism as metaphysics" in his "intellectual autobiography", seems to be making much the same point when he writes:

> I conjecture that there is no biological process which cannot be regarded as correlated in detail with a physical process or cannot be progressively analysed in physiochemical terms. But no physiochemical theory can explain the emergence of a new problem . . . the problems of organisms are not physical: they are neither

physical things, nor physical laws, nor physical facts. They are specific biological realities; they are "real" in the sense that their existence may be the cause of biological effects.

Given the messy richness of "biological effects" it is perhaps not surprising that biologists, much more than chemists, have been conscious of the fact that an unsolved problem is presented to science by the very existence of a set of phenomena which are higher order with respect to those of chemistry and physics. The existence of the problem of the emergence of new phenomena at higher levels of complexity is itself a major problem for the method of science, and one which reductionist thinking has not been able to solve.

Another aspect of the problem of complexity for science has been discussed by Pantin (1968), who makes a useful distinction between "restricted" and "unrestricted" sciences. In a restricted science such as physics or chemistry a limited range of phenomena are studied. Well-designed reductionist experiments in the laboratory are possible, and it is probable that far-reaching hypotheses, expressed mathematically, can be tested by quantitative measurements. The wider and more precise the quantitative predictions, the greater the possibility of failure and hence the greater confidence possible in a hypothesis which actually passes a severe test. In an unrestricted science such as biology or geology, the effects under study are so complex that designed experiments with controls are often not possible. Quantitative models are more vulnerable and the chance of unknown factors dominating the observations is much greater. The social sciences are all "unrestricted" in Pantin's sense, and present considerable problems for the method of science. In addition, they introduce a new kind of difficulty beyond that of mere complexity.

2.2 Social science

Even when the natural sciences face the problem of extreme complexity, the professional scientists concerned are convinced that there is no fundamental issue of principle at stake. Climatologists and meteorologists, for example, deal with large and complex systems involving more variables than can be handled analytically, and it will be a long time, it appears, before meteorologists can tell us whether or not it will rain in Bolton-le-Sands, Lancashire, England, on Thursday next. On the other hand, forecasts of the general weather pattern for England as a whole are now made one month ahead, and are improving in quality. The problems still to be tackled are of a recognized kind, concerning instrumentation, data collection and data *a study of mankind, its societies and customs.*

analysis, rather than fundamental issues which might cast doubt on the possibility of accurate weather forecasting. The future of meteorology as a science is certainly not an issue.

This is a very different situation from that in those unrestricted sciences which we call "social". The status of disciplines like anthropology, economics, sociology, political science, etc., *as sciences* is a question which is still problematic. To an outsider, for example, initial inspection of the literature of sociology gives the impression of its being strong on social findings of the kind which can be collected by asking people to fill in questionnaires, relatively weak on substantive accounts which are the result of sociologists *doing* sociology in the way that chemists *do* chemistry, and relatively strong on discussions of the nature of sociology, what constitutes an "explanation" in sociology, whether or not a value-free sociology is possible, and similar questions. It was a sociologist, Cohen, not an outsider, who wrote ". . . there is a depressing tendency for social theorists to discuss the nature of social theory rather than the nature of social reality". By contrast, the literature of a natural science like chemistry is heavily dominated by substantive contributions within the discipline; simple data collection and discussion of the intellectual status of chemistry are noticeably absent.

This concern with questions *about*, rather than *in*, the disciplines of social science is an indication not that social science attracts dilettantes, but rather that exceptionally difficult problems arise when the methods developed for investigating the natural world which exists outside ourselves are applied to the social phenomena of which we are a part. The founding fathers of social science were in no doubt that the new science was to be science in the image of the natural sciences. It was assumed that empiricism applied to the facts of social life would yield generalizations and predictions on the pattern of natural science. This has not yet happened, and though a century is not a long time in the history of an idea, it does appear that the hiatus in the substantive development of the social sciences is due to the special kind of difficulties they face.

After careful examination of the formidable difficulties facing social science, Nagel (1961) concludes that the problems of determining systematic explanations of social phenomena are not *in logic* insuperable. He admits that "problems are not resolved merely by showing that they are not necessarily insoluble", and the fact is that the problems of a social science patterned on natural science have hardly been solved. It is obvious that one aspect of these problems is that already met with in biology and other unrestricted sciences, namely complexity of subject matter. The phenomena involved are ones with dense connections between many different aspects, making it difficult to achieve the reduction required for a meaningful controlled experiment. As in some of the unrestricted physical sciences, such as geology, the opportunities for experimentation designed to give unequivocal results are very limited. Social institutions are not available for experimentation even if experiments complete with controls could be designed. But in social science it is not only complexity and this non-availability of experimental objects which bring problems. There is also the greater problem of the special nature of the phenomena to be studied.

Our knowledge of the world acquired by science (and perhaps the world itself?) does seem to show symmetries, patterns, regularities. It would seem surprising if social phenomena were not similarly patterned. Indeed, on a common-sense inspection they obviously are, since social life would not be possible if the behaviour of our fellows did not in general meet our expectations. But given the "messy" nature of social phenomena as they appear to us, we can expect the findings of a scientific approach to the investigation of social reality to have certain characteristics which distinguish them from the findings acquired by the natural sciences' investigation of the physical world.

The distinctions between the established sciences and the would-be sciences can be summarized in the fact that at the core of the phenomena studied by social science is the self-consciousness of human beings and the freedom of choice which that consciousness entails. This irreducible freedom stems ultimately from the experimental fact, upon which neurophysiologists agree, that all our mental activity – choosing, believing, etc. – is associated with specific electrical activity in the brain. The arguments are not easy to summarize but hinge on the fact that an observer can *never* obtain an up-to-date account of the state of mind of an agent he is observing which it would be correct for the agent to accept. (See Thorpe, 1974)

As soon as the agent agreed the correctness of the observer's account, his act of belief would render that account out of date by changing the state of his brain. Now suppose the observer were able to make a detailed prediction of the agent's future action based upon some miraculously perfect detailed knowledge of the state of the agent's mind. The agent himself would actually be wrong to believe that prediction before he makes up his mind what action to take (!), since his belief would render the perfect account of his state of mind, upon which the prediction is

dilettante – one who toys with subject or studies it without seriousness.

based, obsolete. Nothing can remove from the agent his freedom to select his action, there is no one outcome which he would be correct to regard as the only possible one. This kind of argument suggests that at best social systems will reveal "trends" rather than "laws", and that the social scientist will be reduced to studying not exactly social reality but only the logic of situations, producing findings of the kind "In situation A, a likely outcome is B", without any guarantee that this will hold in any particular situation. And over the years, with the growth of human knowledge, the "logic of situations", which will involve actors' attribution of meaning, will gradually change.

This discussion hopefully indicates that the method of science, so powerful in the natural sciences, has not yet, and will not easily be applied to the investigation of social phenomena.

2.3 *"Management"*

If we had available a social science on the pattern of the natural sciences, with hypotheses and laws which have been well tested and have survived, and a body of theory which tells a story in which the hypotheses and the laws are meaningful and coherently linked, then that social science would surely help us in the solution of "real-world problems", just as natural science is available to help technologists and engineers solve their problems. It would not *have* to be called upon, of course, just as technology and engineering do not have to call upon science; there are some brilliant and successful technologists and engineers who act intuitively. Nevertheless it is not unreasonable to anticipate that, were it available, an established social science would help us when, as decision takers, we face problems in social systems. By "real-world problems" I mean problems of decision, in social systems, which *arise*, which we find ourselves facing, in contrast to the scientist's problem in a laboratory which he can define and limit. The scientist selects the most difficult problem which in his judgement offers a reasonable chance of solution; real life pushes its problems upon us. Real-world problems are of the kind: what should the British Government do about the supersonic passenger aircraft project, Concorde? How should we design our schools? Should I marry this particular girl? Shall I change my career? Such problems are in fact problems of *management*, broadly defined. The management process, not interpreted in a class sense, is concerned with deciding to do or not to do something, with planning, with considering alternatives, with monitoring performance, with collaborating with other people or achieving ends through others; it is the process of taking decisions in social systems in the face of problems which may not be self-generated.

This being so, we might expect that so-called "management science" is in fact a body of scientific knowledge and principles relevant to the management process. Management science certainly exists in the sense that there are professionals who would think of themselves as "management scientists", and institutions to which they belong; there are books, journals and conferences devoted to management science as well as courses and qualifications. What is noticeably lacking is any great feeling on the part of the people who would apparently get most help from such a science that it really can help them. Managers in industry and in the public sector, leaders of trade unions and shop stewards, politicians and administrators, have not been convinced by its fruits that management science is more than marginally relevant to their task.

The failure of the scientific approach to make much progress so far in its application to the process of management can usefully be examined by looking briefly at the example of operational research (OR), which is the closest management science comes to having a hard scientific core. The Operational Research Society's official definition reads (my emphases):

> Operational Research is the application of the methods of science to complex problems arising in the direction and management of large systems of men, machines, materials and money in industry, business, government and defence. *The distinctive approach is to develop a scientific model of the system,* incorporating measurements of factors such as chance and risk, with which to predict and compare the outcomes of alternative decisions, strategies or controls. The purpose is to help management determine its policy and actions scientifically.

This statement well expresses the brilliant solution which OR has adopted to the difficult problem of applying the methods of science to parts of the real world, as opposed to the artificial situations created in the laboratory. Engineers use the same solution to carry out "experiments" not on the real-world object of study – which is usually not available – but on a model of it, if possible a quantitative model. The strategy of OR is to build a model of the process concerned, one in which the overall performance is expressed in some explicit measure of performance (often economic), then to improve or optimize the model in terms of the chosen performance criterion, and finally to transfer the solution derived from the model to the real-world situation. This is an heroic attempt to be scientific in the real world (as opposed to the laboratory) and the difficulties are great.

What OR can provide is one crucial contribution to a management decision, a rational story of the form: "If you adopt x as the measure of performance then you may optimize with respect to x by the following actions . . .", but it can hardly generate the kind of irrational decision which, in a management situation, often turns out to be a good one.

Historically OR has concentrated most of its efforts on refining its quantitative tools and developing them for specific situations. The argument implicit in the development of OR in the last thirty years is that *problem situations recur*. Once the *form* of the problem has been idealized then the algorithms for its solution may be worked out and refined. Hence we find most OR texts devoting successive chapters to the problem types which are believed to recur. This outlook is expressed by Wild (1972), in a book about the management of production facilities, as follows:

> . . . it is generally recognised that the following problem
> forms exist:
>   Allocation Problems
>   Inventory Problems
>   Replacement Problems
>   Queuing (or Waiting Line) Problems
>   Sequencing and Routing Problems
>   Search Problems (i.e. concerned with location)
>   Competitive or Bidding Problems.

But it is the fact in real life that "the problem" is usually perceived as such because of the content details which make it unique, rather than because of the form which makes it general. This is probably the explanation of the intellectual gap which exists between practising managers and management scientists; and it indicates the formidable problems which still face both OR and management science as a whole as they try to extend the application of the method of science in areas of extreme complexity.

The three problems for science – complexity in general, the extension of science to cover social phenomena, and the application of scientific methodology in real-world situations – have not yet been satisfactorily solved, although some progress has been made. Had they been solved, it is unlikely that systems thinking and the systems movement which unites systems thinkers in many different fields, would exist in their present form. This is not to say that systems thinking has made spectacular progress – indeed, on the whole the substantive results from the systems movement are still meagre – but the existence of the

movement at all is a response to the inability of reductionist science to cope with various forms of complexity. Systems thinking is an attempt, within the broad sweep of science, to retain much of that tradition but to supplement it by tackling the problem of irreducible complexity via a form of thinking based on wholes and their properties which complements scientific reductionism.

3 Systems thinking

3.1 Emergence and hierarchy

"Systems thinking" is not yet a phrase in general use. Eventually, I believe, systems thinking and analytical thinking will come to be thought of as the twin components of scientific thinking, but this stage of our intellectual history has not yet been reached. It is at present necessary to establish, if we can, the phrase's credentials. This and the following section will argue that systems thinking is founded upon two pairs of ideas: those of *emergence and hierarchy*, and *communication and control*.

Biology is an "unrestricted" science, in Pantin's sense, and its phenomena are of a complexity which has severely tested scientific method. Biologists, in fact, have been among the pioneers in establishing ways of thinking in terms of wholes, and it was a biologist, Ludwig von Bertalanffy, who suggested generalizing this thinking to refer to any kind of whole, not simply to biological systems. The second strand in systems thinking comes from a very different source, from electrical, communication and control engineers. A number of other groups have also made contributions, and we can trace the development of systems ideas in, for example, psychology, anthropology and linguistics. But the four main ideas have emerged most clearly in biology and in communication and control engineering, and I shall present them in the context of work in those areas.

Aristotle argued that a whole was more than the sum of its parts, but when Aristotle's picture of the world was overthrown by the scientific revolution of the seventeenth century, this seemed an unnecessary doctrine. Newton's physics provided a mechanical picture of the universe which survived severe tests, and Aristotle's teleological outlook, in which objects in the world fulfilled their inner nature or purpose, seemed tainted by quite unnecessary metaphysical speculation. Nevertheless the history of modern biology is the history of the reinstatement of purpose as a respectable intellectual concept.

No professional experimental scientist would now deny that the evidence is that living systems in all their mechan-

teleology - doctrine of final causes; view that developments are due to the purpose or design that is served by them.

Cognition - action or faculty of knowing, perceiving, conceiving - as opposed to emotion & volition.

isms obey the established laws of physics and chemistry. But this does not mean that reductionism has carried the day; it does not mean that biological phenomena are nothing but physics and chemistry. Biology is now established as an autonomous science which is not reducible to chemistry and physics. Establishing this has established systems thinking.

Microscopic examination of plants and living tissue gave the new science its central discovery – that of the cell, a discovery which leads on to the modern view that there is in living things a hierarchy of structures in the sequence: molecules, organelles (specific entities making up the organization of the cell), cells, organs, the organism. In this hierarchy the organism itself seems intuitively to mark a boundary, organisms having an obvious identity as whole entities, in that they have a boundary which separates them from the rest of the physical world, even though there may be transports across the boundary. The question is whether or not the organism as the ultimate object of concern in biology makes biology autonomous. Or will physical and chemical explanations demolish this autonomy? One of the crucial arguments which counters this reductionism is that a demonstration that all the workings of cells and organs can be explained in terms of known facts of physics and chemistry does not explain *away* the existence of organisms as entities-to-be-explained. But the strength of this argument (in essence epistemological) was not easily established and the issue has remained a live one.

It is the concept of organized complexity which became the subject matter of the new discipline "systems"; and the general model of organized complexity is that there exists a hierarchy of levels of organizations, each more complex than the one below, a level being characterized by emergent properties which do not exist at the lower level. Indeed, more than the fact that they "do not exist" at the lower level, emergent properties are *meaningless* in the language appropriate to the lower level. "The shape of an apple", although the result of processes which operate at the level of the cells, organelles and organic molecules which comprise apple trees, and although, we hope, eventually explicable in terms of those processes, *has no meaning* at the lower levels of description. The processes at those levels result in an outcome which signals the existence of a new stable level of complexity – that of the whole apple itself – which has emergent properties, one of them being the apple's shape.

✗ A sample of the modern debate, which neatly summarizes the anti-reductionist position, is provided by Grene (1974). She points out that in principle a one-level ontol-

ogy – the belief, for example, that with increasing knowledge all science will become an account of the world in the language of, say, atomic events – contradicts itself. This is so because such a belief, to be meaningful, requires an ontology which admits both atomic events *and* cognition. Here at once a second level is smuggled in! It is logically possible, of course, that there might be no levels in between those of atomic events and cognition, but the sciences of chemistry and biology consist of some well-tested conjectures that there are such intermediate levels as are represented by molecules, cells, organelles, organs and organisms. That there is a live issue is illustrated by contemporary debate in molecular biology. The major success of molecular biology is its elucidation of the process by which deoxyribonucleic acid (DNA) is replicated in cell division, thus providing a detailed molecular account of the process by which offspring acquire inherited characteristics from their parents. We now know that the transmission to a new cell of a particular characteristic, such as blue eyes or black hair, is the result of the replication of a particular sequence of organic bases along the molecular chain of DNA. This is the now famous "genetic code". One of the discoverers of the structure of DNA, and hence of a possible mechanism for the operation of the code, Francis Crick (1966), adopts in *Of Molecules and Men* a crudely reductionist position. "The ultimate aim of the modern movement in biology" he claims, "is in fact to explain *all* biology in terms of physics and chemistry." What he fails to notice, as Grene (and also Polanyi, 1968) points out, is that *any* arrangement of the organic bases is compatible with the laws of physics and chemistry. But in biological terms the actual arrangement is *crucial*; certain sequences constitute "a code". The investigator, even if he is Crick himself, in recognizing a code is accepting that "all biology" cannot, in principle, be explained as physics and chemistry. The code is an emergent property at the level of complexity represented by biological phenomena.

The idea that the architecture of complexity is hierarchical and that different languages of description are required at different levels has in recent years led to a developing interest in hierarchy theory as such. Simon (1962) points out that the time required for the evolution of a complex form from single elements depends critically upon the numbers and distribution of intermediate forms which are themselves stable. Simple mathematical analysis of probabilities shows that the time required for a complex system to evolve is much reduced if the system is itself comprised of one or more layers of stable component subsystems. Turning the argument around: the age of planet Earth is such that only hierarchically organized entities have had time to evolve! The structure of the world we inhabit could only be hierarchical.

Hierarchy theory is concerned with the fundamental differences between one level of complexity and another. Its ultimate aim must be to provide both an account of the relationships between different levels and an account of how observed hierarchies come to be formed; what generates the levels, what separates them, what links them? Such theory is still in its infancy but whatever form it eventually takes, it seems likely to be built upon the fact that emergent properties associated with a set of elements at one level in a hierarchy are associated with what we may look upon as constraints upon the degree of freedom of the elements. The emergent properties resulting from application of the constraints will entail a descriptive language at a meta-level to that describing the elements themselves. Thus, in the language of chemistry, any arrangement of the bases in DNA obeys the laws of physical chemistry. But it is constraints upon the ordinary chemistry of the base sequences which produce the specifically biological property of genetic coding, an emergent property which marks a transition from the level we call "chemistry" to that called "biology". This imposition of constraints upon activity at one level which harnesses the laws at that level to yield activity meaningful at a higher level, is an example of regulatory or *control* action. Hierarchies are characterized by processes of control operating at the interfaces between levels. ✗

This brings us to the second pair of root ideas in systems thinking. To emergence and hierarchy we must add *communication* and *control*.

3.2 *Communication and control*

In treating the living organism as a whole, as a system, rather than simply as a set of components together with relationships between components, von Bertalanffy drew attention to the important distinction between systems which are *open* to their environment and those which are *closed*. He defined an open system (1940) as one having import and export of material. More generally, between an open system and its environment there may be exchange of materials, energy and information. Organisms, he points out, are unlike closed systems in which unchanging components settle in a state of equilibrium; organisms can achieve a steady state which depends upon continuous exchanges with an environment. Moreover, the steady state may be thermodynamically unlikely, creating and/or maintaining a high degree of order, where closed systems have no path to travel but the one which leads towards

increasing disorder (high entropy). In a hierarchy of systems such as that represented by the sequence from cell organelle to organism, or, in general, in any hierarchy of open systems, maintenance of the hierarchy will entail a set of processes in which there is *communication* of information for the purposes of regulation or *control*.

This is reflected in the language used in discussions of modern molecular biology. DNA is seen as "storing" and "coding" information (and a very great deal of it; in the 46 chromosomes of each somatic cell of a man, according to Pratt (1962), are instructions which are the informational equivalent of 46 volumes, each containing millions of words). The genetic processes entail chemical "messages" which carry instructions to "activate" or "repress" further reactions, and constitute control processes which guide the development of the organism. Indeed, it is intuitively obvious that a hierarchy of systems which are open must entail processes of communication and control if the systems are to survive the knocks administered by the system's environment. This is even more obvious if we consider not the natural hierarchy of living systems, but man-made hierarchical systems such as machines and industrial plant. The designer of an industrial plant to make a particular chemical product, for example, is forced to be "a systems thinker". He has to consider not only the individual reactor vessels, heat exchangers, pumps, etc., which make up the plant but also, at a different level of consideration, the plant as a whole whose overall performance has to be controlled to produce the desired product at the required rate, cost and purity. He will have to ensure that there exist means by which information about the state of the process can be obtained and used to initiate action to control the reaction within predefined limits; by knowing the variability of the starting materials and the possible environmental disturbances to which the process will be subject, it will be possible, it is hoped, to manipulate automatically a few so-called *control variables* according to a control strategy for the plant as a whole.

Devices incorporating automatic controllers based upon the communication of information about the state of the system were known to the ancient Greeks (Mayr, 1970), but the working out of the theory of control is relatively recent. The mathematics of Watt's 1788 centrifugal regulator for governing the speed of a steam engine, most famous of all control devices, was worked out towards the end of the nineteenth century but it is only in the last forty years that control engineering and control theory have become established as, respectively, a professional activity and a related academic discipline. Nevertheless the ideas from control theory and from information and communication engineering have made contributions to systems thinking no less important than those from organismic biology.

A link between control mechanisms studied in natural systems and those engineered in man-made systems is provided by the part of systems theory known as *cybernetics*, the word coming from the Greek word meaning "steersman". Plato used the word in making an analogy between a helmsman steering a ship and a statesman steering the "ship of state", and Ampère in the nineteenth century used it in discussing the place of political science in a classification of the sciences. Unaware of this, Norbert Wiener suggested the word in 1947 to cover the subject matter of a group of studies which had then been underway in America since the early 1940s. These studies were concerned with the theory of messages, and of message transmission for purposes of control in many different contexts (Wiener, 1948, 1950). Recognizing the generality of the notions of communication and control (whether, for example, in a specific context they refer to the regulation of blood sugar concentration, the motions involved in an owl catching a mouse, or the manipulation of temperatures and pressures in a chemical reactor to control the rate of product formation), Wiener (1948) defined cybernetics as "the entire field of control and communication theory, whether in the machine or in the animal". Under this dictum there is a range of interpretations (Pask, 1961). For Ashby, the leading theoretician in the 1950s and 1960s, cybernetics deals with "all forms of behaviours in so far as they are regular, or determinate or reproducible" (Ashby, 1956). Ashby's interest is not in the real-world manifestations of controllable wholes but in the abstract mathematically expressible image of mechanism which underlies the real embodiments. He works out the synthetic operations which can be performed upon the abstract image and so establishes the formal rules for controllability. For Ashby, the relation between cybernetics and actual machines parallels that between geometry as an abstract study and real objects in three-dimensional space. Geometry, no longer dominated by terrestrial space, provides a general mathematical framework within which terrestrial objects may be treated as a special case.

> Cybernetics is similar in its relation to the actual machine. It takes as its subject matter the domain of "all possible machines". . . . What cybernetics offers is the framework on which all individual machines may be ordered, related and understood. (Ashby, 1956)

And the "machines", of course, may be either natural or man-made.

Wiener's work covers well the core of the ideas contributed to systems thinking by study of "communication and control". Much of the decade of work which led to the publication of Wiener's book in 1948 was carried out in collaboration with J. H. Bigelow and A. Rosenblueth.

Wiener, the mathematician, and Rosenblueth, the medical scientist, both felt that useful developments were likely in the intellectual no man's land between the various established disciplines. In the early 1940s Wiener was trying to develop computing machines for the solution of partial differential equations. At the beginning of World War II Wiener worked with Bigelow on the problem of improving the accuracy of anti-aircraft guns. The difficulty there is to compute automatically the future likely position of the aircraft, to keep the computation up to date as the aircraft moves and to arrange for a shell to detonate at the appropriate spot. For the second time Wiener found himself working on mechanical/electrical systems designed to usurp what was previously thought of as a human function, in this case the huntsman's intuitive assessment of where to aim relative to a moving quarry. Wiener and Bigelow realized the importance and ubiquity of what control engineers call the process of *feedback*, namely, the transmission of information about the actual performance of any machine (in the general sense) to an earlier stage in order to modify its operation. (Usually, in *negative* feedback the modification is such as to reduce the difference between actual and desired performance; positive feedback induces instability by reinforcing a modification in performance, as when a conversation between two people in a crowded room is conducted in louder and louder tones as their output, increasing the general noise level, makes it increasingly difficult for them to hear each other.)

The work with Bigelow, which extended to the construction of machines which tried to predict the extrapolation of curves, also convinced Wiener that "the problems of control engineering and of communication engineering were inseparable". Both centred on a core concern not for mechanical equipment or electrical circuitry but for the more fundamental abstract notion of a message and its transmission.

The separation of the intended message (the "signal") from background distorting "noise" then led to a view of information transmission as a transmission of alternatives, with the unit *amount of information* defined as that transmitted as a single decision (a "yes" or "no", a one or a nought, a dot or a dash) between equally probable alternatives. The idea of a quantitative, statistically-based theory of information transmission was occurring simultaneously to the statistician R. A. Fisher, to Wiener and to Claude Shannon, a communications engineer of Bell Telephone Laboratories. For Wiener, the essential unity of the set of problems centring on communication, control and statistics called for a new name for the field: he was "forced to coin at least one artificial neo-Greek expression". Cybernetics was born.

x   In spite of the perfervid enthusiasm with which some devotees seize upon the general notions of cybernetics, usually in order to apply them promiscuously in other fields, it has not been easy to use the logico-mathematical formulations of cybernetics to derive propositions which are testable in real systems. Nevertheless, it does provide a potentially novel view of many problem areas in which reductionism has previously held sway. For example, the mind–body problem which has dogged philosophy for hundreds of years, viewed cybernetically, seems to be wrongly posed (Bateson, 1971; Sayre, 1976). In a cybernetic analysis of the process in which a person thinks, acts and modifies subsequent behaviour in the light of preceding acts, all these items (including the acts themselves) may be seen as information processing. Bateson argues that the total self-corrective unit which does this processing is not, however, the human being; it is a system whose boundaries extend beyond the human body. The system is a network of information-transmitting pathways, including some external to the actor; in this view, mind is not simply associated with the human body but is immanent in brain, plus body, plus environment.

The practicalities usually associated with cybernetics are those concerned with the design of controllers for man-made systems. This is, of course, the province of control engineers, and much of the experimental work in cybernetics seeks to construct machines which exhibit "intelligent" behaviour, as a means of exploring possible mechanisms for models of the brain. Ashby himself, although responsible for many of the formal theorems of the subject, undertook this work because of a prime interest in biological mechanisms, especially those by which living systems regulate their own behaviour. It is certainly the case that the nature of the ideas *control* and *communication*, and their link to *emergence* and *hierarchy* are most richly apparent in biological systems.

Following arguments advanced by Pattee (1973), a physicist interested in the problem of the origin of life, we may picture the concept *control* through the following picture of biological systems.

The physical universe is a hierarchy; at the lowest levels are nuclear particles, then atoms, then molecules – three levels differentiated by the forces involved; between nuclear particles are forces of about 140 million electronvolts, between atoms in a molecule are "valency" forces of about 5 electronvolts, between molecules are weaker forces of about one-half of an electronvolt. The hierarchy at this stage is characterized by these energy levels, and it is these differences which suggest that it is not foolish to treat systems of nuclei, atoms and molecules as different kinds of the same whole. Above the molecular level, some of the examples of systems consisting of groups of interacting molecules exhibit special properties which cause us to name them "living" systems. Such systems are characterized, among other things, by their exhibiting differentiated processes which may be brought into play by appropriate messages and which serve to create, and re-create, the systems themselves; in the longer term such systems may adapt and evolve more varied forms. In order to understand these properties it is necessary to invoke the idea of hierarchical control. Control is always associated with the imposition of constraints, and an account of a control process necessarily requires our taking into account at least two hierarchical levels. In general, hierarchical control requires three conditions to be met. First, imposition of a constraint must impose new functional relations; this will involve an "alternative description" of the lower level which ignores some of its detailed dynamics. Secondly, the imposition of the constraint – if the system is to be "living" – must be optimal in the sense that it is neither so tight that it leads to rigidity (as do the constraints which govern crystal formation, for example) nor so loose that specific functions are not generated at the lower level (in which case we simply have what physicists recognize as a "boundary condition"). Thirdly, the constraint must act upon the detailed dynamics of the lower level. Finally, in living systems, the variety of alternative descriptions or specific functions which may be developed does not appear to be fixed; over a long time period new forms and functions may evolve. A complete theory of hierarchical control would explain exactly how it is that collections of elements may spontaneously separate out persistent special functions under the constraints of the collection as a whole. As Pattee points out, no such theory yet exists. These are still early days in the systems movement.

This brief examination of the subject matter of cybernetics and of the basic nature of a control mechanism, indicates how close is the link between control and communication. All control processes depend upon communication, upon a flow of *information* in the form of instructions or constraints, a flow which may be automatic or manual. In general, the idea of information is prior to that of feedback, any feedback mechanism in a viable system consisting of a sensor capable of detecting potentially disruptive environmental changes and an effector capable of initiating remedial action. Some of Ashby's most important work has been his demonstration that continuing effective control in a changing environment requires a controller with a variety of responses which can match the variety of the environmental information – the so-called Law of Requisite Variety. Many would argue, in fact, that the concept of information is the most powerful idea so far contributed by the systems movement, comparable in importance to the idea of energy. Both are abstractions, both have considerable explanatory power; both generate conjectures which can be put to the test experimentally. Physics would be a chaotic subject without the idea of energy, defined as the capacity to do work. Systems thinking, similarly, could not survive without the idea of information, although its precise definition raises some problems which are not yet solved. It is important in reaching an understanding of the nature of systems thinking to acknowledge both the importance of information as a concept and the severe limitations of information theory as it exists at present.

Although the rise of civilizations has to a large extent depended upon man's ability to establish long-term continuity of communication beyond mere moment-to-moment discourse, it is only in the last sixty years that communication has been the subject of scientific study, and information has emerged as an important scientific concept.

The basic conceptualization in communication system engineering is that an information source produces a "message" which is coded to produce a "signal"; this signal is transmitted along a "channel", which will inevitably introduce some unwanted disturbances called "noise"; signal plus noise then pass to a "decoder" which regenerates the original message, little distorted, one hopes, for the receiver. Now it is obvious that engineers concerned with such systems will be interested in comparing one with another and that this will require some way of measuring what is transmitted. In particular the measurement of the rate at which the coded message passes through the channel – "channel capacity" as it is called – will require a quantitative measure of what is being transmitted, a quantitative measure of "information". It is the triumph of information theory that it provides this measure, Shannon's 1945 paper being the classic exposition (reprinted in Shannon and Weaver, 1949). The accompanying misfortune, however, is that what is measured under the name of "information" in information theory actually bears very little relation to what we understand by the word in everyday language. In normal usage information is obtained by our attributing meaning to data; I convert the data provided by the positions of the hands of a clock into the information that I am late for an appointment. The quantitative measure of "information" in information theory, however, has nothing at all to do with meaning, the reason for this lying in its origin among engineers. Their concern is for the efficiency of the process whereby a message (*any* message) becomes a signal which is transmitted and received. They are not concerned, *as engineers*, with the content of the message, hence the limitations on the technical definition of "information" in statistical information theory, which applies indifferently to both significant and trivial messages. ✗

Statistical information theory is a considerable and spectacular achievement, bringing into the domain of science a new area of human activity. Simply because of this we should note rather carefully its limitations and discount some of the grander claims made for it. The theory covers more than adequately those aspects of information which are crucial to the communication engineer. In doing this it necessarily assumes that any thousand words of prose has the same information content as any other thousand words. The measures of information content have to do only with the frequency of occurrence of symbols, and not with what they symbolize. This latter is usually called "semantic information", but semantic information theory is in its infancy. Although Wiener treated "amount of information" and "amount of meaning" as synonyms (see Bar-Hillel, 1955), the distinction was recognized by Shannon, who insists that "these semantic aspects of communication are irrelevant to the engineering problem", and by Weaver, whose early paper discussing this was reprinted with Shannon's classic paper in 1949. Weaver suggests that

> The concept of information developed in [Shannon's] theory at first seems disappointing and bizarre – disappointing because it has nothing to do with meaning, and bizarre because it deals not with a single message but rather with the statistical nature of a whole ensemble of messages . . .

Weaver defines three levels of problem: level A, that of "the technical problem" of signal transmission (with which the theory deals); level B, "the semantic problem" of how precisely the symbols convey the desired meaning; and level C, "the effectiveness problem" of how the meaning affects the recipient's conduct. He points out the hierarchical nature of the levels, in that levels B and C "can make use only of those signal occurrences which turn out to be possible when analyzed at" level A, and hopes that his discussion has "cleared the air . . . ready for a real theory of meaning". This has been very slow to emerge, and represents an extremely difficult problem. Bar-Hillel and Carnap (1953) have made a modest step towards it, based upon Carnap's work on inductive probability; they try to set up a measure of the *a priori* probability of very simple declarative statements, and hence are concerned with Weaver's level B in a particularly simple instance. Ackoff (1957) and Ackoff and Emery (1972) bring in level C; they set up a series of tentative definitions and measures related to the objectives of an individual who receives information, his valuation of his objectives, his possible courses of action and the probabilities that he will choose a particular course of action to pursue a particular objective. For example, in the 1972 work they define information as a communication which produces a change in any of the receiver's probabilities of selecting a particular course of action, and motivation as a communication which "produces a change in any of the relative values the receiver places on possible outcomes of his choice" of a course of action.

The unsolved problem is to make such definitions operational. The authors comment:

> Such applications are not easy. They are time-consuming and costly, and may require a degree of control over subjects that is difficult, if not impossible to obtain.

Nevertheless the hope is that

> . . . the existence of such measures, even when not practical or easy to apply . . . provides an *objective standard* for which indexes can be sought.

It is appropriate here to repeat that these are early days in the systems movement.

4 The shape of the systems movement

The previous sections have discussed the emergence in different areas of study of two pairs of ideas which are the core of systems thinking: emergence and hierarchy, communication and control. They provide the basis for a notation or language which can be used to describe the world outside ourselves. Together these ideas provide an outline both for a systems account of the universe and for "a systems approach" to tackling its problems, this latter being complementary to the reductionist approach embodied in the method of the natural sciences. A systems account of the observed world and a systems approach to its problems are found in many different disciplines; together all these efforts constitute what I mean by "the systems movement". It is the set of attempts in all areas of study to explore the consequences of holistic rather than reductionist thinking. The programme of the systems movement might be described as the testing of the conjecture that these ideas will enable us to tackle the problem which the method of science finds so difficult, namely the problem of organized complexity.

It might have happened that the exploration of holistic thinking developed in various disciplines using the language appropriate to each different subject. What in fact has happened is that wholes in many different areas of study, from physical geography to sociology, have been studied using the ideas and the language appropriate to systems of any kind. That the systems movement is, even on a jaundiced view, at least a loose federation of similar concerns – linked by the concept "system" – is the main achievement of Ludwig von Bertalanffy. The greatest individual contribution to this minor intellectual revolution of the 1940s (it is too early to know whether it might eventually be seen as a major one) is probably that of Norbert Wiener. But it was Bertalanffy who insisted that the emerging ideas in the various fields could be generalized in systems thinking; hence it is he who is recognized as the movement's founder. (Gray and Rizzo's *Festschrift*, 1973, gives a panoramic view of his work and interests.) His own thinking as reflected in his writings shows little development from the 1940s until his death in 1972, and Bertalanffy's work is not unfairly described by Lilienfeld (1978) as "rather repetitious and even static in character". Bertalanffy's unchanging view, which might fairly be described as his *vision*, was that there would arise as a result of work in different fields a high-level meta-theory of systems, mathematically expressed. This aspiration is clear in the founding documents of what is now the Society for General Systems Research. In the journal *Philosophy of Science*, 1955, for example, is an announcement (page 331) that "A Society for the Advancement of General Systems Theory is in the process of organization". Those concerned were the biologist Bertalanffy, together with an economist (K. E. Boulding), a physiologist (R. W. Gerard) and a mathematician (A. Rapoport). The purpose was to encourage the development of "theoretical systems which are applicable to more than one of the traditional depart-

meta – of a higher or second order kind.

ments of knowledge". The aims of general systems theory (GST) were to be:

1 To investigate the isomorphy of concepts, laws and models in various fields, and to help in useful transfers from one field to another.

2 To encourage the development of adequate theoretical models in areas which lack them.

3 To eliminate the duplication of theoretical efforts in different fields.

4 To promote the unity of science through improving the communication between specialists.

The main achievement of the organization resulting from this initiative has been the annual publication of the wide-ranging papers in the *General Systems Yearbook*. The general theory envisaged by the founders has certainly not emerged, and GST itself has recently been subject to sharp attacks, notably by Berlinski (1976) and Lilienfeld (1978). Chiding Lilienfeld for bothering to attack "a mirage", Naughton (1979) suggests that there is nothing approaching a coherent body of tested knowledge to attack, rather "a mélange of insights, theorems, tautologies and hunches . . .".

The difficulties of GST, and the kind of temptation it faces, are illustrated by a teasing problem in information theory. The mathematical form of the expression for information content is the same as that for entropy in statistical mechanics but with the sign reversed. Now, since entropy measures degree of disorder, and information may plausibly be regarded as that which reduces uncertainty and hence increases order, it is extremely tempting to equate information with negative entropy ("negentropy"). In an influential little book, Schrödinger (1944) declared that the living organism "feeds on negative entropy", and Wiener (1948) had no doubt that the order which an organism extracts from its environment is synonymous with information:

> Just as the amount of information in a system is a measure of its degree of organisation, so the entropy of a system is a measure of its degree of disorganisation; and the one is simply the negative of the other.

In fact this apparent link between information and entropy, which is simply assumed in much of the literature, is exceptionally difficult to establish rigorously (Bell (1968) and Chapman (1977) discuss the problem, which hinges on the different dimensions of the constants in the two expressions). The similarity of mathematical form between information and negative entropy does not establish any physically meaningful connection between the two

concepts. Mathematical analogies never can establish such connections, but GST has little content beyond such analogies.

The problem with GST is that it pays for its generality with lack of content. Progress in the systems movement seems more likely to come from the use of systems ideas within specific problem areas than from the development of overarching theory.

Although GST does not itself provide a means of picturing the totality of work going on in the systems movement, the distinction just made – between the development of systems thinking as such and the application of systems thinking within other areas, or disciplines – can be extended to provide a reasonable map of all the activity of the movement (Checkland, 1979). This I find useful in "placing" any particular piece of work and in keeping a grasp on the growing literature of this meta-discipline.

To construct the map a number of distinctions have to be made. First, make a distinction between the development of systems ideas as such (as in, say, cybernetics) and in the application of systems ideas within an existing discipline (as in the Cambridge geographers' rewriting of geography from a systems point of view – Chorley and Kennedy, 1971; Chapman, 1977; Bennett and Chorley, 1978). This gives two broad areas of systems work. Secondly, within the work on systems thinking as such, distinguish between purely theoretical development of systems ideas and their interrelationships, and work based on the notion of developing the ideas by seeking to "engineer" systems in the real world, using that word in its broad sense. GST is an example of the former, the development of systems engineering methodology an example of the latter. But "hard" systems engineering is only one example of the development of systems thinking by attempts at problem solving. There are others, and this leads to a third distinction: that between (1) engineering "hard" systems as such; (2) using systems ideas as an aid to decision making (as in operational research); and (3) using systems thinking to tackle "soft" ill-structured problems.

These distinctions are set out in Figure 2.1.

These seven activities within the systems movement make the picture in Figure 2.2. Also indicated are the major influences of one body of systems work upon another. Thus the engineering of hard systems has been powerfully affected by the development of control theory and by information theory as developed by communication engineers; and systems engineering itself gave a powerful impetus to the work on a "soft" systems methodology for ill-structured problems.

Figure 2.1

Significantly missing in Figure 2.1 is an arrow from 3.1 to 4.2; on the whole the RAND/OR/management science world has been unaffected by the theoretical development of systems thinking; it has been *systematic* rather than *systemic* in outlook, in spite of the insistence of the first textbook of operational research that "the comprehensiveness of OR's aim is an example of a 'systems' approach" (Churchman et al., 1957) and its admirable sentiment that "OR is concerned with as much of the whole system as it can encompass" within the constraints of time and resources.

The influences shown are internal to the systems movement. Figure 2.2 can also be extended to include the major influences of external bodies of knowledge. This is done in Figure 2.3 which indicates, for example, that the major influences on RAND systems analysis, OR and management science generally have been the methods of the natural sciences (understandable given the historical origins of OR) and economics.

It is important to be clear about the status of this "map of the systems movement". It is not, as such, a picture of the real-world systems movement; any real-world systems project may well cut across several of the map's categories. In itself, the map is no more than a set of logical distinctions; it is not even a set of distinctions which *have* to be made; it is a set I have chosen to make. What this particular set provides, I argue, is a picture of the systems movement

which does map well on to current real-world systems activity, its intellectual efforts and its literature, and which also enables any particular piece of work or literature to be placed in the context of the movement as a whole.

Looking back over the whole history of the science movement and the emergence within it of the systems activity displayed in Figures 2.2 and 2.3, the nature of this development can be understood in terms of changing concepts of *a machine*. The concept of a machine developed by Newtonian physics is that of a clocklike mechanism, deterministic and preprogrammed. Modern science, with the creation of quantum mechanics, contributes the idea of the statistical machine, the fine detail of whose behaviour is not deterministic. The systems movement then adds the concept of the self-regulated machine which has autonomous control over its own behaviour. Systems thinking has now been exploring the implications of this concept for about thirty years.

The results so far might be fairly described as "significant but not spectacular". Why has progress not been more rapid? One reason is undoubtedly the strong grip which reductionist thinking has on anyone educated in Western civilization. It is not simply that reductive analysis is, in the phrase of Medawar and Medawar (1977), "the most successful explanatory technique that has ever been used in science"; it is also the case that the counterposition to reductionism, based on holism and emergence, does not

deterministic – action, not free, but determined by motives regarded as external forces acting on the will.

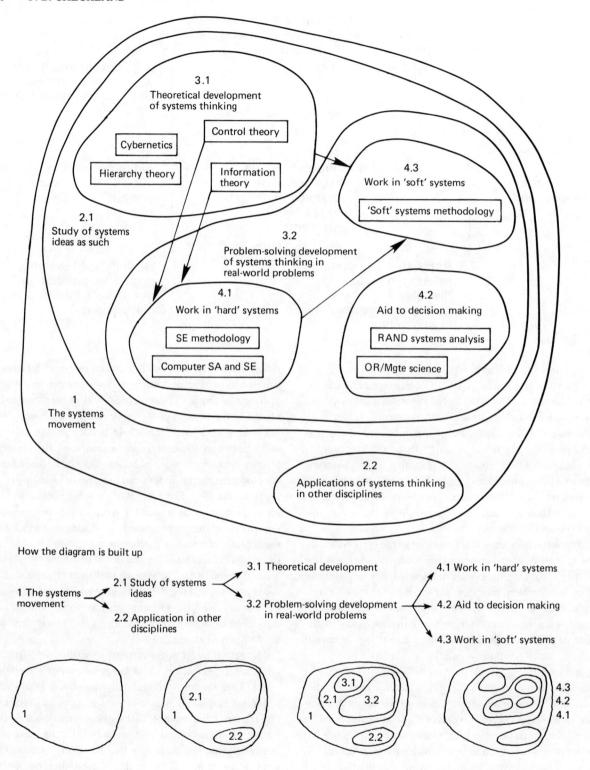

Figure 2.2 The shape of the systems movement (arrows indicate major influences).

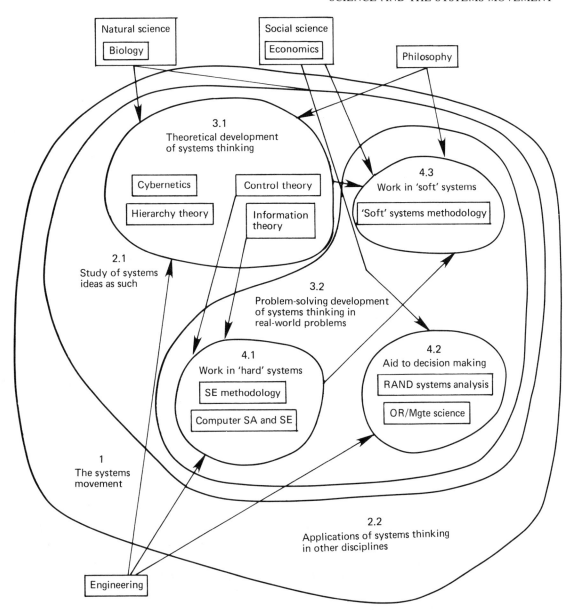

Figure 2.3 The shape of the systems movement indicating major external influences.

provide as clear a philosophy. (The rather woolly Messianic air of some of the GST writings is counterproductive in this respect.) The point is strongly made by Grene (1974):

> ... the anti-reducibility position is, for many people, impossible to accept. Why? Because it breaks through the defences of a simple, one-level physicalism without

providing an alternative metaphysic to take its place. To think anti-reductively demands thinking in terms of hierarchical systems, of levels of reality and the like; but we don't know any longer how to think in that way – and to be told, even to *know*, that the contrary position is absurd does not in itself allow us to embrace wholeheartedly what ought to be the more reasonable alternative. For anti-reductivism is "reasonable" only in the perverse sense that its negation is self-contradictory, not in the more substantive sense of fitting smoothly into a *Weltanschauung* in which, as people educated in the ideal of a "scientific" world view, we can feel at home.

It must be the current task of the systems movement to work towards a version of systems thinking within which we can feel "at home" in a positive sense.

References

Ackoff, R. L. (1957) "Towards a behavioural theory of communication", in Buckley, W. (ed.) (1968) *Modern Systems Research for the Behavioural Scientist,* Aldine, Chicago.

Ackoff, R. L. and Emery, F. E. (1972) *On Purposeful Systems,* Tavistock, London.

Ashby, W. R. (1956) *An Introduction to Cybernetics,* Chapman and Hall, London.

Bar-Hillel, Y. (1955) "An examination of information theory", *Philosophy of Science* **22,** 86.

Bar-Hillel, Y. and Carnap, R. (1953) "Semantic information", *British Journal for the Philosophy of Science* **4,** 14.

Bateson, G. (1971) "The cybernetics of 'self': a theory of alcoholism", in Bateson, G. (1973) *Steps to an Ecology of Mind,* Paladin, St Albans, Herts.

Bell, D. A. (1968) *Information Theory and its Engineering Applications,* Pitman, London.

Bennett, R. J. and Chorley, R. J. (1978) *Environmental Systems,* Methuen, London.

Berlinski, D. (1976) *On Systems Analysis,* MIT Press, Cambridge, Mass.

Bernal, J. D. (1939) *The Social Function of Science,* Routledge, London.

Bertalanffy, L. von (1940) "The organism considered as a physical system", reprinted in Bertalanffy, L. von (1968) *General System Theory,* Braziller, New York.

Butterfield, H. (1949) *The Origins of Modern Science 1300–1800,* Bell, London.

Chapman, G. P. (1977) *Human and Environmental Systems,* Academic Press, New York.

Checkland, P. B. (1979) "The shape of the systems movement", *Journal of Applied Systems Analysis* **6.**

Chorley, R. J. and Kennedy, B. A. (1971) *Physical Geography: A Systems Approach,* Prentice-Hall International, London.

Churchman, C. West et al. (1957) *Introduction to Operations Research,* Wiley, New York.

Cohen, P. (1968) *Modern Social Theory,* Heinemann, London.

Crick, F. (1966) *Of Molecules and Men,* University of Washington Press, Seattle.

Gray, W. and Rizzo, N. D. (1973) *Unity Through Diversity: A Festschrift for Ludwig von Bertalanffy,* Gordon and Breach, New York.

Grene, M. (1974) *The Understanding of Nature,* D. Reidel, Dordrecht.

Hall, A. R. (1963) *From Galileo to Newton 1630–1720,* Collins, London.

Lilienfeld, R. (1978) *The Rise of Systems Theory,* Wiley, New York.

Mayr, O. (1970) *The Origins of Feedback Control,* MIT Press, Cambridge, Mass.

Medawar, P. B. and Medawar, J. S. (1977) *The Life Science,* Wildwood House, London.

Nagel, E. (1961) *The Structure of Science,* Routledge and Kegan Paul, London.

Naughton, J. (1979) "Review of Lilienfeld (1978)", in *Futures* **11**(2).

Pantin, C. P. A. (1968) *The Relations Between the Sciences,* Cambridge University Press, London.

Pask, G. (1961) *An Approach to Cybernetics,* Hutchinson, London.

Pattee, H. H. (ed.) (1973) *Hierarchy Theory: The Challenge of Complex Systems,* Braziller, New York.

Polanyi, M. (1968) "Life's irreducible structure", *Science* **160,** 1308.

Popper, K. R. (1974) "Autobiography of Karl Popper", in Schilpp, P. A. (ed.) (1974) *The Philosophy of Karl Popper,* Open Court, La Salle, Ill. Published separately as *Unended Quest* (1976), Fontana/Collins, London.

Pratt, J. R. (1962) "A 'book model' of genetic information", in Kash, M. and Pullman, B. (1962) *Horizons in Biochemistry,* Academic Press, New York.

Ravetz, J. R. (1971) *Scientific Knowledge and its Social Problems,* Oxford University Press, London.

Sayre, K. M. (1976) *Cybernetics and the Philosophy of Mind,* Routledge and Kegan Paul, London.

Schrödinger, E. (1944) *What is Life?,* Cambridge University Press, London.

Shannon, C. E. and Weaver, W. (1949) *The Mathematical Theory of Communication,* University of Illinois Press, Urbana, Ill.

Simon, H. (1962) "The architecture of complexity", reprinted in *The Sciences of the Artificial* (1969), MIT Press, Cambridge, Mass.

Skair, L. (1973) *Organized Knowledge,* Hart-Davis, Mac-Gibbon, London.

Thorpe, W. H. (1974) *Animal Nature and Human Nature*, Methuen, London.

Wiener, N. (1948) *Cybernetics,* MIT Press, Cambridge, Mass. and J. Wiley, New York (enlarged edition 1961).

Wiener, N. (1950) *The Human Use of Human Beings,* Houghton Mifflin, Boston.

Wild, R. (1972) *Management and Production,* Penguin Books, Harmondsworth.

3 The modern view: a systems approach

by F. E. Kast and J. E. Rosenzweig

Organization theory and management practice have undergone substantial changes in recent years. Traditional theory has been modified and enriched by informational inputs from the management sciences and the behavioral sciences. These research and conceptual endeavors have, at times, led to divergent findings. During the past decade, however, an approach has emerged which can serve as a basis of convergence – the systems approach, which facilitates unification in many fields of knowledge. It has been used in the physical, biological, and social sciences as a broad frame of reference. It can also be used as a framework for the integration of a modern organization theory. General systems theory, its pervasiveness, its relationship to organization theory, and its potential usefulness are discussed in this chapter via the following topics:

General Systems Theory
Pervasiveness of Systems Theory
Systems Approach and Organization Theory
Organization: An Open System in Its Environment
Organization: A Structured Sociotechnical System
Other Properties of Organizational Systems
Managerial Systems
Systems Concepts for Organization and Management

General Systems Theory

Over the past two decades the development of general systems theory has provided a basis for the integration of scientific knowledge across a broad spectrum.[1] *A system is an organized or complex whole: an assemblage or combination of things or parts forming a complex or unitary whole.* The term *system* covers a broad spectrum of our physical, biological, and social world. In the universe there are galaxial systems, geophysical systems, and molecular systems. In biology we speak of the organism as a system of mutually dependent parts, each of which includes many subsystems. The human body is a complex organism including, among others, a skeletal system, a circulatory system, and a nervous system. We come into daily contact with such phenomena as transportation systems, communication systems, and economic systems.

In considering the various types of systems in our universe, Kenneth Boulding provides a useful classification of systems which sets forth a hierarchy of levels as follows:

1. The first level is that of static structure. It might be called the level of *frameworks*; for example, the anatomy of the universe.
2. The next level is that of the simple dynamic system with predetermined, necessary motions. This might be called the level of *clockworks*.
3. The control mechanism or cybernetic system, which might be nicknamed the level of the *thermostat*. The system is self-regulating in maintaining equilibrium.
4. The fourth level is that of the "open system", or self-maintaining structure. This is the level at which life begins to differentiate from not-life: it might be called the level of the *cell*.
5. The next level might be called the genetic–societal level; it is typified by the *plant*, and it dominates the empirical world of the botanist.
6. The *animal* system level is characterized by increased mobility, teleological behavior, and self-awareness.
7. The next level is the *human* level, that is, of the individual human being considered as a system with self-awareness and the ability to utilize language and symbolism.
8. The *social system* or systems of human organization constitute the next level, with the consideration of the content and meaning of messages, the nature and dimensions of value systems, the transcription of images into historical record, the subtle symbolizations of art, music, and poetry, and the complex gamut of human emotion.
9. *Transcendental systems* complete the classification of levels.

These are the ultimates and absolutes and the inescapable unknowables, and they also exhibit systematic structure and relationship.[2]

The first three levels in this hierarchy can be classified as physical or mechanical systems and provide the basis of knowledge in the physical sciences such as physics and astronomy. The fourth, fifth, and sixth levels are concerned with biological systems and are the interest of biologists, botanists, and zoologists. The last three levels are involved with human and social systems and are the concern of the social sciences as well as the arts, humanities, and religion.

General systems theory provides a basis for understanding and integrating knowledge from a wide variety of highly specialized fields. In the past, traditional knowledge has been along well-defined subject-matter lines. Bertalanffy * suggests that the various fields of modern science have had a continual evolution toward a parallelism of ideas. This parallelism provides an opportunity to formulate and develop principles which hold for systems in general. "In modern science, dynamic interaction is the basic problem in all fields, and its general principles will have to be formulated in General System Theory."[3] General systems theory provides the broad macro view from which we may look at all types of systems. "So has arisen systems theory – the attempt to develop scientific principles to aid us in our struggles with dynamic systems with highly interacting parts."[4]

Bertalanffy made another major contribution in setting forth a distinction between closed systems and open systems. Physical and mechanical systems can be considered as closed in relationship to their environment. Thus, the first three levels in Boulding's hierarchy are closed systems. On the other hand, biological and social systems are not closed but are in constant interaction with their environment. This view of biological and social phenomena as open systems has profound importance for the social sciences and organization theory. Traditional theory assumed the organization to be a closed system, whereas the modern approach considers it an open system in interaction with its environment. While the development of general systems theory has provided an overall conceptual view for dealing with all types of phenomena – physical, biological, and social – there have been many additional threads in intellectual development which have contributed to the development of the systems approach.

Pervasiveness of Systems Theory

In complex societies with rapid expansion of knowledge, the various scientific fields become highly differentiated and specialized. In many scientific fields, the concentration over the past several decades has been on analytical, fact-finding, and experimental approaches in highly specific areas. This

* [An article by Bertalanffy setting out the major ideas of General System Theory follows on p. 59. *Ed.*]

has been useful in helping to develop knowledge and to understand the details of specific but limited subjects. At some stage, however, there should be a period of synthesis, reconciliation, and integration, so that the analytical and fact-finding elements are unified into broader, multi-dimensional theories.[5] There is evidence that every field of human knowledge passes alternately through phases of analysis and fact finding to periods of synthesis and integration. Recently systems theory has provided this framework in many fields – physical, biological, and social. Even more important, it provides a basis for communication between scientists in the various disciplinary areas – a problem of immense importance with the high degree of specialization of knowledge.[6]

The application of systems thinking has been of particular relevance to the social sciences. There is a close relationship between general systems theory and the development of functionalism in the social sciences, as described by Martindale:

> The essential unity of the social sciences has been revealed in the flooding of the functionalistic point of view across the boundaries of the special disciplines. This point of view has had both theoretical and methodological dimensions. Theoretically, it consists in the analysis of social and cultural life from the standpoint of the primacy of wholes or systems. Epistemologically, it involves analysis of social events by methods thought peculiarly adapted to the integration of social events into systems.
>
> The functionalistic point of view has been manifest in all of the social sciences from psychology through sociology, political science, economics, and anthropology to geography, jurisprudence, and linguistics.[7]

Although there are several connotations of the word "functionalism", its basic emphasis is upon systems of relationships and the integration of parts and subsystems into a functional whole.[8] Functionalism attempts to look at social systems in terms of structures, processes, and functions and attempts to understand the relationship between these components. It emphasizes that each element of a culture or social institution has a function in the broader system.

Functionalism, under the influence of the earlier works of A. R. Radcliffe-Brown and Bronislaw Malinowski, has become the framework for modern anthropology.[9] They pioneered the view that social customs, patterns of behavior, and institutions do not exist independently but must be considered in relationship to the total culture. All aspects of social life form a related whole, and society can best be understood as an interconnected system. Thus each social action, such as a marriage ceremony or the punishment of a crime, has a function in the culture as a whole and contributes to the maintenance of the social structure.

In sociology, Talcott Parsons led in the adoption of functionalism and the general systems viewpoint.[10] Although Parsons acknowledges his debt to Pareto for the concept of systems in scientific theory, it is Parsons himself who has fully utilized the open-systems approach for the study of social structures.[11] He not only developed a broad social system framework but also related his ideas to the organization. Many of his concepts relating to the structure and processes of social systems will be used later in this book.

In the field of psychology, the systems approach has achieved prominence. The various types of behaviorism in psychological theory have given way to the holism of gestalt psychology and field theory. The very word *gestalt* is German for configuration or pattern.[12] "The Gestaltists early adopted the concept of system, which is more than the sum of its components, and which determines the activity of these components."[13] Kurt Lewin was among the first to apply the tenets of gestalt psychology to the field of individual personality. He found that purely psychological explanations of personality were inadequate and that sociocultural forces had to be taken into account. He viewed personality as a dynamic system, influenced by the individual's environment. Harry Stack Sullivan, in his *Interpersonal Theory of Psychiatry*, went even further in relating personality to the sociocultural system. He viewed the foundation of personality as an extension and elaboration of social relationships. A further extension of psychology to give greater consideration to broader interpersonal and social systems is seen in the rapidly expanding field of social psychology.[14]

Modern economics has increasingly used the systems approach. Equilibrium concepts are fundamental in economic thought, and the very basis of this type of analysis is consideration of subsystems of a total system. Economics is moving away from static equilibrium models appropriate to closed systems toward dynamic equilibrium considerations appropriate to open systems. Leontief and his followers in industrial input–output analysis utilize the systems approach. "Considered from the point of view of the input-output scheme any national economy can be described as a system of mutually interrelated industries or – if one prefers a more abstract term – interdependent economic activities. The interrelation actually consists in the more or less steady streams of goods and services which directly or indirectly link all the sectors of the economy to each other."[15]

The very foundation of the discipline of cybernetics is based upon a systems approach.[16] It is primarily concerned with communication and information flow in complex systems. Although cybernetics has been applied primarily to mechanistic engineering problems, its model of feedback, control, and regulation has a great deal of applicability for biological and social systems as well.

Another similar point of view permeating many of the social and physical sciences is the concept of holism which is closely related to functionalism and the systems approach. Holism is the view that all systems – physical, biological, and social – are composed of interrelated subsystems. The whole is not just the sum of the parts, but the system itself can be explained only as a totality. Holism is the opposite of elementarism, which views the total as the sum of its individual parts. The holistic view is basic to the systems approach. In traditional organization theory, as well as in many of the sciences, the subsystems have been studied separately, with the view to later putting the parts together into the whole. The systems approach emphasizes that this is not possible and that the starting point has to be with the total system.

The foregoing discussion has attempted to show how the systems approach and associate views have become the operating framework for many physical and social sciences. We agree with Chin, who says:

Psychologists, sociologists, anthropologists, economists, and political scientists have been "discovering" and using the system model. In so doing, they find intimations of an exhilarating "unity" of science, because the system models used by biological and physical scientists seem to be exactly similar. Thus, the system model is regarded by some system theorists as universally applicable to physical and social events, and to human relationships in small and large units.[17]

It is important for the student of organization and management to recognize that the developing body of knowledge and applications of the systems approach to complex organizations is but a part of the broad trend in many of the physical and social sciences and that this field is part of a pervasive stream of thought. Furthermore, understanding that organization theory can be put in the context of general systems theory allows for a growing community of interest and understanding with widely diverse disciplines. We will now look more closely at the direct relationship between the systems approach and organization theory.

Systems Approach and Organization Theory

Traditional organization theory used a highly structured, closed-system approach. Modern theory has moved toward the open-system approach. "The distinctive qualities of modern organization theory are its conceptual-analytical base, its reliance on empirical research data, and, above all, its synthesizing, integrating nature. These qualities are framed in a philosophy which accepts the premise that the only meaningful way to study organization is as a system." [18]

Chester Barnard was one of the first management writers to utilize the systems approach.[19] Herbert Simon and his associates viewed the organization as a complex system of decision-making processes. Simon has ranged widely in seeking new disciplinary knowledge to integrate into his organization theories. However, the one broad consistency in both his research and writings has been the utilization of the systems approach. "The term 'systems' is being used more and more to refer to methods of scientific analysis that are particularly adapted to the unraveling of complexity." [20] He not only emphasizes this approach for the behavioral view of organizations but also stresses its importance in management science.

The systems approach has been advocated by a number of other writers in management science. Churchman and his associates were among the earliest to emphasize this view. "The comprehensiveness of O. R.'s aim is an example of a 'systems' approach, since 'system' implies an interconnected complex of functionally related components. Thus a business organization is a social or man-machine system." [21] Although the systems approach has been adopted and utilized in management science, the models typically used are closed in the sense that they consider only certain variables and exclude from consideration those not subject to quantification.

The sociologist George Homans uses systems concepts as a basis for his empirical research on social groups. He developed a model of social systems which can serve as an appropriate basis for small groups and also for larger organizations.[22] In his view, an organization is comprised of an external environmental system and an internal system of relationships which are mutually interdependent. There are three elements in a social system. *Activities* are the tasks which people perform. *Interactions* occur between people in the performance of these tasks, and *sentiments* develop between people. These elements are mutually interdependent.

Philip Selznick utilizes structural functional analysis and the systems approach in his studies of organizations. The institutional leader is concerned with the adaptation of the organization to its external systems. The organization is a dynamic system, constantly changing and adapting to internal and external pressures, and is in a continual process of evolution. The organization is a formal system influenced by the internal social structure and subject to the pressure of an institutional environment. "Cooperative systems are constituted of individuals interacting as wholes in relation to a formal system of coordination. The concrete structure is therefore a resultant of the reciprocal influences of the formal and informal aspects of organization. Furthermore, this structure is itself a totality, an adaptive 'organism' reacting to influences upon it from an external environment." [23] Selznick used this systems frame of reference for empirical research on governmental agencies and other complex organizations.

The systems approach has not only been used by many students of organization theory in the United States but has also provided the model in other countries. The group of social scientists associated with the Tavistock Institute of Human Relations in London is one of the strongest proponents of the open-systems approach. As a result of a number of research studies in the mining, textile, and manufacturing industries in England and other countries, this group developed the concept of the sociotechnical system.[24] They also stressed that the organization is an open system in interaction with its environment.

The systems approach has also been adopted by social psychologists as a basis for studying organizations. Using open-systems theory as a general conceptual scheme, Katz and Kahn present a comprehensive theory of organization.[14] They suggest that the psychological approach has generally ignored or has not dealt effectively with the facts of structure and social organization, and they use systems concepts to develop an integrated model.

There are numerous examples of the utilization of the systems approach at operational levels. For example, the trend toward automation involves implementation of these ideas. Automation suggests a self-contained system with inputs, outputs, and a mechanism of control. Automated production systems for processing of materials are becoming increasingly important in many industries. Another phase which has been automated is information flow. With the introduction of large-scale, electronic data processing equipment, information processing systems have been developed for many applications. Physical distribution systems have received increasing attention. The concepts of logistics, or material management, have been used to emphasize the flow of materials through distribution channels.

The systems approach has been utilized as a basis of organization for many of our advanced defense and space programs. Program management is geared to changing managerial requirements in research, development, procurement, and utilization. With the new, complex programs such as ballistic missiles and advanced space programs it became impossible to think of individual segments or parts of the program as separate entities, and it was necessary to move to a broader systems approach.[25] In many other types of governmental projects, which require the integration of many agencies and activities – transportation problems, pollution control, and urban renewal, for example – the systems approach is being used.

These examples of the increasing trend in adapting the systems approach to modern organization theory and management practice are by no means exhaustive; they merely illustrate current developments. However, they are sufficient to indicate that increasing attention is being given to the study of organizations as complex systems. This modern view treats the organization as a system of mutually dependent parts and variables, which is part of the whole system of society. Modern organization theory and general systems theory are closely related. Many systems concepts taken from the investigation of other types of physical, biological, and social systems are meaningful to the study of organizations.

Organization: An Open System in Its Environment

Systems can be considered in two ways: (1) closed or (2) open and in interaction with their environments. This distinction is important in organization theory. Closed-system thinking stems primarily from the physical sciences and is applicable to mechanistic systems. Many of the earlier concepts in the social sciences and in organization theory were closed-system views because they considered the system under study as self-contained. Traditional management theories were primarily closed-system views concentrating only upon the internal operation of the organization and adopting highly rationalistic approaches taken from physical science models. The organization was considered as sufficiently independent so that its problems could be analyzed in terms of internal structure, tasks, and formal relationships – without reference to the external environment.

A characteristic of all closed systems is that they have an inherent tendency to move toward a static equilibrium and entropy. Entropy is a term which originated in thermodynamics and is applicable to all physical systems. It is the tendency for any closed system to move toward a chaotic or random state in which there is no further potential for energy transformation or work. "The disorder, disorganization, lack of patterning, or randomness of organization of a system is known as its *entropy*."[26] A closed system tends to increase in entropy over time, to move toward greater disorder and randomness.

Biological and social systems do not fall within this classification. The open-system view recognizes that the biological or social system is in a dynamic relationship with its environment and receives various inputs, transforms these inputs in some way, and exports outputs. The receipt of inputs in the form of material, energy, and information allows the open system to offset the process of entropy. These systems are open not only in relation to their environment but also in relation to themselves, or "internally" in that interactions between components affect the system as a whole. The open system adapts to its environment by changing the structure and processes of its internal components.[27]

The organization can be considered in terms of a general open-system model, as in Figure 3.1. The open system is in

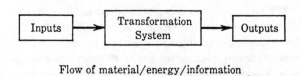

Flow of material/energy/information →

Figure 3.1 General model of organization as an open system.

continual interaction with its environment and achieves a "steady state" or dynamic equilibrium while still retaining the capacity for work or energy transformation. The survival of the system, in effect, would not be possible without continuous inflow, transformation, and outflow. In the biological or social system this is a continuous recycling process. The system must receive sufficient input of resources to maintain its operations and also to export the transformed resources to the environment in sufficient quantity to continue the cycle.

For example, the business organization receives inputs from the society in the form of people, materials, money, and information; it transforms these into outputs of products, services, and rewards to the organizational members sufficiently large to maintain their participation. For the business enterprise, money and the market provide a mechanism of the recycling of resources between the firm and its environment. The same kind of analysis can be made for all types of social organizations. Open-system views provide the basis for the development of a more comprehensive organization theory.

Organization: A Structured Sociotechnical System

In addition to being considered as an open system in interaction with its environment, the organization can also be viewed as a structured sociotechnical system. This view of the organization is set forth by Trist and his associates at the Tavistock Institute. Technology is based upon the tasks to be performed and includes the equipment, tools, facilities, and operating techniques. The social subsystem is the relationship between the participants in the organization. The technological and social subsystems are in interaction with each other and are interdependent. "Trist's concept of the socio-technical system arose from the consideration that any production system requires both a technological organization – equipment and process layout – and a work organization – relating those who carry out the necessary tasks to each other. Technological demands limit the kind of work organization possible, but a work organization has social and psychological properties of its own that are independent of technology."[24]

Under this view an organization is not simply a technical or a social system. Rather, it is the structuring and integrating of human activities around various technologies. The technologies affect the types of inputs into the organization and the outputs from the system. However, the social system determines the effectiveness and efficiency of the utilization of the technology.

Technical subsystems are determined by the task requirements of the organization and vary widely. The technical subsystem for the manufacturing of automobiles differs significantly from that in an oil refinery or in an electronics or aerospace company. Similarly, the task requirements and technology in a hospital are substantially different from those in a university. The technological subsystem is shaped by the specialization of knowledge and skills required, the types of machinery and equipment involved, and the layout of facilities.

Technology frequently prescribes the type of human inputs required. For example, an aerospace company requires the employment of many scientists, engineers, and other highly trained people. Technology also is a prime factor in determining the structure and relationships between jobs.

In addition to the technical subsystem, every organization has within its boundaries a psycho-social subsystem, which consists of the interactions, expectations and aspirations,

sentiments, and values of the participants. However, it must be emphasized that these two subsystems, the technical and the social, cannot be looked at separately but must be considered in the context of the total organization. Any change in the technical subsystem will have repercussions on the social subsystem and conversely.

The organization *structure* can be considered as a third subsystem intermeshed between the technical and the social subsystems. The task requirements and technology have a fundamental influence upon the structure. Structure is concerned with the ways in which the tasks of the organization are divided into operating units and with the coordination of the units. In the formal sense, structure is set forth by the organization chart, by positions and job descriptions, and by rules and procedures. It also concerns the pattern of authority, communications, and work flow. In a sense, the organization structure provides for formalization of relationships between the technical and the psycho-social subsystems. However, it should be emphasized that this linkage is by no means complete and that many interactions and relationships occur between the technical and the psycho-social subsystems which bypass the formal structure.

One way of visualizing the organization as a structured sociotechnical system is shown in Figure 3.2. The goals and

Figure 3.2 Organization as a sociotechnical system.

values, as well as the technical, structural, psycho-social, and managerial subsystems are shown as integral parts of the overall organization. This figure is an aid to understanding the evolution in organization theory. Traditional management theory emphasized the structural and managerial subsystems and was concerned with developing principles. The human relationists and behavioral scientists emphasized the psycho-social subsystem and focused their attention on motivation, group dynamics, and other related factors. The management science school emphasized the economic–technical subsystem and techniques for quantifying decision-making and control processes. Thus each approach to organization and management has emphasized particular primary subsystems, with little recognition of the importance of the others. The modern approach views the organization as a structured, sociotechnical system and considers *each* of the primary subsystems *and* their interactions.

Other Properties of Organizational Systems

The systems approach emphasizes that an organization has a number of interacting subsystems and can only be considered in a holistic or synergistic framework. A number of other characteristics of organizational systems can be identified.

Contrived systems

Social organizations are not natural like mechanical or biological systems; they are contrived. They have structure, but the structure of events rather than of physical components, and it cannot be separated from the processes of the system. The fact that social organizations are contrived by human beings suggests that they can be established for an infinite variety of objectives and do not follow the same life-cycle pattern of birth, maturity, and death as biological systems. Katz and Kahn say:

> Social structures are essentially contrived systems. They are made of men and are imperfect systems. They can come apart at the seams overnight, but they can also outlast by centuries the biological organisms which originally created them. The cement which holds them together is essentially psychological rather than biological. Social systems are anchored in the attitudes, perceptions, beliefs, motivations, habits, and expectations of human beings.[14]

Recognizing that the social organization is a contrived system cautions us against making an exact analogy between it and physical or biological systems.

Boundaries

The view of the organization as an open sociotechnical system suggests that there are boundaries which separate it from the environment. The concept of boundaries helps us understand the distinction between open and closed systems. The closed system has rigid, impenetrable boundaries, whereas the open system has permeable boundaries between itself and a broader supersystem. "Boundaries are the demarcation lines or regions for the definition of appropriate system activity, for admission of members into the system, and for other imports into the system. The

boundary constitutes a barrier for many types of interaction between people on the inside and people on the outside, but it includes some facilitating device for the particular types of transactions necessary for organizational functioning."

The boundaries set the "domain" of the organization's activities. In a physical, mechanical, or biological system the boundaries can be identified. In a social organization, the boundaries are not easily definable and are determined primarily by the functions and activities of the organization. It is characterized by rather vaguely formed, highly permeable boundaries. Frequently, in the study of social organizations, where to draw the boundaries is a matter of convenience and strategy. Thus, in the study of a small work group, we may artificially establish the boundary to include only the activities of the immediate group and may consider interactions with other groups as outside these boundaries. Or, we might set our boundaries to include an entire department, division, company, industry, or total economic system. The boundaries of a social organization are often quite flexible and changeable over time, depending upon its activities and functions.

One of the key functions within any organization is that of boundary regulation between systems. A primary role of management is serving as a linking pin or boundary agent between the various subsystems to ensure integration and cooperation.[28] Furthermore, an important managerial function is that of serving as boundary agent between the organization and environmental systems.

The concept of *interface* is useful in understanding boundary relationships. An interface may be defined as the area of contact between one system and another. Thus, the business organization has many interfaces with other systems: suppliers of materials, the local community, prospective employees, unions, customers, and state, local, and federal governmental agencies. There are many transactional processes across systems boundaries at the interface involving the transfer of energy, materials, people, money, and information.

Hierarchy of systems

In general, all systems – physical, biological, and social – can be considered in a hierarchical sense. A system is composed of subsystems of a lower order and is also part of a supersystem. Thus, there is a hierarchy of the components in the system. Large organizations are almost universally hierarchical in structure. People are organized into groups; groups are organized into departments; departments are organized into divisions; divisions are organized into companies; and companies are part of an industry and economy. Many general systems writers have concluded that this hierarchical relationship is paramount in all types of systems. "Hierarchical subdivision is not a characteristic that is peculiar to human organizations. It is common to virtually all complex systems of which we have knowledge. [There are] strong reasons for believing that almost any system of sufficient complexity would have to have the rooms-within-rooms structure that we observe in actual human organizations. The reasons for hierarchy go far beyond the need for unity of command or other considerations relating to authority."[29]

The hierarchical structure is not only related to levels but is based upon the need for more inclusive clustering or combination of subsystems into a broader system, in order to coordinate activities and processes. In complex organizations there is a hierarchy of processes as well as structure.

Negative entropy

Closed physical systems are subject to the force of entropy which increases until eventually the entire system stops. The tendency toward maximum entropy is a movement to disorder, complete lack of resource transformation, and death. In a closed system, the change in entropy must always be positive. However, in the open biological or social system, entropy can be arrested and may even be transformed to negative entropy – a process of more complete organization and ability to transform resources. This is possible because in open systems, resources (material, energy, and information) utilized to arrest the entropy process, are imported from the external environment. "Living systems, maintaining themselves in a steady state, can avoid the increase of entropy, and may even develop towards states of increased order and organization."[30] Obviously, for the biological system, this process of negative entropy is never perfect. The organism lives and grows for a period of time but is subject to deterioration and death. The contrived, or social, organization which can continue to import new human components and other resources in order to continue its functioning may be capable of indefinitely offsetting the entropy process. However, the only way in which the organization can offset entropy is by continually importing material, energy, and information in one form or another, transforming them, and redistributing resources to the environment.

The steady state or dynamic equilibrium

The concept of *steady state* is closely related to that of negative entropy. A closed system must eventually attain an equilibrium state with maximum entropy – death or disorganization. An open system, however, may attain a state where the system remains in dynamic equilibrium through the continuous inflow of material, energy, and information. This is called a steady state. This relationship between negative entropy and the steady state for living organisms and social systems is suggested by Emery and Trist.

In contradistinction to physical objects, any living entity survives by importing into itself certain types of material from its environment, transforming these in accordance with its own system characteristics, and exporting other types back into the environment. By this process the organism obtains the additional energy that renders it "negentropic"; it becomes capable of attaining stability in a time-independent steady state – a necessary condition of adaptability to environmental variance.[31]

The steady state for the open system, as contrasted to the closed system subject to entropy, occurs while the system can still maintain its functions and perform effectively. Under this concept, an organization is able to adapt to changes in its environment and to maintain a continual steady state. An analogy can be seen in a biological system. The human body is able to maintain a steady state of body temperature in spite of wide variations in the environmental temperature. Obviously, there are limits to the degree to which the biological organism or the social organization can maintain a steady state in response to environmental changes. Massive environmental changes may be so great that it is impossible for the system to adapt. The organism dies, or the social organization is disbanded.

The steady state has an additional meaning; within the organizational system, the various subsystems have achieved a balance of relationships and forces which allows the total system to perform effectively. In biological organisms, the term *homeostasis* is applied to the organism's steady state. For social organizations, it is not an absolute steady state but rather a dynamic or moving equilibrium, one of continual adjustment to environmental and internal forces. The social organization will attempt to accumulate a certain "slack" of resources which helps it to maintain its equilibrium and to mitigate some of the possible variations in the inflow and environmental requirements.

Feedback mechanisms

The concept of feedback is important in understanding how a system maintains a dynamic equilibrium. Through the process of feedback, the system continually receives information from its environment which helps it adjust.

The concept of feedback has been used in looking at a number of biological phenomena. The maintenance of homeostasis, or the balance in a living organism, depends on a continual feedback of information to that organism from its environment. For example, the cooling of the blood from a drop in external temperatures stimulates certain centers in the brain which activate heat-producing mechanisms of the body, and the organism's temperature is monitored back to the center so that temperature is maintained at a steady level. Man uses principles of feedback in many of his physical activities. For example, in riding a bicycle, he receives feedback in regard to direction and balance which cause him to take corrective actions. Feedback can be both positive and negative, although for our purposes the most important consideration is that of negative feedback. Negative feedback is informational input which indicates that the system is deviating from a prescribed course and should readjust to a new steady state. Feedback is of vital importance in the complex organization which must continually receive informational inputs from its environment. Management is involved in interpreting and correcting for this information feedback. This is a vital part of the organizational control function.[32]

Adaptive and maintenance mechanisms

Systems must have two mechanisms which are often in conflict. First, in order to maintain an equilibrium, they must have maintenance mechanisms which ensure that the various subsystems are in balance and that the total system is in accord with its environment. The forces for maintenance are conservative, and attempt to prevent the system from changing so rapidly that the various subsystems and total system become out of balance. Second, adaptive mechanisms are necessary in order to provide a *dynamic* equilibrium, one which is changing over time. Therefore, the system must have adaptive mechanisms which allow it to respond to changing internal and external requirements.

Some forces within the social organization are geared to the maintenance of the system, and other forces and subsystems are geared to adaptation. These counteracting forces will often create tensions, stresses, and conflicts which are natural and should not be considered as totally dysfunctional.[33] Katz and Kahn describe the importance of maintenance and adaptive mechanisms for social organizations.

If the system is to survive, *maintenance substructures* must be elaborated to hold the walls of the social maze in place. Even these would not suffice to insure organizational survival, however. The organization exists in a changing and demanding environment, and it must adapt constantly to the changing environmental demands. *Adaptive structures* develop in organizations to generate appropriate responses to external conditions.[14]

Growth through internal elaboration

In the closed system subject to the laws of physics, the system moves toward entropy and disorganization. In contrast, open systems appear to have the opposite tendency and move in the direction of greater differentiation and a higher level of organization. Bertalanffy points to the continual elaborations of biological organisms: "In organic development and evolution, a transition toward states of higher order and differentiation seems to occur. The tendency toward increasing complication has been indicated as a primary characteristic of the living, as opposed to inanimate, nature."[34]

This same process appears to hold true for most social systems. There is a tendency for them to elaborate their activities and to reach higher levels of differentiation and organization. An examination of certain attributes of complex organizations may help explain this tendency. Complex social organizations are made up of many subsystems, some of which have excess capacity or resources which create a continual pressure toward growth. Furthermore, social organizations will often try to encompass within their boundaries additional activities in order to limit uncertainties and to ensure their survival. The business organization may use vertical integration in order to ensure a continual source of raw materials. The pattern of conglomerate diversification and mergers by many corporations in the United States is another indication of this process. In many cases, these mergers result from product innovation and technological breakthroughs which provide opportunities for the organization to extend its boundaries into new areas. Or it may be attributed to an imbalance of managerial and technical skills which are seeking outlets for their activities and creativity. An indication of this elaboration has been the expansion of many of our large corporations into international activities, significantly increasing the boundaries of their operations.

There is also a tendency for complex organizations to achieve greater differentiation and specialization among internal subsystems. The increased number of specialized departments and activities in complex business organizations is readily apparent. The great proliferation of departments, courses, and subject matter in universities is another example of differentiation and elaboration.

Equifinality of open systems

In physical systems there is a direct cause and effect relationship between the initial conditions and the final state. Biological and social systems operate differently. The concept of *equifinality* says that final results may be achieved with different initial conditions and in different ways. This view suggests that the social organization can accomplish its objectives with varying inputs and with varying internal activities. Thus, the social system is not restrained by the simple cause and effect relationship of closed systems.

The equifinality of social systems has major importance for the management of complex organizations. The closed-system cause and effect relationship adopted from the physical sciences would suggest that there is *one best way* to achieve a given objective. The concept of equifinality suggests that the manager can utilize a varying bundle of inputs into the organization, can transform these in a variety of ways, and can achieve satisfactory output. Extending this view further suggests that the management function is not necessarily one of seeking a rigid optimal solution but rather one of having available a variety of satisfactory solutions to his decision problems.

The foregoing are a few of the characteristics of open systems. To the student who is initially exposed to some of these concepts, they may seem complicated. Much of our educational experience emphasizes closed-system approaches – mathematics and the physical sciences, for example. The open-system view, with the properties set forth in the previous sections, is pertinent for organization theory.

Managerial Systems

Having looked at the characteristics of organizations as open sociotechnical systems, we now turn to a more detailed consideration of managerial systems. Parsons provides a useful framework. He suggests that there are three managerial levels in the hierarchical structure of complex organizations: the technical or production level, the organizational (managerial) level, and the institutional or community level.[35]

The *technical* system is involved with the actual task performance in the organization. In the business firm, the technical functions involve the actual production and distribution of the products or services – the task performance activities of the organization. The technical system is not just involved with physical work but includes many types of technical activities utilizing knowledge. For example, research and development, production control, market research, operations research, and most accounting functions are part of the technical system. The teacher performs a technical task in the school, the doctor a technical task in the hospital, and scientists a technical task in the research laboratory. In complex organizations, many of the technical tasks are performed by professionals and highly trained experts, as well as by skilled and unskilled employees.

The second level, the *organizational*, coordinates and integrates the task performance of the technical system. A primary function of management at this level is to integrate the input of material, energy, and information to the technical level.

The *institutional* level is involved in relating the activities of the organization to its environmental system. The organization must continually receive supporting inputs from the society in order to carry on its transformation activities.

The managerial system spans the entire organization by directing the technology, organizing people and other resources, and relating the organization to its environment. However, there are basic differences in the orientation of the managerial system at these different levels. The technical level is concerned primarily with economic–technical rationality and tries to create certainty by "closing the technical core" to many variables. Thompson says, "Under norms of rationality, organizations seek to seal off their core technologies from environmental influences. Since complete closure is impossible, they seek to buffer environmental influences by surrounding their technical cores with input and output components."[36] The closed-system view is applicable to the "technical core" of the organization.

By contrast, at the institutional level the organization faces the greatest degree of uncertainty in terms of inputs from its environment over which it has little or no control. Therefore, management at this level should have an open-system view and concentrate on adaptive and/or innovative strategies. The organizational manager operates between the technical core and the institutional level and serves to mediate and coordinate the two. This level transforms the uncertainty of the environment into the economic-technical rationality necessary for input into the technical core. Figure 3.3 shows the organization as a composite system using these concepts. In describing this figure, Petit says:

The technical level has a boundary that does not seal it off entirely from the firm's environment but does have a high degree of closure. The organizational level has less closure and consequently is more susceptible to the intrusion of external elements. The institutional level has a highly permeable boundary and therefore is strongly affected by uncontrollable and unpredictable elements in the environment. Inputs enter the firm, are transposed into outputs in the technical subsystem, and then disposed of in the environment.[37]

relatively independently and that therefore it is not realistic to talk of a "line authority" extending from the top or institutional level, through the organization level, and down to the technical level. "I have emphasized the relative independence of the three level-types of organization, an independence that constitutes my main objection to the continuous line-authority picture óf formal organization. This relative independence means that there is at each

Environment of the system

Figure 3.3 The firm as a composite system (Thomas A. Petit, "A Behavioral Theory of Management", *Academy of Management Journal,* December, 1967, p. 346).

linkage point, a range of possible *different* types of articulation."[38] He suggests that there is a break in the line authority between these three levels.

This view represents a major departure from the traditional scalar chain of command. There is a break between the organizational level and the technical level, particularly in the case of professional personnel. The manager cannot, because of his limited knowledge in a specific area, exert absolute authority over professional personnel. He must rely upon them to provide specialized technical expertise which he cannot develop himself. The manager can veto recommendations of the highly trained specialist; however, he cannot propose alternatives. Thus, it is necessary to develop means of articulation and adjustment at the boundaries between these various levels.

However, this does not mean that these different managerial levels can operate independently. Quite the contrary, they are interdependent. For example, the institutional level must perform effectively if the organization is to receive the necessary inputs for the technical level. Also, the technical level must produce outputs efficiently to ensure that the organization receives environmental support.

Thus the managerial system in the organization involves three levels – the technical core activities, intraorganizational interactions, and inter-institutional relationships. In many organizations these roles are separated theoretically. For example, in the university, the board of regents is thought of as fulfilling the institutional role, whereas the president, deans, and department heads are involved with organizational aspects. The professors, under this concept, perform the technical functions. In a hospital, the board of trustees performs the institutional role, the hospital administrator's staff is involved with organizational aspects, while the doctors, nurses, and other specialists perform the technical functions. Theoretically, in the business organization the board of directors relates the institution to its environment, upper and middle management deal with organizational aspects, and other employees perform the technical tasks. However, this distinction is not clear-cut in any of these organizations. For example, the president of a corporation usually has both institutional and organizational roles.

Parsons makes an interesting observation regarding these three levels. He stresses that they frequently are performed

Role of manager

The view of the organization as a sociotechnical system suggests a substantially different role for management than in traditional theory. In the traditional theory, the emphasis was upon economic–technical rationality. This closed-system view was appropriate for the technical level but not for the organizational and institutional levels. The human relations revolution did bring into focus the psycho-social subsystem but neglected the technical, structural, and environmental aspects. The management science approach adopted a closed-system view, focusing on the techniques of managerial decision making.

The view of an open sociotechnical system creates a more difficult role for the management system. It must deal with uncertainties and ambiguities and, above all, must be concerned with adapting the organization to new and changing requirements. Management is a process which spans and links the various subsystems of the organization. Thompson describes the management role as follows:

> The basic function of administration appears to be co-alignment, not merely of people (in coalition) but of institutionalized action – of technology and task environment into a viable domain, and of organizational design and structure appropriate to it. Administration, when it works well, keeps the organization at the nexus of the several necessary streams of action. Paradoxically, the administrative process must reduce uncertainty but at the same time search for flexibility.[36]

It is useful to consider the different types of managers necessary at the three levels in the managerial system. Petit suggests a basis for this classification in terms of the task

performed, point of view, technique employed, time horizon, and decision-making strategy (see Figure 3.4).

The task at the technical level is primarily economic–technical and is concerned with efficiency of output with a given technology. Managers tend to adopt a closed-system view and utilize the methods of scientific management and management science. They have a task orientation with a short time perspective and utilize computational decision-making strategies.

The manager at the organizational level must integrate the technical level with the institutional level. He is more concerned with the psycho-social system of the organization. He serves as a mediator between levels. The decision-making strategy is to effect compromise between the demands of the other levels.

Institutional management must have a broad conceptual frame of reference. Top executives have a long-run perspective and prepare the organization to adapt to environmental changes. Because of the uncertainties in the environment, their decision-making strategy is primarily judgmental.

The systems view suggests that management faces situations which are dynamic, inherently uncertain, and frequently ambiguous. Management is not in full control of all the factors of production as suggested by traditional theory. It is strongly restrained by many environmental and internal forces. The technical system, the psycho-social system, and the environmental system all constrain the management system. Sayles outlines the role of management under the systems approach:

Figure 3.4 The managerial system: technical, organizational, and institutional levels

TYPE OF MANAGER	TASK	VIEWPOINT	TECHNIQUE	TIME HORIZON	DECISION-MAKING STRATEGY
Technical	Technical rationality	Engineering	Scientific management, operations research	Short run	Computational
Organizational	Coordination	Political	Mediation	Short run and long run	Compromise
Institutional	Deal with uncertainty, relate organization to environment	Conceptual and philosophical	Opportunistic surveillance, negotiate with environment	Long run	Judgmental

SOURCE: Adapted from Thomas A. Petit, "A Behavioral Theory of Management", *Academy of Management Journal*, December, 1967, p. 349.

A systems concept emphasizes that managerial assignments do not have these neat, clearly defined boundaries; rather, the modern manager is placed in a network of mutually dependent relationships. . . . The one enduring objective is the effort to build and maintain a predictable, reciprocating system of relationships, the behavioral patterns of which stay within reasonable physical limits. But this is seeking a moving equilibrium, since the parameters of the system (the division of labor and the controls) are evolving and changing. Thus the manager endeavors to introduce regularity in a world that will never allow him to achieve the ideal . . . Only managers who can deal with uncertainty, with ambiguity, and with battles that are never won but only fought well can hope to succeed.[39]

One of the most pervasive functions of management at all levels is decision making. Figure 3.4 indicates that the decision-making strategy differs for various managerial levels. At the technical level, closed-system approaches are appropriate. However, at the organizational and institutional levels, open-system decision-making approaches are necessary.

Summary

The systems approach provides an integrative framework for modern organization theory and management practice. General systems theory includes concepts for integrating knowledge in the physical, biological, and social sciences.

There is a close relationship between general systems theory and the development of functionalism in the social sciences. Functionalism emphasizes integration of parts and subsystems into a functional whole. It has been used as a primary frame of reference in anthropology and sociology. In the field of psychology, the systems concept has achieved prominence. Modern economics also uses this approach, particularly in dynamic equilibrium analysis and input-output studies. The discipline of cybernetics is founded on the systems approach, focusing on communication and information flow in complex systems. Although it has been applied primarily to mechanistic systems, its model of feedback, control, and regulation has applicability for social systems as well.

The systems approach is directly related to organization theory. Traditional theory used closed-system thinking. Modern theory has moved toward considering the organization as an open system interacting with its environment. In contrast to the closed or mechanical system, the open system is not subject to the process of entropy – it can maintain a dynamic equilibrium by importing material, energy, and information from its environment.

The organization can be viewed as a structured sociotechnical system with five primary components – goals and values, and technical, structural, psycho-social, and managerial subsystems.

There are several key characteristics of organizational systems. They are not natural, like physical or biological systems, but are *contrived*. There are *boundaries* which separate the organization from its environment. In general, a system is composed of subsystems of a lower order and is also part of a supersystem; there is a *hierarchy* of systems. In open biological or social systems, entropy can be arrested and may even be transformed to *negative entropy* – a process of more complete organization. The concept of *steady state* is closely related to that of negative entropy. The organization is able to adapt to changes in its environment and to maintain a continual dynamic equilibrium.

The concept of *feedback* is important in understanding how a system maintains a steady state. Through the process of feedback, it continually receives information from its environment which helps it to adjust. A system must have both *adaptive and maintenance mechanisms*. The forces for maintenance are conservative and attempt to prevent the system from changing so rapidly that the various subsystems become out of balance. In contrast, adaptive mechanisms are necessary in order to provide for change. Open systems display *growth through internal elaboration*. They tend to move in the direction of greater differentiation and to a higher level of organization. Finally, open systems have the characteristic of *equifinality* – objectives may be achieved with varying inputs and in different ways.

There are three levels in the managerial system of complex organizations; technical, organizational, and institutional. The *technical level* is involved with actual task performance. The *organizational level* integrates the technical and institutional levels. The *institutional level* relates the activities of the organization to its environment. The view of the organization as a sociotechnical system creates a different role for the manager. He must integrate and balance the various subsystems and their activities in the environmental setting.

References

1 The name "general systems theory" and many of the basic concepts were set forth by the biologist Ludwig von Bertalanffy. For a general discussion of his views, see "The Theory of Open Systems in Physics and Biology", *Science*, Jan. 13, 1950, pp. 23–9; and

"General System Theory: A New Approach to Unity of Science", *Human Biology*, December 1951, pp. 302–61.

2 Boulding, Kenneth E. (1956) "General Systems Theory: The Skeleton of Science", *Management Science*, April, pp. 197–208.

3 von Bertalanffy, Ludwig (1952) *Problems of Life*, John Wiley & Sons, Inc., New York, p. 201. On page 176 he stresses this view: "If we survey the various fields of modern science, we notice a dramatic and amazing evolution. Similar conceptions and principles have arisen in quite different realms, although this parallelism of ideas is the result of independent developments, and the workers in the individual fields are hardly aware of the common trend. Thus, the principles of wholeness, of organization, and of the dynamic conception of reality become apparent in all fields of science."

4 Ashby, W. Ross (1964) in Mesarovic, Mihajlo D. (ed.), *Views on General Systems Theory*, John Wiley & Sons, Inc., New York, p. 166.

5 Eddington suggests that attention has been focused more and more on overall systems as frames of reference for analytical work in various areas. This synthesizing process "marked a reaction from the view that everything to which science need pay attention is discovered by microscopic dissection of objects. It provided an alternative stand-point in which the centre of interest is shifted from the entities reached by the customary analysis (atoms, electric potentials, etc.) to qualities possessed by the system as a whole, which cannot be split up and located – a little here and a little bit there." Eddington, Sir Arthur (1958) *The Nature of the Physical World*, The University of Michigan Press, Ann Arbor, Mich., pp. 103–4.

6 For an overview of the integrative possibilities of the systems approach, see Walter Buckley (ed.) (1968) *Modern Systems Research for the Behavioral Scientist*, Aldine Publishing Company, Chicago.

7 Martindale, Don (1965) *Functionalism in the Social Sciences*, Monograph 5, American Academy of Political and Social Science, February, pp. viii–ix.

8 Robert K. Merton discusses various connotations of the word *function* in *Social Theory and Social Structure*, rev. ed., The Free Press of Glencoe, New York, 1957, pp. 20–25.

9 Radcliffe-Brown, A. R. (1952) *Structure and Function in Primitive Society*, Cohen & West, London, and

Bronislaw Malinowski (1960) *A Scientific Theory of Culture*, Oxford University Press, New York.

10 Talcott Parsons uses the systems approach in much of his writings. His *The Social System*, The Free Press of Glencoe, New York, 1951, presents a comprehensive treatise on his views.

11 For a view of Pareto's works, see Lawrence J. Henderson (1935) *Pareto's General Sociology*, Harvard University Press, Cambridge, Mass.

12 "A *gestalt* is an organized entity or whole in which the parts, though distinguishable, are interdependent; they have certain characteristics produced by their inclusion in the whole, and the whole has some characteristics belonging to none of the parts. The gestalt thus constitutes a 'unit segregated from its surroundings', behaving according to certain laws of energy distribution. It is found throughout human behaviour as well as in physiological and physical events and is thus a fundamental aspect of scientific data." Gould, Julius and Kolb, William L. (eds.) (1964) *A Dictionary of the Social Sciences*, The Free Press of Glencoe, New York, p. 287.

13 Whitaker, Ian (1965) "The Nature and Value of Functionalism in Sociology", in *Functionalism in the Social Sciences*, Monograph 5, American Academy of Political and Social Science, February, pp. 137–8.

14 Katz, Daniel and Kahn, Robert L. (1966) *The Social Psychology of Organizations*, John Wiley & Sons, Inc. New York, is an example of the movement of social psychology into broader systems of analysis.

15 Leontief, Wassily *et al.* (1953) *Studies in the Structure of the American Economy*, Oxford University Press, New York, p. 8.

16 Wiener, Norbert (1948) *Cybernetics*, John Wiley & Sons, Inc., New York.

17 Chin, Robert (1961) "The Utility of System Models and Developmental Models for Practitioners", in Warren G. Bennis, Kenneth D. Benne, and Robert Chin (eds.), *The Planning of Change*, Holt, Rinehart & Winston, Inc., New York, p. 202.

18 Scott, William G. (1967) *Organization Theory*, Richard D. Irwin, Inc., Homewood, Ill., pp. 122–3.

19 Barnard, Chester I. (1938) *The Functions of the Executive*, Harvard University Press, Cambridge, Mass.

20 Simon, Herbert A. (1964) "Approaching the Theory of Management", in Harold Koontz (ed.), *Toward a Unified Theory of Management*, McGraw-Hill Book Company, New York, pp. 82–3.

21 Churchman, C. West, Ackoff, Russell L. and Arnoff, E.

Leonard (1957) *Introduction to Operations Research*, John Wiley & Sons, Inc., New York, p. 7.

22 Homans, George C. (1950) *The Human Group*, Harcourt, Brace & World, Inc., New York.

23 Selznick, Philip (1948) "Foundations of the Theory of Organization", *American Sociological Review*, February, pp. 23–35.

24 Emery, F. E. and Trist, E. L. (1960) "Socio-technical Systems", in C. West Churchman and Michel Cerhulst (eds.), *Management Sciences: Models and Techniques*, Pergamon Press, New York, vol. 2, pp. 83–97; (Article 9) and Rice, A. K. (1963) *The Enterprise and Its Environment*, Tavistock Publications, London.

25 For a discussion of the evolution of this approach in military and space programs, see Kast, Fremont E. and Rosenzweig, James E. (1965) "Organization and Management of Space Programs", in Ordway, Frederick I. III (ed.), *Advances in Space Science and Technology*, Academic Press, Inc., New York, vol. 7, pp. 273–364.

26 Miller, James G. (1965) "Living Systems: Basic Concepts", *Behavioral Science*, July, p. 195.

27 Buckley, Walter, "Society as a Complex Adaptive System", in Buckley, *op. cit.*, pp. 490–1 (see Article 10).

28 This point is made by Rensis Likert in *New Patterns of Management*, McGraw-Hill Book Company, New York, 1961. In his interaction-influence system, he recommends the overlapping-group form of organization in which a "linking-pin function" is performed to integrate activities of the various subsystems in the organization.

29 Simon, Herbert A. (1960) *The New Science of Management Decision*, Harper & Row, Publishers, Incorporated, New York, pp. 40–2.

30 von Bertalanffy, Ludwig (1956) "General System Theory", in *General Systems*, Yearbook of the Society for the Advancement of General Systems Theory, vol. I, p. 4.

31 Emery, F. E. and Trist, E. L. (1965) "The Causal Texture of Organizational Environments", *Human Relations*, February, p. 2.1.

32 The concept of negative feedback is fundamental to the discipline of cybernetics. Mechanisms of feedback are basic to the purposeful behavior in man-made machines, as well as in living organisms and social systems. In discussing the cybernetic hypothesis, Wisdom says, "We may describe machines that embody negative feed-back mechanisms as proceeding by 'trial and error', or as 'error-compensating', or – best – as 'self-correcting'; and we may define 'a simple negative feed-back mechanism' as a mechanism by which part of the input-energy of a machine is utilized at intervals to impose a check on the output-energy. The basic hypothesis of cybernetics is that the chief mechanism of the central nervous system is one of negative feed-back." Wisdom, J. O. (1956) "The Hypothesis of Cybernetics", *General Systems*, Yearbook of the Society for the Advancement of General Systems Theory, vol. I, p. 112.

33 Robert Chin says, "The presence of tensions, stresses or strains, and conflict within the system often are reacted to by people in the system as if they were shameful and must be done away with. Tension reduction, relief of stress and strain, and conflict resolution become the working goals of practitioners but sometimes at the price of overlooking the possibility of increasing tensions and conflict in order to facilitate creativity, innovation, and social change." Chin, *op. cit.*, p. 204.

34 von Bertalanffy, Ludwig, (1950) "The Theory of Open Systems in Physics and Biology", *Science*, Jan. 13, p. 26.

35 Parsons, Talcott (1960) *Structure and Process in Modern Societies*, The Free Press of Glencoe, New York, pp. 60–96. Parsons calls the middle level in the managerial hierarchy "the managerial level". Actually management is involved in each of the three levels, and for our purpose it is more appropriate to call this "the organizational level".

36 Thompson, James D. (1967) *Organizations in Action*, McGraw-Hill Book Company, New York, p. 24.

37 Petit, Thomas A. (1967) "A Behavioral Theory of Management", *Academy of Management Journal*, December, p. 346.

38 Parsons, *Structure and Process in Modern Societies*, p. 95.

39 Sayles, Leonard (1964) *Managerial Behavior*, McGraw-Hill Book Company, New York, pp. 258–9.

4 General system theory – a critical review

by Ludwig von Bertalanffy

Since creative thought is the most important thing that makes people different from monkeys, it should be treated as a commodity more precious than gold and preserved with great care. – A. D. Hall, A Methodology for Systems Engineering.

It is more than 15 years since the writer has first presented, to a larger public, the proposal of a General System Theory.* Since then, this conception has been widely discussed and was applied in numerous fields of science. When an early reviewer found himself "hushed into awed silence" by the idea of a General System Theory, now in spite of obvious limitations, different approaches and legitimate criticism, few would deny the legitimacy and fertility of the interdisciplinary systems approach.

Even more: The systems concept has not remained in the theoretical sphere, but became central in certain fields of applied science. When first proposed, it appeared to be a particularly abstract and daring, theoretical idea. Nowadays "systems engineering" "research", "analysis" and similar titles have become job denominations. Major industrial enterprises and government agencies have departments, committees or at least specialists to the purpose; and many universities offer curricula and courses for training.

Thus the present writer was vindicated when he was among the first to predict that the concept of "system" is to become a fulcrum in modern scientific thought. In the words of a practitioner of the science [R. L. Ackoff]:

In the last two decades we have witnessed the emergence of the "system" as a key concept in scientific research. Systems, of course, have been studied for centuries, but something new has been added. ... The tendency to study systems as an entity rather than as a conglomeration of parts is consistent with the tendency in contemporary science no longer to isolate phenomena in narrowly confined contexts, but rather to open interactions for examination and to examine larger and larger slices of nature. Under the banner of *systems research* (and its many synonyms) we have also witnessed a convergence of many more specialized contemporary scientific developments. ... These research pursuits and many others are being interwoven into a cooperative research effort involving an ever-widening spectrum of scientific and engineering disciplines. We

* This article first appeared in 1962.

are participating in what is probably the most comprehensive effort to attain a synthesis of scientific knowledge yet made.

This, however, does not preclude but rather implies that obstacles and difficulties are by no means overcome as is only to be expected in a major scientific reorientation. A reassessment of General Systems Theory, its foundations, achievements, criticisms and prospects therefore appears in place. The present study aims at this purpose.

According to the Preface to the VIth volume of *General Systems* by Meyer, the greatest number of enquiries made asks for "new statements describing the method and significance of the idea". Another central theme is "the organismic viewpoint". As one of the original proponents of the *Society for General Systems Research* and founders of the organismic viewpoint in biology, the author feels obliged to answer this challenge as well as readily admitted limitations of his knowledge and techniques permit.

1 The rise of interdisciplinary theories

The motives leading to the postulate of a general theory of systems can be summarized under a few headings.

1. Up to recent times the field of science as a nomothetic endeavor, i.e., trying to establish an explanatory and predictive system of laws, was practically identical with theoretical physics. Few attempts at a system of laws in non-physical fields gained general recognition; the biologist would first think of genetics. However, in recent times the biological, behavioral and social sciences have come into their own, and so the problem became urgent whether an expansion of conceptual schemes is possible to deal with fields and problems where application of physics is not sufficient or feasible.

2. In the biological, behavioral and sociological fields, there exist predominant problems which were neglected in classical science or rather which did not enter into its considerations. If we look at a living organism, we observe an amazing order, organization, maintenance in continuous change, regulation and apparent teleology. Similarly, in

human behavior goal-seeking and purposiveness cannot be overlooked, even if we accept a strictly behavioristic standpoint. However, concepts like organization, directiveness, teleology, etc., just do not appear in the classic system of science. As a matter of fact, in the so-called mechanistic world view based upon classical physics, they were considered as illusory or metaphysical. This means, to the biologist for example, that just the specific problems of living nature appeared to lie beyond the legitimate field of science.

3. This in turn was closely connected with the structure of classical science. The latter was essentially concerned with two-variable problems, linear causal trains, one cause and one effect, or with few variables at the most. The classical example is mechanics. It gives perfect solutions for the attraction between two celestial bodies, a sun and a planet, and hence permits one to exactly predict future constellations and even the existence of still undetected planets. However, already the three-body problem of mechanics is unsolvable in principle and can only be approached by approximations. A similar situation exists in the more modern field of atomic physics. Here also two-body problems such as that of one proton and electron are solvable, but trouble arises with the many-body problem. One-way causality, the relation between "cause" and "effect" or of a pair or few variables cover a wide field. Nevertheless, many problems particularly in biology and the behavioral and social sciences, essentially are multivariable problems for which new conceptual tools are needed. Warren Weaver, cofounder of information theory, had expressed this in an often-quoted statement. Classical science, he stated, was concerned either with linear causal trains, that is, two-variable problems; or else with unorganized complexity. The latter can be handled with statistical methods and ultimately stems from the second principle of thermodynamics. However, in modern physics and biology, problems of organized complexity, that is, interaction of a large but not infinite number of variables, are popping up everywhere and demand new conceptual tools.

4. What has been said are not metaphysical or philosophic contentions. We are not erecting a barrier between inorganic and living nature which obviously would be inappropriate in view of intermediates such as viruses, nucleoproteins and self-duplicating units in general which in some way bridge the gap. Nor do we protest that biology is in principle "irreducible to physics" which also would be out of place in view of the tremendous advances of physical and chemical explanation of life processes. Similarly, no barrier between biology and the behavioral and social sciences is intended. This, however, does not obviate the fact that in the fields mentioned we do not have appropriate conceptual tools serving for explanation and prediction as we have in physics and its various fields of application.

5. It therefore appears that an expansion of science is required to deal with those aspects which are left out in physics and happen to concern just the specific characteristics of biological, behavioral, and social phenomena. This amounts to new conceptual models to be introduced. Every science is a model in the broad sense of the word, that is a conceptual structure intended to reflect certain aspects of reality. One such model is the system of physics – and it is an incredibly successful one. However, physics is but *one* model dealing with certain aspects of reality. It needs not to have monopoly, nor is it *the* reality as mechanistic methodology and metaphysics presupposed. It apparently does not cover all aspects and represents, as many specific problems in biology and behavioral science show, a limited aspect. Perhaps it is possible to introduce other models dealing with aspects outside of physics.

These considerations are of a rather abstract nature. So perhaps some personal interest may be introduced by telling how the present author was led into this sort of problem.

When, some 40 years ago, I started my life as a scientist, biology was involved in the mechanism–vitalism controversy. The mechanistic procedure essentially was to resolve the living organism into parts and partial processes: the organism was an aggregate of cells, the cell one of colloids and organic molecules, behavior a sum of unconditional and conditioned reflexes, and so forth. The problems of organization of these parts in the service of maintenance of the organism, of regulation after disturbances and the like were either by-passed or, according to the theory known as vitalism, explainable only by the action of soul-like factors, like hobgoblins as it were, hovering in the cell or the organism – which obviously was nothing less than a declaration of bankruptcy of science. In this situation, I was led to advocate the so-called organismic viewpoint. In one brief sentence, it means that organisms are organized things and, as biologists, we have to find out about it. I tried to implement this organismic program in various studies on metabolism, growth, and biophysics of the organism. One way in this respect was the so-called theory of open systems and steady states which essentially is an expansion of conventional physical chemistry, kinetics and thermodynamics. It appeared, however, that I could not stop on the way once taken and so I was led to a still further generalization which I called "General System Theory". The idea goes back for some considerable time – I presented it first in 1937 in Charles Morris' philosophy seminar at the University of Chicago. However, at this time theory was in bad reputation in biology, and I was afraid of what Gauss, the mathematician, called the "clamor of the Boeotians". So I left my drafts in the drawer, and it was only after the war that my first publications in this respect appeared.

Then, however, something interesting and surprising happened. It turned out that a change in intellectual climate had taken place, making model building and abstract generalizations fashionable. Even more: quite a number of scientists had followed similar lines of thought. So General Systems Theory, after all, was not isolated or a personal idiosyncrasy as I have believed, but rather was one within a group of parallel developments.

Naturally, the maxims enumerated above can be formulated in different ways and using somewhat different terms. In principle, however, they express the viewpoint of the more advanced thinkers of our time and the common ground of system theorists. The reader may, for example, compare the presentation given by Rapoport and Horvath which is an excellent and independent statement and therefore shows even better the general agreement.

There is quite a number of novel developments intended to meet the goals indicated above. We may enumerate them in a brief survey:

(1) Cybernetics, based upon the principle of feedback or circular causal trains providing mechanisms for goal-seeking and self-controlling behavior.

(2) Information theory, introducing the concept of information as a quantity measurable by an expression isomorphic to negative entropy in physics, and developing the principles of its transmission.

(3) Game theory, analyzing in a novel mathematical framework, rational competition between two or more antagonists for maximum gain and minimum loss.

(4) Decision theory, similarly analyzing rational choices, within human organizations, based upon examination of a given situation and its possible outcomes.

(5) Topology or relational mathematics, including non-metrical fields such as network and graph theory.

(6) Factor analysis, i.e., isolation by way of mathematical analysis, of factors in multivariable phenomena in psychology and other fields.

(7) General system theory in the narrower sense (G.S.T.), trying to derive from a general definition of "system" as complex of interacting components, concepts characteristic of organized wholes such as interaction, sum,

mechanization, centralization, competition, finality, etc., and to apply them to concrete phenomena.

While systems theory in the broad sense has the character of a basic science, it has its correlate in applied science, sometimes subsumed under the general name of Systems Science. This development is closely connected with modern automation. Broadly speaking, the following fields can be distinguished:

Systems Engineering, i.e., scientific planning, design, evaluation, and construction of man–machine systems;

Operations research, i.e., scientific control of existing systems of men, machines, materials, money, etc.

Human Engineering, i.e., scientific adaptation of systems and especially machines in order to obtain maximum efficiency with minimum cost in money and other expenses.

A very simple example for the necessity of study of "man–machine systems" is air travel. Anybody crossing continents by jet with incredible speed and having to spend endless hours waiting, queuing, being herded in airports can easily realize that the physical techniques in air travel are at their best, while "organizational" techniques still are on a most primitive level.

Although there is considerable overlapping, different conceptual tools are predominant in the individual fields. In systems engineering, cybernetics and information theory, also general system theory are used. Operations research uses tools such as linear programming and game theory. Human engineering, concerned with the abilities, physiological limitations and variabilities of human beings, includes biomechanics, engineering psychology, human factors, etc., among its tools.

The present survey is not concerned with applied systems science; the reader is referred to Hall's book as an excellent textbook of systems engineering. However it is well to keep in mind that the systems approach as a novel concept in science has a close parallel in technology. The systems viewpoint in recent science stands in a similar relation to the so-called "mechanistic" viewpoint, as stands systems engineering to physical technology.

All these theories have certain features in common. *Firstly*, they agree in the emphasis that something should be done about the problems characteristic of the behavioral and biological sciences, but not dealt with in conventional physical theory. *Secondly*, these theories introduce concepts and models novel in comparison to physics: for example, a generalized system concept, the concept of information compared to energy in physics. *Thirdly*, these theories are particularly concerned with multivariable problems, as mentioned before. *Fourthly*, these models are inter-disciplinary and transcend the conventional fields of science. If, for example, you scan the *Yearbooks* of the *Society for General Systems Research*, you notice the breadth of application: Considerations similar or even identical in structure are applied to phenomena of different kinds and levels, from networks of chemical reactions in a cell to populations of animals, from electrical engineering to the social sciences. Similarly, the basic concepts of cybernetics stem from certain special fields in modern technology. However, starting with the simplest case of a thermostat which by way of feedback maintains a certain temperature and advancing to servomechanisms and automation in modern technology, it turns out that similar schemes are applicable to many biological phenomena of regulation or behavior. Even more, in many instances there is a formal correspondence or isomorphism of general principles or even of special laws. Similar mathematical formulations may apply to quite different phenomena. This entails that general theories of systems, among other things, are labor-saving devices: A set of principles may be transferred from one field to another, without the need to duplicate the effort as has often happened in science of the past. *Fifthly*, and perhaps most important: Concepts like wholeness, organization, teleology and directiveness appeared in mechanistic science to be unscientific or metaphysical. Today they are taken seriously and as amenable to scientific analysis. We have conceptual and in some cases even material models which can represent those basic characteristics of life and behavioral phenomena.

An important consideration is that the various approaches enumerated are not, and should not be considered to be monopolistic. One of the important aspects of the modern changes in scientific thought is that there is no unique and all-embracing "world system". All scientific constructs are models representing certain aspects or perspectives of reality. This even applies to theoretical physics: far from being a metaphysical presentation of ultimate reality (as the materialism of the past proclaimed and modern positivism still implies) it is but one of these models and, as recent developments show, neither exhaustive nor unique. The various "systems theories" also are models that mirror different aspects. They are not mutually exclusive and often combined in application. For example, certain phenomena may be amenable to scientific exploration by way of cybernetics, others by way of general system theory; or even in the same phenomenon, certain aspects may be describable in the one or the other way. Cybernetics combine the information and feedback models, models of

the nervous system net and information theory, etc. This, of course, does not preclude but rather implies the hope for further synthesis in which the various approaches of the present toward a theory of "wholeness" and "organization" may be integrated and unified. Actually, such further syntheses, e.g., between irreversible thermodynamics and information theory, are slowly developing.

The differences of these theories are in the particular model conceptions and mathematical methods applied. We therefore come to the question in what ways the program of systems research can be implemented.

2 Methods of general systems research

Ashby has admirably outlined two possible ways or general methods in systems study:

> Two main lines are readily distinguished. One, already well developed in the hands of von Bertalanffy and his co-workers, takes the world as we find it, examines the various systems that occur in it – zoological, physiological, and so on – and then draws up statements about the regularities that have been observed to hold. This method is essentially empirical. The second method is to start at the other end. Instead of studying first one system, then a second, then a third, and so on, it goes to the other extreme, considers the set of all conceivable systems and then reduces the set to a more reasonable size. This is the method I have recently followed.

It will easily be seen that all systems studies follow one or the other of these methods or a combination of both. Each of these approaches has its advantages as well as shortcomings.

1. The first method is empirico-intuitive; it has the advantage that it remains rather close to reality and can easily be illustrated and even verified by examples taken from the individual fields of science. On the other hand, the approach lacks mathematical elegance and deductive strength and, to the mathematically minded, will appear naïve and unsystematic.

Nevertheless, the merits of this empirico-intuitive procedure should not be minimized.

The present writer has stated a number of "system principles", partly in the context of biological theory and without explicit reference to G.S.T., partly in what emphatically was entitled an "Outline" of this theory. This was meant in the literal sense: It was intended to call attention to the desirability of such field, and the presentation was in the way of a sketch or blueprint, illustrating the approach by simple examples.

However, it turned out that this intuitive survey appears to be remarkably complete. The main principles offered such as wholeness, sum, centralization, differentiation, leading part, closed and open system, finality, equifinality, growth in time, relative growth, competition, have been used in manifold ways (e.g., general definition of system; types of growth; systems engineering; social work). Excepting minor variations in terminology intended for clarification or due to the subject matter, no principles of similar significance were added – even though this would be highly desirable. It is perhaps even more significant that this also applies to considerations which do not refer to the present writer's work and hence cannot be said to be unduly influenced by it. Perusal of studies such as those by Beer and Kremyanskiy on principles, Bradley and Calvin on the network of chemical reactions, Haire on growth of organizations, etc., will easily show that they are also using the "Bertalanffy principles".

2. The way of deductive systems theory was followed by Ashby. A more informal presentation which summarizes Ashby's reasoning lends itself particularly well to analysis.

Ashby asks about the "fundamental concept of machine" and answers the question by stating "that its internal state, and the state of its surroundings, defines uniquely the next state it will go to". If the variables are continuous, this definition corresponds to the description of a dynamic system by a set of ordinary differential equations with time as the independent variable. However, such representation by differential equations is too restricted for a theory to include biological systems and calculating machines where discontinuities are ubiquitous. Therefore the modern definition is the "machine with input": It is defined by a set S of internal states, a set I of input and a mapping f of the product set $I \times S$ into S. "Organization", then, is defined by specifying the machine's states S and its conditions I. If S is a product set $S = \pi_i T_i$, with i as the parts and T is specified by the mapping f. A "self-organizing" system, according to Ashby, can have two meanings, namely: (1) The system starts with its parts separate, and these parts then change toward forming connections (example: cells of the embryo, first having little or no effect on one another, join by formation of dendrites and synapses to form the highly interdependent nervous system). This first meaning is "changing from unorganized to organized". (2) The second meaning is "changing from a bad organization to a good one" (examples: a child whose brain organization makes it fire-seeking at first, while a new brain organization makes him fire-avoiding; an automatic pilot and plane coupled first by deleterious positive feedback and then

improved). "There the organization is bad. The system would be 'self-organizing' if a change were automatically made" (changing positive into negative feedback). But "*no machine can be self-organizing in this sense*" (author's emphasis). For adaptation (e.g., of the homeostat or in a self-programming computer) means that we start with a set S of states, and that f changes into g, so that organization is a variable, e.g., a function of time $\alpha(t)$ which has first the value f and later the value g. However, this change "cannot be ascribed to any cause in the set S; *so it must come from some outside agent, acting on the system* S *as input*" (our emphasis). In other terms, to be "self-organizing" the machine S must be coupled to another machine.

This concise statement permits observation of the limitations of this approach. We completely agree that description by differential equations is not only a clumsy but, in principle, inadequate way to deal with many problems of organization. The author was well aware of this emphasizing that a system of simultaneous differential equations is by no means the most general formulation and is chosen only for illustrative purposes.

However, in overcoming this limitation, Ashby introduced another one. His "modern definition" of system as a "machine with input" as reproduced above, supplants the general system model by another rather special one: the cybernetic model, i.e., a system open to information but closed with respect to entropy transfer. This becomes apparent when the definition is applied to "self-organizing systems". Characteristically, the most important kind of these has no place in Ashby's model, namely, systems organizing themselves by way of progressive differentiation, evolving from states of lower to states of higher complexity. This is, of course, the most obvious form of "self-organization", apparent in ontogenesis, probable in phylogenesis, and certainly also valid in many social organizations. We have here not a question of "good" (i.e., useful, adaptive) or "bad" organization which, as Ashby correctly emphasizes, is relative on circumstances; increase in differentiation and complexity – whether useful or not – is a criterion that is objective and at least on principle amenable to measurement (e.g., in terms of decreasing entropy, of information). Ashby's contention that "no machine can be self-organizing", more explicitly, that the "change cannot be ascribed to any cause in the set S" but "must come from some outside agent, an input" amounts to exclusion of self-differentiating systems. The reason that such systems are not permitted as "Ashby machines" is patent. Self-differentiating systems that evolve toward higher complexity (decreasing entropy) are, for thermodynamic reasons, possible only as open systems, i.e., systems importing matter containing free energy to an amount over-compensating the increase in entropy due to irreversible processes within the system ("import of negative entropy"). However, we cannot say that "this change comes from some outside agent, an input"; the differentiation within a developing embryo and organism is due to its internal laws of organization, and the input (e.g., oxygen supply which may vary quantitatively, or nutrition which can vary qualitatively within a broad spectrum) makes it only possible energetically.

than an inanimate communication channel. Both, however, are consequences of the organism's character as an open system.

Incidentally, it is for similar reasons that we cannot replace the concept of "system" by the generalized "machine" concept of Ashby. Even though the latter is more liberal compared to the classic one (machines defined as systems with fixed arrangement of parts and processes), the objections against a "machine theory" of life remain valid.

These remarks are not intended as adverse criticism of

STIMULUS   **MESSAGE**   **MESSAGE**   **RESPONSE**

Figure 4.1   Simple feedback model.

The above is further illustrated by additional examples given by Ashby. Suppose a digital computer is carrying through multiplications at random; then the machine will "evolve" toward showing even numbers (because products even × even as well as even × odd give numbers even), and eventually only zeros will be "surviving". In still another version Ashby quotes Shannon's Tenth Theorem, stating that if a correction channel has capacity H, equivocation of the amount H can be removed, but no more. Both examples illustrate the working of closed systems: The "evolution" of the computer is one toward disappearance of differentiation and establishment of maximum homogeneity (analog to the Second Principle in closed systems); Shannon's Theorem similarly concerns closed systems where no negative entropy is fed in. Compared to the information content (organization) of a living system, the imported matter (nutrition, etc.) carries not information but "noise". Nevertheless, its negative entropy is used to maintain or even to increase the information content of the system. This is a state of affairs apparently not provided for in Shannon's Tenth Theorem, and understandably so as he is not treating information transfer in open systems with transformation of matter.

In both respects, the living organism (and other behavioral and social systems) is not an Ashby machine because it evolves toward increasing differentiation and inhomogeneity, and can correct "noise" to a higher degree

Ashby's or the deductive approach in general; they only emphasize that there is no royal road to General Systems Theory. As every other scientific field, it will have to develop by an interplay of empirical, intuitive and deductive procedures. If the intuitive approach leaves much to be desired in logical rigor and completeness, the deductive approach faces the difficulty of whether the fundamental terms are correctly chosen. This is not a particular fault of the theory or of the workers concerned but a rather common phenomenon in the history of science; one may, for example, remember the long debate as to what magnitude – force or energy – is to be considered as constant in physical transformations until the issue was decided in favor of $mv^2/2$.

In the present writer's mind, G.S.T. was conceived as a working hypothesis; being a practicing scientist, he sees the main function of theoretical models in the explanation, prediction, and control of hitherto unexplored phenomena. Others may, with equal right, emphasize the importance of axiomatic approach and quote to this effect examples like the theory of probability, non-Euclidean geometries, more recently information and game theory, which were first developed as deductive mathematical fields, and later applied in physics or other sciences. There should be no quarrel about this point. The danger, in both approaches, is to consider too early the theoretical model as being closed and definitive – a danger particularly important in a field like general systems which is still groping to find its correct foundations.

3 Homeostasis and open systems

Among the models mentioned, cybernetics in its application as homeostasis, and G.S.T. in its application to open systems lend themselves most readily for interpretation of many empirical phenomena. The relation of both theories is not always well understood, and hence a brief discussion is in place.

The simplest feedback scheme can be represented as follows (Fig. 4.1). Modern servomechanisms and automation, as well as many phenomena in the organism, are based upon feedback arrangements far more complicated than the simple scheme (Fig. 4.1) but the latter is the elementary prototype.

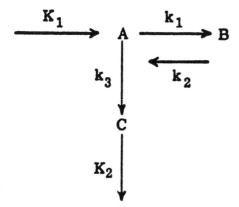

Figure 4.2 Model of a simple open system. The component A is introduced into the system and transformed, in a reversible reaction, into B; it is catabolized in an irreversible reaction, into C which eventually is excreted. K_1, K_2 are constants of import and export, respectively; k_1, k_2, k_3 are reaction constants. The model approximately corresponds, for example, to protein turnover in an animal organism, A representing amino acids, B proteins, and C products of excretion.

In application to the living organism, the feedback scheme is represented by the concept of homeostasis.

Homeostasis, according to Cannon,[1] is the ensemble of organic regulations which act to maintain the steady states of the organism and are effectuated by regulating mechanisms in such a way that they do not occur necessarily in the same, and often in opposite, direction to what a corresponding external change would cause according to physical laws. The simplest example is homeothermy. According to Van't Hoff's rule in physical chemistry, a decrease in temperature leads to slowing down of the rate of chemical reactions, as it does in ordinary physico-chemical systems

[1] Article 11.

and also in poikilothermic animals. In warm-blooded animals, however, it leads to the opposite effect, namely, to an increase of metabolic rate, with the result that the temperature of the body is maintained constant at approximately 37°C. This is effectuated by a feedback mechanism. Cooling stimulates thermogenic centers in the brain thalamus which "turn on" heat-producing mechanisms in the body. A similar feedback pattern is found in a great variety of physiological regulations. Regulation of posture and the control of actions in animals and man toward a goal are similarly controled by feedback mechanisms.

In contradistinction to cybernetics concerned with feedback arrangements, G.S.T. is interested in dynamic interaction within multivariable systems. The case particularly important for the living organism is that of open systems. It amounts to saying that there is a system into which matter is introduced from outside. Within the system, the material undergoes reactions which partly may yield components of a higher complexity. This is what we call anabolism. On the other hand, the material is catabolized and the end products of catabolism eventually leave the system. A simple model of an open system is indicated in Figure 4.2.

A few main characteristics of open as compared to closed systems are in the fact that, appropriate system conditions presupposed, an open system will attain a steady state in which its composition remains constant, but in contrast to conventional equilibria, this constancy is maintained in a continuous exchange and flow of component material. The steady state of open systems is characterized by the principle of equifinality; that is, in contrast to equilibrium states in closed systems which are determined by initial conditions, the open system may attain a time-independent state independent of initial conditions and determined only by the system parameters. Furthermore, open systems show thermodynamic characteristics which are apparently paradoxical and contradictory to the second principle. According to the latter, the general course of physical events (in closed systems) is toward increasing entropy, leveling down of differences and states of maximum disorder. In open systems, however, with transfer of matter import of "negative entropy" is possible. Hence, such systems can maintain themselves at a high level, and even evolve toward an increase of order and complexity – as is indeed one of the most important characteristics of life processes.

The open-system model also has a wide application. According to its character, it is particularly applicable to phenomena showing non-structural, dynamic interaction of processes, such as those of metabolism, growth, metabolic aspects of excitation, etc.

Speaking more generally, living systems can be defined as hierarchically organized open systems, maintaining themselves, or developing toward a steady state. Disease is the life process regulating toward normalcy after disturbance, owing to the equifinality of biological systems and with the assistance of the physician. In this way, the *vis medicatrix naturae* of old is divested of its metaphysical paraphernalia; it is not a vitalistic agent but an expression of the dynamics of living systems, maintaining and reestablishing, so far as possible, the steady state.

In this way, the theory of open systems accounts for basic characteristics of the living organism which have baffled physicists, biologists, and philosophers, and appeared to be violations of the laws of physics, explainable only by vitalistic factors beyond the competence of science and scientific explanation.

Thus "feedback" and "open systems" are two models for biological and possibly behavioral phenomena. It should be made clear that the term "homeostasis" can be used in two ways. It is either taken in the original sense as proffered by Cannon and illustrated by examples like maintenance of body temperature and other physiological variables by feedback mechanisms – or else the term is often used as a synonym for organic regulation and adaptation in general. This is a question of semantics. However, it is a wise rule in the natural sciences to use terms in the sense originally attached to them by their authors. So I propose to use the word homeostasis in its narrower but well-defined sense, and this has important consequences, as it reveals certain limitations which are often forgotten.

As was already emphasized, regulations of the homeostasis or feedback type are abundant in the mature higher organism. However, it is clear from the scheme (Fig. 4.1) or any other flow diagram that feedback represents a machine-like arrangement, that is, an order of processes based upon fixed arrangements and representing linear, though circular, causal trains. The primary phenomena of organic regulation, e.g. the regulations in early embryonic development, in regeneration, etc., appear to be of a different nature. It seems that the primary regulations in the organism result from dynamic interaction within a unitary open system that reestablishes its steady state. Superimposed upon this by way of progressive mechanization are secondary regulatory mechanisms governed by fixed structures especially of the feedback type.

Although the homeostasis model transcends older mechanistic models by acknowledging directiveness in self-regulating circular processes, it still adheres to the machine theory of the organism. This also applies to a second aspect. An essential component of the mechanistic view is a utilitarian conception which is deeply connected with the economic outlook of the 19th and early 20th centuries. This is well known, for example, in the history of Darwinism: Struggle for existence and survival of the fittest are a biological version of the economic model of free competition. This utilitarian or economic viewpoint also prevails in the concept of homeostasis: The organism is essentially envisaged as an aggregate mechanism for maintenance of minimum costs. However, there seem to be plenty of non-utilitarian structures and functions in the living world.

The concept of homeostasis also retains a third aspect of the mechanistic view. The organism is essentially considered to be a reactive system. Outside stimuli are answered by proper responses in such a way as to maintain the system. The feedback model (Fig. 4.1) is essentially the classical stimulus-response scheme, only the feedback loop being added. However, an overwhelming amount of facts shows that primary organic behavior as, for example, the first movements of the fetus, are not reflex responses to external stimuli, but rather spontaneous mass activities of the whole embryo or larger areas. Reflex reactions answering external stimuli and following a structured path appear to be superimposed upon primitive automatisms, ontogenetically and phylogenetically, as secondary regulatory mechanisms. These considerations win particular importance in the theory of behavior as we shall see later on.

In this sense, it appears that in development and evolution dynamic interaction (open system) precedes mechanization (structured arrangements particularly of a feedback nature). In a similar way, G.S.T. can logically be considered the more general theory; it includes systems with feedback constraints as a special case, but this assertion would not be true vice versa. It need not be emphasized that this statement is a program for future systematization and integration of G.S.T. rather than a theory presently achieved.

4 Criticism of general system theory

A discussion of G.S.T. must take account of the objections raised, both to clarify misunderstanding and to utilize criticism for improvement.

A "devastating" criticism of "General Behavior Systems Theory" by Buck would hardly deserve discussion were it not for the fact that it appeared in the widely read *Minnesota Studies in the Philosophy of Science*, a leading publication of modern positivism. In passing, it should be noted that the lack of interest in, or even hostility of logical positivists against, G.S.T. is a rather remarkable phenomenon. One would expect that a group whose program is "Unified Science" should be concerned with a novel approach to this problem, however immature it may still be. The opposite is the case; no contribution or even pertinent criticism came forward from these quarters. The reason is not difficult to see. Abandoning the debatable but challenging position of Logical Positivism and replacing it by a rather tame "Empirical Realism", modern positivists have come back to what is generally agreed among modern scientists, avoiding commitments which trespass and would imply an adventure of thought. It needs to be said that modern positivism has been a singularly sterile movement. It is paradoxical that the declared "philosophers of science" have neither contributed any empirical research nor new idea to modern science – while professional or half-time philosophers who were justly censored for their "mysticism", "metaphysics", or "vitalism", indubitably did. Eddington and Jeans in physics, Driesch in biology, Spengler in history are but a few examples.

Buck's critique is not directed against the present author but against J. G. Miller and his Chicago group. Its essence is in the "So what?" argument: Supposing we find an analogy or formal identity in two "systems", it means nothing. Compare, for example, a chessboard and a mixed dinner party; a general statement expressing the alternation of black and white squares on the one hand, and of men and women on the other can be made. "If one is tempted to say 'All right, so they're structurally analogous, so what?' my answer is 'So, nothing.'" In the same vein, Buck pokes fun at some of Miller's more hazardous comparisons, such as the behavior of slime molds and Londoners during the *blitz*. He asks, "What are we to conclude from all this? That Londoners are a form of slime mold? That myxamoebae are a sort of city dweller?" Or "if no conclusion, why bother with the analogy at all?"

As proof of the emptiness of analogies Buck offers the example of a scientist, A, who finds a formula for the rate of formation of frost in a refrigerator; of another, B, formulating the rate of carbon deposit in an automobile motor; and a "general systems theorist," C, who notices that both formulas are the same. The similarity of mathematical expressions and models is, according to Buck, "sheer coincidence" – it does not prove that a refrigerator is an automobile or vice versa, but only that both are "systems" of some sort. This, however, is a meaningless statement; for

One is unable to think of anything, or of any combination of things, which could not be regarded as a system. And, of course, a concept that applies to everything is logically empty.

Regardless of the question whether Miller's is a particularly felicitous presentation, Buck has simply missed the issue of a general theory of systems. Its aim is not more or less hazy analogies; it is to establish principles applicable to entities not covered in conventional science. Buck's criticism is, in principle, the same as if one would criticize Newton's law because it draws a loose "analogy" between apples, planets, ebb and tide and many other entities; or if one would declare the theory of probability meaningless because it is concerned with the "analogy" of games of dice, mortality statistics, molecules in a gas, the distribution of hereditary characteristics, and a host of other phenomena.

The basic role of "analogy" – or rather of isomorphisms and models in science – has been lucidly discussed by Ashby. Hence a few remarks in answer to Buck will suffice.

The "So what?" question mistakes a method which is fundamental in science although – like every method – it can be misused. Even Buck's first example is not a meaningless pseudoproblem; in the "analogy" of chessboard and dinner party topology may find a common structural principle that is well worth stating. Generally speaking, the use of "analogy" (isomorphism, logical homology) – or, what amounts to nearly the same, the use of conceptual and material models – is not a half-poetical play but a potent tool in science. Where would physics be without the analogy or model of "wave", applicable to such dissimilar phenomena as water waves, sound waves, light and electromagnetic waves, "waves" (in a rather Pickwickian sense) in atomic physics? "Analogies" may pose fundamental problems, as for example, the analogy (logically not dissimilar from that of chessboard and dinner party) of Newton's and Coulomb's law which raises the question (one of the most basic for "Unified Science") of a general field theory unifying mechanics and electrodynamics. It is commonplace in cybernetics that systems which are different materially; e.g., a mechanical and an electrical system, may be formally identical; far from considering this as a meaningless So what? the researcher has to work out the common structure (flow diagram), and this may be of incomparable value for practical technology.

A similar lack of understanding is manifest in the criticism of the system concept. By the same token ("One is unable to think of anything" which would not show the properties in question) mechanics would have to be refused as "logically empty" because every material body shows mass, acceleration, energy, etc. In the following paragraphs of his paper, Buck has some glimpse of this truism, but he soon comes back to ridiculing Miller's use of "analogies".

Although Buck justly criticizes certain unfortunate formulations, his misunderstanding of the basic problems involved makes one wonder how his essay found its way into a treatise on "Philosophy of Science".

At an incomparably higher level stands the criticism by the Soviet authors, Lektorsky and Sadovsky. The writers give a sympathetic and fair presentation of Bertalanffy's G.S.T. sketching diligently its gradual evolution from "organismic biology" and the theory of open systems. In view of the above criticism by Buck, the following quotation is of interest:

Bertalanffy emphasizes the idea that a general system theory is not an investigation of hazy and superficial analogies. . . . Analogies as such have little value, since differences can always be found among phenomena as well as similarities. Bertalanffy declares that the kind of isomorphism with which general system theory is concerned is a consequence of the fact that in some respects corresponding abstractions and conceptual models can be applied to different phenomena.

"We can only welcome [the] goal [of G.S.T.]," write Lektorsky and Sadovsky, "i.e., the attempt to give a general definition of the concept of 'organized system', to classify logically various types of systems and to work out mathematical models for describing them . . . Bertalanffy's theory of organization and of organized complexes is a special scientific discipline. At the same time it certainly fulfills a definite methodological function" (i.e., avoiding duplication of effort in various disciplines by a single formal apparatus). "Its mathematical apparatus can be utilized for analyzing a comparatively large class of systemed objects of interest to biologists, chemists, biochemists, biophysicists, psychologists and others."

The criticism of the Russian authors is directed against imperfections of G.S.T. which, unfortunately, cannot be denied: "Bertalanffy's definition is rather a description [not pretending to precision] of the class of events which we may call systems than a strictly logical definition." "The description contains no trace of logical elegance." "Elementary methods of analysis and synthesis are insufficient for the analysis of systems." Fairly enough the authors concede that "The flaws we have noted speak only for the fact that general system theory, like any scientific theory, should develop further and in the process of development should strive for more adequate reflection of the objects of investigation."

The "main flaws of the theory", according to Lektorsky and Sadovsky, are in the lack of "methodology" (i.e., presumably of rules to establish and to apply system principles) and in considering G.S.T. "a philosophy of modern science". With respect to the first item, the present study is devoted to just this problem. The second point is a misunderstanding. G.S.T. in its present form is one – and still very imperfect – model among others. Were it completely developed, it would indeed incorporate the "organismic" world view of our time, with its emphasis on problems of wholeness, organization, directiveness, etc., in a similar way as when previous philosophies have presented a mathematical world view (philosophies *more geometrico*), a physicalistic one (the mechanistic philosophy based upon classical physics), etc., corresponding to scientific development. Even then, this "organismic" picture would not claim to be a "Nothing-but" philosophy: It would remain conscious that it only presents certain aspects of reality (richer and more comprehensive than previous ones, as corresponds to the advance of science), but never exhaustive, exclusive or final.

According to the authors, Marxist–Leninist philosophy "formulates a series of most important methodological principles of analysis of complex systems"; Soviet scientists "attempt to give a general definition of the notion of systems and to obtain a classification". Difficulties in international communication make it unfortunately impossible to the present writer to evaluate these claims.

Another criticism backed by the same *weltanschauung* is that of Kamaryt. The main arguments are:

1. Underestimation of the structural and morphologic aspects of organization of the theory of open systems (and implicitly in G.S.T.). The theory of open system does not "solve" the problem of life, its origin and evolution which is successfully attacked in modern biochemistry, submicroscopic morphology, physiological genetics, etc. The reply to this is that the functional and processual aspect has been emphasized in the theory, particularly in contradistinction to structural, homeostatic mechanisms. But neither the importance of the latter is denied, nor of course the specificity of the material basis of life. "Morphology and physiology are different and complementary ways of studying the same integrated object." If one wishes, this may be called a "dialectic unity of structure and function".

2. Neglect of "qualitative specificity" of biological open system and of the specific "chemodynamics" of the first.

The reply is: Thermodynamic considerations (of machines, chemical reactions, organisms, etc.) permit balance statements regarding the system as a whole, without entering into, or even knowing partial reactions, components, organization, etc., in detail. Hence part of the "theory of open systems" is concerned with such over-all balances of the system as a whole. If, however, the theory is applied to individual processes such as formation of proteins, behavior of tracers in the organism, ionic steady states, etc., the "specificity" of the respective components enters as a matter of course.

5 Advances of general system theory

The decisive question is that of the explanatory and predictive value of the "new theories" attacking the host of problems around wholeness, teleology, etc. Of course, the change in intellectual climate which allows us to see new problems which were overlooked previously, or to see problems in a new light, is in a way more important than any single and special application. The "Copernican Revolution" was more than the possibility somewhat better to calculate the movement of the planets; general relativity more than an explanation of a very small number of recalcitrant phenomena in physics; Darwinism more than a hypothetical answer to zoological problems; it was the changes in the general frame of reference that mattered. Nevertheless, the justification of such change ultimately is in specific achievements which would not have been obtained without the new theory.

There is no question that new horizons have been opened up but the relations to empirical facts often remain tenuous. Thus, information theory has been hailed as a "major breakthrough" but outside the original technological field contributions have remained relatively scarce. In psychology, they are so far limited to rather trivial applications such as role learning, etc. When, in biology, DNA is spoken of as "coded information" and of "breaking the code" when the structure of nucleic acids is elucidated, this is more a *façon de parler* than added insight into the control of protein synthesis. "Information theory, although useful for computer design and network analysis, has so far not found a significant place in biology." Game theory, too, is a novel mathematical development which was considered to be comparable in scope to Newtonian mechanics and the introduction of calculus; again, "the applications are meager and faltering" (the reader is urgently referred to Rapoport's discussions on information and game theory which admirably analyze the problems here mentioned). The same is seen in decision theory from which consider-

able gain in applied systems science was expected; but as regards the much-advertised military and business games, "there has been no controlled evaluation of their performance in training, personnel selection, and demonstration".

A danger in recent developments should not remain unmentioned. Science of the past (and partly still the present) was dominated by one-sided empiricism. Only collection of data and experiments were considered as being "scientific" in biology (and psychology); "theory" was equated with "speculation" or "philosophy", forgetting that a mere accumulation of data, although steadily piling up, does not make a "science". Lack of recognition and support for development of the necessary theoretical framework and unfavorable influence on experimental research itself (which largely became an at-random, hit-or-miss endeavor) was the consequence. This has, in certain fields, changed to the contrary in recent years. Enthusiasm for the new mathematical and logical tools available has led to feverish "model building" as a purpose in itself and often without regard to empirical fact. However, conceptual experimentation at random has no greater chances of success than at-random experimentation with biological, psychological, or clinical material. In the words of Ackoff, there is the fundamental misconception in game (and other) theory to mistake for a "problem" what actually is only a mathematical "exercise". One would do well to remember the old Kantian maxim that experience without theory is blind, but theory without experience a mere intellectual play.

The case is somewhat different with cybernetics. The model here applied is not new; although the enormous development in the field dates from the introduction of the name, Cybernetics, application of the feedback principle to physiological processes goes back to R. Wagner's work nearly 40 years ago. The feedback and homeostasis model has since been applied to innumerable biological phenomena and – somewhat less persuasively – in psychology and the social sciences. The reason for the latter fact is, in Rapoport's words that

usually, there is a well-marked negative correlation between the scope and the soundness of the writings. . . . The sound work is confined either to engineering or to rather trivial applications; ambitious formulations remain vague.

This, of course, is an ever-present danger in all approaches to general systems theory: doubtless, there is a new compass of thought but it is difficult to steer between the scylla of the trivial and the charybdis of mistaking neologisms for explanation.

The following survey is limited to "classical" general system theory – "classical" not in the sense that it claims any priority or excellence, but that the models used remain in the framework of "classical" mathematics in contradistinction to the "new" mathematics in game, network, information theory, etc. This does not imply that the theory is merely application of conventional mathematics. On the contrary, the system concept poses problems which are partly far from being answered. In the past, system problems have led to important mathematical developments such as Volterra's theory of integro-differential equations, of systems with "memory" whose behavior depends not only on actual conditions but also on previous history. Presently important problems are waiting for further developments, e.g., a general theory of non-linear differential equations, of steady states and rhythmic phenomena, a generalized principle of least action, the thermodynamic definition of steady states, etc.

It is, of course, irrelevant whether or not research was explicitly labeled as "general system theory". No complete or exhaustive review is intended. The aim of this unpretentious survey will be fulfilled if it can serve as a sort of guide to research done in the field, and to areas that are promising for future work.

Open systems

The theory of open systems is an important generalization of physical theory, kinetics and thermodynamics. It has led to new principles and insight, such as the principle of equifinality, the generalization of the second thermodynamic principle, the possible increase of order in open systems, the occurrence of periodic phenomena of overshoot and false start, etc. The possibility of measuring organization in terms of entropy ("chain entropy" of high molecular compounds showing a certain order of component molecules) deserves further attention.

The extensive work done cannot be reviewed here. . . . It should be briefly mentioned, however, that apart from theoretical developments, the field has two major applications, i.e., in industrial chemistry and in biophysics.

The applications of "open systems" in biochemistry, biophysics, physiology, etc., are too numerous to permit more than brief mentioning in the present study. The impact of the theory follows from the fact that the living organism, the cell as well as other biological entities essentially are steady states (or evolving toward such states). This implies the fundamental nature of the theory in the biological realm, and a basic reorientation in many of its specialties. Among others, the theory was developed and

applied in such fields as e.g., the network of reactions in photosynthesis, calculation of turnover rates in isotope experiments, energy requirements for the maintenance of body proteins, transport processes, maintenance of ion concentrations in the blood, radiation biology, excitation and propagation of nerve impulses, and others. The organism is in a steady state not only with respect to its chemical components, but also to its cells; hence the numerous modern investigations on cell turnover and renewal have also to be included here. Beside the work already cited, results and impending problems in biophysics and related fields may be found in Netter (1959).

There are certainly relations between irreversible thermodynamics of open systems, cybernetics, and information theory, but they are still unexplored. First approaches to these problems are those by Foster, Rapoport and Trucco, and by Tribus. Another interesting approach to metabolizing systems was made by Rosen (1960) who instead of conventional reaction equations, applied "relational theory" using mapping by way of block diagrams.

Beyond the individual organism, systems principles are also used in population dynamics and ecologic theory. Dynamic ecology, i.e., the succession and climax of plant populations, is a much-cultivated field which, however, shows a tendency to slide into verbalism and terminological debate. The systems approach seems to offer a new viewpoint. Whittacker has described the sequence of plant communities toward a climax formation in terms of open systems and equifinality. According to this author, the fact that similar climax formations may develop from different initial vegetations is a striking example of equifinality, and one where the degree of independence of starting conditions and of the course development has taken appears even greater than in the individual organism. A quantitative analysis on the basis of open systems in terms of production of biomass, with climax as steady state attained, was given by Patten.

The open-system concept has also found application in the earth sciences, geomorphology and meteorology, drawing a detailed comparison of modern meteorological concepts and Bertalanffy's organismic concept in biology. It may be remembered that already Prigogine in his classic mentioned meteorology as one possible field of application of open systems.

Growth-in-time

The simplest forms of growth which, for this reason, are particularly apt to show the isomorphism of law in different fields, are the exponential and logistic. Examples are, among many others, the increase of knowledge of number of animal species, publications on drosophila, of manufacturing companies. Boulding and Keiter have emphasized a general theory of growth.

The theory of animal growth after Bertalanffy (and others) – which, in virtue of using overall physiological parameters ("anabolism", "catabolism") may be subsumed under the heading of G.S.T. as well as under that of biophysics – has been surveyed in its various applications.

Relative growth

A principle which is also of great simplicity and generality concerns the relative growth of components within a system. The simple relationship of allometric increase applies to many growth phenomena in biology (morphology, biochemistry, physiology, evolution).

A similar relationship obtains in social phenomena. Social differentiation and division of labor in primitive societies as well as the process of urbanization (i.e., growth of cities in comparison to rural population) follow the allometric equation. Application of the latter offers a quantitative measure of social organization and development, apt to replace the usual, intuitive judgments. The same principle apparently applies to the growth of staff compared to total number of employees in manufacturing companies.

Competition and related phenomena

The work in population dynamics by Volterra, Lotka, Gauss and others belongs to the classics of G.S.T., having first shown that it is possible to develop conceptual models for phenomena such as the "struggle for existence" that can be submitted to empirical test. Population dynamics and related population genetics have since become important fields in biological research.

It is important to note that investigation of this kind belongs not only to basic but also to applied biology. This is true of fishery biology where theoretical models are used to establish optimum conditions for the exploitation of the sea (survey of the more important models: Watt). The most elaborate dynamic model is by Beverton and Holt developed for fish populations exploited in commercial fishery but certainly of wider application. This model takes into account recruitment (i.e., entering of individuals into the population), growth (assumed to follow the growth equations after Bertalanffy), capture (by exploitation), and natural mortality. The practical value of this model is illustrated by the fact that it has been adopted for routine purposes by the Food and Agriculture Organization of the United Nations, the British Ministry of Agriculture and Fisheries and other official agencies.

Richardson's studies on armaments races, notwithstanding their shortcomings, dramatically show the possible impact of the systems concept upon the most vital concerns of our time. If rational and scientific considerations matter at all, this is one way to refute such catch words as *Si vis pacem para bellum*.

The expressions used in population dynamics and the biological "struggle for existence", in econometrics, in the study of armament races (and others) all belong to the same family of equations. A systematic comparison and study of these parallelisms would be highly interesting and rewarding. One may, for example, suspect that the laws governing business cycles and those of population fluctuations according to Volterra stem from similar conditions of competition and interaction in the system.

In a non-mathematical way, Boulding has discussed what he calls the "Iron Laws" of social organizations: the Malthusian law, the law of optimum size of organizations, existence of cycles, the law of oligopoly, etc.

Systems engineering

The theoretical interest of systems engineering and operations research is in the fact that entities whose components are most heterogeneous – men, machines, buildings, monetary and other values, inflow of raw material, outflow of products and many other items – can successfully be submitted to systems analysis.

As already mentioned, systems engineering employs the methodology of cybernetics, information theory, network analysis, flow and block diagrams, etc. Considerations of G.S.T. also enter. The first approaches are concerned with structured, machine-like aspects (yes-or-no decisions in the case of information theory); one would suspect that G.S.T. aspects will win increased importance with dynamic aspects, flexible organizations, etc.

Personality theory

Although there is an enormous amount of theorizing on neural and psychological function in the cybernetic line based upon the brain–computer comparison, few attempts have been made to apply G.S.T. in the narrower sense to the theory of human behavior. For the present purposes, the latter may be nearly equated with personality theory.

We have to realize at the start that personality theory is at present a battlefield of contrasting and controversial theories. Hall and Lindzey have justly stated: "All theories of behavior are pretty poor theories and all of them leave much to be desired in the way of scientific proof" – this being said in a textbook of nearly 600 pages on "Theories of Personality".

We can therefore not well expect that G.S.T. can present solutions where personality theorists from Freud and Jung to a host of modern writers were unable to do so. The theory will have shown its value if it opens new perspectives and viewpoints capable of experimental and practical application. This appears to be the case. There is quite a group of psychologists who are committed to an organismic theory of personality, Goldstein and Maslow being well-known representatives. Biological considerations may therefore be expected to advance the matter.

There is, of course, the fundamental question whether, first, G.S.T. is not essentially a physicalistic simile, inapplicable to psychic phenomena; and secondly whether such model has explanatory value when the pertinent variables cannot be defined quantitatively as is in general the case with psychological phenomena.

1. The answer to the first question appears to be that the systems concept is abstract and general enough to permit application to entities of whatever denomination. The notions of "equilibrium", "homeostasis", "feedback", "stress", etc., are no less of technologic or physiological origin but more or less successfully applied to psychological phenomena. System theorists agree that the concept of "system" is not limited to material entities but can be applied to any "whole" consisting of interacting "components". . . . Systems engineering is an example where components are partly not physical and metric.

2. If quantitation is impossible, and even if the components of a system are ill-defined, it can at least be expected that certain principles will qualitatively apply to the whole *qua* system. At least "explanation on principle" (see below) may be possible.

Bearing in mind these limitations, one concept which may prove to be of a key nature is the organismic notion of the organism as a spontaneously active system. In the present author's words:

Even under constant external conditions and in the absence of external stimuli the organism is not a passive but a basically active system. This applies in particular to the function of the nervous system and to behavior. It appears that internal activity rather than reaction to stimuli is fundamental. This can be shown with respect both to evolution in lower animals and to development, for example, in the first movements of embryos and fetuses.

This agrees with what von Holst has called the "new conception" of the nervous system, based upon the fact that primitive locomotor activities are caused by central automatisms that do not need external stimuli. Therefore, such movements persist, for example, even after the connection of motoric to sensory nerves had been severed. Hence the reflex in the classic sense is not the basic unit of behavior but rather a regulatory mechanism superimposed upon primitive, automatic activities. A similar concept is basic in the theory on instinct. According to Lorenz, innate releasing mechanisms (I.R.M.) play a dominant role, which sometimes go off without an external stimulus (in-vacuo or running idle reactions): A bird which has no material to build a nest may perform the movements of nest building in the air. These considerations are in the framework of what Hebb called the "conceptual C.N.S. of 1930–1950". The more recent insight into activating systems of the brain emphasizes differently, and with a wealth of experimental evidence, the same basic concept of the autonomous activity of the C.N.S.

The significance of these concepts becomes apparent when we consider that they are in fundamental contrast to the conventional stimulus-response scheme which assumes that the organism is an essentially reactive system answering, like an automaton, to external stimuli. The dominance of the S–R scheme in contemporary psychology needs no emphasis, and is obviously connected with the *zeitgeist* of a highly mechanized society. This principle is basic in psychological theories which in all other respects are opposite, for example, in behavioristic psychology as well as in psychoanalysis. According to Freud it is the supreme tendency of the organism to get rid of tensions and drives and come to rest in a state of equilibrium governed by the "principle of stability" which Freud borrowed from the German philosopher, Fechner. Neurotic and psychotic behavior, then, is a more or less effective or abortive defense mechanism tending to restore some sort of equilibrium (according to D. Rappaport's analysis of the structure of psychoanalytic theory: "economic" and "adaptive points of view").

Charlotte Buhler, the well-known child psycholgeist, has aptly epitomized the theoretical situation:

In the fundamental psychoanalytic model, there is only one basic tendency, that is toward *need gratification* or *tension reduction*. . . . Present-day biologic theories emphasize the "spontaneity" of the organism's activity which is due to its built-in energy. The organism's autonomous functioning, its "drive to perform certain movements" is emphasized by Bertalanffy. . . . These concepts represent *a complete revision of the original homeostasis principle* which emphasized exclusively the tendency toward equilibrium. It is the original homeostasis principle with which psychoanalysis identified its theory of discharge of tensions as the only primary tendency. (Emphasis partly ours.)

In brief, we may define our viewpoint as "Beyond the Homeostasis Principle":

(1) The S–R scheme misses the realms of play, exploratory activities, creativity, self-realization, etc.;
(2) The economic scheme misses just specific, human achievements – the most of what loosely is termed "human culture";
(3) The equilibrium principle misses the fact that psychological and behavioral activities are more than relaxation of tensions; far from establishing an optimal state, the latter may entail psychosis-like disturbances, as e.g., in sensory-deprivation experiments.

It appears that the S–R and psychoanalytic model is a highly unrealistic picture of human nature and, in its consequences, a rather dangerous one. Just what we consider to be specific human achievements can hardly be brought under the utilitarian, homeostasis, and stimulus–response scheme. One may call mountain climbing, composing of sonatas or lyrical poems "psychological homeostasis" – as has been done – but at the risk that this physiologically well-defined concept loses all meaning. Furthermore, if the principle of homeostatic maintenance is taken as a golden rule of behavior, the so-called well-adjusted individual will be the ultimate goal, that is a well-oiled robot maintaining itself in optimal biological, psychological and social homeostasis. This is a *Brave New World* – not, for some at least, the ideal state of humanity. Furthermore, that precarious mental equilibrium must not be disturbed. Hence in what somewhat ironically is called progressive education, the anxiety not to overload the child, not to impose constraints and to minimize all directing influences – with the result of a previously unheard-of crop of illiterates and juvenile delinquents.

In contrast to conventional theory, it can safely be maintained that not only stresses and tensions but equally complete release from stimuli and the consequent mental void may be neurosogenic or even psychosogenic. Experimentally this is verified by the experiments with sensory deprivation when subjects, insulated from all incoming stimuli, after a few hours develop a so-called model psychosis with hallucinations, unbearable anxiety, etc. Clinically it amounts to the same when insulation leads to prisoners' psychosis and to exacerbation of mental disease by isolation of patients in the ward. In contrast, maximal stress need not necessarily produce mental disturbance. If conventional theory were correct, Europe during and after the war, with extreme physiological as well as psychological stresses, should have been a gigantic lunatic asylum. As a matter of fact, there was statistically no increase either in neurotic or psychotic disturbances, apart from easily explained acute disturbances such as combat neurosis.

We so arrive at the conception that a great deal of biological and human behavior is beyond the principles of utility, homeostasis and stimulus-response, and that it is just this which is characteristic of human and cultural activities. Such new look opens new perspectives not only in theory, but in practical implications with respect to mental hygiene, education, and society in general.

What has been said can also be couched in philosophical terms. If existentialists speak of the emptiness and meaninglessness of life, if they see in it a source not only of anxiety but of actual mental illness, it is essentially the same viewpoint: that behavior is not merely a matter of satisfaction of biological drives and of maintenance in psychological and social equilibrium but that something more is involved. If life becomes unbearably empty in an industrialized society, what can a person do but develop a neurosis? The principle which may loosely be called spontaneous activity of the psychophysical organism, is a more realistic formulation of what the existentialists want to say in their often obscure language. And if personality theorists like Maslow or Gardner Murphy speak of self-realization as human goal, it is again a somewhat pompous expression of the same.

Theoretical history

We eventually come to those highest and ill-defined entities that are called human cultures and civilizations. It is the field often called "philosophy of history". We may perhaps better speak of "theoretical history", admittedly in its very first beginnings. This name expresses the goal to form a connecting link between "science" and the "humanities"; more in particular, between the "social sciences" and "history".

It is understood, of course, that the techniques in sociology and history are entirely different (polls, statistical analysis against archival studies, internal evidence of historic relics, etc.). However, the object of study is essentially the same. Sociology is essentially concerned with a temporal cross-section as human societies *are*; history with the "longitudinal" study how societies *become* and develop. The object and techniques of study certainly justify practical differentiation; it is less clear, however, that they justify fundamentally different philosophies.

The last statement already implies the question of constructs in history, as they were presented, in grand form, from Vico to Hegel, Marx, Spengler and Toynbee. Professional historians regard them at best as poetry, at worst as fantasies pressing, with paranoic obsession, the facts of history into a theoretical bed of Procrustes. It seems history can learn from the system theorists, not ultimate solutions but a sounder methodological outlook. Problems hitherto considered to be philosophical or metaphysical can well be defined in their scientific meaning, with some interesting outlook at recent developments (e.g., game theory) thrown into the bargain.

Empirical criticism is outside the scope of the present study. For example, Geyl and many others have analyzed obvious misrepresentations of historical events in Toynbee's work, and even the non-specialist reader can easily draw a list of fallacies especially in the later, Holy-Ghost inspired volumes of Toynbee's *magnum opus*. The problem, however, is larger than errors in fact or interpretation or even the question of the merits of Marx's, Spengler's or Toynbee's theories; it is whether, in principle, models and laws are admissible in history.

A widely held contention says that they are not. This is the concept of "nomothetic" method in science and "idiographic" method in history. While science to a greater or less extent can establish "laws" for natural events, history, concerned with human events of enormous complexity in causes and outcome and possibly determined by free decisions of individuals can only describe, more or less satisfactorily, what has happened in the past.

Here the methodologist has his first comment. In the attitude just outlined, academic history condemns constructs of history as "intuitive", "contrary to fact", "arbitrary", etc. And, no doubt, the criticism is pungent enough vis-à-vis Spengler or Toynbee. It is, however, somewhat less convincing if we look at the work of conventional historiography. For example, the Dutch historian, Peter Geyl, who made a strong argument against Toynbee from such methodological considerations, also wrote a brilliant book about Napoleon, amounting to the result that there are a dozen or so different interpretations – we may safely say, *models* – of Napoleon's character and career within academic history, all based upon "fact" (the Napoleonic period happens to be one of the best documented) and all

flatly contradicting each other. Roughly speaking, they range from Napoleon as the brutal tyrant and egotistic enemy of human freedom to Napoleon the wise planner of a unified Europe; and if one is a Napoleonic student (as the present writer happens to be in a small way), one can easily produce some original documents refuting misconceptions occurring even in generally accepted, standard histories. You cannot have it both ways. If even a figure like Napoleon, not very remote in time and with the best of historical documentation, can be interpreted contrarily, you cannot well blame the "philosophers of history" for their intuitive procedure, subjective bias, etc., when they deal with the enormous phenomenon of universal history. What you have in both cases is a conceptual model which always will represent certain aspects only, and for this reason will be one-sided or even lopsided. Hence the construction of conceptual models in history is not only permissible but, as a matter of fact, is at the basis of any historical interpretation as distinguished from mere enumeration of data, i.e., chronicle or annals.

If this is granted, the antithesis between idiographic and nomothetic procedure reduces to what psychologists are wont to call the "molecular" and "molar" approach. One can analyze events within a complex whole – individual chemical reactions in an organism, perceptions in the psyche, for example; or one can look for over-all laws covering the whole such as growth and development in the first or personality in the second instance. In terms of history, this means detailed study of individuals, treaties, works of art, singular causes and effects, etc., or else over-all phenomena with the hope of detecting grand laws. There are, of course, all transitions between the first and second considerations; the extremes may be illustrated by Carlyle and his hero worship at one pole and Tolstoy (a far greater "theoretical historian" than commonly admitted) at the other.

The question of a "theoretical history" therefore is essentially that of "molar" models in the field; and this is what the great constructs of history amount to when divested of their philosophical embroidery.

The evaluation of such models must follow the general rules for verification or falsification. First, there is the consideration of empirical bases. In this particular instance it amounts to the question whether or not a limited number of civilizations – some twenty at the best – provide a sufficient and representative sample to establish justified generalizations. This question and that of the value of proposed models will be answered by the general criterion; whether or not the model has explanatory and predictive value, i.e., throws new light upon known facts and correctly foretells facts of the past or future not previously known.

Although elementary, these considerations nevertheless are apt to remove much misunderstanding and philosophical fog which has clouded the issue.

1. As had been emphasized, the evaluation of models should be simply pragmatic in terms of their explanatory and predictive merits (or lack thereof); *a priori* considerations as to their desirability or moral consequences do not enter.

Here we encounter a somewhat unique situation. There is little objection against so-called "synchronic" laws, i.e., supposed regularities governing societies at a certain point in time; as a matter of fact, beside empirical study this is the aim of sociology. Also certain "diachronic" laws, i.e., regularities of development in time, are undisputed such as, e.g., Grimm's law stating rules for the changes of consonants in the evolution of Indo-Germanic languages. It is commonplace that there is a sort of "life-cycle" – stages of primitivity, maturity, baroque dissolution of form and eventual decay for which no particular external causes can be indicated – in individual fields of culture, such as Greek sculpture, Renaissance painting or German music. Indeed, this even has its counterpart in certain phenomena of biological evolution showing, as in ammonites or dinosaurs, a first explosive phase of formation of new types followed by a phase of speciation and eventually of decadence.

Violent criticism comes in when this model is applied to civilization as a whole. It is a legitimate question – Why often rather unrealistic models in the social sciences remain matters of academic discussion, while models of history encounter passionate resistance? Granting all factual criticism raised against Spengler or Toynbee, it seems rather obvious that emotional factors are involved. The highway of science is strewn with corpses of deceased theories which just decay or are preserved as mummies in the museum of history or science. In contrast, historical constructs and especially theories of historical cycles appear to touch a raw nerve, and so opposition is much more than usual criticism of a scientific theory.

2. This emotional involvement is connected with the question of "Historical Inevitability" and a supposed degradation of human "freedom". Before turning to it, discussion of mathematical and non-mathematical models is in place.

Advantages and shortcomings of mathematical models in the social sciences are well known. Every mathematical model is an oversimplification, and it remains questionable whether it strips actual events to the bones or cuts away vital parts of their anatomy. On the other hand, so far as it goes, it permits necessary deduction with often unexpected results which would not be obtained by ordinary "common sense".

In particular, Rashevsky has shown in several studies how mathematical models of historical processes can be constructed.

On the other hand, the value of purely qualitative models should not be underestimated. For example, the concept of "ecologic equilibrium" was developed long before Volterra and others introduced mathematical models; the theory of selection belongs to the stock-in-trade of biology, but the mathematical theory of the "struggle for existence" is comparatively recent, and far from being verified under wildlife conditions.

In complex phenomena, "explanation on principle" by qualitative models is preferable to no explanation at all. This is by no means limited to the social sciences and history; it applies alike to fields like meteorology or evolution.

3. "Historical inevitability" – subject of a well-known study by Sir Isaiah Berlin – dreaded as a consequence of "theoretical history", supposedly contradicting our direct experience of having free choices and eliminating all moral judgment and values – is a phantasmagoria based upon a world view which does not exist any more. As, in fact, Berlin emphasizes, it is founded upon the concept of the Laplacean spirit who is able completely to predict the future from the past by means of deterministic laws. This has no resemblance with the modern concept of "laws of nature". All "laws of nature" have a statistical character. They do not predict an inexorably determined future but probabilities which, depending on the nature of events and on the laws available, may approach certainty or else remain far below it. It is nonsensical to ask or fear more "inevitability" in historical theory than is found in sciences with relatively high sophistication like meteorology or economics.

Paradoxically, while the cause of free will rests with the testimony of intuition or rather immediate experience and can never be proved objectively ("Was it Napoleon's free will that led him to the Russian Campaign?"), determinism (in the statistical sense) can be proved, at least in small-scale models. Certainly business depends on personal "initiative", the individual "decision" and "responsibility" of the entrepreneur; the manager's choice whether or not to expand business by employing new appointees, is "free" in precisely the sense as Napoleon's choice whether or not to accept battle at Austerlitz. However, when the growth curve of industrial companies is analyzed, it is found that "arbitrary" deviations are followed by speedy return to the normal curve, as if invisible forces were active. Haire states that "the return to the pattern predicted by earlier growth suggests the operation of *inexorable forces* operating on the social organism" (our emphasis).

It is characteristic that one of Berlin's points is "the fallacy of historical determinism (appearing) from its utter inconsistency with the common sense and everyday life of looking at human affairs". This characteristic argument is of the same nature as the advice not to adopt the Copernican system because everybody can see that the sun moves from morning to evening.

4. Recent developments in mathematics even allow to submit "free will" – apparently the philosophical problem most recalcitrant against scientific analysis – to mathematical examination.

In the light of modern systems theory, the alternative between molar and molecular, nomothetic and idiographic approach can be given a precise meaning. For mass behavior, system laws would apply which, if they can be mathematized, would take the form of differential equations of the sort of those used by Richardson mentioned above. Free choice of the individual would be described by formulations of the nature of game and decision theory.

Axiomatically, game and decision theory are concerned with "rational" choice. This means a choice which "maximizes the individual's utility or satisfaction", that "the individual is free to choose among several possible courses of action and decides among them at the basis of their consequences", that he "selects, being informed of all conceivable consequences of his actions, what stands highest on his list", he "prefers more of a commodity to less, other things being equal", etc. Instead of economical gain, any higher value may be inserted without changing the mathematical formalism.

The above definition of "rational choice" includes everything that can be meant by "free will". If we do not wish to equate "free will" with complete arbitrariness, lack of any value judgment and therefore completely inconsequential actions (like the philosopher's favorite example: It is my free will whether or not to wiggle my left little finger) it is a fair definition of those actions with which the moralist, priest, or historian is concerned: free decision between alternatives based upon insight into the situation and its consequences and guided by values.

The difficulty to apply the theory even to simple, actual situations is of course enormous; so is the difficulty in establishing over-all laws. However, without explicit formulation, both approaches can be evaluated in principle – leading to an unexpected paradox.

The "principle of rationality" fits – not the majority of human actions but rather the "unreasoning" behavior of animals. Animals and organisms in general do function in a "ratio-morphic" way, maximizing such values as maintenance, satisfaction, survival, etc.; they select, in general, what is biologically good for them, and prefer more of a commodity (e.g., food) to less.

Human behavior, on the other hand, falls far short of the principle of rationality. It is not even necessary to quote Freud to show how small is the compass of rational behavior in man. Women in a supermarket, in general, do not maximize utility but are susceptible to the tricks of the advertiser and packer; they do not make a rational choice surveying all possibilities and consequences; and do not even prefer more of the commodity packed in an inconspicuous way to less when packed in a big red box with attractive design. In our society, it is the job of an influential specialty – advertisers, motivation researchers, etc. – to *make* choices irrational which essentially is done by coupling biological factors – conditioned reflex, unconscious drives – with symbolic values.

And there is no refuge by saying that this irrationality of human behavior concerns only trivial actions of daily life; the same principle applies to "historical" decisions. That wise old mind, Oxenstierna, Sweden's Chancellor during the Thirty Years' War, has perfectly expressed this by saying: *Nescis, mi fili, quantilla ratione mundus regatur* – you don't know, my dear boy, with what little reason the world is governed. Reading newspapers or listening to the radio readily shows that this applies perhaps even more to the 20th than the 17th century.

Methodologically, this leads to a remarkable conclusion. If one of the two models is to be applied, and if the "actuality principle" basic in historical fields like geology and evolution is adopted (i.e., the hypothesis that no other principles of explanation should be used than can be observed as operative in the present) – then it is the statistical or mass model which is backed by empirical evidence. The business of the motivation and opinion researcher, statistical psychologist, etc., is based upon the premise that statistical laws obtain in human behavior; and that, for this reason a small but well-chosen sample allows for extrapolation to the total population under consideration. The generally good working of a Gallup poll and prediction verifies the premise – with some incidental failure like the well-known example of the Truman election thrown in, as is to be expected with statistical predictions. The opposite contention – that history is governed by "free will" in the philosophical sense (i.e., rational decision for the better, the higher moral value or even enlightened self-interest) is hardly supported by fact. That here and there the statistical law is broken by "rugged individualists" is in its character. Nor does the role played in history by "great men" contradict the systems concept in history; they can be conceived as acting like "leading parts", "triggers" or "catalyzers" in the historical process – a phenomenon well accounted for in the general theory of systems.

5. A further question is the "organismic analogy" unanimously condemned by historians. They combat untiringly the "metaphysical", "poetical", "mythical" and thoroughly unscientific nature of Spengler's assertion that civilizations are a sort of "organisms", being born, developing according to their internal laws and eventually dying. Toynbee takes great pains to emphasize that he did not fall into Spengler's trap – even though it is somewhat difficult to see that his civilizations, connected by the biological relations of "affiliation" and "apparentation", even (according to the latest version of his system) with a rather strict time span of development, are not conceived organismically.

Nobody should know better than the biologist that civilizations are no "organism". It is trivial to the extreme that a biological organism, a material entity and unity in space and time, is something different from a social group consisting of distinct individuals, and even more from a civilization consisting of generations of human beings, of material products, institutions, ideas, values, and what not. It implies a serious underestimate of Vico's, Spengler's (or any normal individual's) intelligence to suppose that they did not realize the obvious.

Nevertheless, it is interesting to note that, in contrast to the historians' scruples, sociologists do not abhor the "organismic analogy" but rather take it for granted. For example, in the words of Rappoport and Horvath:

> There is some sense in considering a real organization as an organism, that is, there is reason to believe that this comparison need not be a sterile metaphorical analogy, such as was common in scholastic speculation about the body politic. Quasibiological functions are demonstrable in organizations. They maintain themselves; they sometimes reproduce or metastasize; they respond to stresses; they age, and they die. Organizations have discernible anatomies and those at least which transform material inputs (like industries) have physiologies.

Or Sir Geoffrey Vickers:

> Institutions grow, repair themselves, reproduce themselves, decay, dissolve. In their external relations they show many characteristics of organic life. Some think that in their internal relations also human institutions are destined to become increasingly organic, that human cooperation will approach ever more closely to the integration of cells in a body. I find this prospect unconvincing (and) unpleasant. [N.B. so does the present author.]

And Haire:

> The biological model for social organizations – and here, particularly for industrial organizations – means taking as a model the living organism and the processes and principles that regulate its growth and development. It means looking for lawful processes in organizational growth.

The fact that simple growth laws apply to social entities such as manufacturing companies, to urbanization, division of labor, etc., proves that in these respects the "organismic analogy" is correct. In spite of the historians' protests, the application of theoretical models, in particular, the model of dynamic, open and adaptive systems to the historical process certainly makes sense. This does not imply "biologism", i.e., reduction of social to biological concepts, but indicates system principles applying in both fields.

6. Taking all objections for granted – poor method, errors in fact, the enormous complexity of the historical process – we have nevertheless reluctantly to admit that the cyclic models of history pass the most important test of scientific theory. The predictions made by Spengler in the *Decline of the West*, by Toynbee when forecasting a time of trouble and contending states, by Ortega y Gasset in the *Uprise of the Masses* – we may as well add *Brave New World* and *1984* – have been verified to a disquieting extent and considerably better than many respectable models of the social scientists.

Does this imply "historic inevitability" and inexorable dissolution? Again, the simple answer was missed by moralizing and philosophizing historians. By extrapolation from the life cycles of previous civilizations nobody could have predicted the Industrial Revolution, the Population Explosion, the development of atomic energy, the emergence of underdeveloped nations, and the expansion of Western civilization over the whole globe. Does this refute the alleged model and "law" of history? No – it only says that this model – as every one in science – mirrors only certain aspects or facets of reality. Every model becomes dangerous only when it commits the "Nothing-but" fallacy which mars not only theoretical history, but the models of the mechanistic world picture, of psychoanalysis and many others as well.

We have hoped to show in this survey that General System Theory has contributed toward the expansion of scientific theory; has led to new insights and principles; and has opened up new problems that are "researchable", i.e., are amenable to further study, experimental or mathematical. The limitations of the theory and its applications in their present status are obvious; but the principles appear to be essentially sound as shown by their application in different fields.

References

Ackoff, R. L. (1959) "Games, decisions, and organizations". *General Systems* IV, 145–50.

—— (1960) "Systems, organizations, and interdisciplinary research", *General Systems* V, 1–8.

Arrow, K. J. (1956) "Mathematical models in the social sciences", *General Systems* I, 29–47.

Ashby, W. R. (1958a) "General systems theory as a new discipline", *General Systems* III, 1–6.

—— (1958b) *An Introduction to Cybernetics*, 3rd impr., Wiley, New York.

—— (1962) "Principles of the self-organizing system", in H. von Foerster, G. W. Zopf, Jr. (eds.), *Principles of Self-organization*, Pergamon Press, New York, pp. 255–78.

Attneave, F. (1959) *Application of Information Theory to Psychology*, Holt, New York.

Beer, St. (1960) "Below the twilight arch. A mythology of systems", *General Systems* V, 9–20.

Bell, E. (1962) "Oogenesis", C. P. Raven (review), *Science* 135, 1056.

von Bertalanffy, L. (1947) "Vom Sinn und der Einheit der Wissenschaften", *Der Student*, Wien, 2, No. 7/8.

—— (1949) "Zu einer allgemeinen systemlehre", *Biologia Generalis* 19, 114–29.

—— (1950) "An outline of general system theory", *Brit. J. Philos. Sci.* 1, 134–65.

—— (1953) *Biophysik des fliessgleichgewichts*, (Transl. by W. Westphal), Vieweg, Braunschweig.

—— (1956) "General system theory", *General Systems* I, 1–10.

—— (1956) "A biologist looks at human nature", *Scientific Monthly* 82, 33–41.

—— (1952) *Problems of Life. An Evaluation of Modern Biological and Scientific Thought*. Torchbook edition, Harper, New York, 1960a.

—— (1960b) "Principles and theory of growth", in W. W. Nowinski (ed.), *Fundamental Aspects of Normal and Malignant Growth*, Elsevier, Amsterdam, pp. 137–259.

—— (1933) *Modern Theories of Development. An Introduction to Theoretical Biology*. Torchbook edition, Harper, New York, 1962.

von Bertalanffy, L., Hempel, C. G., Bass, R. E., and Jonas, H. (1951) "General system theory: A new approach to unity of science", *Human Biol.* 23, 302–61.

Beverton, R. J. H. and Holt, S. J. (1957) "On the dynamics of exploited fish populations", *Fishery Investigation*, Ser. II, vol. XIX, H.M.S.O. London.

Boulding, K. E. (1953) *The Organizational Revolution*, Harper, New York.

—— (1956) "Toward a general theory of growth", *General Systems* I, 66–75.

Bradley, D. F. and Calvin, M. (1956) "Behavior: Imbalance in a network of chemical transformation", *General Systems* I, 56–65.

Bray, J. R. (1958) "Notes toward an ecology theory". *Ecology* 9, 770–6.

Bray, H. G. and White, K. (1957) *Kinetics and Thermodynamics in Biochemistry*, Academic Press, New York.

Buck, R. C. (1956) "On the logic of general behavior systems theory", in H. Feigel and M. Scriven (eds.), *Minnesota Studies in the Philosophy of Science*, vol. I, Univer. of Minnesota Press, Minneapolis, pp. 223–38.

Buhler, Ch. (1959) "Theoretical observations about life's basic tendencies", *Amer. J. Psychother.* 13, 501–81.

Chorley, R. J. (1962) "Geomorphology and general systems theory", *United States Geological Survey, Professional Paper*, 500–B.

Dost, R. H. (1953) *Der Blutspiegel. Kinetik der Konzentrationsabläufe in der Körperflussigkeit*. Thieme, Leipzig.

Egler, F. E. (1953) "Bertalanffian organismicism", *Ecology* 34, 443–6.

Feigl, H. (1956) "Some major issues and developments in the philosophy of science of logical empiricism", in H. Feigl and M. Scriven (eds.), *Minnesota Studies in the Philosophy of Science*, vol. I, Univer. of Minnesota Press, Minneapolis, pp. 3–37.

Foster, C., Rappoport, A., and Trucco, E. (1957) "Some unsolved problems in the theory of non-isolated systems", *General Systems* II, 9–29.

Gessner, F. (1952) "Wieviel Tiere bevölkern die Erde?", *Orion*, 33–5.

Geyl, P. (1957) *Napoleon for and Against*, Cape, London.

—— (1958) *Debates with Historians*, Meridian Books, New York.

Haire, M. (1959) "Biological models and empirical histories of the growth of organizations", in M. Haire (ed.), *Modern Organization Theory*, Wiley, New York, pp. 272–306.

Hall, A. D. (1962) *A Methodology for Systems Engineering*, Nostrand, Princeton.

Hall, A. D. and Fagen, R. E. (1956) "Definition of system", *General Systems* I, 18–28.

Hall, C. S. and Lindzey, G. (1957) *Theories of Personality*, Wiley, New York.

Hayek, F. A. (1955) "Degrees of explanation", *Brit. J. Philos. Sci.* 6, 209–25.

Hearn, G. (1958) *Theory Building in Social Work*, Univer. of Toronto Press, Toronto.

Hersh, A. H. (1942) "Drosophila and the course of research", *Ohio J. of Science* 42, 198–200.

Holt, S. J. "The application of comparative population studies to fisheries biology – an exploration", in E. D. Le Cren and M. W. Holdgate (eds.), *The Exploitation of Natural Animal Populations*, Blackwell, Oxford.

Kamaryt, J. (1961) "Die Bedeutung der Theorie des offenen Systems in der gegenwaertigen Biologie", *Deutsche Z. fuer Philosophie* 9, 2040–59.

Keiter, F. (1951–2) "Wachstum und Reifen im Jugendalter", *Koelner Z. fuer Soziologie* 4, 165–74.

Kment, H. (1959) "The problem of biological regulation and its evolution in medical view", *General Systems* IV, 75–82.

Kremyanskiy, V. I. (1960) "Certain peculiarities of organisms as a 'system' from the point of view of physics, cybernetics, and biology", *General Systems* V, 221–30.

Lektorsky, V. A. and Sadovsky, V. N. (1960) "On principles of system research (related to L. Bertalanffy's general system theory)", *General Systems* V, 171–9.

McClelland, Ch. A. (1958) "Systems and history in international relations. Some perspectives for empirical research and theory", *General Systems* III, 221–47.

Meyer, R. L. (1961) Preface, *General Systems* VI, III–IV.

Miller, J. G. *et al.* (1953) Symposium. "Profits and problems of homeostatic models in the behavioral sciences", *Chicago Behavioral Sciences Publications No. 1.*

Naroll, R. S. and von Bertalanffy, L. (1956) "The principle of allometry in biology and the social sciences", *General Systems* I, 76–89.

Netter, H. (1959) *Theoretische Biochemie*, Springer, Berlin.

Oppenheimer, R. (1956) "Analogy in science", *Amer. Psychol.* 11, 127–35.

Patten, B. C. (1959) "An introduction to the cybernetics of the ecosystem: The trophic-dynamic aspect", *Ecology* 40, 221–31.

Prigogine, I. (1947) *Etude thermodynamique des phénomènes irréversibles*, Dunod, Paris.

Rapoport, A. (1956) "The promise and pitfalls of information theory", *Behav. Sci.* 1, 303–15.

—— (1957) "Lewis F. Richardson's mathematical theory of war", *General Systems* II, 55–91.

—— (1959) "Critiques of game theory", *Behav. Sci.* 4, 49–66.

—— (1960) *Fights, Games, and Debates*, Univer. of Mich. Press, Ann Arbor.

Rapoport, A. and Horvath, W. J. (1959) "Thoughts on organization theory and a review of two conferences", *General Systems* IV, 87–93.

Rappaport, D. (1960) "The structure of psycho-analytic theory", *Psychol. Issues* 2, Monogr. 6, pp. 39–64.

Rashevsky, N. (1952) "The effect of environmental factors on the rates of cultural development", *Bull. Math. Biophysics* 14, 193–201.

Rosen, R. (1960) "A relational theory of biological systems", *General Systems* V, 29–55.

Schulz, G. V. (1951) "Energetische und statistische Voraussetzungen fuer die Synthese der Makromolekeule im Organismus", *Z. Elektrochem. u. angew. phys. Chemie* 55, 569–74.

Thompson, J. W. (1961) "The organismic conception in meteorology", *General Systems* VI, 45–9.

Toynbee, A. J. (1961) *A Study of History, Vol. XII. Reconsiderations*, Oxford Univer. Press, New York.

Tribus, M. (1961) "Information theory of the basis for thermostatics and thermodynamics", *General Systems* VI, 127–38.

Vickers, G. (1957) "Control, stability and choice", *General Systems* II, 1–8.

Watt, K. E. F. (1958) "The choice and solution of mathematical models for predicting and maximizing the yield of a fishery", *General Systems* III, 101–21.

Weaver, W. (1948) "Science and complexity", *American Scientist* 36, 536–644.

Whittaker, R. H. (1953) "A consideration of climax theory: The climax as a population and pattern", *Ecol. Monographs* 23, 41–78.

Weiss, P. (1962) "Experience and experiment in biology", *Science* 136, 468–71.

Wiener, N. (1948) *Cybernetics*, Wiley, New York.

Zacharias, J. R. (1957) "Structure of physical science", *Science* 125, 427–8.

Reprinted from von Bertalanffy, L. (1962) "General System Theory – A Critical Review", in *General Systems* VII, 1–20, with permission of the Society for General Systems Research.

Section II

Introduction

The engineering and design of complex man–machine systems, such as word-processing stations, manufacturing production lines, chemical plants and a variety of control rooms, require a range of activities which rapidly increase in type and number as new developments in technology appear. In engineering terms alone, the tasks are very demanding and once human characteristics are considered too they become formidable. The articles in this section characterize different aspects of the application of systems ideas to these hard systems, i.e., those systems where the objectives can be defined, the relationships accurately depicted and where quantification is often possible. It may seem strange to include articles on psychology and *man*–machine systems alongside manufacturing systems and systems engineering, but the approach that all four articles take is primarily an engineering one.

Singleton spells out the details of a method for designing systems and incorporating human factors considerations in that design. The approach is essentially systems management as practised by the United States military and extensively used in the space programme. It is a systematic development of both technical and human capabilities and requirements, with particular emphasis on the human side. Kenyon De Greene too tackles the management approach to man–machine design, but whereas Singleton is anxious to demonstrate the necessary skills to consider systems and to come to grips with the human side in an orderly way, De Greene is intent on establishing the need for a subject area of *systems psychology*. As in several later articles we have deliberately retained the author's own explanations of what the subject of systems is, both to allow readers to encounter different explanations and also to highlight the roots of the ideas and the variety of interpretations possible. Singleton, for example, is content to specify roots which are clearly in the systems engineering world, whereas De Greene considers it necessary to review a wider systems movement which is primarily general

systems- and cybernetics-based. Particular attention is drawn to De Greene's section entitled "What happens when the systems approach is not followed?" (p. 103), since not only is it an amusing set of disasters and failures but it also highlights the complex nature of so many engineering systems and the human involvement in them.

The paper by Gwilym Jenkins is a classic example of systems engineering as it is understood in the United Kingdom. The method is exhaustive, thorough and practical, and yet still allows the broader considerations that are necessary even in the design of technical systems. It was Jenkins who founded the Department of Systems Engineering at Lancaster University and it is this method which, when later applied to softer social systems, prompted the development of the soft-systems method detailed in Peter Checkland's article in Section VI.

In the article by Parnaby we see systems concepts applied to manufacturing, an area where a systems engineering approach ought to fit easily. Yet, as Parnaby explains, such systems are complex too and the consideration of complexity must be careful and thorough.

Associated reading

Systems engineering is a well-worked area and the references given by Jenkins provide an excellent starting point.

Many aspects of human factors, man–machine systems and systems engineering are dealt with in the Open University's course Systems Performance: Human Factors and Systems Failures. Of the two set books associated with that course the first, *Catastrophic Failures* by V. Bignell, G. Peters and C. Pym (Open University Press, 1977) is a selection of case studies of major disasters in similar vein to De Greene's examples of what happens when the systems approach is not followed. The second book, *Human Aspects of Man-made Systems* by S. C. Brown and J. N. T. Martin (Open University Press, 1977) is a collection of twenty articles on human considerations.

In addition, Singleton's book *Man—Machine Systems* (Penguin, 1974) and De Greene's book *Systems Psychol-*

ogy (McGraw-Hill, 1970) both extend the ideas presented in the extracts given here.

5 Systems and psychology
by Kenyon B. De Greene

Introduction

It's a typical day. The car starts OK, but you think with a flash of irritation that it really shouldn't have been necessary to remove the engine just to replace the starter motor. At the stop signal, it seems the flow of cross traffic will never end. You've got to present a briefing to military higher management at the other end of the country this afternoon and you're not satisfied. The pieces just don't seem to fit together. Perhaps that combination of tranquilizers and sleeping pills had left you unduly grouchy, but your wife shouldn't have bugged you about spending so much time on your job and neglecting the kids and all. An hour to catch your plane and cars piled up on the freeway as far as the eye can see. Start, move a few feet, and stop, start. . . . You reflect on the events in this morning's paper. Big jet pancakes down in the ocean eight miles short of the runway, killing 147. More student and minority group riots. Danger of imminent starvation in Africa and Asia. Strikes curtail services in still another city. You're still worried about your briefing. If you only had a better gauge that the men (how many *are* really necessary) could really do the job in that environment. You glance over your left shoulder. Traffic going the other way isn't much better. Car piled with skis and boats and people headed for the mountains and desert, even though it's a weekday. Airport's a couple of miles ahead now, but you can't see the tower through the smog. Surely there ought to be a way of getting an overall grasp of things, things that should fit nicely together but always seem to be operating at cross purposes. People pretty well manage to foul things up. People. Human nature again. If only the headshrinkers. . . . You'll have to walk about half a mile to your plane from the parking place you were just able to ace away from that other guy. But no sweat, there's still time for a quick cup of coffee, and you'll get points from your brisk walk in that new exercise system. System! You remember a book you leafed through at the company book stall on the quad. There was sort of a catchy quotation: "When we try to pick out anything by itself, we find it hitched to everything else in the universe." McGraw-Hill as you recall. Right! *Systems Psychology*. Have to look into it when you get a chance and see what it's about. . . .

This book* is about people and how they relate to complex technology and its consequences – how they relate to machines, buildings, communications, roads, and one another. Because human behavior varies from one situation to another, it is also about how people relate to environments. You may already be familiar with the *Three-M* – man–machine–medium – concept of interaction and its more recent extension to include a fourth and fifth *M*, mission and management. In this book, we determine whether apparently diverse and unrelated problems can be investigated in a *general yet systematic* manner, a manner that at once provides a basis for both definition and solution of these problems. Of basic concern is the *effectiveness* of people and the missions to which they contribute. We look at the way people behave and the effects of various conditions on their behavior.

At the same time, we examine the capabilities and limitations of machines. We thus are concerned with the man–machine *interface* – how man and machine can complement one another most effectively in accomplishing some end. Optimum design of the man–machine package alone does not guarantee the effectiveness we desire, however, and our success in man–machine design, even optimized to meet the constraints of a physicochemical environment, may introduce problems that seem less easy to handle. Our concept of effectiveness must be extended to include the variables of individual need, reward, expectation, and attitude. Not all problem situations structured through engineering will involve the same *psychological factors*. Sometimes it is necessary to single out specific factors – for example, alertness, vigilance, or decision making – for special study and consideration. However, under operating conditions of, say, piloting an aircraft, vigilance and decision making are functions of the pilot's needs at a given moment.

* [i.e., *Systems Psychology*, *Ed.*]

Clearly, *interrelatedness* and *interaction* among things are important themes in systems science. As we attempt to lend order and meaning to complicated situations, we apply the framework concepts and methods of *systems*, represented along the two dimensions of *time* and *depth*, which characterize, respectively, the sequence of activities by which a system accomplishes a given *purpose*, and the amount of knowledge available and applicable at given times. It is necessary first to postulate a hierarchy of subwholes,* leading eventually to the level of the individual human being, who can conveniently be viewed as a *"black-box* component" that, by some poorly understood *transfer function*, converts *inputs* into *outputs*. Unraveling the mechanisms involved in the human transfer function is a primary ongoing responsibility of psychology and physiology. You will notice the engineering language used here: Black-box component can be translated into the more psychological *stimulus–organism–response (S–O–R) paradigm*, or model.

It is sometimes convenient to single out constructs such as perception, motivation, learning, thinking, and intelligence. But these constructs are interrelated and are, in turn, reflections of other, perhaps more basic processes and of the environment at any instant. This difficulty has long been evident in the field of accident investigation. Suppose a pilot has had a quarrel with his wife and later, on a routine flight, in good weather, collides with another aircraft. Is the "cause" of this accident perception, attention, emotion, poor judgment, or what? Let's say we attribute it to degraded attention. We must then ask: Was attention degraded because of poor equipment design, conflicting task demands, boredom, or preoccupation with marital difficulties? The point we must never forget is this: While it is necessary to identify an abstraction such as "vigilance" for study in the laboratory, the vigilance of one situation may have little predictive value for the vigilance in another situation.

This book† attempts to integrate several established practices in psychology and in engineering. Part I covers the sequence of processes of analysis, synthesis, and evaluation applicable to the engineering of all systems. Because we are concerned primarily with human behavior, matters of particular interest to psychology applied within the context of systems engineering are covered in greater detail; specific-

* This process introduces epistemological difficulties, discussed later, that are associated with terminology and the meaningfulness of constituents and abstractions. (Note the use of *constituents* rather than *units*, *components*, or *elements*.)

† [i.e., *Systems Psychology*, Ed.]

ally, this is the field of *human factors*‡ or engineering psychology.

As viewed by the U.S. Air Force, the management of human factors within systems engineering involves development of partially sequential, partially parallel, but interrelated specialties. These *personnel subsystem elements* (see the preceding footnote and the last section of this chapter) are considered in Parts I and IV of this book. The concept of man as a constituent of man–machine systems is expressed in Part II, where we examine input, throughput, and output in terms of *information*, *decision*, and *control theory*, respectively. In Parts II, III, and V, we discuss perception, attention, cognitive processes, perceptual-motor behavior, individual differences, and motivation, usually in the context of a particular system operational requirement. The modifying effects of physicochemical and psychosocial environmental factors on behavior are discussed in Part V.

Specific system problem areas of salient concern to the psychologist, and not treated widely elsewhere, are considered in detail in Parts III and VI. Throughout the book, attempts are made to integrate psychology with other disciplines, to determine a common language for the intercommunication of ideas, and to develop a body of systems psychological methods applicable to the study of any system problem. Particular emphasis is placed on the recognition, definition, measurement, and, where possible, quantification of basic psychological factors; the identification of human capabilities and limitations; the relating of psychological factors to systems factors; the prediction of effective and ineffective human behavior; and the highlighting of situations in which failure to follow these procedures leads to degraded human and system performance, human frustration or misery, danger, waste of resources, and other unsatisfactory results. Applications include those in which psychologists have had extensive experience and those in which we urge far greater participation.

‡ For the benefit of our human factors readers who are not psychologists, we acknowledge the important contributions of physiologists, physicians, anthropologists, sociologists, engineers, and mathematicians to the field. Choice of either term – *human factors* or *engineering psychology* – is a matter of personal preference, in part reflecting the professional organization addressed (Human Factors Society or Society of Engineering Psychologists, a division of the American Psychological Association).

Here, human factors is considered a broader term, which includes training, manpower determinations, analysis, evaluation, equipment design, and so forth. On the other hand, engineering psychology can be equated most readily to human engineering – equipment, facilities, and environments designed for compatibility with human capabilities and limitations.

In the remainder of this chapter, we examine, in some detail, different ways of looking conceptually at systems, at psychology, and at psychology within the systems context. A number of dramatic examples are provided of failure to see things as systems, particularly with regard to psychological factors in systems. The chapter concludes with an examination of the practical aspects of systems engineering and management.

Systems science and psychology

Every educated person recognizes that a "system" imposes an order or consistency on similar interrelated constituents (for example, solar system, nervous system, tax-evasion system); yet there is no integrated body of system knowledge acceptable to the educated public as a whole. We will use the term *systems science* here in the most inclusive sense to include conceptual, theoretical, and applied developments.* There usually is no close relationship between the theoretical, as represented most typically in the *Yearbook of the Society for General Systems Research*, and the applied, as represented by the burgeoning advances in systems engineering and the derived systems management. In fact, it is often stated that applications lack valid theoretical underpinnings. This is perhaps as it should be for a field in the stage of initial rapid growth, but we should caution against theorizing apart from insightful interpretation of our experiences building systems, and conversely, continuing to implement outside of a conceptual *system for systems*. (Following popular practice, we use the term *systems*, instead of *system*, as a noun modifier.)

In this section, we examine various conceptual ways of approaching the study of systems and then attempt to integrate psychology and systems. Systems engineering and management methodology are discussed later in this chapter.

What is a system?

A look into a dictionary reveals that definition of the word *system* entails consideration of a set or arrangement, of relationship or connection, and of unity or wholeness. Further, the term has had longstanding use both as general methodology for achieving order and as a specific modifier in sciences such as astronomy, mathematics, chemistry, geology, and biology. In the most general sense, then,

* For example, a definition of systems science given by the Institute of Electrical and Electronic Engineers professional group in Systems Science and Cybernetics (see Rowe, 1965) is: *The scientific theory and methodology that is common to all large collections of interacting functional units that together achieve a defined purpose.*

system can be thought of as synonymous with *order*; the opposite of chaos.

Experience has led to modification of this simple definition, in most cases in terms of *level* or *hierarchy*, *purpose*, and *environment*. Hall and Fagen (1956) provide the following definition:

> A system is a set of objects together with relationships between their attributes.

As Hall and Fagen see it, *objects* are simply the parts, or components of a system – for example, stars, atoms, neurons, switches, and mathematical laws. *Attributes* are the properties of objects – for example, the temperature of a star. *Relationships* tie the system components together, and which relationships are meaningful at a given time is a matter of discretion by the investigator. It is important to determine interconnections and dependencies, as well as the static or dynamic nature of the relationship.

The *environment* of a system has been defined by Hall and Fagen as follows:

> For a given system, the environment is the set of all objects a change in whose attributes affects the system and also those objects whose attributes are changed by the behavior of the system.

Subdivision of a universe into system and environment is obviously often quite arbitrary. Yet to specify completely an environment, one must know all the factors affecting or affected by the system. This is easier in the physical sciences than in the life, behavioral, and social sciences. Differentiation between system and environment is an immensely complex problem in the last two.

Any system can be further subdivided hierarchically into subsystems, which can in turn be subdivided into sub-subsystems, components, units, parts, and so forth (Figure 5.1 and Table 5.2).†

Objects that are parts of one system or subsystem can be considered parts of the environment of another system or subsystem. Also, systems may unite as subsystems of a still larger system, and under some conditions subsystems can be considered systems. Often the behavior of subsystems is not completely analogous to that of the system itself.

Systems may be studied at macroscopic or microscopic levels, depending on one's training, specialization, and philosophy. Analytic, "atomistic", "elementaristic", or "molecular" approaches versus "holistic" or "molar" approaches are discussed later.

† We discuss problems of terminology involving these subdivisions later in this section.

Many workers do not consider as systems those natural organizations or structures that lack *purpose*, where purpose is construed to be the discharge of some function. For example, minerals can be classified into one of six systems (halite into the cubic system and calcite into the hexagonal system); however, some authors (Gérardin, 1968) argue that crystals cannot be said to form a system, because they perform no function, are end-products in themselves, and do not change except by application of external force. For man-made systems, purpose or mission is an important, integral feature. A general definition of such a system might be: an assemblage of constituents (people and/or hardware and/or software) that interact to fulfill a common purpose transcending the individual purposes of the constituents.

Systems properties and types

A survey of the systems literature reveals a plethora of definitions, but there is almost universal acceptance of the following:

1. Basic system constituents (components, elements, parts, objects) may or may not be similar and possess peculiar characteristics (attributes, behaviors).
2. What constitutes a *basic* constituent is an arbitrary decision within a hierarchical arrangement and a function of one's specialization and the exigencies of the moment.
3. Upon incorporation into the system, constituents are modified through *interactions* with other constituents.
4. The system's characteristics are usually quantitatively greater than, and qualitatively different from, the inferred sum of the characteristics of the constituents.
5. The system exists within an environment, defined as a function of the hierarchical level chosen, that modifies the behavior of the system and may be modified by it: The *boundary* between system and environment should be clearly recognizable.
6. Some systems have a recognized purpose.

Systems are often considered to possess other, often interrelated properties (see, for example, von Bertalanffy, 1956; Hall and Fagen, 1956). The properties outlined below represent a good approximation of *first-order* properties from which it is possible to make second-order derivations, third-order derivations, and so on. For example, out of the disruption of equilibrium, we can observe what might be called *drive* or goal-direction, which in turn can lead to *competition*. Recognition of secondary and tertiary properties is particularly important in biological and social sciences.

From certain dominant properties, we can designate *types* of systems – for example, feedback control systems, adaptive control systems, self-organizing systems, or information systems.

Equilibrium. Equilibrium may be static but is usually dynamic and occurs in concepts of chemistry, geology, biology, and other sciences. A familiar example is *homeostasis.**

Change over time. Changes that occur over time (especially *growth* and *decay*) are important in almost all sciences.

Dominance or centralization. One subsystem may play a dominant role in the behavior of the system. With caution, we can offer the nervous and endocrine systems in vertebrates as examples.

Independence. The hierarchical nature of systems has been noted, as well as the arbitrary nature of system designation. However, there is some virtue in excluding from consideration as systems those entities that cannot exist independently. Thus, the nervous system cannot operate outside the body; the propulsion system of a spacecraft has no ongoing function outside that spacecraft.

Feedback. The system output is sampled, measured, and fed back to the input with subsequent modification, if necessary, of the output. Feedback is especially important to the control mechanisms of organisms and machines, and it provides one of the major bases for cybernetics, discussed later in this section. Feedback systems are typically called *closed-loop* systems. Systems without feedback are called *open-loop* systems. These terms should not be confused with *open* and *closed systems*, respectively (see below).

The type and amount of feedback is important to system stability and equilibrium. The terms *positive and negative feedback* are commonly used. Familiar machine examples of feedback are servomechanisms such as antiaircraft fire-control mechanisms, ship-steering mechanisms, and target-seeking guided missiles. In mammalian psychophysiology, increased secretions of adrenal cortical, thyroid, and gonadal hormones inhibit the secretion of the relevant anterior pituitary hormones in a negative-feedback loop; the release of epinephrine by the adrenal medulla in stress helps enhance the action of the sympathetic nervous system by a positive-feedback mechanism. Integration of control mechanisms in animal and machine is, of course, the main role of *cybernetics* discussed later.

* [See Article 11. *Ed.*]

Entropy and information. In the strictest sense, entropy indicates the theoretical amount of energy (as in steam) in a thermodynamic system that cannot be transformed into mechanical work. It is a function of the probabilities of the states of gas particles. In a closed system, entropy must increase to a maximum with eventual cessation of the physical process and equilibrium. The concept of entropy has also been applied to information systems, where one can speak of "source entropy", "channel entropy", and the like. Entropy can be considered a measure of probability in that the most probable distribution is one of randomness or disorder. It is thus the opposite of information, which can be used as a measure of order in a system.

Open and closed systems. Open systems exchange information, energy, or materials with their environments. Biological systems are the best examples of open systems. One of the most important jobs of the biologist and psychologist is understanding the transfer function whereby inputs (information, energy, or materials) are converted into outputs. Many "test-tube" physical–chemical reactions occur in closed systems (see entropy above), which are considered isolated from their environments.

Differentiation. Related to growth and especially characteristic of biological systems, differentiation refers to the formation, over time, of new constituents from old. *Reproduction* is closely related to differentiation.

Adaptation. Adaptation refers to the ability to modify a system in accord with environmental demands to assure continued function. Individual learning and biological evolution are examples. There is tremendous interest in developing artificial systems possessing qualities of biological systems. Such systems are referred to as *self-regulating*, *self-adapting*, or *self-organizing*. The self-organizing system is described by Yovits *et al.* (1962) as one "which changes its basic structure as a function of its experience and environment".

Predetermined control. Predetermined control of a sequence of structural or functional changes is a consequence of information coding. It is characteristic of living systems in which control over reproduction, growth, differentiation, and behavior reflects information coded in all genes, in organizer tissues in embryological development, and in nervous tissue. Predetermined control is an important feature also of computerized systems. In some man–machine systems, termed *procedural* systems, it is possible to specify beforehand the sequence of operator tasks. The alternative is a *contingency* system.

Naturalness or artificiality. This might appear to be a simple dichotomy, but the distinction fades with man's ability to synthesize proteins and to design systems on the basis of natural bionic analogs.

Compatibility with the environment. The biological world provides myriad examples of organisms marvelously adapted to an environment or, conversely, extinct because the changing environment has passed them by. In a related sense, artificial systems may not function if the environment for which they were designed changes (*cf.* general-purpose and special-purpose computers). Similarly, we may find that one system does not interface well with another when we attempt to build a new system on an old base (the "grow like Topsy" approach) or to effect retrofits. The job of system integration indeed may be formidable in such cases.

Randomness. If constituents are assembled at random, the situation is chaos and a system cannot be said to exist. Yet all physical, biological, and social systems have random properties or functions. Vacuum-tube noise is considered due to random emission of electrons from the cathode. Many people believe that, at first, connections among neurons in the retina and brain may be purely random. There is evidence that random errors and accidents occur in complex systems.

Ways of looking at systems

Systems are observed, studied, and evaluated primarily to: (1) improve the system or its successor; (2) determine general theories or methods for new system development; and (3) advance science. Study of man-made, natural, and semi-natural systems more or less fulfills all three objectives, depending on the purposive or adventitious human contribution to the original "design".

A growing body of systems science methods is beginning to reconcile the conflicting definitions of what a system is and differences among systems. These methods include: (1) generalization across systems; (2) analysis and synthesis; and (3) modeling and simulation. These general approaches must be modified in terms of system level and definition of environment and the degree of practical relationship to the "real world".

Generalization across systems. Examination of the examples given in the earlier discussion of system properties reveals that different systems may have much in common. In several cases, workers in different specialties have arrived independently at similar concepts. The term *isomorphism* (*an* isomorphy) refers to structural similarities among systems in different fields. The concept of isomorphism suggests that the various fields of science can be united at basic levels through underlying principles. An analog based on only two variables – input and output – has the lowest degree of isomorphism, and the underlying function may be vastly dissimilar. Such an oversimplified model is most useful as a representation of a subsystem, which is then linked to other simplified subsystems. *The lack of precision and detail should not transcend the subsystems.* Isomorphism can also refer to structural–functional relationships between a living prototype and a model. Practical attempts to determine isomorphic properties of different systems are particularly spectacular in bionics.

Analysis and synthesis. Complexity in all systems can be approached by breaking the whole into simpler constituents – that is, by analysis. Often, however, there is reason to suspect the significance of the abstracted constituents when we attempt to synthesize them as a means of explaining and predicting the whole. This has long been a major problem within psychology, a most recent example of which is provided by efforts to predict human error.

Modeling and simulation. Models and simulations are analogies ranging from physical operating devices with definite shapes to block diagrams, figures, and computer programs (*abstract* or *mathematical models*). They aid in explaining natural phenomena. Whether present mathematics can be applied is a function of the extent to which a given system can be analyzed. Realistic models can be constructed fairly easily for physical systems but not for complete biological and social systems, in which real system relationships are obscure, the actual number of variables may not be known, and quantification poses a formidable problem. Modeling and simulation have an advantage for these systems, however, in that they allow detachment of the observer from the system he is studying and therefore reduce personal bias.

Selection of level and environment. All systems possess hierarchical structure: A system at one level may be considered a subsystem at another. Similarly, how much of the environment is included in the system helps determine the system properties. Knowledge gleaned at one level may have limited applicability to another level.

Relationship to the "real world". Even if a particular level and environment are chosen for study, only some of the properties of systems may find application in the study of real-world engineering problems. The systems engineer and manager are particularly concerned with interactions, pro-cessing, feedback, environmental compatibility, evolution and change, and purpose (mission); the systems theorist is more concerned with such factors as entropy and differentiation. Accordingly, we can recognize a "systems approach" that may be partially qualitative, even intuitive, and lack the theoretical basis of systems science.

Examples of systems

Over the years, systems have been classified in a number of ways on the basis of properties such as those discussed earlier. It is interesting to combine the properties in different ways or to describe definite entities in terms of relevant properties. A more formidable problem arises, however, when we try to achieve unanimity of agreement as to what *is* and *is not* a system. Most people will agree that a man is a system and that a submarine is a system, and that each can be characterized in terms of certain properties; most also will agree that a single perceptual-motor action is not a system and that an electron is not a system. On the other hand, many will disagree as to whether a crystal or a city is a system, primarily because of differing conceptions of *purpose, normal independence,* and *clearly recognizable boundary.* Ultimate resolution of these disparities *is* a responsibility of systems science, but for purposes of this discussion, we will consider some nonequivocal examples of systems arranged in order of complexity.

Wilson (1965) illustrates a simple mechanical system that shows rudimentary features of negative and positive feedback and exemplifies that the whole is greater than sum of the parts. This system has only five constituents: a pipe, a valve, a supportive arm, a spring, and a container. Its mission is to fill the container to a certain level and shut off the valve automatically. When the constituents are *properly connected* – that is, the fulcrum is placed near the container – the increasing weight of the liquid results in greater tension on the spring, which closes the valve. The system mission is faithfully discharged. Conversely, an improper connection of the constituents – moving the fulcrum to the middle of the pipe – precludes start of the mission. If the system is started in the middle of its operating cycle, the valve opens progressively wider as the container fills. The miller's grain-feeder (Gérardin, 1968), known by at least the eighteenth century, illustrates an early practical design of a similar mechanical system with aspects of automatic control.

A telephone network illustrates an intermediate level of complexity. It can be viewed at the level of a local exchange, a nationwide network, or a worldwide network connected by radio, undersea cable, and communications satellites.

Each succeeding level can be viewed as a system or a subsystem of a larger system. At different levels, specialty subsystems, such as central switching and direct dialing, can be recognized. Despite its immense number of constituents, a telephone network is not the most complicated of systems. Its several basic functions are relatively simple, straightforward, and generalizable from one level to the next, and thus are amenable to considerable automation.

Nearly the most complicated systems are the large-scale, computerized information-acquisition, -processing, and -display, control and command-and-control systems. In the broadest sense, these systems acquire radar, sonar, microwave, ionizing radiation, system status, biomedical, voice, and other data from a variety of terrestria land solar system environments. Conversions of information, digital to analog, parallel to serial, and vice versa, and data compressions are almost always necessary. Almost every aspect of computer and display technology is relevant. Large numbers of personnel are required, sometimes in a great variety of types and skills. The many environmental stresses are both acute and chronic. Vehicles are controlled directly or indirectly and are themselves complex systems that may or may not cooperate with the system. This large systems category includes the various Air Force "L" systems, the manned spaceflight systems, and the naval control systems. The Semi-Automatic Ground Environment (SAGE) air defense system, the Air Force Satellite Control Facility, and the Apollo manned spacecraft system are considered in some detail throughout this book, because they exemplify system problem areas particularly well and because several of the authors have had experience with them.

The mission of SAGE is to detect, track, identify, intercept, and destroy enemy bomber aircraft. It has no antiballistic missile destruction capability. Major inputs are the dynamic position and speed data from radar and flight plans. Large, duplexed, digital computers compute aircraft tracks, determine identifications, calculate intercept points, etc. Various data are displayed on computer-related cathode-ray tubes. Enemy bombers are intercepted by manned aircraft or by Nike or Bomarc missiles. At one time, four-storied, duplexed SAGE Direction Center blockhouses were distributed over most of the contiguous United States and Canada. Now being phased out, SAGE is of particular interest because: (1) it can be viewed as the "granddaddy" of the electronic command and control systems, a laboratory of what was done correctly and incorrectly; (2) it exemplifies the long lead times between system conceptualization and system implementation; (3) in a related sense, it dramatizes the possibility that by the

time a system is operational, its mission may be quite incidental – SAGE went into operation just as the enemy threat changed from "air-breathing" bomber to ballistic missile, a still unsolved problem; (4) almost no attention was paid at high engineering and management levels to human factors and other psychological problems; and (5) it contributed a great deal to the design of computerized systems – for example, the presently important concepts of man–computer interaction, time-sharing, and display buffer design owe much to SAGE.

The Air Force Satellite Control Facility (SCF) has evolved considerably since its inception. The general aspects of the system and its mission can be gleaned from an article by White (1963), although the system has changed in detail since White's publication appeared. The mission of the SCF is to track, receive, and process telemetry data, test and check out, and control satellites. The SCF does not launch satellites, although it monitors prelaunch checkout and launch, which is a responsibility of other agencies at Cape Kennedy and at Vandenberg Air Force Base in California. Once launched, the satellite is tracked by, and telemetry data are received from, a worldwide network of tracking stations. Raw data received by these tracking stations are processed, compressed if necessary, converted, and transmitted mostly via digital data link to the Satellite Test Center in Sunnyvale, near San Francisco, California. After analysis of the tracking and telemetry data, especially the latter, voice commands are sent to the tracking station, which transmits them in nonvoice form to the satellite, correcting its attitude and so on. This is an oversimplification, and data are not always easily transmitted or easily analyzed. For our purposes, the major lessons learned from the SCF are: (1) it is an outstanding example of system development wherein operation requirements came too fast, too heavily, and from too many separate users, without central planning – what had started out as a fairly simple research and development (R&D) effort for testing the Discoverer unmanned satellite within several years became a superimposed mass of satellite-support equipment, methods, and personnel; (2) it provides an example of managerial debate as to whether a system is "operational" or "R&D", raising questions as to the applicable type of management control; (3) it has long demonstrated a challenging number of human factors problems connected with the allocation of functions between man and computer, automation of other functions, information availability, diagnosis and troubleshooting, problem solving, display and control design, personnel numbers and training, and formulation of operational procedures.

The mission of Apollo 11 was to bring three American men into a lunar orbit, land two of them on the moon, bring all three together again, and return them to Earth. Apollo involves a marvelous integration of test and checkout, launch, tracking and telemetry, data processing and display, control and recovery capabilities. It is perhaps *par excellence* the example of successful planning and the management of thousands of contractors and tens of thousands of specialist workers to bring about the successful implementation of a mission. For our purposes, it is of particular interest because: (1) it demonstrates that sophisticated management of complex processes can lead to the solution of quite formidable *technical* problems; (2) it can serve as a type example for application to the sociotechnical area; (3) in all systems, unforeseen interactions can result in costly waste and in tragedy; and (4) it exemplifies the concept of system hierarchy. The "system" can be considered the complete spacecraft-launch vehicle assemblage plus the worldwide network of tracking stations, the launch and recovery facilities, the Integrated Mission Control Center (IMCC) in Houston, Texas, and the simulation and training facilities; or we could consider the "system" as comprising only the spacecraft itself, consisting of an Escape Module (Launch Escape System jettisoned shortly after earth launch), Service Module, Command Module, and Lunar Module.* During descent to and ascent from the moon, the system could consist of either the Lunar Module (containing two astronauts) or Command Module (containing one astronaut). During the return cislunar voyage, and reentry and earth recovery, the system is the combined Service-Command Modules and the Command Module, respectively. Of course, the unmanned spacecraft or an individual astronaut can also be considered the system.

Systems such as those discussed above are *nearly* the most complicated with which we must deal. What then is more complex? The entire universe? Probably not, if complexity may be defined in terms of the overall problems with which we must live – and survive. The universe is complex and inspiring, but *in toto* has little effect upon our everyday lives. The most complicated system, or system environment, can be delineated as comprising the earth, Earth's moon, the sun and the five nearest planets to the sun. How is this a system? Consider our earlier properties and the concept of boundary. Boundary need not be a

physical wall or even the effective force of the sun's gravitation. It can also be managerial, organizational, economic, psychological, conceptual. There is no question that space exploration, undersea exploration, poverty, automation and technological change, education, population growth, human happiness, democracy, and communism are today inextricably intertwined. This monstrous system, absolutely the most important for you and for us during our lifetimes and probably for a long time thereafter, can be characterized, however crudely, in terms of boundary; inputs, throughputs, and outputs; equilibrium; feedback loops; growth, differentiation, and decay; dynamic interactions; control and other properties. In this most macroscopic of macrosystems, the North American air defense network (NORAD) of which SAGE can be viewed a subsystem, the SCF, and Apollo, as well as individual cities and nations, can be recognized only as important subsystems (Figure 5.1). The interactions are quite evident. Important contributory factors of this system are discussed in the last three chapters of this book. We believe that one of the most useful discoveries of the twentieth century will be the application of systems know-how to the solution of problems in *sociotechnical* systems.

The partially human-designed, semispontaneous, and fortuitous systems and organizations of mankind possess many of the systems properties defined earlier. Yet there are important differences: man-made equipment-oriented systems reflect the purposes of a few users and are designed largely to function *in spite of* environments. Seminatural systems reflect the vagaries of numerous economic, social, and political needs, and geographic and climatic environments. Organizations, as in business and industry, are examples of systems in which man–man interactions predominate over man–machine interactions.

System interactions occur in these less, as well as in the more, structured systems. The interactions and their results may be apparently *unpredictable*, *uncontrollable*, and as in our present technological society, *unmanageable*. Psychology has the chance of its lifetime to demonstrate its worth in dealing with these late twentieth-century problem areas, especially in relation to growth and decline, need and goal direction, stability, and internally and externally generated stress and change.

The search for universals

Three separate approaches to the identification of underlying principles of structure and behavior have developed in response to observations of isomorphies among systems and the development of similar concepts in different fields

---

* At earth launch, the Lunar Module is physically separated from the Command and Service Modules by the S-IVB (third) stage of the three-stage Saturn V launch vehicle. A reconfiguration of the modules is required shortly after injection into the cislunar path.

on the one hand, and the increasing specialization of knowledge on the other. To varying extents, general systems theory, cybernetics, and bionics seek universals that can relate the specifics of different sciences and technologies.

General systems theory. By the 1950s, it was evident that scientific specialization was leading to increasing difficulties of communication across disciplines. A number of philosophies, methods, and approaches, based on attempts to understand organization and the behavior of wholes, integrative mechanisms, dynamic interaction, and environmental effects, had evolved over the last 100 years in several sciences. However, this evolution took place in one discipline independently of developments in other disciplines. Examples include the field concept of physics, homeostasis and synergy in biology, servo theory in engineering, and Gestalt psychology.

Pressures to integrate similarities and relationships among the sciences, to enhance communication across disciplines, and to derive a theoretical basis for *general* scientific education had several philosophical roots, of which we will mention three (see von Bertalanffy, 1956; Boulding, 1964).*

1. Science in the late nineteenth and early twentieth centuries was largely analytic, with the whole being reduced to even smaller units, the study of which would allegedly result in understanding the whole. Eventually, many theorists hoped to achieve unity within science by reduction to the particles and mechanisms of physics. Thus, molecules were broken down into atoms; atoms into electrons, protons, and other particles; organisms into cells; behavior into reflexes; perception into sensations; the mind into ideas; and so forth. Simple additive and static cause–effect explanations were offered in describing the properties of the whole. Concepts of organization and of interaction were ignored. Countering this *reductionistic* approach was the increasing awareness of the importance of interaction and of dynamics that emerged in several fields of science during the first third of the twentieth century. Such terms as *field theory, Gestalt, holistic, organismic, adaptiveness,* and *goal-direction* reflect this newer tenor. The independent development of these concepts in different sciences can be considered a forerunner of the development of a general systems theory.

2. The second stimulus toward development of a general systems theory – and limitation of specific-system approaches – came from the so-called Heisenberg Principle of Indeterminacy. Thus, information cannot be applied to or withdrawn from a system without changing it, and the very process of observation or study distorts the system itself and hence the meaning of results. A wide variety of experiences, especially in the biological, behavioral, and social sciences, substantiates this objection. For example, in experimental psychology the experimenter's behavior itself or the design of his equipment may offer subtle cues to the human subjects; in opinion polling, respondents tend to give answers they believe will seem "right" to the pollster.

3. Many systems are probabilistic or stochastic rather than deterministic. A single observation can tell us little or nothing about the probability of occurrence of the event observed. Again this holds especially true in the biological, behavioral, and social sciences.

In 1956, a group of scientists established the Society for General Systems Research (originally called the Society for the Advancement of General Systems Theory). The Society issues a yearbook of articles on systems approaches from virtually all the sciences. Young (1964) has surveyed general systems theory after nearly a decade of its existence, summarizing the attempts of workers to apply general systems theory to their specific fields. *Emphasis on specific applications to enhance the general theory was found to be far greater than the applications of general systems theory to specific disciplines.* Work could be broken down into four categories:

1. *Systematic and descriptive factors.* This category dealt with classifications of types of systems, their data and internal organization, and system environments. Particular attention was given to openness and closedness, organismic or nonorganismic properties, centralization, independence, differentiation, interaction, and boundaries.

2. *Regulation and maintenance.* This category dealt with control and stabilization. Concepts of equilibrium, feed-back and communication, and control were important.

3. *Dynamics and change.* This category dealt with nondisruptive internal and external environmental changes. Of particular importance were adaptation, learning, growth, and goal-seeking.

4. *Decline and breakdown.* This category dealt with disruption and dissolution, and emphasized stress, overload, entropy, and decay.

* The term "general systems theory" was coined by von Bertalanffy.

Young states that the typical literature is strong on regulation and maintenance and weak on decline and breakdown. Social scientists are showing an increased, sometimes overriding, interest in the general systems field, perhaps because of training and interests at the given time. The usefulness of the literature is diminished by the tendency of some authors to cite general concepts without indicating how these concepts helped specific applications.

Material on general systems can be found in the *Yearbook of the Society for General Systems Research* and in the Institute of Electrical and Electronic Engineers *Transactions on Systems Science and Cybernetics*. Boulding (1956) is a good general reference.

Cybernetics. Since World War II, there have been several concerted, often highly mathematical attempts to determine universals applicable to the explanation of the behavior of both organisms and machines. Work has been directed to increasing understanding of organisms (and societies) and making machines more adaptive, more flexible, and more in tune with given environments. In this book, we will consider two main developments: *cybernetics* and *bionics*.* Cybernetics can be thought of as an attempt to understand organisms through making analogies to machines, and bionics as an attempt to develop better machines through understanding of biological design principles. Cybernetics traditionally has emphasized understanding of a given process *per se*, while bionics seeks understanding of a given process as a means of generalizing to another situation. Both cybernetics and bionics involve theory, model building, experimentation, and application; they have been compared with the two sides of a coin.

A few individuals have participated in developments in both cybernetics and bionics; similarly, there have been tangential developments, closely akin to these, but given other names such as *self-organizing systems* (Yovits *et al.*, 1962), *adaptive systems*, *learning machines*, *automata*, and *artificial intelligence*, which have yet to be interrelated. These approaches appear to rely more heavily on "armchair", rational, and intuitive methods, while cybernetics and bionics emphasize empirical and experimental methods.

As we attempt to deal with the increasing complexity of our world, those most complex of things, living organisms, can provide clues to better design for small and compact power supplies, for reliability, for greater adaptability, for

---

* In some parts of Europe, bionics is considered to be synonymous with applied cybernetics.

more effective organization, and so forth. Of particular interest to both cybernetics and bionics are the following:

1. The reception ("sensation") and recognition ("perception") of information.
2. Integrative processes.
3. Storage and retrieval of information.
4. Self-regulatory ("homeostatic") processes.
5. Adaptive ("learning") processes.
6. Control processes.

The world first became widely aware of cybernetics in 1948 when Norbert Wiener published the first edition of *Cybernetics or Control and Communication in the Animal and the Machine* (the second edition appeared in 1961). However, Wiener had formulated his ideas earlier in World War II, when he was faced with problems of automatic aiming of antiaircraft guns. It was necessary to shoot the projectile not at the aircraft itself, but along a trajectory such that the two would intersect in space sometime in the future. Accordingly, it was necessary to predict the future position of the aircraft. Wiener was able to formulate equations describing a closed-loop system (the input to a computer was part of the output signal). Thus, the computer, utilizing a feedback loop, could calculate the time of the trajectory of a projectile and predict the point at which the gun should aim. Working with Arturo Rosenblueth, a biologist, and with other prominent engineers, mathematicians, biologists, and psychologists, Wiener formulated principles common to machines, animals, and societies. The term *cybernetics* itself comes from the Greek word for *steersman*, a tribute to the fact that a ship's steering engines provide one of the earliest types of feedback mechanism. Wiener's book was eclectic and contained discussions of normal and abnormal physiological, psychological, and sociotechnical processes, as well as of information, communications and feedback *per se*.

Wiener viewed cybernetics as encompassing the entire field of control and communication theory, whether in the animal or the machine. The study of *automata*, machine or animal, was regarded as a branch of communication engineering, and was concerned with the concepts of information amount, coding and message, with noise, and so on. Automata are related to the outside world through sensors/receptors and control mechanisms/effectors, which are interconnected by central integrating mechanisms.

Wiener recognized that the value of cybernetics would be shaped by the limitations of the data we can obtain. Yet he felt there were two areas in particular offering practical results: the development of prostheses and the development of automatic computing machines. Subsequent developments have borne out Wiener's expectations, particularly in the second area.

The importance of cybernetics to the psychologist or physiologist interested in neuro-endocrine integrative action, self-organizing behavior, homeostasis, perception, learning, and so forth should be quite evident. In another area, Wiener was remarkably prophetic: he expressed concern over our abilities to construct machines of almost any degree of sophistication of performance, believing that we are confronted with "... *another social potentiality of unheard-of-importance for good and for evil* ..." (emphasis added). Just as the industrial revolution *devalued* the human arm through competition with machinery, so the present technological revolution is bound to devalue the human brain, at least in its more routine processes. Wiener believed, as we emphasize later, that the alternative is a society based on human values other than buying and selling – *a society that would require a great deal of planning and struggle.* He hoped that a better understanding of man and society, as "fall-out" of cybernetics efforts, would outweigh the concentration of power (in the hands of the most unscrupulous) incidental to the applications of cybernetics, but he concluded in 1947, "... that it is a very slight hope".

Cybernetics is an integrated body of concepts applicable to orderly study within physical, biological, and social sciences, and in the "crossroads" interdisciplinary sciences between. In each case, problems can be represented in terms of information content and flow and in terms of feedback and control. Yet, like some other concepts, cybernetics has proved no universal panacea. Its initial reception was lurid with the connotation, "The robots are here." Extensions were interesting and led to coining of new terms – *cyborg* for an organism with a machine built into it with consequent modification of function, *cybernation* for automation involving especially information and control systems – but cybernetics generally did not live up to expectations. The term itself remained an obscure one in the United States, although it became popular in Germany and in the Soviet Union, where theoretical cybernetics is considered to include information theory, automata theory, programming theory, and the theory of games. More recently, interest in cybernetics has renewed in the United States, as reflected in the establishment of the Professional Group in Systems Science and Cybernetics (1965) within the Institute of Electrical and Electronics Engineers and the American Society for Cybernetics (1968).

Cybernetics applications include adaptive teaching machines and pattern perception devices; the best examples are provided by automata and by prostheses. *Locomotion automata*, which may be bi- or quadrupedal, are of potential value for use in difficult terrain, such as mountains, polar regions, swamps, and the lunar surface. In a simple quadruped automaton, each leg has only two output states: on the ground pushing backward and in the air pushing forward. The sequence of motions for each leg and the gait are controlled by a binary-sequence generator using a different program for each gait and based on *finite-state* logic (the machine can have only a finite number of states) (Kalisch, 1968; Swanson, 1968). Other applications deal with powered prostheses. The most sophisticated concepts involve sensing and amplifying bioelectric potentials from muscles, or even better, nerves in the stump of the severed limb itself. Devices based on utilization of muscle potentials and including an electric motor enable the patient to perform fairly precise activities such as writing and to lift weights of about 10 pounds. Other cybernetic machines under study include those that amplify a normal operator's strength, enabling him to lift 1,500 pounds, or increase his locomotion speed to 35 mph over rough or dangerous terrain.

An automaton possessed of adaptive ("homeostatic") behavior was Ashby's (1960) *homeostat*, an electromechanical device, which always returned to equilibrium by means of switches, regardless of input. Another was Shannon's mechanical mouse, which was programmed to "learn" a checkerboard maze after one trial by "remembering" the direction in which it had left a given square for the last time (Lindgren, 1968). A Russian automaton, based on a hierarchy of heuristic computer programs, purportedly also possesses feeling and consciousness (Lindgren, 1968).

Bionics. Bionics is another of the important interdisciplinary areas that emerged toward the late 1950s and early 1960s. The term was coined by U.S. Air Force Major J. E. Steele in 1958, but first received widespread recognition at the first bionics symposium in 1960 (*Bionics Symposium: Living Prototypes – the Key to New Technology*, 1960). Since 1960, other bionics congresses have been held (e.g., *Bionics Symposium: Information Processing by Living Organisms and Machines*, 1964). The word "bionics" suggests a coalescence of biology and electronics, but bionics protagonists emphasize the integration of *analysis* (from biology) and *synthesis* (from engineering design). This is reflected in an official insignia: the scalpel representing analysis, an integral sign representing synthesis. Over the years biologists, psychologists, engineers, and mathematicians have participated in bionics efforts.

Bionics can be defined as the study of living systems to identify concepts applicable to the design of artificial systems; alternatively, it can be defined as the study of systems whose functions have been derived from the study of living systems.

The philosophical and rational basis for bionics rests on the time-based, dynamic organism–environment interactions that have characterized all living systems since the first appearance of life on earth some two to three billion years ago. The environment stresses the organism, which either adapts to fit a particular ecological niche.at a given time or perishes. Hence, living systems can be thought of as being good, sometimes even the best, approximations of adjustments to the demands of given environments at a given time.

The next question concerns the appropriate degree of isomorphism between the natural and artificial system. Attempts to pattern design too rigidly after the living prototype often lead to dead ends, as shown by early (sometimes fatal) attempts to fly by avian methods. Modeling is widely used in bionics and provides a bridge between different specialists. Model building, however, always presents the possibility of too great abstraction and mathematical precision at the cost of minimum relation to the real world. Also, there has long been a tendency both in biology and in psychology, and now perhaps also in bionics, to concentrate on knowledge that may be incomplete, distorted out of context, incidental, or artifactual. Examples are the undue emphasis on the electrical activity of the nervous system and on reflex activity, and attempts to equate nervous system and computer functioning. Nevertheless, a rigid insistence on complete understanding of a biological process may retard useful serendipitous discovery. It seems desirable, therefore, to qualify the definition of bionics to include processes that directly and wholly explain a natural phenomenon, those that seem to explain *some* aspects of a natural phenomenon, those recognized as incidental, and those that clearly are only analogies.

Bionics thus can be seen to be the study of living organisms with the intention of deriving technological knowledge. As the flight of aircraft and of spacecraft demonstrate, the capabilities of the artificial systems – *along some dimensions* – may greatly exceed those of the original prototypes. Actual or potential system design applications based on *living prototypes* are summarized in Table 5.1.

Often the living prototype indicates only that a process *is* possible, but information as to how the process works is scant. Thus, in many bionics studies, limited biological or psychological knowledge is extended by simulation and modeling and by intuition on the part of the bionicist.

The question has been raised as to the usefulness of the bionics approach. That there are probably more workers in the area of artificial neurons or *neuromimes** than in any other derives from the hope that greater understanding of the nervous system will aid in the construction of smaller, more flexible computers. On the other hand, neural modeling should provide better understanding of the nervous system *per se*. What we know about the neuron has enabled us to build electronic analogs that simulate neuron behavior. Many different kinds of neuromimes have been built, depending on the interests of the designers. Some emphasize central processes such as memory; others emphasize peripheral processes such as excitation-inhibition, threshold, summation, and refractoriness. Van Bergéijk and Harman (1960) have attempted to produce as precise an analog of the peripheral nervous system as possible, and report that this approach has helped elucidate both anatomical and physiological features.

Reichardt (1961) and his interdisciplinary coworkers at the Max Planck Institut für Biologie, Tübingen, Germany, have studied visual processes in the beetle *Chlorophanus*. This beetle responds optokinetically (in terms of head or eye movements) to relative movements of light in its optical environment. The most elementary succession of light changes found capable of eliciting an optomotor response consisted of two stimuli in adjacent ommatidia (facets) of the compound eye. A stimulus received by one ommatidium can interact only with that received by the adjacent ommatidium or those adjacent to the latter. Transformation and interaction within the central nervous system were found to agree with known principles. The results were expressed in the language of control systems, suggesting that the beetle could derive velocity information from a moving, randomly shaded background. This finding led to the design of a ground-speed indicator for aircraft based on the function of two of the hundreds of facets comprising the compound eye (see Savely's article in Steele, 1960).

A very readable book that discusses most of the developments in bionics has been written by Gérardin (1968). Specific original papers of representative interest are those of Rosenblatt (1958), Lettvin et al. (1959), Newell and Simon (1961), and Simon (1961).

---

* There is a need for nomenclature to differentiate between the natural and analog entity. Following van Bergéijk (1960), we can consider the suffix *mime* to indicate the most general type of artificial cell or organ. Accordingly, a neuristor would be one type of neuromime.

Table 5.1 Bionic developments (Prepared partially from text in Gérardin, 1968)

PROTOTYPE	APPLICATION
Olfactory receptors of moths and butterflies; infrared receptors of pit vipers	Lightweight sensors
Compound eye of beetle *Chlorophanus*	Aircraft ground-speed indicator
Compound eye of king crab *Limulus*; retina of frog	Automatic recognition of pattern, movement
Eel and ray electrical-field generation, detection	Submarine detection
Bat and cetacean echo-location behavior and related physiology; bat-moth interactions	Radar and sonar with better antijamming and antievasive capabilities
Bat ear structure and echo location	Location aid to the blind
Neuronal (generally peripheral) electrophysiology	Artificial neuron or neuristor to propagate a "signal" without attenuating it*
Retina and brain of higher vertebrates	Pattern-perception and learning machines (perceptrons)
Animal short-term memory (apparently electro-chemical or synaptic) and long-term memory (apparently chemical and inter- and intracellular involving both neurons and neuroglia)	Computer memory
Human problem solving	Adaptive (heuristic) problem-solving computer programs
Dolphin swimming behavior and double (turbulence-reducing) skin	Streamlined torpedo
Migratory, orientation, homing behavior; related physiology of birds, turtles, fish, insects	Navigation devices
Bioluminescence	Cold (100% efficient) light

* Neuristors are capable of performing complex calculations, leading to attempts to build computers using them as basic constituents.

Systems psychology: a new field

Conceptually, systems theory and psychology have long had much in common. Concepts that have arisen independently include those of field and environment, dynamics, interaction, and evolution and change. Most significantly, both organisms and systems consist of wholes that transcend the sum of the dynamically interacting parts. In turn, each part affects the properties of the whole. The organism can be thought of in terms of a hierarchy expressed from most general and tenuous to most elementary and precise: the social grouping of organisms and the man–machine system; the total intact organism; the organ system such as the nervous system; the tissue such as nervous tissue; the individual cell such as the neuron; the cell nucleus; the complex molecule or colloid such as deoxyribonucleoprotein; the simpler molecules such as the nucleotides, nucleosides, purines, and pyrimidines; and finally the atom and subatomic particle. At the upper end of this hierarchy, psychology interrelates with sociology, cultural anthropology, economics, and political science; at the lower end with physiology, biochemistry, and biophysics. Systems concepts and methods are applicable at all levels, and psychological problems at each level can be couched in systems terms. Examples at each end of the continuum are provided by simulation studies of the industrial organization and by relating memory to nucleic acid and protein metabolism within the neuron cell body and associated neuroglia.

In a similar vein, systems are arranged as *macrosystems* such as the Apollo systems as defined earlier; as *systems* such as the Apollo spacecraft; and as *subsystems, sub-subsystems,* or *modules, components* (individual subassemblies), *units,* and *parts.* Psychological factors or psychology-related problems can be defined at each level, for example, by the use of computers in military decision making involving national defense, at one extreme, and by training required for the assembly of printed-circuit boards at the other. A major problem derives from the lack of consistency in use of systems terminology. Such terms as *unit, part, component,* and *element* are used interchangeably. We have used the neutral term *constituent,* as appropriate, to indicate the most general case. The same semantic difficulties apply to such terms as *job, task, element,* and others in the behavioral hierarchy. In some chapters, the term *element* is used in a general sense, although there are objections to doing so. The nomenclature and definitions given in Table 5.2, and used throughout this book, are based generally on usage in the aerospace industry and specifically on practice at Northrop Corporation on the Skybolt air-to-ground missile project.

Table 5.2 Definitions of basic terms in systems hierarchy

GENERAL

Mission. A statement of *what* the system is to do to solve a given problem and *when* and *where* – an expression of purposes and objectives. It can be arbitrarily segmented in terms of identifiable beginning and end points. Mission determination involves many subjective or judgmental factors.

Requirement. A statement of an obligation the system must fulfill to effect the mission. Requirements are expressed first in qualitative terms and progressively in quantitative performance terms relative to some criterion(ia). They further delineate the system mission.

Function. A general means or action by which the system fulfills its requirements. Functions are usually expressed in verb form (monitor, control) or participial form (monitoring, controlling). They are the first expression of the *hows* of the system. They are expressed progressively more precisely. Ideally, functions are conceived apart from implementation by men and/or by machines; in practice, they are usually expressed along with machine design implications.

EQUIPMENT	BEHAVIORAL
Subsystem. At its *most basic level*, a single module, or combination of modules, plus independent components that contribute to modular functions, all interconnected and interrelated within a system and performing a specific function. Examples: guidance and control subsystem, propulsion subsystem.	*Job operation.* A combination of duties and tasks necessary to accomplish a system function. A job operation may involve one or more positions or career specialties or fields.
Module (sub-subsystem). A combination of components contained in one package or so arranged that together they are common to one mounting, which provides a complete function(s) to the subsystem and/or systems in which they operate. Examples: guidance and control computer, astrotacker.	*Position.* A grouping of duties and responsibilities constituting the principal work assignment of *one* person. The position may be that of operator, maintainer, controller, etc. Positions related in terms of ability, education, training, and experience can be grouped as career specialties and fields. Synonym: *job.*
Component. A combination of units or parts independent of, or an independent entity within, a complete operating module or subsystem, providing a self-contained capability necessary for proper module, subsystem, and/or system operation. Can be replaced as a whole. Examples: DC power supply, digital display readout.	*Duty.* A set of operationally related tasks within a given position. These may involve operating, maintaining, training, and supervising, etc.
Unit. A combination of parts constituting a definable entity of a component, possessing a functional potential essential to the proper operation of that component. Example: chip.	*Task.* A composite of related (discriminatory–decision–motor) activities performed by an individual, and directed toward accomplishing a specific amount of work within a specific work context. Involves, for example, a group of associated operations or inspections.
Part. The smallest *practical* equipment subdivision of a system; an individual piece having an inherent functional capability, but unable to function without the interaction of other parts or forces; ordinarily not subject to further disassembly without destruction. Examples: transistor, diode, resistor, capacitor.	*Subtask.* Actions fulfilling a limited purpose within a task – for example, making a series of related machine adjustments.
	Task element. A basic S–O–R constituent of behavior comprising the smallest *logically* definable set of perceptions, decisions, and responses required to complete a task or sub-task. Involves, for example, identifying a specific signal on a specific display, deciding on a single action, actuating a specific control, and noting the feedback signal of response adequacy. Synonym: *behavior* or *job behavior.*

SOURCE: Modified from text in Headquarters Air Force Systems Command, *Personnel Subsystems*, (1969) and from practices at Northrop Corporation.

Figure 5.1 summarizes the above aspects of systems hierarchy. Macro-macrosystems can be subdivided into many other ways – for example, in terms of communications; transportation, or use of resources. An immensely complicated figure would be required to indicate *organizational* hierarchy and all subdivisions at the lower hierarchical levels. Identification and analysis of all segments of the mission profile and the constituent functions, tasks, and the like require detailed documentation, and constitute one of the main businesses of *human factors. Systems* science is concerned with determination of interrelationships among the various concepts, levels, and terms. This does not imply, however, simple linear, additive, multiplicative, or deterministic relationships, either laterally or hierarchically. For example, at the moment we can clearly relate system job performance neither to the biochemistry of the brain nor to task-element performance. Hopefully someday we will be able to do much of both.

Figure 5.1 Examples of systems subdivision and organismic, equipment, and behavioral hierarchy (see Table 5.2 for definitions of basic terms).

Systems and organisms can also be studied and described in terms of *feedback control*. Independently of physical scientists, biologists and psychologists came up with the concepts of *milieu internale* and homeostasis, and extensions thereof, which describe the maintenance of constancy of physiological, behavioral, and social parameters, internal to the organism or group, despite wide variations in stimuli. However, the organism is immensely complex when compared to the machine: Control loops in the organism are superimposed upon one another, and its internal nonlinear feedback mechanisms may be dissimilar to those in the machine.

Conceptualization of organisms and systems in hierarchical terms like those indicated earlier has been associated with the development of philosophies concerned with methods of approach. Can the complex whole best be understood at that level, or by studying the individual constituents? Is analysis that defines the behavior of these constituents isolated from the system a more meaningful approach than synthesis, the attempt to deduce behavior of the system from knowledge of the constituent functions? Terms such as *holism, Gestalt, molar, molecular, atomism, elementarism, associationism, reductionism, stimulus-response unit, mechanism,* and *vitalism,* long used by psychologists or biologists, attest to the continuing lack of agreement.

Finally, systems techniques have the heuristic or epistemological benefit of providing rigor in the definition of psychological terms such as *intelligence, learning, thinking,* and *feeling.* This is especially evident when we try to answer such questions as: Do machines think? What is artificial intelligence? How does problem solving relate to decision making? In our attempts to provide answers to these questions, assist colleagues in other fields to understand how psychology can contribute to solving their problems, and evaluate the statements they so frequently vouchsafe, we are forced to consider even more far-reaching questions. For example: What *is* psychology? How good are its basic methods? Are the right problems being recognized, defined, and attacked? Does psychology have a body of theory and an approach amenable to the study of *real-world* problems? How good and how useful is psychological research? How can we better apply psychological research to the crushing problems of technology and society? Is psychology poorly understood by the layman and by other scientists and engineers so that its findings, while valid and generalizable, are poorly applied? Throughout this book, we attempt to provide answers to each of these questions, mostly within the context of specific subject areas.

The nature of psychology and psychological theory. A science must be defined in terms of the events of a given time in history; the efforts of its practitioners, the problems they recognize and identify, the tools they use, and interfaces with other sciences. It is not always clear just *what* psychology is. Certainly, the customary definitions do not provide a realistic framework for a science that encompasses a greater vertical range than any other, including at one extreme human behavior in groups and organizations, and at the other the biophysics and biochemistry of learning. More and more, psychologists find themselves associated with specialists in other fields – clinicians with psychiatrists, educational psychologists with teachers, engineering psychologists with engineers – cut off from their fellows who share the science of mind, of man, of behavior, and of experience.

We can expect a shifting of boundaries within science, the emergence of interdisciplinary "cross-roads sciences", which eventually achieve an intrinsic sufficiency of their own, and the absorption of subsciences that have not proved their worth. This may sound like an unduly pragmatic view, and there is indeed danger in compromising development of basic knowledge in the name of immediate returns on research grants. There is just as great a danger in retreating into the contented isolation of our laboratories while the world collapses without, secure in our grasp of an idea, or method, or shibboleth of questionable relevance.

The history of science provides us with many examples of intellectual *culs de sac.* There is always the risk of misunderstanding the problem, selecting the wrong level or the fortuitous artifactual, rather than the lasting and real, or of simply grasping the most convenient. It is always tempting to build elaborate theories on limited or premature data, only to become caught up in the excitement and momentum of the times and pushing applications that may be invalid at best and downright harmful at worst. Jones and Gray (1963) cite the selection of neuron pulse interval or pulse frequency, while ignoring pulse amplitude or width, as an example of grasping a phenomenon that is easier to deal with conceptually or mathematically in model building: the problem and unit of measure has been selected to fit available mathematics, rather than new mathematics developed to fit the problem. The traditional attempts of psychology to explain learning and memory in terms of simple conditioned reflexes or in terms of electrophysiological events (ignoring the chemical) probably represent premature theorizing based on limited fact. Goslin (1968) has reviewed the field of standardized ability tests and testing, and has pointed out the many questions of validity and predictability and the real danger of individual and social harm.

A considerably body of psychological theory and data has been based on experimentation with the albino variety of the brown rat, *Rattus norvegicus.* What if all this research is at best incidental and at worst artifactual and decidedly wrong? Some insight into this serious problem is offered by Lockard (1968), who presents considerable evidence that the albino rat is an *atypical* organism – a poor one, indeed, on which to base generalizations of behavior – that its very evolution is adventitious and artificial, and that results based thereon are bound to be distorted. Here is an excellent example of our misguided hope in finding a standard unit (as in physical science); there are biologically many types of white rats.

When the engineering psychologist turns to the experimental psychologist and asks for basic data on human performance, he is likely to find that there are no data or that the data are inapplicable to real-world problems of analysis, design, and operation. Again and again, workers have complained about the lack of application, even relevancy, of the results of psychological experimentation to pressing engineering and social requirements (Chapanis, 1967; Alluisi, 1967, and Meister, 1964; and Boulding, 1967, and Mackie and Christensen, 1967). At the same time engineers, computer programmers, chemists, mathematicians, and others are assuming, and – to an extent more than psychologists – mastering problems long considered within the domain of psychology. At present, problem solving, especially man–computer problem solving, is quite *in*. But where is the basic groundwork in psychology developed over the years as an aid to the psychologists and others now specializing in the field? Why were so many of us psychologists running rats through mazes over several decades and so few studying human thinking and problem solving? Simultaneously, in the streets throughout the world, social and sociotechnical problems cry out for solution – and the cry is becoming louder – in terms of skill definitions *vis-à-vis* automation and technological change, in terms of training, education, attitudes, emotions, mental disease, and so forth. Psychology's record of accomplishment in helping to ameliorate the world's woes, perhaps also in advancing basic science, has not been great, especially considering the number of psychologists. Demonstrable results often come from outside psychology. The major advance in the treatment of the mentally ill in the last decade or so has stemmed from developments in pharmacology, not from developments in clinical psychological analysis and therapy. Separate abstractions such as personality, mental illness, intelligence, learning, and memory may see unity through extension of Pauling's (1968) concept of *orthomolecular psychiatry* to include gene action and specified biophysical and biochemical processes involving membrane permeability, metabolism, waste product accumulation, and the like.

Psychology, as we have now seen, is a remarkably diverse science that often seems at odds with itself and with its neighbor sciences. Internecine battle has long raged within psychology: clinician against experimentalist, "brass-instrument" man against "field theorist", "rat man" against "head shrinker", pure scientist against applied worker. Many psychologists believe that this conflict has been for the better and will lead to a truly stable eclectic science. Actually, this is far from true, and at no time more evident than when we try to answer the question, just what *are* the psychological factors in systems? At first the answer seems deceptively simple. We could say, why they're perception, learning, memory, motivation, emotion, psychomotor behavior, and so on. Closer inspection, however, reveals that these entities themselves are interrelated, varied within themselves, and time- and context-dependent. There seem to be at least two types of memory, for example, short term and long term, differing at the cellular level. There are undoubtedly several levels of perception, learning, and emotion, which might be called "peripheral", "subcortical", and "cortical".

Further, in operational situations we find it necessary to deal with factors like judgment and intuition that have long been pariahs to objective psychology. Even when we reduce the psychological factors to basics like visual acuity, vigilance, and reaction time, we find that these are dependent on the temporal and environmental context. Clearly what is needed is a *general* and *flexible* approach, adaptable to different problems, levels, times and environments. Systems theory seems to provide this approach. Throughout psychology, it is meaningful to conceptualize a person – or a human group, or a brain, or a mitochondrion – as a constituent processing energy, materials, and information; interacting within a given environment, at a given time, and at a given state of equilibrium and internal consistency. Systems theory should provide a common framework for posing, studying, and solving systems problems that seem to involve as apparently disparate factors as pattern perception, alertness, decision making, language, fatigue and stress, individual skill and performance differences, morale, and interpersonal relations.

It is probably premature to try to develop a comprehensive theory encompassing the *continuum*: automatic – man-machine – sociotechnical – social systems. An intermediate step is to use various models: information processing, feedback control, probabilistic, input–throughput–output, and man–machine–environmental. Further, it is probably fair to state that *there is no comprehensive theory tying together what we know about human behavior in systems*. In view of the many problems discussed later in this book, any systems psychological theory clearly must account for factors long faced by psychological theory in general. What are these factors? One approach is suggested by Coan's (1968) recent study of basic trends in psychological theory over time and at any given time. Coan determined 34 variables (divided into emphasis on content, methodology, basic assumption or mode of conceptualization) related to 54 theorists by the ratings of a couple of hundred experts in the history and theory of psychology. The theories included those of personality, abnormal behavior, learning, brain mechanisms, homeostasis, peripheral nervous activity, mental abilities, individual differences, sensation, integrative activity of the nervous system, and so forth.* For each psychological theorist, the experts' ratings were averaged and a 54 × 34 matrix obtained. Factor analysis and multiple-regression analysis revealed six factors and a placement of each theorist along a continuum represented by that factor. The factors are summarized as follows:

1. Subjectivistic versus objectivistic.
2. Holistic versus elementaristic; these two factors emerged as the factors of greatest variance, but other factors were also necessary.
3. Transpersonal versus personal, or experimental versus clinical.
4. Quantitative versus qualitative.
5. Dynamic versus static.
6. Endogenist ("biological") versus exogenist ("social" or, we might add, "environmental").

The six factors were intercorrelated and further analysis revealed two more general factors:

1. Synthetic (subjectivistic, holistic, and qualitative) versus analytic (objectivistic, elementaristic, and quantitative).
2. Functional (dynamic, personal, and internal and biological) versus structural (static and transpersonal).

In turn, the two second-order factors had a correlation of 0·55, leading to isolation of a final general factor: fluid (relaxed) orientation versus restrictive (controlling, compartmentalized) orientation. These theoretical orientations were seen to be a function of the personality of the scientist, a point systems researchers could do well to bear in mind. Does the need for systematization or mathematical rigor in fact reflect inner insecurities? Coan's work is summarized in Figure 5.2.

From the trends revealed in his work, Coan observes that neither at the factor level nor at the variable level is there a basis for confidently extrapolating to future developments. The clearest trend was toward greater objectivism. The

* Unfortunately, Coan emphasized classical theorists to the detriment of pragmatic theorists such as organization theorists.

participation of psychologists in system theory and system development over the past two and one-half decades suggests an approach (remember there is not yet a theory) that can be characterized as objectivistic, elementaristic, transpersonal, quantitative, dynamic, and exogenist. This approach *could* serve as a launching point for a comprehensive theory of human behavior in both man–machine and sociotechnical systems (which should be viewed not as dichotomous but rather as operating along a continuum). This theory must incorporate the input–throughput–output paradigm, and it must be expressible in terms of the modification or processing of inputs, probably in terms of information processing. Most important, it must express interactions at different levels and the same level, and predict the effects of interactions on the disruption and maintenance of equilibrium. Other systems properties could be factored in to a lesser extent. From here there could be an infinite quest for universals, perhaps the "elements" or "tasks" or "behaviors". One factor of particular importance is *expectation*: when the system situation, operation, or environment does not accord with an individual's expectation, degraded behavior occurs: the pilot loses control of his aircraft, the maintenance man's morale decreases, the minority group member or college student riots.

The definition, value, and directions of systems psychology. What we've said so far suggests the time has arrived to say, "Whoa, let's take stock of ourselves!" We must define systems psychology within its context of the other sciences, and carefully evaluate its future directions. Formally we define systems psychology as *the science and technology of understanding, describing and predicting; and generalizing the total effective performance and need-gratification behavior of intact organisms (usually human beings) under conditions of interaction with other intact organisms or machines within given environments.*

From preceding discussions, we may define *systems psychology* more generally as a new interdisciplinary specialty characterized by a *level*, a *breadth*, and a *method of approach*. At its most basic, the *level* is that of the individual intact organism (almost invariably, but not exclusively, a human being) interacting with at least one other entity, either man or machine, at about the same hierarchical level of complexity. Usually, at least ten of these basic constituents are involved. *Breadth* refers to similar consideration of man–man interactions within an environment, and man–machine interactions within an environment, and combinations thereof. The *method of approach* is that of systems

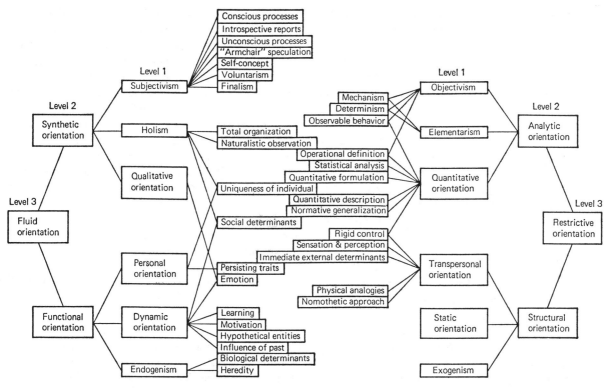

Figure 5.2 Three levels of factors common to psychological theories (From Coan, 1968).

theory *and* practice as discussed in detail throughout this chapter. It is general enough to permit qualitative, quantitative, or mixed techniques as appropriate.

Clearly, systems psychology cannot stand alone, and recognition of its relationships to other fields is important. If the same methods are applied at the level of the brain, the scientist is a physiological psychologist or physiologist. If the focus is on applying knowledge as to *specific* human capabilities and limitations, especially performance capabilities and limitations, to equipment design, the worker is an engineering psychologist; finding the requisite information is the work of an experimental psychologist. The man interested in the interaction of people in groups is a social psychologist.

We already have *specialists* capable of dealing with all sorts of system-related problems. Why establish still another science? One reason is that it is often difficult to relate problems to disciplines. Is self-regulated decrease in viable births, consequent to over-crowding, apparently involving sensory–neural–endocrine mechanisms and observed in mammals from rats to elephants, the province of physiological psychology or social psychology? Is the study of attitudes toward machines a concern of engineering psycho-

logy, industrial psychology, or social psychology? The choice of problems within our discipline is largely a function of how we define our jobs. A second reason is that, in practice, scientific generalists are few and far between. Industrial psychology, nominally broad, has proved to be rather static and has generated few, if any, exciting ideas. Human factors has made much progress in integrating human engineering, training, and man-power determination, but so far has largely ignored motivation, attitudes, and social factors in systems.

Systems psychology has roots in physiological, experimental, general, individual, and social psychology, as well as in physiology, the other social sciences, engineering, the computer and information sciences, and mathematics. It is both an applied and a theoretical/conceptual field, but at the present time, emphasis is on applications. Although systems psychology possesses methods appropriate to its level (for example, computer modeling and simulation), it is reciprocally dependent on other sciences and technologies: *One of the most healthful relationships entails recognizing and defining complex real-world problems in terms amenable to solution by the contributory sciences and referring these problems to the relevant specialty science.*

It is not sufficient to establish systems psychology as a well-defined and worthwhile science: We must insist on a careful evaluation of where we are going. Your response might now be, "Eureka! The millenium has arrived." A look to the past in psychology suggests caution, however. Uncertain of its own identity, psychology has all too often tried to emulate the rigor of the physical sciences. We have already mentioned the "standard rat". In the early days of experimental psychology, the human subject was known as the "reagent". The present author, whose initial university education was in chemistry and biology, is still uncomfortable with applications to psychology of such terms as *genotype* and *phenotype*, *molar* and *molecular*. Currently, many of the *in*-concepts and terms derive from information and control theory, but terms like *bit* and *coding* and *channel* should not be used to camouflage a poorly defined problem. Psychology must stand on its own two feet.

We must encourage the development of theory of man-related systems, but not at the expense of basic data collection. As psychologists, we should not be ashamed of perhaps emphasizing fieldwork over experiment. Meteorology, astronomy, geology, zoology, botany, anthropology, and sociology too must rely largely on field observations and measurements. Attempts to predict novae, earthquakes, or volcanic eruptions largely on the basis of laboratory abstractions would seem doomed to failure. Complex sociotechnical systems in particular require that basic field data be collected before subaspects of the systems problem can be relegated to the laboratory for detailed study.

Finally, we must urge the expansion of interdisciplinary, systems-related education in a changing psychology. One example is Fein's (1961) discussion of education in the computer-based sciences in 1975; the present book is another.

Systems science is general, widely applicable; we believe that, when judiciously used, it will reshape psychology and psychology's effect upon the world. And you, the reader, should you care to launch yourself into a career as a systems psychologist, will find your world very exciting indeed – and pleasantly remunerative, if you plan carefully, discipline yourself, and don't mind some risk and uncertainty.

How systems come into being

In the last section, we examined the theoretical basis of systems and psychology, an area that we will help advance. At the same time, however, there is a multitude of immediate systems to implement, of "brush fires to put out". The remainder of this chapter and much of the rest of this book is devoted to the practical demands of systems analysis, engineering, evaluation, and management. The most relevant theoretical, experimental, and empirical findings that provide substance to human factors will be discussed in appropriate sequence. A first step in learning to work with systems involves understanding how they originate and develop. In this section, we offer four examples of levels of rigor, taken from the natural and artificial worlds.

The origin, development, and evolution of systems can be conceptualized in terms of spontaneity, type, and degree of control; prior planning and integration; and exigencies of the time. Thus, the development of biological systems is mainly a function of control coded in the genes by the sequence of the nitrogenous bases adenine, cytosine, thymine, and guanine within the deoxyribonucleic acid molecule; by organizers within certain tissues during embryonic development (as appropriate); and by environmental constraints introduced, especially by the presence of chemical and ionizing radiation agents. Such systems are effectively preprogrammed and integrated.

Next come systems based on the most thorough possible long-range analyses of mission, operational, and performance requirements (Ferguson, 1965), involving much prior planning and freedom from ephemeral exigencies. This category includes most modern engineering systems such as the Apollo manned spacecraft system.

In the past, however, and to some extent still, systems have "grown like Topsy". Long-range planning has been absent, often because of military pressures to "get the system operational on schedule". In other cases, subsystems have been superimposed on subsystems, as, for example, in the SCF, outlined earlier, which included specialized – that is, "program-peculiar" – test support facilities (antennas, computers, communications, recorders, conversion equipment, telemetry ground stations, and so on). This specialization reduced the effectiveness of the network of control, tracking, and communications facilities by increasing station "turnaround time", and by necessitating replicate and redundant equipment, additional specialized personnel, and computer programs, and so on. Subsequently, attempts have been made to simplify and integrate the network toward development of a real system. But many interesting human factors problems still remain unsolved in the areas of display, control, man–machine task allocation, and personnel numbers. Unpublished studies by the present author, for example, suggest that personnel reallocations could result in cost savings sufficient to pay for a new computer-generated cathode-ray-tube display system.

Most civil or social systems are just reaching this state. Hence, we can expect obsolescent or obsolete transportation or urban networks superimposed on one another before a true system is evolved. Similarly, buildings in cities tend to be designed apart from their function in the total urban ecology.

Human roles in systems: the degree of mannedness

Human capabilities in the *operation* of such equipment as aircraft and radar were recognized as long ago as World War II. This recognition gave rise to fields variously called aviation psychology, applied experimental psychology, engineering psychology, human engineering, and ergonomics. Even after the importance of human capabilities and limitations in the operation of equipment had been recognized, albeit at the subsystem or "knob and dial" level, equipment continued to be poorly designed for *maintainability*. Still later, it was recognized that *controllability* is an attribute that can be differentiated from operability by virtue of complexity and the dynamic behavior of at least some equipment or vehicles.

At the present time there is considerable interest in man's role as *decision maker* and *manager*. A related role, particularly in complex military and space systems, is that of *analyst*. For example, analysts help evaluate the military threat, and are indispensable to the evaluation and interpretation of satellite tracking, trajectory, and telemetry (both hardware and biomedical) data. The role of analysis in system development is self-evident.

Other roles of men in systems include those of *planner*, *designer*, *producer*, and *evaluator*. These roles can be conceptualized and studied in terms of the amount of human involvement, and real-time or non-real-time nature of human participation, and the types of psychological factors involved. Systems are sometimes dichotomized as manned, e.g., projects Mercury, Gemini, and Apollo; or unmanned, e.g., projects Ranger, Surveyor, and Mariner (all these involve space missions). However, it is more meaningful to speak of *degrees of mannedness*. By definition, all man-made systems involve the participation of human beings.

Human roles also vary with time. Most attention has been paid to the more dramatic real-time operations and control activities. There *is* justifiable concern with human capabilities and limitations involved in, say, piloting an aircraft or spacecraft and in ground-based air traffic control. Yet system success or failure may depend as much on planning, inspection, quality control, computer program design, maintenance, and similar factors.

Finally, behavioral and life scientists have long emphasized clearly identifiable perceptual-motor skills and related physiological (e.g., reaction to high g forces) and anthropometric (reach and dimension) parameters. Poorly understood concepts such as "judgment" were implied. Today, decision making, short- and long-term memory, problem solving, and creativity are receiving much attention. Motivational and emotional factors are still largely ignored in systems contexts, although they are of considerable importance to the field of psychology as a whole. The problem of interfacing these psychological factors with equipment and environmental parameters and with anticipation, analysis, planning, management, and real-time operations is a major one in systems psychology – and in this book.

What happens when the systems approach is not followed?

In conceptualizing and experimenting in the laboratory, if we make a mistake, leave out a variable, or neglect an interaction, we end up with an imprecise theory or limited or misleading results. The same type of mistake in the design or operation of a system can kill hundreds or potentially millions of people, can cost millions or billions of dollars, or can degrade the dignity of our lives.

For example, as this manuscript goes to press, there is considerable congressional, military, industrial, and public concern with military systems that have "gone wrong" in one way or another. In some cases, system hardware was never constructed. In other cases the systems were cancelled, prototype equipment and all, before they became operational. It is estimated that the cost of 68 such "historic" weapons systems over the past 15 years was about $10 billion.* Examples are the B-70 manned supersonic bomber, Skybolt B-52-launched air-to-ground missile, and a nuclear-powered aircraft. In addition to these historic examples, we must consider the contemporary F-111A and B fighter-bomber aircraft, C5A heavy transport aircraft, Cheyenne jet combat helicopter, and Air Force Manned Orbital Laboratory (MOL) spacecraft. We discuss some of these systems in more detail later. The point we emphasize is that we can learn much from our mistakes. We all make mistakes – whether government planner, military planner, industrial system developer, or urban planner. A critical look at what we have done, where we stand, and where we are going is in no way to be interpreted as "finger pointing".

The systems method provides a means for the orderly, integrated, and timely development of systems. Where

* For a list of these "systems that failed", see the *Congressional Record*, vol. 115, no. 59, April 15, 1969.

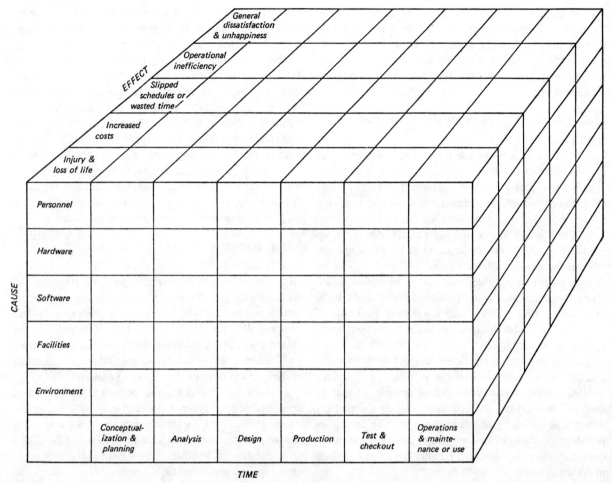

Figure 5.3 First-level cause-effect-time matrix for indicating system degradation. *Note:* Progressively more refined matrices may be constructed. Use extreme caution in establishing cause-effect relationships.

people are involved, careful consideration must be given to human capabilities and limitations. *When these guidelines are not followed, penalties must be paid in terms of increased costs, decreased performance, slipped schedules, accidents, and loss of life.*

A number of examples of failure to follow systems guidelines are outlined in this section. Whereas the *individual events* within each example are probably stochastic, the gross picture in each case has been qualitatively replicated and the cases are of *unequivocal* pedagogic value. Thus, there *have* been several Boeing 727 landing crashes under similar conditions, several midair aircraft collisions under similar conditions, several misinstallations of constituents in missile systems under similar conditions, and so on. All the examples demonstrate some aspect of "human error" (whatever the scientific limitations of that term).

The study of human errors and accidents – classification, prediction, investigation, and prevention – is, of course, an organized specialty in human factors. Accidents themselves provide a valuable source of data to systems psychological understanding of human capabilities and limitations and to design. Throughout this book, however, the theme recurs of human error and how to prevent it. The hardware- and software-related* examples that follow stress dollar losses, loss of lives, decreased operation efficiency, and near

* In this chapter, *hardware* means equipment, including communications equipment; *software* means computer programs and documentation; *facilities* means buildings, roads, airstrips, docks, etc. These three, plus *personnel*, are the four major constituent subdivisions of the systems with which we will deal most of the time. Interfaces are important both between and within major constituents.

national chaos. System degradations can be roughly classified using the matrix illustrated in Figure 5.3. As more information becomes available, progressively finer matrices can be employed. Remember that *every event occurs within a context; therefore, simple cause–effect relationships are usually impossible to establish*. Even a concatenation or field of interacting events may be much harder to establish than the causal events in the cases we now discuss.

Effect of failure to plan for multiple contingencies

The great Northeast power failure: national chaos narrowly avoided. The great Northeast power failure, the largest in American history (see Friedlander, 1966), provides a dramatic example of failures in systems thinking, planning, and management. On November 9, 1965, because of an unexpected flow of power, a circuit breaker tripped at a hydroelectric plant on the Niagara River in Ontario, triggering a power blackout that lasted many hours and involved 30 million people in the Northeast United States and parts of Canada.

Interconnected power systems comprise previously isolated local power company utilities tied together. But *system integration is often poorly advanced*. Each constituent utility company has different output capacities, dynamic inertia, speed-regulating methods, and loading systems. The interconnected systems are designed to meet a *single* large-scale contingency, but not a *combination* of simultaneous disturbances. Thus, when the circuit breaker in Ontario tripped, power shifted to other lines, which, because their own load-carrying capacities were now overloaded, tripped out in *cascade*. Significantly, the backup relay that triggered the disturbance had been set in 1963 at a capacity below that of the line, and perhaps unrelated to subsequent actual power flows. Thus, at about 5.16 P.M. on November 9, 1965, the power flow apparently reached the level at which the relay was set. The relay functioned properly, and its circuit breaker tripped out the line. *Operating personnel were not aware of the relay setting.*

Normally, in power systems, design provides for protection against loss of power generation, not against loss of a very large block of load. In this case, the outage of five transmission lines separated the Canadian power generation from its normal load, leading to a power reversal and superimposing additional power onto New York lines, exceeding the capacity of the New York system and leading to its breakup.

Thus, a simple power-limit pullout led to a chain reaction of power failures. This involved direction reversals of load, cascade tripping off of other units, loss of synchronization among utility units, automatic shutdown of generators to prevent damage, severing of lines to other power pools, and fragmentation of the Northeast power pool into four constituents, some of which possessed an excess of load and some an excess of generation. All this took only four seconds. Further sequential breakdowns of similar nature then occurred, with an end result of a widespread power blackout within about 12 minutes.

The results of the power failure included both damages to the generators themselves and interesting side effects relative to communications, transportation, and mass human behavior. These latter events dramatize that no system, whether power, transportation, communication, air defense, police, or what, exists out of context of parallel, subordinate, and supraordinate systems. In this case, television, some radio, teletype, and news printing were lost; railway and traffic lights ceased functioning; electrically driven gasoline pumps at service stations would not operate; 600,000 people were trapped for hours in subways, and thousands more in elevators; and operations were not possible at most airports. Fortunately, the telephone company, some hospitals, and other agencies possessed auxiliary power sources. Had the power failure taken place on a moonless, blizzardy night, a major catastrophe could have occurred. Implications for sabotage or attack on the nation are self-evident, as for mass panic behavior of the "War of Worlds" sort.

Further, restoration of power after the failure took many hours: Each utility company checked its own relays, circuit breakers, and switches; these companies' frequencies were synchronized with other parts of the system; city underground grid circuits were checked; the power generation sources, themselves to a greater (thermal) or lesser (hydro) extent dependent on electricity, were restored. At the time, the nature and location of the failure were unknown. This dramatizes again the need for sensing mechanisms, display of system status, and personnel trained in recognition of symptoms and contingency procedures.

Major lessons learned were recognition of the need for close human override of automatic equipment; planning for contingencies and improbable events; sensing, display, and monitoring of dynamic system status; better personnel training; and some backup, redundant, or emergency equipment. Further, the system failure dramatically demonstrated the integrated power system interface with other systems, and the resulting, even larger metropolitan or regional system. In avoiding a recurrence, guidance could perhaps be taken from such aerospace systems as SAGE (where track and other data must be maintained by Direction Centers adjacent to an "outage") or the SCF (where contact can be lost between the main control center and an outlying tracking station). An overall supervisory control system is also indicated.

Other power failures have occurred since the great November 9, 1965, power blackout.

Effects of improper analysis of operator requirements

SAGE: blue light and blinking displays. The SAGE air defense system is a salient example of increased computer programming and environmental costs, and reduced efficiency, resulting from the failure to analyze, in depth, operator and controller task information requirements. Too much information – and clutter – was displayed at each console. This increased the load on the display-generating computer program, which then was unable to refresh the (flickering) display on each cathode-ray tube rapidly enough to maintain a character brightness level legible under the conditions of tube and phosphor development of the time. To avoid this problem, the familiar broad-band blue lighting system was used, involving blue filters over ordinary fluorescent light sources and orange filters over the cathode-ray tube faces. The displays could be read and certain other tasks performed under the same level of blue illumination. However, the lighting system imparted an eerie atmosphere to SAGE Direction and Combat Centers, and personnel often complained of headaches after exposure to the blue light. To our knowledge, no studies were made of the behavioral or physiological consequences of exposure to this atypical environment. The system interactions among personnel information requirements, computer programming design, hardware availability, display design, and environmental design are evident. For a consideration of other problems in SAGE and similar systems, see Israel (1965).

Apollo Command Module: fire kills three astronauts. The launch pad fire in the Apollo Command Module in January 1967 exemplifies dramatically a failure of systems engineering and management. The interacting factors included the 100 percent oxygen breathing atmosphere (selected for all U.S. manned space programs), increased combustibility of normally noncombustible materials in a pure-oxygen atmosphere, failure to apply available knowledge of such fire danger, nonfireproof space suit worn by the astronauts, the length of time required to open the escape hatch, and the electric arcing permitted by the circuitry design. Three

men died – yet prevention of this accident required no new advances in science or engineering. In systems work, little "knowns" seem often to add up to big "unknowns". The aftereffects of this accident included widespread managerial changes within both the National Aeronautics and Space Administration (NASA) and the contracting organizations, and a year's delay in implementation of the United States manned space program.

Effects of improper methods in design, production, and test and checkout

Nimbus B/Thorad/Agena: incorrect gyro installation leads to spacecraft destruction. On May 18, 1968, a Nimbus B/Thorad/Agena space vehicle was launched at the Western Test Range, Vandenberg Air Force Base, California. The space vehicle consisted of a Thorad (long-tank Thor) primary launch vehicle, a second-stage Agena orbital vehicle, and a Nimbus B spacecraft. The Nimbus was the largest, most heavily instrumented NASA meteorological (weather-mapping) satellite. Within two minutes after launch, during the Thorad-powered portion of the flight, direct visual, tracking, and telemetry data indicated that the vehicle was exhibiting increasing oscillations in yaw and deviating considerably to the left of the prescribed trajectory, finally crossing the range safety boundary. The range safety officer then destroyed the vehicle.

The accident investigation board* found that the malfunction of the Thorad launch vehicle was caused by a misinstallation of the yaw-rate gyro, which provided negative pitch-rate data to the autopilot yaw-control channel, rather than the correct yaw-rate feedback signals. Such a misinstallation required rotation of the gyro (looking forward) 90 degrees clockwise about its long axis. *It was a clear case of human error* associated with: (1) "incorrect installation of the gyro in a correctly fabricated and installed gyro-mounting bracket", or (2) "installation of the gyro in an improperly made gyro bracket", according to the accident investigation report. Specific deficiencies are outlined below.

Manufacturing. Dowel pin holes were drilled in a fixture permitting their mislocation, which resulted in a "proper appearing", but actually incorrect, installation.
Installation. The installation drawings did not show the dowel pin holes in place, and the projections used did not accord with the natural view of the worker. In addition,

* This discussion is based partially on the board's report; see also *Aviation Week*, May 27 and August 19, 1968.

it was possible to depress the guide pin inadvertently, thus losing an orientation to correct installation.

Installation of the long-tank Thor gyro in the vertical position was awkward because of the physical location of the mounting bracket. The installer had to reach 2 to 3 feet above his head to mount the gyro (a one-man operation) because the permanent step ladder was too low. A variety of rate gyro brackets, intended for use on different models of the Thor booster, could be interchanged, installed on the wrong vehicle, or misinstalled. *Test and Inspection Procedures.* Procedural inadequacies made it impossible to accurately determine correctness of installation. For example:

- It was possible to obtain valid-appearing data even from an improperly installed gyro, because it was nearly impossible physically for the operator to move the gyro precisely into its intended plane.
- Check lists of *critical items* to inspect when verifying an installation were not provided.
- Even when members of the accident investigation board were present (such observation was known to the personnel concerned), numerous attempts were made to misconnect electrical connectors, sensitive equipment was nearly damaged, etc.
- The acceptance testing procedures and specifications of the primary contractor permitted acceptance of an incorrectly installed gyro.
- Procedures for conducting gyro tests (not related to differences in test equipment) differed among launch sites, at the factory, and even on the same launch complex during different phases of prelaunch testing.
- During testing, operators did not wear their headsets, leading to miscommunication of information.

This case exemplifies the omission of long understood human factors principles associated with design, manufacture, testing, procedures, and supervision. We also can note again the importance of taking a systems overview that recognizes the reinforcing of interacting effects of a sequence of events. *The cost: estimated at $62 million!*

Apollo/Saturn: improper labeling leads to engine shutdown. An improper installation of signal wires led to premature shutdown of two of the five second-stage engines on the Apollo 6/Saturn 502 space vehicle launched April 4, 1968 (*Aviation Week*, April 15, 1968). This was the second unmanned flight of the Saturn 5, and the error might well have contributed to the requirement for an additional unmanned

flight prior to the first manned flight and precluded hoped-for cost and time savings. NASA had hoped that a third unmanned flight, already programmed, could be cancelled. Postflight analysis revealed that a workman had followed the installation instructions properly, but that the wires had been mislabeled. The cost of another unmanned flight, if necessary to man-rate the launch vehicle, would be approximately $200 million. From the system standpoint, such an error could result from poor human engineering design for maintainability (including technical manuals), inadequate training or personnel selection, lack of motivation, inferior management, or some combination of these factors.

Mariner/Atlas/Agena Venus flyby: computer program error leads to vehicle destruction. In mid-1962, a Mariner/Atlas/Agena combination was launched from Cape Canaveral, Florida. The mission involved flight of the Mariner to the vicinity of the planet Venus. During operation of the second or sustainer stage of the Atlas, it was determined that the vehicle was off course and had to be destroyed. Subsequent investigation revealed a transcription error in coding the computer program, which resulted in the omission of *a hyphen* from the guidance equations before the equations were fed into the missile-guidance computer. The cost: over $35 million! This case exemplifies the importance of designing computer programs that do not assign rigidly prescribed meanings to easily overlooked or forgotten things like commas, spaces, and hyphens, and that ensure the identification of errors as they occur. It also illustrates that, although the actual perpetrator of an error or accident is usually an operator, factory worker, maintenance man, clerk, and so on, the error or accident situation may have received its essential structure long before, during problem formulation, analysis, or design.

Effects of failure to predict man–machine–environmental interactions in operations

DC-7B takeoff crash: evasive maneuver in response to optical illusion. That degraded perception can lead to fatal aircraft accidents is illustrated by the following two cases attributed to optical illusions. In the first case (*Aviation Week*, January 2, 1967),* an Eastern Airlines DC-7B climbing on departure from John F. Kennedy International Airport (New York City) on February 8, 1965, crashed in the Atlantic Ocean off Long Island about 6.26 P.M. (and hence in

* From time to time, the weekly *Aviation Week and Space Technology* presents detailed reports on the results of aircraft accident investigations. It is recommended that you keep a file of these if you wish to begin specializing in this field.

darkness), killing all 84 persons aboard. The Civil Aeronautics Board (CAB) determined the probable cause to be evasive action taken by the DC-7B to avoid an *apparent* collision with a Pan American Boeing 707 descending to land. This maneuver placed the DC-7B aircraft in an attitude from which recovery in time was not possible.

Detailed analysis indicated that one or more illusions, associated with a paucity of stimuli, misleading cues, or a conflict among sensory cues – separately amenable to laboratory study but difficult to isolate operationally – may have been involved. Other perceptual factors such as vertigo led to disorientation. Following recognition of disorientation, as much as 36 seconds would have been required to reestablish orientation using instruments. Under conditions of this particular flight, this period was too long.

The abrupt avoidance maneuver had originally been precipitated by the belated ability of the pilot of the DC-7B to detect the jet aircraft visually. The initial evasive maneuver of the DC-7B was paralleled by an evasive maneuver by the 707, which appeared to negate the former. A second evasive maneuver, a rapid pull up and roll to the right, led to spatial disorientation of the crew of the DC-7B. This vertical bank could be corrected only within a time period less than that required for instruments. Postaccident flight tests indicated five out of six pilots experienced similar illusions of collision under equivalent flight conditions.

Ground radar separation of the two aircraft had disappeared at the time of the initial turn of the DC-7B toward the 707, although in reality the aircraft were separated by 1,000 feet vertical elevation. The CAB recommends that pilots avoid vectoring aircraft on directly converging courses because of problems associated with spatial disorientation. Also, the Federal Aviation Administration (FAA) promulgated a procedure requiring that 2,000- rather than 1,000-foot vertical separation be maintained between inbound and outbound flights in areas where illusions have occurred. Development of automatic collision-sensing and display systems also show promise in preventing future accidents of this kind.

The above case exemplifies the interactions among visual angle and visual field, themselves a function of cockpit design, window size, and placement; depth and movement perception based on size, change, and rate-of-change cues; decision making; mission profile and maneuvers; lack of a horizon and night-time flying conditions; contingency phenomena and operational procedures in both aircraft and at ground control; psychophysiological cues and responses to visual, labyrinthine, and probably kinesthetic stimuli; reaction times and other aspects of task time stress; and cockpit display design. There is no alternative to our development of a total systems understanding.

Boeing 707-Lockheed 1049C midair collision: cloud forms distort perception. The midair collision of a Trans World Airlines (TWA) Boeing 707 and an Eastern Airlines Lockheed 1049C (*Aviation Week*, January 9, 1967) is another example of failure to consider all the variables in a dynamically operating system. This accident occurred on December 4, 1965, while the TWA and Eastern aircraft were enroute to John F. Kennedy International Airport and to Newark (New Jersey) Airport, respectively. The Boeing 707 was approaching the New York area, under an Instrument Flight Rules (IFR) flight plan at an assigned altitude of 11,000 feet. The Lockheed aircraft was approaching the area under an IFR flight plan at an assigned altitude of 10,000 feet. In close sequence, the crews of both aircraft perceived an apparent collision course and took evasive maneuvers, the Lockheed aircraft being pulled up and the Boeing then being rolled first to the right and then to the left. The aircraft then collided at approximately 11,000 feet. Both aircraft suffered structural damage; the Lockheed aircraft, forced to land in an open field, was destroyed by impact and fire. Four persons on the Lockheed aircraft suffered fatal injuries and 49, nonfatal injuries. There were no injuries aboard the Boeing 707. The CAB attributed the collision to misjudgment of altitude separation by the crew of the Lockheed aircraft because of an optical illusion created by the up-slope effect of cloud tops, followed by the previously described evasive measures. At the time of the collision, the area was overcast with cloud tops at just above 10,000 feet. Cloud tops tended to be higher to the north than to the south, resulting in an illusion of upward slope toward the north.

The above example dramatizes better than any laboratory abstraction the figure/ground relationships in perception. In this case, illusion appears to have been a function of the distances between the aircraft, their angular velocities, and the observed rate of change of the range-rate of each aircraft, all superimposed on the false horizon cues provided by the sloping clouds.

Boeing 727 landing crash: display design and inclement weather. A landing crash and burn of an American Airlines Boeing 727 aircraft occurred during darkness and inclement weather at Greater Cincinnati Airport. Fifty-eight of the 62 persons on board were fatally injured (*Aviation Week*, October 24, 1966). The CAB determined that the probable cause of the accident lay in the crew's failure to monitor properly the altimeters during a visual landing approach into environmental conditions leading to reduced visibility. However, careful scrutiny provides detail of a subtler nature involving psychological factors of attention, perception, motivation, and judgment interacting with task structure and load and with display design:

- Late departure from La Guardia (New York) Airport, together with increasing thunderstorm activity around Cincinnati, apparently prompted the crew to expedite their landing. A landing delay or instrument approach would have been a more prudent judgment. Much more psychological research should be performed on motivation, decision making, problem solving, and judgment under conditions of time- and load-stress and fatigue.

- Just before the crash, both pilots were preoccupied with maintaining visual reference to the runway, so that they neglected the altimeters.

- It is well known to human factors scientists that poor altimeter design has been associated with numerous aircraft accidents over the years. In this case, the three altimeters were Kollsman drum-pointer types; thousands of feet were indicated on a rotating drum visible through a slot, and hundreds of feet were indicated by a radial pointer. The range of the altimeters was from minus 1,500 feet to plus 50,000 feet. Crosshatching was printed on the drum adjacent to the critical values between plus 1,000 and minus 1,500 feet. Human factors and other developments leading to the incorporation of audible and additional visual alarms at low altitudes should prove valuable.

- System design should reflect contingency, low-probability, stress factor, and interaction events, particularly for critical segments of a mission profile, such as aircraft takeoff, approach, and landing. These factors should receive particular attention in information display design.

The systems approach as a problem-solving and decision-making methodology

Systems methods applied to practical engineering problems are now intrinsic facets of our technology. These are largely pragmatic, even intuitive, and have grown through trial and error in the face of complex, previously unmanageable problems. Thus, in many ways, the systems approach is one of conceptual problem solving, an attitude or ability to perceive wholes, different levels, and interrelationships, rather than a formal regimen! It cannot be said that practice usually follows the general systems theory discussed earlier in this chapter; on the contrary, theory often has been derived from observation of, and experience with, real-life problem areas and cases. The large-scale systems methods employed so far can thus be said to be more rational, empirical, and observational than experimental. Nevertheless, an appreciable engineering and management methodology has emerged, which has been associated with rather spectacular improvements in costs, efficiency, safety, and timeliness, and which is currently being applied to broader and broader vistas. For purposes of discussion, this methodology can be considered to have four iterative, usually overlapping and reinforcing segments: *analysis, engineering, management,* and *evaluation.* Collectively, these contribute to the *system-development process,* usually more realistically considered the *system-development cycle.*

Systems analysis

Systems analysis may have a future orientation in which the realism of requirements is degraded by increasing uncertainties (see, for example, Quade, 1966). Ferguson (1965) cautions against expecting formalized, unchanging requirements. Further, in dealing with social systems, most of the input derives from the poorly understood, poorly quantifiable, and the uncertain.

Two examples of the uses and limitations of systems analysis are provided by the B-70 high-altitude supersonic bomber and the F-111 (TFX) fighter-bomber, both reflecting decisions from high levels within the United States government.

In each case, lively political controversy was generated, involving the Department of Defense, the Congress, the Air Force, and other agencies; the Department of Defense's insistence on rigor in the analysis of weapons systems requirements prevailed over more partisan political pressures. The B-70 eventually cost about $1·5 billion; two experimental aircraft were built, one of which eventually crashed, with loss of the pilot's life, during a public relations filming (see Carter, 1968). As originally planned, the program was to lead to a $20 billion fleet of these aircraft. The program was, in Carter's words, "a classic example of failure to analyze rigorously the mission to be performed and the state of the technology the mission requires". One of the most severe limitations of the program was its dependence on the development of an extremely high-resolution radar, associated processing and display equipment, and (perhaps an impossible) *human interpretation capability.* The Department of Defense questioned that this equipment could be available by 1967, as planned, or, indeed, even by 1970. Further, even if the aircraft (later renamed the RS-70) could be developed, *cost/effectiveness* studies indicated that cheaper, less vulnerable, and more effective weapons systems were available. The RS-70 made a poor showing when compared to the Polaris missile-carrying submarine and even to the antiquated B-52. In retrospect, it appears that application of rigorous systems analysis saved the taxpayers some $8·5 billion.

The case of the F-111 aircraft is still unclear. Development of this aircraft was also clouded by political factors, in this case involving industrial contractors as well. Further consideration of these factors is beyond the scope of this book. Suffice it to say that the Department of Defense attempted to reduce the cost of developing separate weapons systems for the Air Force and Navy by developing two versions, the Air Force F-111A and Navy F-111B, of the same basic aircraft. Unfortunately, the program has been plagued with difficulties. Both versions have cost considerably more than originally programmed. The Navy version has been cancelled; among other reasons, the Navy maintains the aircraft is too heavy and cumbersome to operate off a carrier. Several F-111A aircraft have crashed, both in the United States and, under combat conditions, in Southeast Asia.

Systems engineering

Systems engineering connotes design of equipment, communications, computer programs, documentation, job or task assignments for personnel, or usually, some combination of all these factors. Where systems analysis leaves off and systems engineering begins is an arbitrary judgment: Systems analysis can be considered an integral part of systems engineering; alternatively, following Gilmore *et al.* (1967), for example, we might consider the dividing line to be the selection of performance requirements by the customer, user, or design team. Systems engineering, of course, usually has a hardware-design implication, as opposed to a pencil/paper or computer model and simulation implication. Systems engineering design starts when a system is fairly well defined. Traditionally, intuitions, judgments, economics, politics, and expediency have played as great a role in the selection of a design as has analysis, whether poor, good, or nonexistent.

The essence of systems engineering lies within recognizing and understanding constituent specialties – for example, structures, electronics, power and fuel, and crew – and allowing these to function only within the context of integrating these efforts into a whole. The systems engineer must be able to stimulate, direct, and utilize much work that is not "systems engineering", but only specialty or constituent engineering.

Systems engineering developments have taken place within industry; methodology has been generalized from case histories and is based more on inference derived from direct observation than on experimentation or model building. According to Hall (1966), the universities have been rather uncritical in accepting even extreme claims from industry; there is a need for the active development of better curricula, more scholarly analysis and less promotionalism in the present literature, and the formulation and testing of models against actual situations.

Systems management

We have seen that there are systems of all levels of complexity. The systems of primary concern in this book – weapons, aerospace, sociotechnical – are of *immense* complexity. The United States civilian space program, for example, has involved 20,000 contractors; some 300,000 engineers, technicians, and production workers; and expenditures of $35 billion over a decade, of which $24 billion alone has been spent on the manned space effort. This complexity of techniques, disciplines, specialists, contractors, concepts, resources, and building blocks must be brought together in an orderly manner. Engineering systems management or, more simply, systems management techniques have provided an impressive start in the right direction: that of *total system design and management.*

Systems management encompasses techniques developed since the early 1950s, primarily by the Air Force in connection with advanced aircraft, missile, and space systems. NASA's unmanned and manned space programs and the Navy's nuclear submarine projects have also contributed substantive ideas.* Systems management is a time-phased, monitorial, evaluative, and integrative activity involving the recognition of technical (for example, analytic) criteria; the assignment of organizational and contractual responsibilities; the definition of milestones; and the assignment of required documentation, hierarchies of contributing organizations, and feedback responses to initial documentation. In parallel with, and utilizing, systems analysis and engineering, it proceeds from the general to the specific, from the hypothetical to the real, and from the conceptual through research and development and production to the operational. The systems concepts of interface, evolution, and integration are of paramount importance.

* The Program Evaluation and Review Technique (PERT), a form of *network analysis* developed for the Navy, deserves special mention.

Before examining the main ideas of systems management in more detail, we will first review the situation before the early and mid-1960s. Neither the user nor the contractor was certain how the system would turn out until it appeared in the field. Often hardware was delivered, but no crews; if there were crews, they were untrained. Often, the operations and maintenance philosophy had not been thought out. Typically, the system was not available on schedule, was difficult to use, and required costly and time-consuming retrofit changes. To determine and correct deficiencies in the management of systems engineering, Air Force Systems Command (AFSC) of the U.S. Air Force conducted a series of management surveys (see, for example, AFSCP 375-2, 1963). Significant lessons were gained from 24 major contractors. Twenty-six major findings were cited. Those of particular relevance to this book include:

- Underestimation of costs.
- Limited standards of manpower utilization (the largest single element of costs) and the related, inefficient utilization of engineering manpower.
- Costly proliferation and duplication of reports.
- Insufficient systems analysis, systems design, and detailed design integration, leading to a cascading effect on production, logistics, and the like, and requiring costly design changes to correct early over-sights.
- Inadequate consideration of reliability in detailed design.
- Unrealistic engineering development and test schedules, leading to slipped schedules and increased costs.
- Late delivery of end items.
- Technical data late, costly, and inaccurate; related technical manuals not validated, late, and of poor quality.

As you might expect from the points emphasized so far, these deficiencies were seldom isolated problems but were *interrelated*, symptomatic of common management problems. As a result of these and other findings, the U.S. Air Force has developed a comprehensive body of systems management techniques, which have been extended to other branches of the Department of Defense. Much of applied systems management has also been derived from the cost/effectiveness systems analysis studies of the RAND school, which has received enthusiastic support in the Department of Defense. A descendant of the concept, the Planning–Programming–Budgeting System (PPBS), which attempts to provide a bridge between the already extant military planning and budgeting, is becoming rather widely accepted in state governments as well.

Systems management can be defined as *the process of planning, organizing, coordinating, controlling, and directing the combined efforts of contractors and other relevant organizations to accomplish system program objectives. It involves an integration, in a time-phased manner, of organizations, responsibilities, knowledge, and data and documentation.* The details of the Air Force program are given in the AFR 375-1 through 375-5 series and the AFSCM 375-1 through 375-5 series. Systems management concepts as applied to personnel subsystem (human factors) management are presented in the *Handbook of Instructions for Aerospace Personnel Subsystem Design* (HIAPSD), AFSCM 80-3.* Most important of the 375 series for our purposes is AFSCM 375-5, *Systems Engineering Management Procedures* (1964). A review of this document and its uses, available to the general reader, is provided by Gelbwaks (1967).

The management of the systems engineering process entails as early and accurate an identification as possible of *total system* requirements, control over the evolution of requirements and designs, integration of technical specialty efforts including human factors, and development of basic data and documentation. In the broadest sense, systems management is applied over the life cycle of the system, including conceptualization, design, development, test and evaluation, operations and maintenance, and senescence and replacement. In actuality, one could make a distinction between *systems development management* and *systems operational management*: The basic Air Force regulation AFR 375-1 states, for example, "systems management does not apply to *actual use* of a system during the operational phase". Thus, the degree and type of management control, the nature of the scientific or technical and engineering processes, and the organizations involved differ among say a conceptual system, an operational system, and a system about to be phased out. In the past, so-called "R&D systems" have been largely free of management control.

The heart of the management of complex systems lies in the identification and control over specific events in the life history of the system. The life cycle of *Air Force Systems* is divided into four formal phases which in turn may be further divided into subphases. The four phases and their salient events can be summarized as follows:

1. *Conceptual phase:* determination of a system concept that will satisfy the stated (mission) requirements and is

* The names and codes for military organizations frequently change, as does the nomenclature for documentation. HIAPSD has been revised and updated, and the design (but not the management) portions have been reissued as AFSC DH 1-3 (1969).

indicated by analysis as suitable, feasible, and acceptable in terms of *performance*, *cost*, and *schedule*; and specification of functions, system interfaces, and gross performance and design requirements.

2. *Definition phase:* definition in greater detail of the basic concept, personnel, computer programs, equipment, facilities, costs, and schedules leading to acquisition phase contractor selection.

3. *Acquisition phase:* design, production, and test (Categories I and II) of the system; the acquisition phase may overlap with the operational phase.

4. *Operational phase:* system test (Category III) and evaluation to determine accomplishment of the mission objectives; and actual operation of the system.

Within and, particularly, among the phases, specific documents are prepared and released by given organizations; these documents call for responses on the part of other organizations and are reflected in feedback modifications of the original documentation.

Such system development depends at each phase on the *previous* development of *basic building blocks*. A series of R&D categories has been established by the Department of Defense in the sequence: basic research, exploratory development, advanced development, and so on, eventually leading to the operational system. Psychologists have the opportunity to participate in basic research and all phases of the system life cycle. They have made contributions in universities, industry, and military and associated non-military organizations.*

There is a burgeoning specialty area dealing with management and the manager, and psychologists have the opportunity to make major contributions both within the field of management, viewed as a system, and with regard to the interpersonal capabilities and limitations of the individual manager. The term *behavioral science* sometimes is used in a very specialized sense to describe the study of human behavior in organizations; in practice, it is more circumscribed with a small-group-dynamics emphasis. Fields of concentration include such areas as leadership, sensitivity

---

* Systems analysis, engineering, and management skills, as opposed to specialty training, are not common. For this reason, the Air Force has used intermediary "think tank" organizations such as the RAND, Aerospace, and Mitre corporations, which perform advanced research, study, and planning, or act as intermediaries between the military user and the design, and frequently operations and maintenance, industrial contractor. Such organizations frequently have General Systems Engineering and Technical Direction (GSE/TD) responsibilities.

training in which the manager hopes to develop a better awareness of himself and his effect on other people, and organizational change.

Management information and control systems are bona fide systems that present all the challenges of complex systems and provide the psychologist with all the opportunities to apply the techniques and information to which this book is devoted. Later, we discuss motivation, morale, job satisfaction, supervision, and group relations – all topics of particular interest to management psychology. For additional general reading on systems management see Johnson *et al.* (1967); on management psychology, see Leavitt (1964) and Leavitt and Pondy (1964); and on management systems, see Schoderbek (1967).

Experience with systems management programs has shown that effective documentation (including use of computer methods) is an absolute necessity for systems development. However, there is evidence of too strict adherence to *procedure*. Numerous industrial contractors have complained about stifled creativity and enforced conformity especially during the early conceptual phase, tight control over their design activities, and the time spent filling out and maintaining accountability forms that (the contractors maintain) could better be spent on design itself. Similarly, there is some evidence of misapplication of tight control to smaller, one-of-a-type or conceptual systems.

Also, it must be remembered that systems management approaches and techniques are evolving. We have a good thing, but it's not foolproof. Consider the C5A heavy-transport aircraft, developed under sophisticated systems management concept, which nevertheless has been estimated to cost twice as much per aircraft as originally budgeted. We must constantly refine our methods, adapt our techniques to fit experiences, and work toward the advancement of systems theory.

Systems evaluation

Systems evaluation begins with the first consideration of pencil–paper alternatives and continues through the use of nonwired, wired but static, and dynamic *mockups* and *simulators*, related in various degrees of fidelity to expected environmental conditions. Sophisticated simulations play a large role in such systems evaluations. As the operational date draws nearer, more and more realistic evaluations become possible. Thus, in the Air Force systems management terminology, *Category I testing* typically involves in-plant (within the factory) subsystem testing and evaluation utilizing design engineer personnel; *Category II testing* is system testing in the field, usually with mixed design and user personnel; and *Category III testing* is system testing in the field under near-operational conditions. "Testing" cannot be separated from "evaluation" in these contexts. Personnel subsystem testing and evaluation is a specialized aspect of particular importance to this book.

The value of systems testing and evaluation – and of systems analysis – rests on successful *definition of criteria*, which presents a major, largely unresolved problem, especially in social systems.

Applied systems psychology: engineering psychology and human factors

In the practical, applied sense, systems psychology has meant engineering psychology and human factors. Engineering psychology, originally largely an outgrowth of experimental psychology,* is concerned mainly with the design of equipment, facilities, and environments to match the capabilities and limitations of people; and to a lesser extent with the selection and training of personnel. Engineering psychology originated in World War II (see Christensen, 1964; Grether, 1968), when it became clear that operational deficiencies in bombing, artillery targeting, submarine sonar detection, and aircraft were associated with poor equipment design and personnel selection and training.† Psychologists were asked to examine these problems, and when the war ended, several research laboratories and independent consulting companies were established. Interdisciplinary work with engineers began with the study of aircraft cockpits, radar and sonar displays, panel layouts, individual displays and controls, fire-control systems, and so on. Human factors groups were founded, grew, and proliferated in numerous military and industrial organizations. Many significant books were published and well received; some were revised and published in later editions (see especially Chapanis *et al.*, 1949; Morgan *et al.*, 1963;‡ Gagné, 1963; Woodson and Conover, 1964; and Meister and Rabideau, 1965). The military released *design-criterion* documentation – guidance and specifications – which generally is evolving toward applicability across all departments of the Department of Defense.

* The term *applied experimental psychology* was an early synonym.

† Even before World War II, designers were concerned with simplifying the aircraft pilots' job. Information from such instruments as the artificial horizon, rate-of-turn indicator, altimeter, and directional gyro was integrated at a single point of observation and displayed on a cathode-ray tube (Anonymous, 1938).

‡ This so-called "Joint Services (Army-Navy-Air Force) Guide" is scheduled for release in an updated version.

Considerable progress in engineering psychology has been made, but the route has not always been clear, the road often rough, and much remains to be done by imaginative, aggressive people interested in specializing in the field. For example, there is considerable confusion in terminology. Engineering psychology and human factors are *not* synonymous: Some 40 percent of people who consider themselves to be human factors experts are *not* psychologists. Further, in practice it is easy to confuse engineering psychology with human engineering, which as we shall see is a single aspect of human factors. Also, in practice, human engineering has been much more subsystem-, even modular-oriented (we should say subsystem- or modular-limited) than should be the case. Then there is a whole group of people who variously call themselves training experts and training directors, who have their own society, the *American Society of Training Directors*, and who may have little association with human factors people. The same is true of the aerospace medicine specialists and the *Aerospace Medical Association*. Finally, we must consider our colleagues in Europe whose specialty, ergonomics, entails both the work of human engineers in the United States and things like work measurement (see, for example, Murrell, 1965). For these reasons, we will use the terms *human factors scientist* and *human factors psychologist* to indicate the expert, psychologist and otherwise, who is concerned with all the interacting elements of the personnel subsystem discussed in the next section. However, he is usually also a specialist in one area – for example, engineering psychology or anthropometry. With regard to psychology in the development of a *given* system, engineering psychology, training psychology, and personnel psychology might be thought of as specialties of human factors psychology. When the human factors psychologist begins to generalize across systems at all levels and to work toward development of basic theories and methods of application, he becomes a *systems psychologist*.

Even more crucial than semantic problems has been that of securing the rightful place of systems psychology among the other sciences and establishing the practical value of its findings. The early work cited above made good sense to most observers, including military managers, and after 1957, contractual requirements, particularly within the Air Force "family", forced the inclusion of human factors considerations – and the hiring of human factors specialists! Release of design-criterion documentation aided this effort immensely. Yet the human factors man, as a human engineer, usually found himself doing what became known as "knob-and-dial" work, minutiae such as indicating the color coding of controls. Design was already frozen when he came into the picture, and isolated from the planning phase, he was powerless to alter situations that, according to his expertise, clearly violated sound principles relating to human capabilities and limitations. At the same time, in other parts of the organization, other human factors specialists were working, usually with great replication of effort, on training requirements, plans, and programs; manpower determinations; and test and evaluation. Appreciation of human factors contributions was often quite perfunctory. Many corporations, both profit and not-for-profit, employed thousands of engineers, but at most a few human factors workers.

Clearly, there was a need both to integrate human factors efforts and to bring this integrated activity at least a couple of years "upstream" into the problem-definition, conceptualization, and planning stages of the system. Coupled with this management shift was the preeminent need to convince high-level decision makers in industrial organizations, the military, and government what human factors and psychology can do.

The establishment of the personnel subsystem concept and program was a step of fundamental importance in meeting the first two needs. Meeting the last need is a matter of (1) diversification of effort; (2) taking a good look at ourselves and where we are going; (3) developing a basic body of theory and methodology, including, but not limited to, quantified methodology; and (4) education, training, and selling ourselves. Human factors scientists now participate at the several stages in the development of many different kinds of systems: weapons and nonweapons; aerospace, ground-based, and undersea; governmental and commercial. They study problems as varied as those involving communication with computers, automobile safety, telephone-user preferences, and aerospace pilot models. For a review of human factors activities up to the mid 1960s, see Lindgren (1966a, 1966b).

The personnel subsystem: a framework for systems management

The importance of the total systems approach, involving development of the appropriate subsystems in *parallel*, is now widely recognized. Thus, a human or crew or personnel subsystem can be recognized and defined, and planned and designed in relation to the structure, power, electronic, environmental control, and other subsystems. Gone are the days, hopefully forever, when aircraft are delivered with no (trained) crews; or costly retrofits are required to make the aircraft or ground system operable or safe.

Systems interactions *within* human factors must also be

recognized. The relationships among oxygen partial pressure breathing requirements of Apollo astronauts, the flammability of materials and consequent degradation of safety, the design of the space suit, and the design of the escape hatch have been mentioned. Similarly, there is a clearly recognizable tradeoff among human engineering, training, and personnel selection. The better human engineered a system, the easier and less specialized the training and the more typical the crew member chosen. For example, flexibility in personnel assignment is reduced by a lack of standardization in type and layout of equipment performing similar or identical functions in satellite tracking stations. And placement of some controls in the navigator's position of certain models of the B-52 manned bomber appear to require the arm reach of an orangutan, an Air Force (personnel) Specialty Code hard to fill!

To manage the integrated development of human factors both internally and in relation to other efforts such as reliability engineering, civil engineering, and equipment design, and in the overall context of systems management, the Air Force (about 1960) defined the personnel subsystem (PS) program. PS is a time-phased program involving management, analysis, design, selection, training, and test and evaluation.* It emphasizes man's capabilities and limitations, and their effects on system performance, from the earliest phases of consideration of a (possible) system, through the conceptual, definition, acquisition, and operational phases. Even an obsolescent or senescent system can provide general concepts and specific performance data for incorporation into a new-generation system.

The personnel subsystem concept involves definition of a number of so-called *elements*, which can be interpreted roughly as subfields within human factors and aggregates of the subfields. The number of these elements changes with experience. The 14 defined in Table 5.3 are now in the process of being integrated into a more manageable number; this involves some change in nomenclature. For example, many of the PS elements deal with training and could be grouped together for purposes of generalization. However, it should be noted that the listing in Table 5.3 is to some extent sequential. Thus, for the most part, analysis precedes design and the determination of types and numbers of personnel or training requirements and plans. The personnel equipment data can be thought of as prerequisite to human engineering, QQPRI, and so forth. Similarly, training concepts are basic to the preparation of training

---

* The term *effectiveness engineering* has been utilized to describe an integrated approach to human factors, maintainability, reliability, safety, cost analysis, and value engineering.

Table 5.3 Personnel subsystem elements (Prepared from text in Headquarters Air Force Systems Command, 1967)

---

1. *Personnel equipment data* (*PED*). Centrally controlled, multilevel, multisource, analytic data on personnel interactions with equipment, environments, etc.
2. *Human engineering.* Application of knowledge of man's capabilities and limitations relative to equipment, facilities, environments, jobs, procedures, computer programs, and performance aids, to achieve optimum safety, comfort, and effectiveness compatible with system requirements
3. *Life support.* Application of physiological, anthropometric, and psychological principles to ensure man's integrity, health, safety, and comfort
4. *Qualitative and quantitative personnel requirements information* (*QQPRI*). Determination of the kinds and numbers of persons required in the system for operating, maintaining, controlling, etc.
5. *Trained personnel requirements.* List of personnel requiring system-specific training to support the system through the acquisition phase
6. *Training concepts.* Early planning based on estimates of Air Training Command and of the User Command
7. *Manpower authorizations.* Early allocations required for advanced planning
8. *System manning and trained personnel requirements.* Specialized planning produced for higher headquarters when special manpower problems are anticipated
9. *Training equipment planning information.* Recommendations on the types and quantities of training equipment required
10. *Training equipment development.* Procedures for developing and producing training equipment
11. *Training facilities.* Real estate and buildings used exclusively for training
12. *Technical publications.* Development of manuals to support operations, maintenance, and training
13. *Training plans.* Methods and schedules to effect training
14. *Personnel subsystem test and evaluation* (*PST&E*). Coordinated subsystem and system testing under preoperational conditions

---

plans. Note, however, that system development is usually *iterative*: Test and evaluation data may modify the original requirements and initial design.

Summary and conclusions

This chapter has set the theme of the book.* The artificial systems with which we are primarily concerned lie along a continuum of different types, degrees, and relative directness of human participation. For convenience, we can designate four types of systems: *automatic, man–machine, sociotechnical,* and *social.* Man does participate as manager, planner, analyst, designer, production worker, operator, controller, maintainer, supervisor, evaluator, and user. In any given position, error, accident, or inefficiency may occur. A consideration of man's capabilities and limitations thus is critical to successful system operation.

It is tempting to seek guidance in the traditional fields of psychology: perception, intelligence, learning, motivation, and so on. To an extent we have done so, as reflected in some of the chapter titles, but this is an insufficient model. It can be embellished by viewing man as a system constituent, which at a given time and in a given environmental context acts on, changes, or processes something – at the level of psychology, usually information, but also energy or materials.

* [*Systems Psychology,* Ed.]

As a system constituent, man modifies and is modified by his fellow constituents – the machines, other men, and facilities; by the communicative connections among these constituents; and by the general ambiance. When the outside forces – physical, chemical, biological, and social – exceed a tolerance level set at the moment within the man, or these forces interact with internal psychological forces to reduce that tolerance, we can say that *stress* has occurred. Associated with stress can be severely degraded performance, both on specific tasks and in terms of general efficiency. In all cases, inputs to the system constituent are converted somehow into outputs. The search for the appropriate transfer functions is one of our ongoing responsibilities; therefore, the S–O–R paradigm can be added to the model for the book and is accordingly reflected in the chapter organization.

It is probably futile for psychology to proceed by itself apart from integration within the mainstream of science and technology. The body of a science can be an ephemeral thing. This does not mean aping the terminology of physics, chemistry, biology – or of information theory! Sciences can mutually reinforce themselves, each science both giving specifics and receiving generalities. General systems theory, cybernetics, and bionics are attempts toward this mutual support. Progress in psychology should follow from using the generally applicable systems concepts and methods. Otherwise, there is a formidable communications barrier in trying to translate psychological terms into, for example, engineering terms; there is a real danger in being left by the wayside. We have defined a new field, *systems psychology*, because there is no appropriate term within psychology, and because specialties like engineering psychology, industrial psychology, and human factors have been limited in practice. Systems psychology is necessary because of the shifting boundaries of knowledge; because all new science and technology *must* be interdisciplinary; and because of the hierarchical nature, complexity, and generalizability of our effort. Systems psychology, a branch of systems science, then, provides the theoretical framework of our effort.

Burgeoning almost completely apart from the somewhat erratic developments of systems theory, the pragmatic advances of systems analysis, systems engineering, and systems management have shaken our society to its roots. Psychology itself has found expression in human factors. Since World War II, great progress has been made, but major battles remain to be won. A major advance has been the development of the personnel subsystem concept and program within systems engineering and management. This concept also is reflected in the chapter structure of this book.

A major problem still derives from the self-identity of psychology and of human factors; their direction, orientation, and extension; and general education in their practical usefulness. When a systems approach incorporating psychological factors is *not* followed in design and management, literally *terrible* things can result at worst, frustrating and costly things at best. We can be of greatest service to our organization, our society, our nation, and our world by developing our theory, coalescing our methods, assuming a large-scale perspective of problems, and *aggressively* attacking these problems. It's an exciting world, offering adventure at each step. You, our young champion, are a far cry from the poor, jaded chap who entered this chapter.

References and bibliography

Anonymous (1938) "Simplifying the Pilot's Task", *Scientific American*, December, 159(6), 308.

Anonymous (1968a) "Use of Existing Spares Urged for Early Nimbus Replacement", *Aviation Week and Space Technology*, May 27, 88(22), 31.

Anonymous (1968b) "Nimbus Abort Laid to Gyro Misalignment", *Aviation Week and Space Technology*, Aug. 19, 89(8), 17.

Ashby, W. R. (1960) *Design for a Brain*, New York: Wiley.

Boulding, K. E. (1956) "General Systems Theory: The Skeleton of Science", *Management Science*, April 2, 197–208.

Boulding, K. E. (1964) "General Systems as a Point of View", in Mesarovic, M. D. (ed.), *Views on General Systems Theory*, Proceedings of Second Systems Symposium at Case Institute of Technology, New York: Wiley.

Butsch, L. M. and H. L. Oestreicher (Cochairmen) (1964) *1963 Bionics Symposium: Information Processing by Living Organisms and Machines*, Wright-Patterson AFB, Ohio: Aeronautical Systems Division, Technical Report ASD-TDR-63-946, March.

Carter, L. J. (1968) "The McNamara Legacy: A Revealing Case History – Death of the B-70", *Science*, Feb. 23, 159(3817), 859–63.

Christensen, J. M. (1964) *The Emerging Role of Engineering Psychology*, Wright-Patterson AFB, Ohio: Aerospace Medical Research Laboratories, Technical Report AMRL TR-64-88, September.

Chapanis, A., *et al.* (1949) *Applied Experimental Psychology: Human Factors in Engineering Design*, New York: Wiley.

Coan, R. W. (1968) "Dimensions of Psychological Theory", *American Psychologist*, 23(10), 715–22.

Fein, L. (1961) "The Computer-Related Sciences (Synnoetics) at a University in the Year 1975", *American Scientist*, June, 49(2), 149–68.

Ferguson, J. (1965) "Military Electronic Systems for Command and Control", *IEEE Transactions on Military Electronics*, April, MIL-9(2), 80–7.

Friedlander, G. D. (1966) "The Northeast Power Failure – A Blanket of Darkness", *IEEE Spectrum*, 3(2), 54–73.

Gagné, R. M. (ed.) (1963) *Psychological Principles in System Development*, New York: Holt, Rinehart and Winston.

Gelbwaks, N. L. (1967) "AFSCM 375-5 As a Methodology for System Engineering", *IEEE Transactions on Systems Science and Cybernetics*, June, SSC-3(1), 6–10.

Gérardin, L. (1968) *Bionics*, New York: McGraw-Hill.

Gilmore, J. S., *et al.* (1967) *Defense Systems Resources in the Civil Sector: An Evolving Approach, an Uncertain Market*, Washington, D.C.: U.S. Arms Control and Disarmament Agency, Paper E-103, July.

Goslin, D. A. (1968) "Standardized Ability Tests and Testing", *Science*, Feb. 23, 159(3817), 851–5.

Grether, W. F. (1968) "Engineering Psychology in the United States", *American Psychologist*, 23(10), 743–51.

Hall, A. D. and R. E. Fagen (1956) "Definition of System", in Bertalanffy, L. von and Rapoport, A. (eds.), *General Systems Yearbook of the Society for the Advancement of General Systems Theory*, I, 18–28.

Hall, A. D. (1966) "The Present Status and Trends in Systems Engineering", *IEEE Transactions on Systems Science and Cybernetics*, August, SSC-2(1), 1–2.

Headquarters Air Force Systems Command (1967) *Handbook of Instructions for Aerospace Personnel Subsystems Design*, Andrews AFB, Washington, D.C.: AFSCM 80–3.

Headquarters Air Force Systems Command (1969) *Personnel Subsystems*, Andrews AFB, Washington, D.C.: AFSC DH 1–3.

Israel, D. R. (1965) *System Design and Engineering for Real-Time Military Data Processing Systems*, Bedford, Mass.: Electronic Systems Division, Technical Report ESD-TDR 64-168, January (AD 610 392*).

Johnson, R. A., *et al.* (1967) *The Theory and Management of Systems*, New York: McGraw-Hill.

Jones, R. W. and J. S. Gray (1963) "System Theory and Physiological Processes", *Science*, May· 3, 140(3566), 461–6.

Kalisch, R. B. (1968) "The Locomotion Quadruped", *OAR Research Review*, VII(8), 4–5.

Leavitt, H. J. (1964) *Managerial Psychology* (2nd ed.), Chicago: The University of Chicago Press.

Leavitt, H. J. and L. R. Pondy (eds.) (1964) *Readings in Managerial Psychology*, Chicago: The University of Chicago Press.

Lettvin, J. Y., *et al.* (1959) "What the Frog's Eye Tells the Frog's Brain", *Proceedings of the IRE*, 47(11), 1940–51.

Lindgren, N. (1966a) "Human Factors in Engineering: Part I – Man in the Man-Made Environment", *IEEE Spectrum*, 3(3), 132–9.

Lindgren, N. (1966b) "Human Factors in Engineering: Part II – Advanced Man–Machine Systems and Concepts", *IEEE Spectrum*, 3(4), 62–72.

Lindgren, N. (1968) "Purposive Systems: The Edge of Knowledge", *IEEE Spectrum*, 5(4), 89–100.

Lockard, R. B. (1968) "The Albino Rat: A Defensible Choice of a Bad Habit?", *American Psychologist*, 23(10), 734–42.

Meister, D. and G. F. Rabideau (1965) *Human Factors Evaluation in System Development*, New York: Wiley.

Morgan, C. T., *et al.* (eds.) (1963) *Human Engineering Guide to Equipment Design*, New York: McGraw-Hill.

Murphy, C. S. (Chairman) (1966) "Crew Monitoring Cited in 727 Crash (Civil Aeronautics Board Accident Investigation Report)", *Aviation Week and Space Technology*, Oct. 24, 95–122.

* Defense Documentation Center (DDC) Acquisition Number.

Murphy, C. S. (Chairman) (1967a) "Collision-Course Illusion Cited in Accident (CAB Accident Investigation Report)", *Aviation Week and Space Technology*, Jan. 2, 86(1), 84–98.

Murphy, C. S. (Chairman) (1967b) "Optical Illusion Cited as Cause of Collision (CAB Accident Investigation Report)", *Aviation Week and Space Technology*, Jan. 9, 86(2), 81–97.

Murrell, K. F. H. (1965) *Human Performance in Industry*, New York: Reinhold.

Newell, A. and H. A. Simon (1961) *Computer Simulation of Human Thinking*, Santa Monica, Calif.: The RAND Corporation Paper, P-2276, April 20.

Normyle, W. J. (1968) "Nimbus B to Test New Weather Sensors", *Aviation Week and Space Technology*, May 6, 88(19), 71–9.

Pauling, L. (1968) "Orthomolecular Psychiatry", *Science*, April 19, 160(3825), 265–71.

Quade, E. S. (1966) *Some Problems Associated with Systems Analysis*, Santa Monica, Calif.: The RAND Corporation Paper, P-3391, June (AD 634 375).

Reichardt, W. (1961) "Autocorrelation, a Principle for the Evaluation of Sensory Information by the Central Nervous System", in Rosenblith, W. A. (ed.), *Sensory Communication*, 303–17, M.I.T. Press and Wiley.

Rosenblatt, F. (1958) "The Perceptron: A Probabilistic Model for Information Storage and Organization in the Brain", *Psychological Review;* November, 65(6), 386–408.

Rowe, W. D. (1965) "Why Systems Science and Cybernetics?", *IEEE Transactions on Systems Science and Cybernetics*, November, SSC-1(1), 2–3.

Schoderbek, P. P. (ed.) (1967) *Management Systems: A Book of Readings*, New York: Wiley.

Simon, H. A. (1961) *Modeling Human Mental Processes*, Santa Monica, Calif.: The RAND Corporation Paper, P-2221, February.

Steele, J. E. (Chairman) (1960) *Bionics Symposium: Living Prototypes – The Key to New Technology*. Wright-Patterson AFB, Ohio: Wright Air Development Division, Technical Report 60-600, December.

Swanson, R. W. (1968) "Automata in Motion", *OAR Research Review*, VII(10), 12–13.

Thomas, B. K., Jr (1968) "Apollo 6 Wiring Flaw Found as Next Mission Is Studied", *Aviation Week and Space Technology*, April 15, 88(16), 28–9.

van Bergéijk, W. A. (1960) "Nomenclature of Devices Which Simulate Biological Functions", *Science*, Oct. 28, 132(3435), 1248–9.

van Bergéijk, W. A. and L. D. Harman (1960) "What Good Are Artificial Neurons?", *Bionics Symposium: Living Prototypes – The Key to New Technology*, Wright-Patterson AFB, Ohio: Wright Air Development Division, Technical Report 60-600, December, 395–406.

von Bertalanffy, L. (1956) "General Systems Theory", *General Systems Yearbook of the Society for the Advancement of General Systems Theory*, I, 1–10.

White, V. (1963) "A Multiple Satellite Real-Time Control Network", *IEEE Transactions on Military Electronics*, October, MIL-7(4), 285–95.

Wiener, N. (1948) *Cybernetics, or Control and Communication in the Animal and the Machine*, New York: Wiley.

Wilson, W. E. (1965) *Concepts of Engineering System Design*, New York: McGraw-Hill.

Woodson, W. E. and D. W. Conover (1964) *Human Engineering Guide for Equipment Designers* (2nd ed.), Berkeley, Calif.: University of California Press.

Young, O. R. (1964) "A Survey of General Systems Theory", in von Bertalanffy, L. and Rapoport, A. (eds.), *General Systems Yearbook of the Society for General Systems Research*, IX, 61–80.

Yovits, M. C., *et al.* (eds.) (1962) *Self-Organizing Systems 1962*, Washington, D.C.: Spartan Books.

6 Man-machine systems
by W. T. Singleton

1 Introduction

It would be reasonable to introduce a book on systems by explaining what the term means, but this is not so easy to do formally. One problem is that a definition requires that something is described in more fundamental terms, but there are very few concepts which are more fundamental than that of a system. The physicist has a similar difficulty when he tries to explain what he means by energy; he usually resorts to explaining energy in terms of power and then completes the tautological circle by explaining power in terms of energy. His problem is that energy is a quite fundamental idea, analogous to an axiom in mathematics; one just has to accept it and synthesize other ideas and explanations from it. Another problem is that the term "system" has more than one meaning. According to the Oxford English Dictionary it has three: first, a set of connected things, for example, the solar system, a body of knowledge or a doctrine; secondly, a religious system and an orderly arrangement; and thirdly, a botanical classification system. Within this book* the first of these three will be used.

If we grant also that the physicist has developed more fundamental ideas than the ones we are going to use we can try to explain what is meant by a system in terms of basic physical ideas such as time, energy and information. A system is a set of related objects. "Related" implies that information and energy are exchanged or shared between them, this in turn implies that they change in time. To put it another way, all important systems are dynamic; there are static systems but they do not come within the scope of our study, e.g., a brick wall is a system but not a very interesting one. An "object" is a point of interference with energy, it is located and identified by the sense organs. For these to function, the object must interfere in some characteristic way with energy thereby generating information, for example when light is reflected.

* [i.e., *Man–Machine Systems*, Ed.]

It is tempting also to propose that a system must have an *objective*, that is, a purpose or a reason for existence. This brings us to the first subdivision of systems: there are *natural systems* and there are *man-made systems*. Natural systems obviously do not have objectives; it is not profitable to discuss the reason for the existence of the solar system or the purpose of a tree or the objective of a river.

An *engineer* is a person who designs or constructs. Systems-engineering, then, is concerned with man-made systems although we must add the proviso that these man-made systems are constructed from components which have their origins in natural systems. Sometimes indeed the natural systems are transferred intact into man-made systems. The most general example of this is the human operator, a natural system but a necessary component of almost all man-made systems. It is sometimes argued that systems engineering is a new name for the traditional general engineer. This somewhat parochial view accepts that the tendency for engineers to become more specialized and therefore narrower may have gone too far. Systems engineering is an attempt to reverse this trend and to re-emphasize that good design requires a broad but balanced approach with weighted consideration of the range of all possible alternatives to the solution of particular problems, with adequate attention to the ways in which the solution of one problem will interact with potential solutions of other design problems within the system. This is a parochial view, valid as far as it goes but it goes nowhere near far enough. Design can no longer be confined within the limits set by the traditional engineering professions.

The change from thinking about machine design to thinking about systems design is not a gradual evolution but a discontinuity; an abrupt change in basic philosophy comparable to the change which occurred when the engineer took over design problems from the blacksmith and carpenter. The original approach to making machines involved a personal experience of the task for which the machine was required and an intuitive knowledge of the relevant properties of materials – a "feel" for wood and metal. The machine was constructed from the materials by a process of trial and error. As the ambitions of machine makers increased it gradually became apparent that these skills were inadequate. A systematic numerical knowledge of materials and power sources emerged, and techniques were developed for trying ideas without using the real materials, e.g., the scale drawing. The engineer had arrived. Notice that the arrival of the specialist created at least one undesirable tendency, the designer was no longer necessarily a user or even a maker; this created a potentiality for communication failure. The machine became an end in itself with the needs of the user and the requirements of the operator relegated to the role of tiresome unquantifiable constraints. The timing of this change was different in different industries, but the turn of this century is a reasonable average point. The era of pure engineering only lasted for about half a century. The hardware-centred approach was perhaps a necessary phase to provide the stimulus for the development of technology based on the physical sciences but it was only a temporary one. The change to systems engineering ended the era almost as suddenly as it began. As machines have got more and more complex there has been a switch to this new approach which has three characteristics: a consideration of function independently of mechanisms, a detailed attention to objectives and a consideration of man as an integral part of the system. It is this last point, of course, which justified the involvement of the human scientists in problems of design.

Table 6.1 Characteristics of systems thinking

Cause	Characteristics	Consequence
Development of varieties of ways of carrying out the same activity	Consideration of functions independently of mechanisms	Improved systematic choice between alternative solutions
Increased complexity of new systems. Feasibility of system performance prediction	Detailed attention to objectives	Fewer expensive design errors. Reduced frequency and magnitude of modifications
Hardware performance becoming comparable with, and superior to, human performance	Consideration of man as an integral part of the system	Improvement of system performance by improving human performance

To understand the emergence of systems thinking it is useful to identify the factors which have made it possible and necessary (Table 6.1). The underlying cause is the successful development of engineering technology. The engineer has not only solved problems, he has in many cases provided a whole variety of ways of solving a given problem. This aspect has given rise to the need for functional thinking. If the only engine available is a steam engine then there is no restriction in thinking about a design problem with a steam engine in mind as the prime mover. When, however, there are electric motors, air motors, hydraulic motors, petrol engines, diesel engines, etc., available, it increases versatility to do the initial thinking about a design problem in functional terms such as prime movers and power sources. Too early a switch to thinking in physical terms such as electric motors may unnecessarily restrict the solution of the problem.

As technology has developed and the complexity of products has increased, the cost of both the design process and the product has increased correspondingly. One has to be increasingly careful in arriving at design decisions on what the objectives of the product are and on exactly how they are to be met. For example, in designing a simple dynamo, one can afford to be relatively vague about what the ultimate performance will be and about what kind of materials and sizes to use for which components, but in designing a nuclear power station this kind of waiting to see simply will not do; one has to know exactly what the objectives are as well as when and how they will be achieved. It is only possible to embark on a very ambitious design such as nuclear power stations when one can predict with confidence the performance of the product before it is produced.

Another consequence of successful technology is that the performance and needs of the operator become an important set of variables. When machines are primitive, no one worries about the operator, any discomfort is more than compensated for by the excitement of a new machine and the limits on the system performance are set by the mechanisms. Eventually the action of the mechanism gets faster or more reliable than the reaction of the operator; further improvements in system performance are now best achieved by studies of the operator rather than more studies of the mechanism. For example, in the early days of the motor car the problems are to do with hardware, the designer is struggling to develop an engine that does not fail every few miles and a suspension which does not break on every hole in the road. The one who has the greatest success in these matters sells the most motor cars. Eventually the technology does develop. Engines and suspensions all become highly reliable, there is nothing to choose between the various products from this point of view. The successful designer is now the man who switches his attention to the comfort of seats, the positions of controls, effective visibility and so on, in general the human operator problems. This is where there is now scope for improvement and the possibility of doing better than one's competitors. The same transition occurs in relation to safety aspects of cars. In the early days it is a problem of better brakes and more reliable steering mechanisms. When these problems have been successfully overcome, safety becomes a problem of human judgements and attitudes.

All these are internal factors within the professions associated with designing and making things. There are also external aspects of the designer himself as a human operator and the broader impact on the whole society now pervaded by technology.

Technology has gone through an explosive development phase in the last century. The initiation of this phase depended largely on one factor which is usually forgotten, the productivity of farmworkers. The primary condition of survival is adequate nutrition. Mankind has been held back because for most of human history a worker could only generate enough food to feed himself and his family. As the productivity of farmworkers increased it became possible to release a few active people from the task of generating food and providing the related protection from the environment. A few of these people devoted their energies to the design and construction of machines. When this happened we embarked on a process of development with positive feedback. The machines increased the productivity of agriculture still further, freeing even more people to think about even more machines. The stage was then set for exponential growth. In this phase at least, it seemed that a man plus a more elaborate machine produces sufficiently more to reward the investor in the machine, to pay for it and still increase the rewards of the operator. There have to be other developments in parallel such as legal, fiscal and administrative systems, but all of these are possible with increased reservoirs of spare worker capacity. It seems that the more one spends the more one has to spend, the more knowledge advances the faster it advances. Eventually there has to be either disintegration or a levelling of the growth curves. These apparently exponential curves must turn out to be the early parts of sigmoid curves. In fact there are some signs that this is now happening. The underlying factor which is now causing some levelling-off seems

to be the rate at which individuals either can change or are prepared to change. Within the technological world these strains have been apparent now for several decades. There is a limit on the rate at which an individual can learn and a ceiling on how much he can know. At the scientific level research workers have become more and more specialized to the point which is proving self-defeating. For example, too much psychology makes one become a specialist within a narrow part of psychology but then, it turns out that to make progress one needs to know not only psychology, but also physiology and physics and engineering. Thus the individual psychologist cannot concentrate on thinking productively about psychology because he does not have the relevant knowledge of other related disciplines. If he spends his time learning the related disciplines he has no time to think about psychology; whether he does one or the other he certainly does not have time to keep up to date with all the work of the other psychologists. Inevitably the rate of advancement of real knowledge decreases.

There is a corresponding braking factor on technology. For the past century not only has technology advanced, but the rate of advance has increased. Thus we are off in another vicious circle. As knowledge advances systems get more complex. As systems become more complex they take longer to produce, but although they take longer to produce they become obsolete faster. In weapon systems and in aeronautics this process reached the absurd stage about a decade ago when systems were obsolete before they became operational. We are probably already through this phase. The VC10 will have a longer operational life than the Britannia basically because although people (airline passengers) were prepared to pay for the marginal improvement of the 1960s airliner over the 1950s airliner, they are not prepared to pay the much larger cost of the 1970s airliner over the 1960s airliner.

Nevertheless the designers are still trying to cope. The process was foreseen twenty years ago and it became very serious in the field of weapon systems (Singleton, 1971a). So much so that it became apparent that success in competition between nations depended on the development time for new systems. In an era of rapid technical change the competitor with the shortest development time is bound to win. The principle applies not only in military situations but also in industrial situations and it was the basic stimulus for the development of systems techniques. The broad aim is the faster development of better systems.

It may seem odd, at first sight, that there is no discussion of motivation within this book.* Given that systems princi-

* [i.e., *Man–Machine Systems, Ed.*]

ples depend on the concept of objectives or goals and it is recognized that these are set by people and that systems are steered towards them by people, it might seem reasonable to incorporate some discussion of the drive towards these goals; in other words to discuss morale, motivation and incentives. This is not included because this book is about man–machine interaction. To follow the argument that such design problems cannot be considered without looking at needs and drives would be to invite the corresponding arguments from the other end of the spectrum; that design problems cannot be considered without looking at engineering problems of mechanisms.

The systems approach is used in the context of human motivation. There are a variety of different approaches which are based on systems concepts (Emery, 1969). Man–machine systems philosophy has some common factors with other systems philosophies, notably the emphasis on objectives and the importance of interaction effects or context, but the unique characteristic is the emphasis on man–machine interaction. For this reason also there is no discussion of interactions between people. This is obviously involved in all kinds of system problems: designs are done by teams, every machine operator has a supervisor, there are many machines that require more than one operator and there are many systems which involve complex communication between operators as well as between men and machines. However, the man–man interface has different problems and different principles from the man–machine interface. These former aspects have been discussed by Brown (1954), Pym (1968) and Warr (1971).

In common with other system approaches, this book is not really about how to deal with a problem but rather how to separate, identify and approach problems. Even the middle section of the book, which is concerned with analysis, contains description only at the "what to do" rather than "how to do it" level. There are two reasons for this. First, systems theory is essentially relevant to the structuring of problems rather than their solution. Secondly, there are no formal procedures which can be described in detailed sequence which will solve a problem involving human behaviour. Any method, whether it involves observation, interview, survey or experiment, must have a high content of creativity applied by the investigator to the particular problem in hand. There are, of course, detailed standard procedures (Singleton, 1971b), but these are different from systems methodology which supplies a context for the procedure and they are never recipes which, if followed, will guarantee the right answer.

Having said what the book is not about it would be appropriate to conclude this section by repeating what it is about. It is to do with the design of work, on the assumption that work nowadays is never done by men, nor is it done by machines; it is always done by man–machine systems. The man–machine system has proved enormously successful because men and machines are so different, each compensates for the weaknesses of the other. There are therefore problems of deciding what men should do and what machines should do in the pursuit of any objective. This is what man–machine allocation of function is about. Again because they are so different there are inevitable problems of ensuring that men and machines communicate effectively. This is what the design of man–machine interfaces is about. The smooth efficient interaction of men and machines cannot be achieved entirely by design. Certain kinds of men are best for certain kinds of machine control and furthermore they need to learn in order to achieve the highest level of efficiency. This is what selection and training are about.

Human performance, as a designer or an operator, is so complex that specialized techniques are needed to identify and separate the various human functions. This is what systems methodology and analytical techniques are concerned with. The whole makes up an integrated package of human knowledge, developed almost entirely within the last twenty years, which ought to be known about by engineers, designers, psychologists and administrators. If they all knew something about it, they would at least be able to communicate with each other more successfully. They might thereby generate rather more mutual sympathy and perhaps even empathy.

2 Systems methodology

The purpose of the systems approach is twofold: to cope with increasingly complex systems designs and to reduce development times for new systems.

There are three aids to the solution of problems generated by sheer complexity: the clarification of objectives, the separation of functions from the means of achieving them and the structuring of the design process itself.

Objectives

The traditional directive to the design engineer is that he should do the best he can with a given sort of problem. Exactly what is the best attainable and what resources of time or money are needed to achieve it are evolved slowly by dialogue and iteration between the sponsor of the project and the designer. There are many products for which this is still the optimum design procedure but as technology has advanced there has been a parallel increase in rigour of approach from two points of view. On the one hand, more definite objectives are necessary because of the size of effort required. The more time and money that are involved the greater the pressure is to know what will finally emerge. On the other hand, more definite directives are acceptable to the designer because of his confidence in his own technology together with the degrees of freedom which it provides.

Details of objectives in the form of specifications are usually best provided in terms of inputs, outputs, times and costs. The different kinds of inputs and outputs must be specified, preferably in numerical terms, although ranges or probabilistic distributions often represent the greatest precision attainable. For example, no sponsor would ask for a new aircraft design which will fly as fast as possible with as long a range as possible. What happens is that high-density routes are identified, and this determines the required range, and an even number of trips within a 24-hour cycle fixes the speed. It is obviously not as simple as this; there are large numbers of constraints but the ones mentioned illustrate how an idea is refined to a specification before it is given to the designer. To take a less complex example, no sponsor would ask for a "good" domestic washing machine. He would first of all look at the size and rate of change of the market and at its current distribution between various competitors. He would then

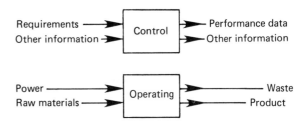

Figure 6.1 General double-block diagram of objectives.

look at the cost of advertising required to break into a given section of the market at a given level and would thus arrive at a fairly precise specification. In general the objectives stage provides the framework and the stimulus for two kinds of parallel studies: technical feasibility and market requirements.

Specifications are best presented in the form of double-block diagrams as shown in Figure 6.1. Every system has a control part which deals essentially with information and an operating part which deals essentially with things, stuff and power. Some applications of this diagram to particular systems are shown in Figure 6.2. These are only at the very general level, one stage beyond Figure 6.1. It is necessary to go to further stages in order to identify and separate all the inputs and outputs and to describe their ranges of acceptability.

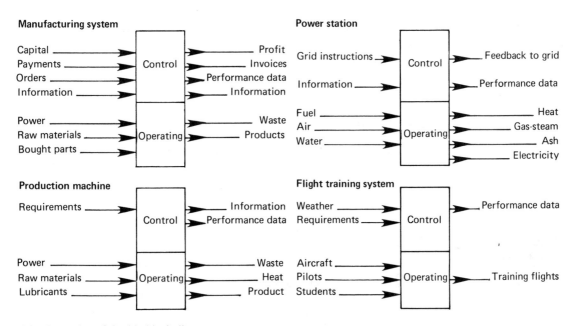

Figure 6.2 Examples of double-block diagrams.

Functions

A function is an activity or set of activities described strictly in terms of activities and not in terms of means of achieving them. For example, power generation is a function but a petrol engine is not, it is a means of achieving that function. Unfortunately most designers, particularly engineers, are not taught to think in functional terms. Their education and training is mainly in terms of physical mechanisms and it is extremely difficult to persuade them to think at the more abstract level of functions; there is an element of truth in the old slander that the mechanical engineer cannot understand anything unless he can screw it in a vice and hit it with a hammer. Electrical engineers are somewhat better perhaps because electricity itself is an abstract concept rather than a physical entity. Of course there is another side to the argument and the engineer can often, with justice, point to the limitations of industrial designers and others who propose solutions to design problems which cannot possibly be realized in physical terms. Clearly there is a need for both and for an optimum timing of the switching between thinking in physical terms and thinking in functional terms. A start at the functional level is more and more essential because of the increasing variety of ways in which a particular problem can be solved physically. Pose a problem to a mechanical engineer and he will come up with a mechanical solution; pose the same problem to a hydraulics engineer and he will arrive at a feasible solution in hydraulic terms. To avoid this it is useful to think initially in functional terms, thereby avoiding the pre-empting of the solution.

Thus, in principle, the system designer has mechanical, hydraulic, pneumatic, electrical, electronic, chemical and electrochemical methods and mechanisms at his disposal. To choose between them and to provide a common language through which all the specialists can communicate we need functional-type thinking. Incidentally the whole range of types of mechanism are used within the human operator which is the ultimate example of complex but extraordinarily effective heterogeneous design. The opposite extreme of insensitive mixing of mechanisms is still too common. In the machine-tool industry, for example, there are many basically mechanical devices with a bit of hydraulics or electrics obviously tagged on as an afterthought. It ought to be possible to avoid and to eliminate this kind of clumsy design by generating functional studies on the basis of which various physical solutions can be evaluated and integrated systematically. The psychologist usually has no great difficulty about thinking functionally since this is his raison d'être. All psychological concepts which are not also physiological are essentially functional. For design problems the role of the human operator within the system is also best arrived at from a functional analysis of required system activities.

3 The structure of the design process

Another inevitable consequence of the greater complexity of systems is that all separate design decisions become increasingly interactive and yet increasingly remote from the overall objectives of the system. Thus a structure for the design process itself is needed so that particular decision points can be perceived within the context of the whole process, and their consequences can also be more easily predicted. Perhaps most important, a structure will help to ensure that decisions are made in the optimum

Figure 6.3 Reduction of development times.

sequence or pattern. In order that such a structure should be general it must necessarily be phrased in rather global terms, but there are several levels at which this can be done. Perhaps the most general is that shown in Figure 6.3 where the whole design process for any system is summarized in just four blocks. This illustrates a number of fundamental points about design. For example, assuming that each block takes at least two years to achieve, it becomes clear why complex systems can take eight to ten years from initial conception to operational availability. The strategic thinking which led to the substitution of the process shown in Figure 6.3b for that in Figure 6.3a has been described elsewhere (Singleton, 1971a). It is obvious that the process shown in Figure 6.3b is inherently faster than that shown in Figure 6.3a. It does, however, make greater demands on the designers. First, it assumes that it is possible, from a specification, to make some systematic decisions about the functions to be performed by men and the functions to be performed by machines. Secondly, it assumes that it is possible to create the personnel subsystem without having the final hardware available as a basis for selection and training. Thirdly, it assumes that the separately created subsystems, personnel and hardware, can be successfully integrated. To redescribe these activities in systems terminology the assumptions are respectively that we know about allocation of function between man and machine, about off-line selection and training and about man–machine interface design.

The description of what we do know about these areas is the core of this book. Note that they are all essentially human factors or ergonomic problems for which a knowledge of psychology is at least as important as a knowledge of engineering. These problems exist and always have existed for every design. The difference in the systems approach is that they are recognized as fundamental problems which require systematic solutions. The engineering approach in the past has been to regard them possibly as important but certainly as diffuse, not subject to rigid analytical methods and generally best left to others rather than to engineers. The traditional solution to the allocation of function problem is to do what can be done by machines and just leave the rest as a kind of literally indescribable remainder for the human operator. There is a case for this approach but it was stronger when hardware performance was so poor generally that the human operator could always be relied on to compensate for and to supplement the machine. It is an unfortunate fact of history that selection and training have developed independently of design problems. They are difficult enough for known machines

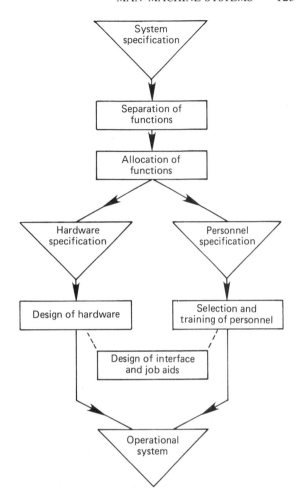

Figure 6.4 The systems design process.

and known tasks and it is only in very recent years that techniques have developed for task synthesis and extrapolation to skill descriptions. There have been associated developments in simulation, task training and team training so that it is now practicable to conceive of the development of the personnel subsystem in a concurrent rather than a sequential phase to the hardware development. Interface design has also developed beyond the stage of evolution by experience, at least for the lower levels of skilled operator. Thus, just as a systems approach is not necessary until technology has developed from the physical sciences, it is equally not feasible until other technologies of training and interface design have developed from the human sciences. Interface design is itself a particular aspect of total work-space design which also includes studies of environmental problems.

The total design process can be described as shown in Figure 6.4. It must be conceded at once that the methodology and techniques along the personnel line are nowhere near as precise as those along the hardware line, but the design decisions are at least of equal importance.

For all these diagrams feedback loops have been omitted. They obviously exist since designing remains an iterative and not a serial process. The interactions take place at all stages and not simply through the whole process. One does not merely work through to the product and then reverse the specification in the light of user experience. This remains the crucial final interaction but it is wasteful, especially for large systems. Effective interaction takes place at all stages and all levels through the design process; this is one way in which the systems philosophy differs in degree rather than in kind from more traditional approaches.

One general difficulty about translating the systems philosophy into practice is in the identification of the boundaries of the system under consideration. The origin of this problem is in the inherent hierarchical nature of systems. Every system is made up of other systems and is itself a component of a larger system. It is too easy in designing one system to complain about the restraints imposed by the larger system; for example, in designing a production system it is virtually standard to point out that the whole problem would be so much easier if only the marketing policy could be changed. It always seems easier to tackle the larger problem and the systems approach encourages this tendency. Sometimes it reveals valuable insights and at other times it merely confuses the issue. For example, in designing a motor car it might in principle be helpful to consider that this is not necessarily the optimum means of transport, but more often, especially if one is employed by the design department of a car manufacturing company, such thoughts are a distracting irrelevance.

It is of some help to recognize that, as a design problem, every system is somewhere in the hierarchy between the simplest man–machine (one man plus elementary aids) and the whole world. In designing the simple man–machine, the problems of the world are only marginally involved; equally in the design of the world the problems of the simple man–machine are only marginally involved. For a given design a trio is under consideration: the system, its parent system and its subsystems. In thinking about that system the designer must consider but must not get too involved in either the parent system or the subsystems. There are of course designers for whom these subsystems become the system and the system becomes the parent system. The zone of critical interest for a particular designer at a particular time must be kept in focus while recognizing that the total hierarchy exists.

Throughout this chapter most of the examples have been taken from man–machine systems where the design problems are clearly to do with mechanisms and tasks. Most people find this the easiest way to perceive the meaning of the systems approach. There are, of course, other kinds of systems in which there may be little hardware and where procedures rather than men and machines are the dominant design problem. However, there is one set of problems common to all system designs, the problems of the people associated with that system, either as operators or users. Within the operators there are three categories: those primarily concerned with the setting-up aspects, the operating aspects and the maintenance aspects. Again it is misleading and over-simplifying to conceive of the human operator as concerned with on-line control. Automation removes this particular set of human functions but it does not remove the human factor problems of setting-up and maintenance.

Here we are concerned with systems as systems involving men, machines and procedures. These separate categories are each important in their own right and warrant the attention of separate specialists. The remainder of the book is concerned mainly with the human factors aspects, the people problems of systems design.

4   Separation of functions
Limitations of physical thinking
Functional thinking has been developed to compensate for the limitations of thinking in terms of physical entities. This latter is essentially conservative or convergent and it is also limited in range of comprehension.

The conservative aspect is best described by a number of examples which illustrate three different, although related, phenomena. First, the range of possible solutions is restricted to those encompassed by the particular kind of physical components. For example, one part of a car ignition system has, until recently, always been thought of as a mechanical distributor – a metal wiper rotating round a number of contacts corresponding to the number of cylinders. It requires a bit of functional thinking to escape from this concept and to consider electronic methods of generating a sequence of sparks at varying speeds. Second, there is a tendency to innovate simply by change of scale rather than of method. For example, thinking about the principle of earth moving in terms of a spade shovelling inevitably leads to the design of a drag-line which is essentially a giant shovel pulled by wires and pulleys instead of by tendons and joints. One has to think functionally of general ideas such as the possibility of suspending the earth in water and pumping it away. Thirdly, it is difficult, by physical thinking, to arrive at fundamental changes of method. For example, for half a century or more shoe-making machinery was designed on the principle of imitating the way the cobbler worked; this resulted in the most extraordinarily complicated mechanical devices for gripping a sole on to a last, putting tacks in the right position and hammering them home. Thinking in terms of the function of attaching a sole to an upper results in the development of appropriate adhesives and of welding techniques.

The problem of range of comprehension obviously becomes increasingly serious as machines get more complex. For example, it is possible to discover how a steam engine works by tracing the flow of heat, steam and water, and studying the relative timing of valves and the movements of the mechanical parts. This physical tracing technique will not work for a computer. The human brain cannot comprehend what is happening by looking simultaneously at all the different flows of current or potential changes in all the wires. The only way to understand what a computer is doing as a whole is to think in terms of inputs, outputs, arithmetic units, stores, data, programs, and so on. All of these are functional terms. Of course it is possible, having identified the functional units, to concentrate on one relatively very small part of the whole and then trace what is happening in electrical or mechanical terminology.

Both to facilitate comprehension and to stimulate flexibility of innovation we need to conceptualize systems at a more and more abstract or symbolic level. In particular it is necessary to separate the functional concept of a system from its physical realization; that is, to contemplate what it does as an issue quite separate from how it does it physi-

cally. Thus, one of the basic and early steps in the system design process is to separate out the functions required to achieve the overall objectives and only later to translate these functions into physical processes. The technique for both of these steps, identifying functions and switching from functional to physical units, is the block diagram. The power and the universality of the block diagram has even led to the definition of the system designer as a man who draws block diagrams.

Advantages of block diagrams

The conceptual advantage of block diagrams is the ease with which the meaning of the separate blocks can shift up and down any scale of generality or complexity and across the conceptually difficult borderline between functional and physical entities. There are also very important practical advantages of the technique; it is possible to generate and display such diagrams on paper, blackboards, slides, and so on.

The block diagram is an elegant technique which facilitates design because it has properties which match the needs of the human operator in thinking about a design problem. Returning to the systems design process, the designer must form a concept of some system and this system, by definition, is an assembly of components related by a common purpose. Because of the limitations of his short-term memory and internal display system, the designer can only perceive a large-scale system as a whole by condensing it into a small number of complex parts, and equally he cannot comprehend these parts without subdividing them into assemblies of even smaller parts. In other words, to think about a system of any size the designer must be able to shift rapidly up and down a hierarchy of building blocks. This technique avoids the limitations of his internal mental capacities already mentioned. One reasonable analogy of this process is the way in which a microscopist copes with the limitations of a fixed-

Figure 6.5 Four-block diagrams of the human operator.

size viewing field. By reducing magnification he can shift from looking in detail at a small part of the total field to look at the total field in much less detail. For a particular purpose at a particular time he selects the appropriate compromise between the general broad view and the detailed narrow view. The analogy is not exact because the microscopist only shifts along one dimension – magnification; the block diagram provides several dimensions – physical–functional shifts, size shifts, complexity shifts, abstraction shifts and inversions.

The problem of inversions is illustrated in Figure 6.5. The lower half of the figure is a functional diagram which may appear to be the equivalent of the top half, but the two halves are in fact very different.

Limitations of block diagrams

The limitations are mainly the inevitable by-products of the advantages. The block diagram is a valuable communication device for members of a team from different disciplines, but because of its versatility it is difficult to arrive at an agreed diagram for a given system. Diagrams of the same system, drawn by two different people, rarely turn out to be identical unless they are very simple. It is common practice in examination papers on systems design to ask questions such as "Draw a block diagram of x"; x might be almost anything, a machine tool, a post office, a university department or a municipal bus system. Physical scientists and engineers are often disturbed to find that two answers to such a question can be marked equally high and yet be entirely different, and that it is not possible to produce a model answer against which to mark other efforts.

The flexibility of block diagrams in switching from functional to physical representations is also a source of difficulty in that it is very easy to generate a diagram which is neither the one nor the other, but a misleading mixture. This is a special case of the problem of level of abstraction. A diagram which is not at a consistent level of abstraction causes difficulties particularly at the allocation of function stage. Similarly the ease of shift up and down the level of complexity can facilitate the production of a diagram containing blocks at very different levels of complexity; this also is misleading. Some faults may be obvious but there can be much more subtle slips of this kind which are serious obstacles to design thinking until they are identified. In general a useful block diagram must have an element of unity, but the sheer variety of dimensions tempting the designer into disunity causes real problems. The most difficult faults to identify are those in which a diagram and its inversion have got confused.

Figure 6.6 A block-line diagram and a path-node diagram for the redecoration of a room.

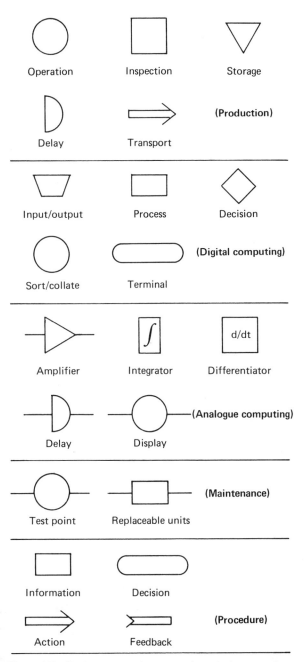

Figure 6.7 Some commonly accepted symbol conventions.

is often discussed in the psychological literature. This is not a useful concept because the development of perception always involves more than one sensory mode. The error has arisen because of the attempt to identify a function (perception) with a physical data channel (eye–brain). An even grosser error is to identify the sequence of physical channel elements with functional elements by suggesting that the eye is concerned with sensation and the brain with perception. Finally, the flexibility of representation of the lines of a diagram can tempt the designer into generating hybrids where sometimes the line means that stuff passes, sometimes that data pass and sometimes merely that time has passed. An early mistake of this kind can cause members of a design group to be at cross purposes for a long time until the origin of the confusion is identified. All these errors may appear to be logically obvious and readily avoidable by tidy thinkers. Unfortunately it does not turn out in practice to be such a simple matter. For complex systems, even experienced design teams can get into considerable communication and conceptual difficulties by subtle and inadvertent errors of the kind discussed in this section. Very careful and time-consuming effort and discussion of block diagrams are an essential investment in the early stages of any system design.

Display aspects of block diagrams

Designing displays is a problem of using the properties of some physical medium to match the structure of the information to be presented. This information is determined by the requirements and limitations of the observer. The observer in our case is a designer who wishes to form a concept of some system, and this system by definition is an assembly of components related by a common purpose. The human operator is accustomed to thinking in up to four dimensions (when sticking close to reality he can conceive of one time and three space dimensions) and it happens that there are four dimensions available in a block diagram. Any graphical display has up–down and left–right dimensions. The block diagram also has the block–line dichotomy and each of these can be treated as a dimension. For example, the length or style of a line can have meaning and so can the shape or size of the block. In principle all of these dimensions can be interchanged: a block–line diagram can be inverted to a path–node diagram where the paths can represent what was previously in blocks and the lines become nodes. From this point of view, designing a block diagram involves determining what the designer requires and distributing this information among the available dimensions.

The apparent similarity of physical and functional block diagrams of the same system can lead to the false assumption of identity of physical units and functional units. This problem is not so serious in hardware systems where, in fact, one criterion of good design is that the functional units are separately packaged in physical units, but this does not apply to biological systems. For example, visual perception

There are a number of conventions or stereotypes which restrict the total available choice. The decision on whether to use a block–line or the equivalent path–node diagram depends on the number of states to be displayed within each dimension. A line or a path can be varied in length which is an analogue presentation of state information, and a block can be varied in shape which is a symbolic distinction of state information. Of course, a block could be varied in size but this is undesirable because of the ambiguity as to whether length or area is linearly related to the state being displayed. In any graphical display, interchanging whatever is represented from left to right with that represented up to down, or vice versa, will not distort the information, although it may make it more difficult to perceive because of display stereotypes. For example, from the reading and writing convention we are accustomed to left to right sequences and thus time lapse is naturally represented in this way. Up–down is ambiguous since reading and writing move up to down but, on graphs, movement from down to up usually denotes that something is increasing. Thus, whether the primary input is on the upper or lower left and the primary output is on the upper or lower right are arbitrary but the left–rightness is not.

Generally, analogue presentation is better for continuous information and symbolic presentation for discrete information. Thus, lines or paths are best for time, but there is a serious complication if feedback loops are included so that the identification of a sequence in time, such as a cause and effect, becomes impossible. Some accepted conventions for block shapes are shown in Figure 6.7.

Procedure for preparation of system diagrams

1 Define and list all inputs and outputs.
2 Allocate the meaning of the available dimensions
   up–down
   left–right
   lines–blocks.
3 Determine range and sequence of required diagrams
   physical–functional
   level of abstraction
   level of complexity.
4 Avoid hybrid diagrams
   a lines should have only one meaning: sequence, time, energy, stuff, data or information
   b do not confuse dimensions and states within a dimension
   c blocks should have only one meaning (processes or things) unless different shapes are used.

Conclusion

It is now possible to make a bald statement which would not have been acceptable at the beginning of this chapter – namely, that separation of functions is a matter of drawing the right set of block diagrams. What is meant by "right" depends on the particular kind of system, on the quality of the design team and so on. There is no single universally acceptable solution. Nor is there a single appropriate way of generating the diagrams. For system designs which are a marginal change from already operational systems it is easiest to start by a physical analysis of the existing systems followed by a translation into the functional equivalent. For systems for which there is little previous experience it is better to start with a functional diagram. It may be optimum to do both separately and compare the results. Sometimes diagrams are best generated by individuals or small teams and the teams get larger as the detail of description increases. There seems to be no substitute for or no equivalent to the block diagram as a technique for defining and communicating what is required at all levels, from broad objectives to detailed physical solutions.

References

Brown, J. A. C. (1954) *The Social Psychology of Industry,* Penguin, London.

Emery, F. E. (1969) *Systems Thinking,* Penguin, London.

Pym, D. (1968) *Industrial Society*, Penguin, London.

Singleton, W. T. (1971a) "Psychological aspects of man–machine systems", in Warr, P. B. (ed.), *Psychology at Work*, Penguin, London.

Singleton, W. T. (1971b) "General theory of presentation of information", in Bernstat, R. K. and Garnet, K. D. (eds.), *Displays and Controls,* Swels & Zeitlinger, Lisse, The Netherlands.

Warr, P. B. (ed.) (1971) *Psychology at Work,* Penguin, London.

7 Concept of a manufacturing system

by J. Parnaby

There is no single concept of a manufacturing system covering all industries in every detail. It is necessary to examine the fundamental properties and characteristics of a range of systems and to consider the way they are synthesized and operated before consolidating general conclusions. What is seen depends very much on the viewpoint and the narrowness of the focusing range. Nevertheless there is much to be gained from a fundamental study of all aspects of manufacturing systems and their interactions since there are opportunities for technology transfer between industries.

Manufacturing systems must be designed by taking into account both steady state and dynamic performance, whilst ensuring there is an adequate number of controllable variables to compensate the effects of uncontrolled disturbances. The technological process part of the manufacturing system is synthesised from interacting unit-operating subsystems, and this itself is a subsystem of the overall business system. The business subsystem has a complex multivariable nature and for its effective control it is important that information flows and plans or set points are well defined to allow people to be effective controllers of the system.

System design and system control must be effectively integrated.

Manufacturing system

In general terms, a manufacturing system is one in which raw materials are processed from one form into another, known as a product, gaining a higher or added value in the process. The output products from one manufacturing system may be the inputs to another. There is thus considerable interaction. Such systems incorporate particular product-dependent applications of science and technology via their processes and associated machinery and are usually complex. They directly involve many people who carry the process know-how and they interact in many complex ways with our social system and physical environment.

We live in a dynamic and competitive world where market competition is met at interfirm level and intercountry level. For a manufacturing industry to survive it must keep pace with change, and each and every firm must be efficient in achieving its objectives. Efficiency in terms of return on capital employed, or profit, has to be achieved these days in the face of increasingly complex interactions and constraints of a technical and sociological nature.

One representation of a manufacturing system, in an overall sense, is given in Figure 7.1 in input–output analysis form. This figure, whilst interesting, is not particularly useful other than to remind us that not all inputs to the system are controllable by management, and disturbances in these must be mitigated by manipulations in controllable inputs such as resources and plans.

Figure 7.1 gives the impression of manufacturing systems in general being a homogeneous group. However, this is not so for a number of reasons, not least of which is the differing natures of the products, as can be deduced from the list given in Table 7.1 of different manufacturing systems making up British manufacturing industry. Engineering companies and processing companies are represented in Table 7.1.

Certain features are common, for example:

1 A manufacturing system should be an integrated whole. It is composed of different subsystems, each of which interacts with the whole system. The system will have a number of objectives and the system must be operated in such a way as to optimize some weighted function of the objectives (Beishon and Peters, 1972).

2 The manufacturing system will be synthesized by selecting sets of energy consuming subsystems for raw materials processing from the typical list in Table 7.2, linking these together and operating or controlling the resulting system and its interactions with its environment.

3 To operate the system requires an administration information-flow system and decision-making processes.

4 The processes taking place in the unit operations and reactors must all be constrained to satisfy the laws of mass and energy conservation and of chemical combination.

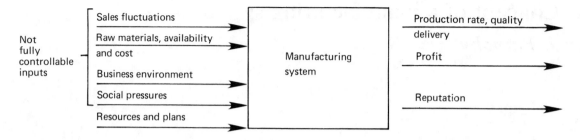

Figure 7.1   Overall view, input-output analysis.

Table 7.1   Manufacturing industry

Food, drink, tobacco	Textiles
Chemicals and allied industries	Leather, leather goods and fur
Metal manufacture	Clothing and footwear
Engineering and electrical goods	Bricks, pottery, glass, cement, etc.
Shipbuilding and marine engineering	Timber, furniture, etc.
Vehicles	Paper, printing and publishing
Other metal goods	Others!

However, there are many differences resulting from the various different combinations of subsystems met in each company as a result of product differences from company to company and also the differing interactions with the social and business environment. Each company in its way is a unique manufacturing system with its own set of problems, many of which also are unique in certain detailed aspects (Riggs, 1970).

Again, there is a superficial apparent uniformity in that the block diagram in Figure 7.2, this time showing subsystems grouped on a functional (Lockyer, 1974) or departmental basis, appears to apply to all manufacturing companies. Clearly all will have a production function within which combinations of unit operations and reactions from Table 7.2 will be found. Clearly also the nature of the technology must affect the structure of the system, the way it is controlled and the types of staff employed, and one cannot really design and operate the system without an understanding of the technology.

In defining a manufacturing system, therefore, it is necessary to do so from a number of different viewpoints ranging from the overall macroscopic description of Figures 7.1 and 7.2 or Table 7.1, to a detailed microscopic analysis of the physical and chemical processes taking place and the static and dynamic interactions involved. It is natural when describing manufacturing systems to use as a language the process flow-block diagram to clarify the

logic and help to correctly match inputs and outputs for the various subsystems. Typical examples of production process system flow-block diagrams are given in Figure 7.3 (Riggs, 1970; Lockyer, 1974; Vilbrandt and Dryden, 1959).

One essential basic requirement of all manufacturing systems, regardless of the types of production processes, machinery used and business environment, is that of long-term stable operation in the face of continually changing constraints and external disturbances. This creates a need for a supply of information to facilitate control decision making by management and requires (Kochhar and Parnaby, 1977) the following three basic functions to be deliberately incorporated:

1   data acquisition and sorting function,
2   information flow function,
3   systems control function.

In order to further illustrate characteristics of manufacturing systems, it is necessary to next consider the interacting aspects of systems design and control.

Design of the manufacturing system

Just as systems can, with great care and an experienced professional approach, be designed to be controllable, the converse is certainly also true if care is not taken. Every subsystem of the whole is required to process certain inputs and produce certain outputs. To obtain the desired outputs

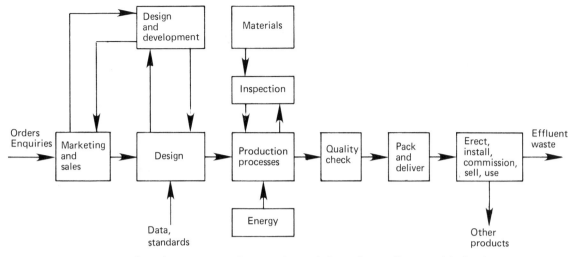

Figure 7.2   Equipment manufacturing company (arrows denote information and/or materials flow).

Table 7.2   Elemental subsystem building blocks

A: Unit operations — physical processes	B: Chemical processes
1. *Visco-elastic fluid flow* Pumping, mixing, casting, moulding, extrusion	1. *Organic, inorganic reactions or combinations*
2. *Heat transfer* (Possibly channelling heat to or from chemical reactions.) Annealing, melting, heating	2. *Electrolysis*
3. *Mass transfer* Gas absorption, stripping, leaching, adsorption, ion exchange, conveying, solvent extraction, painting, coating, welding, plating	
4. *Separation* Filtration, sedimentation, elutriation, flocculation	
5. *Combined heat and mass transfer* Humidification, dehumidification, crystallization, drying, distillation	
6. *Cutting* Drilling, milling, shaping, sawing, planing, slicing, etc.	
7. *Elastic — plastic forming* Deep-drawing, vacuum forming, etc.	
8. *Assembly*	
9. *Inspection* Physical examination, chemical examination	

the correct inputs must be available. When all subsystems are put together the input and output interactions must be compatible (Rudd and Watson, 1968; Forrester, 1969).

Examples

1 The food manufacturing industry interacts with the agriculture system, with its time cycles of production, as well as with the chemical industry which supplies various additives such as colourings and flavours.

2 A man operating a machine tool must clearly have all the skills and knowledge of the product required to operate his machine whilst he must also have the broader skills required to allow him to fit harmoniously into the workshop social environment.

3 If a process reactor is supplied with liquid raw materials by a pump, then

> *a* the output variables of flow rate and pressure from the pump must always match the input variables required by the reactor to ensure the correct output rate of homogeneous, well-reacted product from the reactor;
>
> *b* the flow-rate/pressure characteristics of the pipeline connecting pump and reactor must correctly match the pump characteristics;
>
> *c* the pump input torque-speed characteristic must be carefully matched to the electric drive motor (Holmes, 1977).

Further consideration of the design of the simple production process system of example 3 above reveals the need for two stages in system design.

Figure 7.3 Production process block diagrams.

Steady-state design

Matching the elements of a system together based upon averaged input–output performance characteristics assumed to be constant at all times. This gives a figure for average overall performance.

Dynamic design

In example 3 above there are two largely uncontrollable variables which are likely to exhibit random changes and so continually alter system performance:

   a fluid properties: temperature, viscosity, density, reactivity, purity;

   b reactor environment: wind, rain, air temperature, internal clogging.

If the fluid properties vary, then the pump speed must change to compensate for flow-rate changes, so making demands for torque changes on the electric motor. If the reaction conditions change due to fluid property or flow-rate changes or environment changes then the reaction rates may be inhibited or increased and such possible changes must be examined.

The anticipation of the effects of dynamic changes in uncontrollable variables as well as in controllable variables at the system design stage is known as dynamic design and requires response times for the system elements to be known either empirically or theoretically.

As a consequence of dynamic or time-dependent changes in uncontrollable variables, it is necessary for the system to be provided with a means of control of system performance. This is a very fundamental property of real manufacturing systems which never operate under steady-state conditions (Forrester, 1969; Parnaby et al., 1978). For the reactor-pump system it would be necessary to control production rate and product quality. This requires that data be continuously collected relating to these two variables prior to controlling changes by changing pump speed. Thus, five interrelated stages of manufacturing system design have been identified:

1 Subsystem input–output analysis working backwards from the product requirements.
2 Steady-state design using specifications from stage 1.
3 Dynamic design.
4 Specification of data-collection system required.
5 Control system design.

The above five stages are fundamental to the design of any part of the manufacturing system and are not specific only to the design of process plants. Example 4 illustrates this fact by reference to a different type of simplified production process system.

Example 4: Design and control of manufacturing system centred on a machine shop

Stage 1: Input–output analysis

Starting from a parts explosion for the product, the following typical variables and the types of subsystem for which inputs and outputs are necessary are defined:

types of machinery and assembly processes needed;
skills required of all personnel and personnel types needed;
product variables and associated tolerance limits.

Figure 7.4 gives some sample input–output descriptions for elements typically found in such a system.

Stage 2: Steady-state design

Here would be specified the number and types of departments, machines, staff and operators and steady-state operating levels based upon typically:

a an assumed average constant performance rate for each machine and person;
b an assumed average rate of flow of orders for the products;

c an assumed average estimated work content for each product;
d choice of operational rota systems for all sections.

Stage 3: Dynamic design

This would be based upon assessments of likely sources of variations in performance from the average steady-state values, e.g., machine breakdowns, operator absenteeism and performance variation, changes in raw materials processability characteristics, product changes, sales-level variation, changes in legislation, activities of competitors, etc. End-products of this stage would include sizing of interstage buffer inventories, stock or order policies, maintenance plans, sizes of data sampling time intervals to suit the dynamic response of each subsystem, assembly plans, policy for overtime working and work subcontracting.

Stage 4: Data collection system design

It would be necessary to specify which variables were to be frequently sampled and the time intervals for sampling, suited to the particular requirements of each subsystem for efficient control. Thus, information relating to the following variables might typically be collected at regular intervals:

level of work in progress in each subsystem;
state of each machine, i.e., working/not working;
queue levels in each subsystem;
general stock levels;
level of scrapped work;
state of completion of each product ordered;
manpower availability;
level of sales.

In other words detailed information relating to the states of all manpower, machinery and materials involved in the production process as well as for design offices and other areas would be collected.

Stage 5: Control system design

This would involve the careful definition of procedures for providing and changing control set points or plans, such as:

a Authorized work schedules, i.e., list of total waiting work required to meet sales/forecasts in the various categories, e.g., drilling, milling, grinding, welding, assembly, painting, etc., in hours of estimated operation to match customer orders. A coded list of operations required in sequence would also be provided for each component part.

b Loading schedules: detailed route plans showing consecutive machine operations for each component and

Figure 7.4 Examples of input-output analysis.

detailed hourly, daily, weekly or monthly plans showing the actual jobs associated with each order allocated to machines or operators taking into account the estimated time needed for each operation and the length of each working day.

  c Materials schedules showing the detailed raw materials and bought-in, component, sub-assembly lists required for each order, together with a time-scale plan for the ordering of supplies, allowing for delivery of materials to a detailed time schedule as required by the loading schedule.

  d Inspection schedules: inspection points, frequency and quantity of samples required for efficient product quality control.

  e Cost schedules: unit-cost standards for each operation carried out, together with procedures for warning when departures from planned component costs are taking place.

  f Delivery schedules: plans showing when each customer order is estimated to be completed if the schedules in *a* to *e* are closely followed.

  The services *a* to *f* must be provided by a department or subsystem having a responsibility for production control within the manufacturing system. Clearly there is considerable scope for using a computer to assist with the detailed information flows required for control.

Control of the manufacturing system

The dynamic processes involved in a manufacturing system must be ordered and controlled if they are to efficiently meet the system objectives. At the same time they must be adaptive, i.e., able to change their structures and characteristics, in order to survive. Their adaptive nature comes from the dominant involvement of people in the control procedures and decision-making strategies at all levels. Manufacturing systems involve many people and exist to serve people, and clear recognition of this fundamental point is essential to good control. Management at all levels clearly has to see it has a controller function and must ensure it has adequate information flow systems, computers, etc. to facilitate control (Hammond and Oh, 1973; Alford, 1973).

  As manufacturing systems are so complex in general, it is not possible for a control theory approach to be used for continuous real-time overall optimization. Instead a theoretically based heuristic procedure is necessary where major control functions are applied to maintain overall control discontinuously (Hammond and Oh, 1973; Alford, 1973).

  For example, in the production control layer, supervisors maintain continuous real-time control of production (Hollwey et al., 1978) by reference to sales, in parallel with a cost control layer which operates with a different time scale and different sampling time intervals but nevertheless in real time so far as effective control of costs is required. There is regular routine flow of information between these two layers but, in addition, at irregular intervals the cost control system interacts strongly with the control set points for production control in an overriding way owing to emergencies, effects of cost inflation on standard cost data, etc. Similarly, there may nowadays be an energy control system layer which only interacts strongly with production when energy usage or cost set points require major changes. Furthermore, sudden market changes can take priority and cause overruling of routine production control systems.

  Within the production system itself, for similar reasons of complexity, one can often identify several levels of control which have tended to operate in a pseudo-independent way (Hammond and Oh, 1973; Alford, 1973). However, the increasing distributed use of linked mini-computers and micro-processors promises the opportunity during the next decade of a better overall integrated form of control, whilst at the same time allowing individual managers to have adaptively controllable units more effectively under their control (Parnaby, 1979).

  Figure 7.5 shows schematically the levels of control typically found in a production subsystem and indicates how the following two areas of control have to integrate in practice:

  process control – automated control of technological processes to manual set points with overall managerial supervision;
  production control – control by people, based on information flow systems involving computers, of processes involving people and machines.

In discrete manufacturing, such as machine tool or motor car manufacture, the production control system will be dominant owing to high product complexity and number of items. In a processing industry such as chemicals manufacturing, process control systems will be dominant (Parnaby and Billington, 1976; Parnaby, 1977).

  In addition to ensuring that control of individual layers of the manufacturing systems, such as the production subsystem, is satisfactory, it is necessary that overall control of the manufacturing system is maintained in the face of market and other environmental disturbances. Figure 7.6 illustrates high-level overall feedforward control of the total manufacturing system based upon predictions of

Figure 7.5 Levels of control and information flows in a production subsystem

future requirements. Such a form of control is happening now in all manufacturing systems even if in some the forecasting roles of elements A and B and the models of element C (Kochhar et al., 1978) are simply intuitive ideas in the minds of managers, or if the marketing strategy involves merely the spreading of rumours over a pint of beer in the pub on a Friday night. However, an awareness of the implications of Figure 7.6 may help to improve such rudimentary forms of control. Figure 7.7 shows a form of on-line real-time production control system desirable to facilitate feedforward control. Note that each VDU user in Figure 7.7 sees a different system and a different control problem. Each must have information available at time

intervals suited to the nature and dynamic response of the particular control function he carries out to ensure truly on-line real-time control as in process control.

Conclusions

There is no clear concept of a manufacturing system acceptable to everyone. Much depends upon the viewpoint, the nature of the industry and the type of product. However, there are certain properties and characteristics which may be regarded as somewhat fundamental. One of these is a clear need for good control systems to counteract the many external disturbances interacting with manufacturing systems. Control has, of course, clearly to recognize

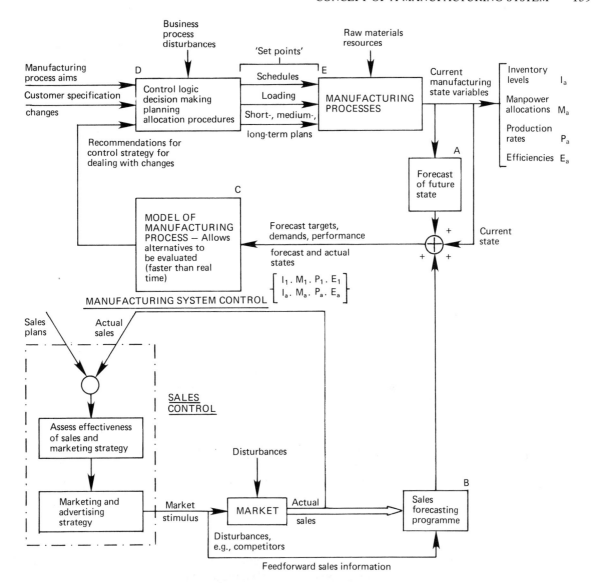

Figure 7.6 High-level feedforward control block diagram.

the many constraints, including legislation. In manufacturing systems the basic overall structural and performance logic can easily be obscured by a mass of paperwork and detail as well as by stultifying administrative systems. It must be clearly recognized that such systems are dynamic and must be adaptive to survive.

There is the basic dilemma of ensuring that the overall system operational and control philosophy and objectives are clear, whilst paying sufficient attention to detail at all levels, which creates a major demand for leadership from

managers and engineers. Effective leadership requires, amongst other things, a sound education in fundamentals relative to manufacturing systems design and control. Until recently the traditional undergraduate education of many production engineers was concentrated unduly on metal working systems and did not reflect the major importance of the production function in all other industries listed in Table 7.1. However, recently developed new engineering degree courses in the broader area of manufacturing (systems) engineering (University of Bradford,

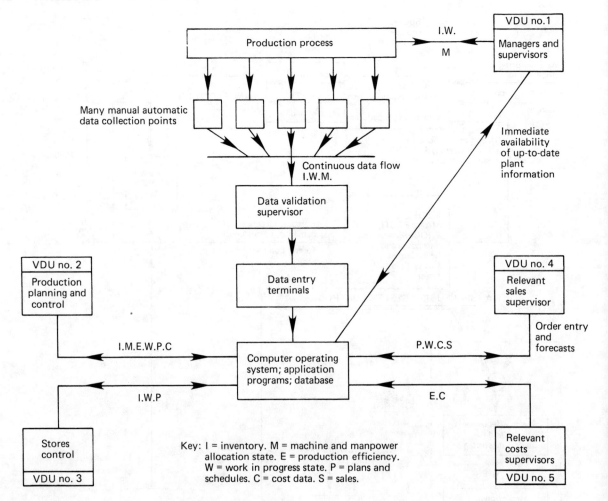

Figure 7.7 Elements of an on-line real-time production control system.

1975) have rectified this deficiency and pay sufficient attention to scientific principles governing all the processes in Table 7.2 as well as to control and systems principles. Adequately broadly trained engineers are an essential ingredient of any recipe for improving the performance of the British manufacturing system.

References

Alford, C. A. (1973) "Design aspects of computer control in discrete manufacturing", *I.E.E. Trans. Manuf. Tech.* **1,** 26.

Beishon, J. and Peters, G. (eds.) (1972) *Systems Behaviour,* Harper and Row, London, for the Open University.

Forrester, J. W. (1969) *Industrial Dynamics*, MIT Press, Cambridge, Mass.

Hammond, J. L. and Oh, S. J. (1973) "Evolution of systems approaches to computer control in discrete manufacturing, *I.E.E. Trans. Manuf. Tech.* **1,** 4.

Hollwey, M. W. M., Kochhar, A. K., Parnaby, J. and Ephraim, O. M. (1978) "Using a real time minicomputer for production control",*J. Inst. Prod. Engrs.* **55**, 37.

Holmes, R. (1977) *The Characteristics of Mechanical Engineering Systems,* Pergamon Press, London.

Kochhar, A. K. and Parnaby, J. (1977) "The choice of computer systems for real-time production control",*J. Inst. Prod. Engrs.* **56**, 29.

Kochhar, A. K. et al. (1978) "Comparison of stochastic

identification techniques for dynamic modelling of plastics extrusion processes", *Proc. I. Mech. E.* **192,** 299.

Lockyer, K. G. (1974) *Factory and Production Management,* Pitman, London.

Parnaby, J. (1977) "The design and control of homogenising systems for minerals processing", *Trans. Inst. Chem. Engrs.* **55,** 104.

Parnaby, J. (1979) *Product manufacturing technology utilising minicomputers and microcomputers,* Proceedings of the Jubilee Conference (Rubber and Plastics Research Association, Shrewsbury).

Parnaby, J., Battye, E. A. A., Hassan, C. P. and Hadwell, C. P. (1978) "Computer controlled injection moulding and extrusion", *Plastics and Rubber: Processing* **3,** 89.

Parnaby, J. and Billington, D. (1976) "Computer modelling and control of manufacturing systems – with particular reference to the tailoring industry", *Trans. Instn. Elect. Engrs.* **123,** 835.

Riggs, J. L. (1970) *Production Systems,* Wiley, New York.

Rudd, D. F. and Watson, C. C. (1968) *Strategy of Process Engineering,* Wiley, New York.

University of Bradford (1975) Honours Degrees in Manufacturing Systems Engineering, Course brochures and syllabuses.

Vilbrandt, F. C. and Dryden, C. E. (1959) *Chemical Engineering Plant Design,* McGraw-Hill, New York.

8 The Systems approach
by Gwilyn M. Jenkins

Summary

The objective of this paper is to discuss the philosophy underlying a systems approach to the solution of problems. The most important conclusions may be summarized as follows:

1. A *piecemeal approach* to problems within firms and in local and national government is *no longer good enough* if firms and nations are to compete, and indeed to collaborate, efficiently.

2. This is so because technology, firms, organizations and affairs in general are becoming *increasingly complex* and because policy decisions *increasingly require the expenditure of large sums of money* – so that the consequences of *bad decision making* are becoming *increasingly costly*.

3. A *systems approach* to problems demands that a *piecemeal approach* is replaced by an *overall approach*. Systems Engineering is the science of designing complex systems, by the efficient use of resources in the form of *Men, Money, Machines* and *Materials*, so that the individual sub-systems making up the overall system can be designed, fitted together, checked and operated so as to achieve the *overall objective* in the most efficient way.

4. The rapid development of Systems Engineering during the last few years has been stimulated not only by the increasing complexity of businesses but also by the increasing potential of large analogue, digital and hybrid computers which enable an overall *model* of the system to be *optimized*.

5. One of the greatest benefits of Systems Engineering is that it exerts a *unifying influence* on management by tying together the many specialist techniques needed to solve complex problems.

6. The systems engineer is seen as the *generalist* who always takes an *overall view* and who always takes particular care to ensure that the system objectives are correct, are communicated to all concerned, and are achieved with maximum efficiency.

7. One of the most important consequences of the systems approach is that it highlights the fact that *fundamental changes* are needed in the way that both individuals and organizations go about their work. In particular, it demands that problem solving needs to be carried out on a more *interdisciplinary* basis and that many firms and organizations need to be organized in a more *integrated* way than at present.

8. Thus, Systems Engineering is seen as a *key factor* in improving *management practice*, and hence, in making big improvements to the efficiency of firms and organizations.

9. Finally, the paper draws attention to the *urgent need* at this point in time to inject *systems thinking* at all levels into industry, commerce, and into local and national government.

The paper is in three parts. Part A is concerned with answering the questions "What is Systems Engineering?" and "What is a Systems Engineer?" Part B answers the question "How does a Systems Engineer go about solving any problem?" *

A. The nature and objectives of Systems Engineering
A.1. Systems and their properties

The expression "All Systems Go" is now an established part of popular jargon. It means that the overall system, consisting of millions of electronic components, making up a space rocket and hundreds of men, making up the management and technical teams, has been designed in such a way that each component and human being is ready to play its *designed role* efficiently in making the rocket achieve its predetermined objective. Such an impressive feat of engineering and project management calls for sophisticated systems engineering skills. Before discussing these skills in

* [The original article contained a further part discussing the question, "How can systems thinking help to improve efficiency within firms and other organizations?" *Ed.*]

greater detail, it is useful by way of introduction to say what is meant by a system.

The notion that it is useful to regard such diverse entities as a domestic water heater, an industrial plant, a company, a space rocket, a hospital, a port and the entire regional government set-up of a country as *systems*, must surely go down as a very important contribution to twentieth-century thought. That the word is not new is seen from its Greek origin "systema", which derives from "syn" meaning "together" and "histemi", which means "to set". A typical dictionary definition of a system would read "A *plan* or scheme according to which things are *connected* into a *whole*", as in a system of philosophy or in the solar system. Thus, the key words, *plan, connected* and *whole*, which will recur throughout this paper, are present even in popular definitions of the word system.

Although a system has a well-established popular meaning, from the point of view of systems engineering a more precise and extended definition is needed [1]. In the following discussion, six important properties of systems are listed and illustrated by considering a relatively simple system in the form of a chemical plant.

Systems as complex groupings of human beings and machines

A chemical plant usually consists of a very large number of different items of equipment, together with stocks of raw materials, intermediate products and finished products and also services in the form of water, steam and electricity. To operate the plant, a plant manager is required, and he will need to be assisted by several foremen and process workers, usually working three eight-hour shifts per day. For efficient running of the plant, these "line personnel" must be backed up by a host of technical and commercial "service personnell", for example maintenance engineers, research chemists, accountants and salesmen. Thus, the first property of a system is that it is *a complex grouping of human beings and machines*.

Sub-systems and flow-block diagrams

An important characteristic of systems is that they may be broken down into *sub-systems*. The way in which this breaking down is done in any particular situation will depend on the nature of the system being studied and therefore on the extent to which detail is important. To decide on the amount of sub-system detail needed may require an analysis in depth of the system and its interactions.

A convenient and readily understood way of displaying how systems may be broken down into sub-systems is provided by a *flow-block diagram*, as indicated in Figure 8.1. This shows a simplified flow-block diagram of a chemical plant for making acrolein (C_3H_4O) by the catalytic oxidation of propylene (C_3H_6) * [2]. The diagram displays the individual sub-systems or process units, making up the whole plant, as *blocks* and the links or *flows* between them, as arrows. In the present example, the flows refer to materials and energy. More generally, the flows between individual sub-systems may refer to Money, Materials, Energy, Information or Decisions.

Flow-block diagrams provide an invaluable tool for helping to clarify one's thinking about a particular system. It is remarkable how much light can be shed on a complex problem by the mere act of constructing a flow-block diagram.

Sub-systems interact with each other

The overall efficiency of the acrolein plant depends on the correct functioning of all the sub-systems shown in Figure 8.1. This is because the plant units have *interacting tasks* to perform. In addition, some material is *recycled* from one part of the plant to an earlier stage and this in turn produces further interactions. An example of a simple interaction is provided by the fact that the more concentrated the acrolein leaving the absorption column, the less is the demand on the distillation column; thus the design of the absorption and distillation columns may be balanced against each other. Similarly, a small reactor will be cheaper but may give a lower conversion to acrolein and hence may demand more recycling of unconverted raw materials and also bigger absorption and distillation columns. At the same time the catalyst is expensive and has a limited life; it can be shown that this has an effect on the most economic size of the reactor tubes. Because of these interactions, and many more besides, it is impossible to arrive at the best design of the plant, or even at the best design for an individual piece of equipment, by considering each item separately. This brings us to the third general property of systems, namely that *the individual sub-systems interact with each other*. The performance of a given sub-

* In the process propylene and air are mixed with recycled gas and passed into a tubular reactor where they react over a catalyst to produce acrolein plus other gases. The outlet gases are cooled and then passed on to an absorption column where some gases are absorbed in water, the undissolved gases from the top of the column being recycled to the reactor. The liquid from the bottom stream of the absorber is passed into the distillation column where the acrolein is distilled and removed at the top of the column and the liquid (mostly water) from the bottom of the column is then returned to the absorption column for further use.

Figure 8.1 Simplified flow-block diagram of an acrolein plant as an example of a simple system with interacting sub-systems.

Figure 8.2 A sub-system as some process which transforms input flows of money, materials, energy, information and decisions into corresponding output flows.

system interacts with the performance of other sub-systems and hence it cannot be designed in isolation from these other sub-systems.

In general, a sub-system may be regarded as some process which *transforms* certain *input* flows of money, materials, energy, information or decisions into corresponding *outputs*, as shown in Figure 8.2.

It is a fact that the outputs from one sub-system provide the inputs for other sub-systems which is responsible for the interactions between the various sub-systems. Understanding the detailed nature of these interactions is one of the primary concerns of the Systems Engineer.

Systems form part of hierarchies of systems

The process of breaking down a system into sub-systems can be taken further as we look at the system in greater detail. Thus, at a later stage in the design of a chemical process, it will be necessary to specify individual plant units in much greater detail and to include their instrumentation and control equipment. The breaking down process could be continued even further until one was concerned with minute detail such as the frequency with which pumps should be serviced or even the ordering of the grease for the maintenance mechanic's grease gun!

Figure 8.3 Hierarchy of systems associated with the wider system of which an individual plant forms part.

In turn, as indicated in Figure 8.3, the plant being studied may be part of a complex of plants making several products from common feedstocks and using common and interlocking utility supplies. Again, the complex may be one of several plants and complexes on a single large industrial site. In turn, the production facilities of the entire company may consist of several manufacturing sites *to which* raw materials have to be transported, *at which* production has to be planned on a company-wide basis and *from which* finished products have to be delivered to marketing areas. If the whole firm is to operate efficiently, it must *coordinate* and *integrate* the functions of planning and investment, research, design and development, production and equally importantly, selling and marketing. This can be done efficiently only if proper account is taken of other firms, especially those in the chemical industry. In turn the chemical industry, along with other industries, forms part of an even wider system, the British Economy of this country, possibly itself to form part of an even wider system, the European Common Market.

Thus, the fourth property of systems is that *they form part of a hierarchy of systems*. There will usually be strong interactions between the various systems which occur at the same level of a hierarchy and between systems at different levels in the hierarchy. However, the systems "at the top" are the most important because they exert considerable influence on the systems lower down in the hierarchy.

Systems have conflicting objectives

The fifth property of a *system is that it should have an objective*. Getting the objectives right is not an easy matter but it is the key to successful systems design. For example, in the case of designing a plant, is the objective "to minimize capital costs" or "to minimize operating costs" or "to achieve the highest possible safety standards" or "to maximize reliability" or "to maximize the ease of maintenance" or what? In fact, for a given system, it is not difficult to write down a long list of possible objectives. However, these objectives will usually tend to be in conflict with each other. For example, lower capital costs result in higher operating costs, higher safety and reliability standards increase both capital and operating costs but may increase throughput and profit, and so on.

In general, *all systems have conflicting objectives*, so that some form of compromise is essential. Therefore, a balance or *trade-off* must be sought between the conflicting objectives if the best overall result is to be obtained. Thus, in the present example, a compromise between the conflicting requirements of low capital costs, low operating costs, high safety standards, high reliability and ease of maintenance must be obtained by calculating their contribution to some overall objective, such as the financial rate of return on the plant over its expected future lifetime. Reaching the best compromise between conflicting objectives poses many important questions which usually require detailed investigation at the beginning of a systems study.

Systems must be designed to be able to achieve their objectives

The sixth, and most important, property of a system is that it must be *designed* in such a way that it is capable of achieving its overall objective. Achieving the overall objective may be a difficult and complicated question and may involve analysis, planning and designing over a long time period. This is what Systems Engineering is all about. Before going on to discuss its role in greater detail, a summary is given of the main properties of systems.

Summary of properties of systems

1. A system is a *complex grouping* of human beings and machines.

2. Systems may be broken down into *sub-systems*, the amount of sub-system detail depending on the problem being studied. *Flow-block diagrams* provide a readily understood way of describing these sub-systems.

3. The *outputs* from a given sub-system provide the *inputs* for other sub-systems. Thus the performance of a given sub-system *interacts* with the performance of other sub-systems and hence can not be studied in isolation.

4. The system being studied will usually form part of a *hierarchy* of such systems. The systems at the top are very important and exert considerable influence on the systems lower down.

5. To function at all, a system must have an *objective*, but this is influenced by the wider system of which it forms part. Usually, systems have multiple objectives which are in conflict with one another, so that an *overall objective* is required which effects a compromise between these conflicting objectives.

6. To function at maximum efficiency, a system must be *designed* in such a way that it is capable of achieving its overall objective in the best way possible.

A.2. The four M's and Systems Engineering

A system has been defined as any complex grouping of human beings and machines with a definite objective, such as an entire industrial plant, a whole firm or a rocket system, which is made up of a very large number of electronic components, each affecting the overall performance of the rocket. *Systems Engineering is the science of designing complex systems in their totality* to ensure that the component sub-systems making up the system are designed, fitted together, checked and operated in the most efficient way [1], [3]. It is not a new discipline, since its history is deeply rooted in good industrial design practice. However, it brings a new emphasis on *overall performance*, as opposed to the performance of individual parts of the system.

An important central feature of Systems Engineering is the building of *quantitative models* so that some overall measure of the performance of the system can be *optimized*. One of the advantages of the systems approach is that it is possible to look at entirely different problems coming from different areas of technology and business in a way that emphasizes their common features when regarded as systems.

The word "engineer" in Systems Engineering is used in the everyday sense of "designing, constructing and operating works of public utility", a definition which includes a much wider range of people than would be recognized as engineers by the professional engineering institutions! Hence, Systems Engineering is the activity of planning, designing, constructing, checking and operating complex systems. This definition has much in common with the original Greek meaning of the word system, namely "to set together". Many sub-systems need to be integrated together for the whole system to work effectively. Thus, systems engineering is the science of setting, or knitting together, or engineering, systems so that jointly they perform more efficiently in pursuit of a common objective.

It is now possible to state more precisely what is meant by the expression "All systems go", mentioned in the introduction. "All systems go" means that in the launch controller's view, each piece of electronic equipment is working properly and is making its designed contribution to the overall performance of the rocket. To reach a state where the launch controller is able to say with confidence that "All systems go", the rocket designers must have previously defined the total system and its objective. Its objective may be to launch a capsule into a predetermined path to reach the Moon. The total system consisting of rocket, launching pad and technical crew must then be designed to achieve this objective. The designers will need to analyse the requirements of the total system and then break them down into smaller systems capable of finer definition until every component and human being *has its planned place and role* in a suitably defined subsidiary system. Nothing less is acceptable from a systems engineering point of view.

The four M's

Perhaps a simpler way of saying all this is that Systems Engineering is concerned with the *optimal use of resources* of all kinds. The major resources are the four M's, namely Men, Money, Machines and Materials or, as once translated by an earthy Yorkshire executive, Blokes, Brass, Gadgets and Muck! It has been objected by some that Systems Engineering will result in the regimentation of people to such an extent that they may become technological robots. On the contrary – a systems approach to many problems in British industry during the last twenty-five years would have shown that too much emphasis was being placed on Money, Machines and Materials and not enough on Blokes. Greater emphasis on people would have achieved the dual result of making firms much better places in which to work and also of increasing efficiency, profits and benefits all round.

Reasons for the rapid development of Systems Engineering

Systems Engineering is becoming increasingly important because of the increasing *complexity* of business and of modern affairs in general. If all that were concerned was running a small family business, or the local parish council, there would be no particular need for Systems Engineering. However, many problems nowadays are far more complicated. Governments are forced to consider future national energy requirements and to balance up supply and demand of oil, coal, natural gas, hydro-electric power and atomic power. City administrations have to control vast financial resources in the areas of health, sanitation, education and transport. Large oil companies operate huge refineries where plant units are strung together in series and in parallel so that the performance of any one affects the efficiency of the whole. Many separate systems need to come together if a satisfactory solution is to be obtained for such complex problems. Thus, the science of knitting together separate systems is rapidly becoming an important branch of science – the science of Systems Engineering.

Alongside the increasing complexity of affairs, the ability to perform the sometimes very complicated calculations needed for systems engineering studies has been made possible by rapid developments in the development of large digital, analogue and hybrid computers. Such computers have now become indispensable weapons in the system engineer's armoury since they enable him to explore in considerable detail the economics of different ways of operating a system and to select those ways that are most efficient, resulting in optimization of the system.

Interdisciplinary approach

In addition to providing a method by which complex problems, activities and organizations can be analysed, Systems Engineering also provides a framework within which to tie together many separate and possibly divergent disciplines, which otherwise might fail to make an effective contribution to the overall optimization of the problem. Thus Systems Engineering is a team activity and brings together specialists with such diverse backgrounds as natural science, engineering, mathematics, statistics, economics, accountancy and behavioural science. By contrast, the Systems Engineer himself is a generalist, a man trained to think in terms of an overall approach to problem solving, of getting the objectives right and seeing that they are achieved efficiently. As such, it is essential that he is able to liaise and *communicate* effectively with the various specialists whose advice is essential and to stimulate their creativity within this interdisciplinary approach. In fact, the role of the Systems Engineer is very much like that of the general practitioner whose main concern is with the general health of his patient but who, from time to time, will call in specialists for guidance. The systems team will contain specialists and Systems Engineers but the main job of the Systems Engineer is to sort out what is happening, and why, and how it can be done better. Then, together with the specialists, he ensures that the agreed objectives are realized as efficiently as possible in minimum time and at minimum cost and that a good case is presented to the decision makers who will eventually have to sanction the implementation of the designed system.

Disasters that could have been avoided with Systems Engineering

That there is urgent need to apply a systems approach throughout industry is highlighted by the following examples of the consequences of a piecemeal approach which the writer has seen during the last few years:

1. A plant translated too quickly from laboratory stage to full-scale plant, without a proper systems study, failed to operate at all on the large scale and had to be redesigned at considerable expense.
2. A plant, which had been engineered excellently, was built but was written off immediately and did not manufacture a single ton of product. This was because the firm's assessment of the market had been at fault and was outstripped by the assessment of a rival company.
3. A large integrated plant complex lost a great deal of money during the first two years of its life because plant reliability and raw material availability had not been assessed properly.
4. A fibre manufacturer responded quickly to an increase in demand by installing additional spinning capacity without ensuring that its raw material supply was adequate and so lost money by tying up valuable capital resources.

Mistakes of this kind, which are so obvious in hindsight, are caused by a piecemeal approach to problems. It is such disasters that the disciplined approach of Systems Engineering is designed to prevent and can prevent.

Success stories that went with good Systems Engineering

By contrast, the following represent some successful applications of systems engineering which the author has seen at close quarters during the past few years:

1. A plant designed using a systems engineering approach was estimated to be at least 10% cheaper than a plant designed by conventional methods [2].

2. A systems study leading to the installation of an on-line computer on a paper making machine led to an increase in profitability of 9% and the cost of the computer was recovered within two years [4].

3. Short term production planning of an olefines complex resulted in savings of the order of £200,000 per annum [5, 6].

4. A systems study of a petrochemical plant resulted in improvements to the process and in savings of approximately £80,000 per annum at a total cost of £6,000, including the cost of systems effort [7].

Such examples could be multiplied several times over and testify to the efficiency of the extra discipline instilled by a systems approach. Detailed stages in the development of a systems engineering project will be described later. Figure 8.4 and the following discussion summarize the main sequence of events in a typical systems study.

Summary of stages in a systems approach to problems

1. *Systems analysis.* Systems Engineering starts with a common-sense analysis of what is going on, and why, and whether it might be done better. Then the system and its objectives have to be defined and data gathered about its likely performance.

2. *Systems design (or systems synthesis).* First, the future environment of the system has to be *forecast*. Then a quantitative *model* has to be built and used to *simulate* or explore a number of different ways of operating the system, finally choosing the system or systems which are in some sense "best", thus optimizing the system.

3. *Implementation.* The results of the system study must be presented and approval sought for their implementation. The optimized system will then have to be built, that is suitable hardware and/or software constructed. The project will require careful planning at this stage to ensure that the full benefits of the system approach are realized.

After construction, the system will need to be checked for performance, reliability, etc.

4. *Operation.* A point will be reached when the system will need to be handed over to those who have to operate the system on a routine basis. This is where great care is needed to avoid misunderstanding and inefficiency and probably represents *the area which is least well done in any project*. Finally the effectiveness of the operational system will need to be assessed, and if unsatisfactory, the system "tuned", or reoptimized, to operate in an environment which may turn out to be different from that for which it was designed.

Figure 8.4 Broad stages in the development of a systems engineering project.

Benefits which follow from using a Systems Engineering approach

Several benefits follow from applying a systems approach. The following are the most important:

1. The majority of systems in industry and government have not been designed at all – like Topsy, they have just happened! New systems get added on to old systems and the result becomes a mess. An example of this is provided by the piecemeal development of an industrial site where plant after plant is added without a full examination of the consequences in terms of overall efficiency. Even if there were well defined objectives originally, these change gradually in time without any consequent change in the

system. Hence, the most important benefit of taking an overall systems approach is *that it affords an opportunity to stand back, take a good look at the system and to start formulating new objectives.*

2. Getting the objectives right is the most important part of any study. If the objectives are wrong, most of the subsequent effort is going to be wasted. In this context, it is easy to delude oneself into thinking that a well-defined mathematical objective is relevant. It may be that the real objective is more difficult to define and more vague. Nevertheless, it must be brought out into the open, no matter how subjective certain features of it turn out to be. Hence the second benefit of Systems Engineering is that by its disciplined method of attack on problems, it focuses attention on the important issues – *the correct objective will tend to be brought to the foreground as opposed to an irrelevant objective which might be kept in the background.* Once the objective has been formulated and agreed, it should be explained carefully to all those involved with the system, *down* to the men who will have to operate the system and *up* to the senior managers whose support is necessary both for implementation and efficient operation. Because of his overall approach, the systems engineer is the best person to define *what* should be optimized and hence is the best man to carry out the optimization.

3. There is still a great tendency in industry and in government to base decisions on *guesswork*. For example, the use of guesswork in the design of industrial plants has often led in the past to large safety factors being used in the design, resulting in excessive capital and operating costs. The third important benefit of Systems Engineering is that it *replaces guesswork by model building and optimization.* Careful consideration is then given to the consequences of alternative ways of designing the system. However, it should be emphasized that model building and optimization, if they are to be effective, must supplement and enhance intuition, judgement and inventiveness and not replace them!

4. The fourth important benefit is that by taking an overall view, *problems will be tackled in their correct order of importance.* Time will not be wasted in exploring avenues which, although interesting in themselves are not important to the realization of the overall objective. For example, there is little point in worrying about what is happening on the 17th plate of a distillation column in a chemical plant if the 17th plate has no effect on the overall economic performance of the plant. By contrast, the objectives of Systems Engineering are to pin-point those

areas which are cost sensitive and to see that these are studied carefully.

5. Related to the fourth benefit is the fact that if simple devices and techniques result in big improvements, *these will be applied as soon as possible*, leaving the last 5% or 10%, say, of the improvements to the development of more sophisticated techniques later on, provided, of course, that the effort involved in getting this last 10% of improvement is worthwhile and could not more usefully be spent elsewhere. In other words, a good systems engineer should be applying Systems Engineering to find out where he should be doing Systems Engineering!

A.3. The origins and scope of Systems Engineering

It is claimed by Schlager in [8] that the term "Systems Engineering" was probably first used in the Bell Telephone Laboratories in the early 1940s. The widespread development of Systems Engineering since that time is demonstrated by references [9] to [29], which represent a few of the many books and articles written on the subject during the last 15 years. Systems Engineering was born and has been developed in two quite distinct areas – in military and space technology systems during and since World War II and also in industrial problems, particularly in the oil, chemical and power generation industries.

Systems Engineering in military and space applications has been dominated by the U.S.A. and has fitted in very well with the practice whereby government agencies specify the overall system requirements and then sub-contract major sub-systems to individual firms. By contrast, in the non-military area, British development, although as yet in its infancy, compares very favourably with that in other countries. This is especially true in relation to the application of systems thinking to the activities of a whole firm.

Engineering and Systems Engineering

Differences of opinion seem to exist as to the scope and nature of Systems Engineering. There are many engineers who would argue that good engineering and Systems Engineering are synonymous. For example, Affel in [22] writes "I still find it hard to convince myself that there is a difference between systems engineering and just good engineering". In a similar vein, J. M. English [29] says "Since engineers have always been concerned with developing systems, they always have been doing systems engineering or (synonymously) engineering design. . . . Design is the function which characterises the engineer." The author would agree that "Design" is the central activity in engineering (and unfortunately an activity which is sadly neglected in many university engineering departments) and, therefore, that good engineering and good systems engineering go hand-in-hand. However, in the author's opinion, such a narrow view of Systems Engineering seems to miss two very important points.

The first is that even in situations where an engineer is usually involved, for example in the design of a chemical plant, there is a systems problem to be solved before conventional engineering can begin. Thus the design of a plant must be seen as part of the Investment Planning System of the Company. The systems problem is concerned with answering such questions as "Why should we make this product anyway as compared with other products?" If the answer to this is in the affirmative, "What is the best way to manufacture it as cheaply as possible on a large scale?" "Does the venture still look economically viable, bearing in mind the activities of competitors?" "How big should the plant be and where should it be located?", and so on. Finally, a systems problem has to be solved first to determine the interactions which the various plant units must meet in order that they can play their designed role in optimizing an overall economic criterion. It follows that when the systems job is finished, there is still a major engineering job to be done to convert the system specifications for each individual unit into detailed engineering design and hardware. However, this detailed engineering design can turn out to be pointless and wasteful in resources unless the systems job has been properly executed.

The second and more important reason that there is a difference between engineering and Systems Engineering is that the same systems thinking which can be applied to the design of hardware systems, such as space rockets, plants or ships, can also be applied, for example, to parts of firms, or whole firms, or to local government. Conventionally a firm is not regarded as a system analogous to a space rocket. But the systems engineer claims that, by definition, a firm is a system of at least similar complexity and, moreover, that to look at a firm in this way provides an opportunity for improving its efficiency markedly. Thus the systems approach to design can be applied to these much wider Commercial, Management and "software" systems just as well as to the "hardware" systems with which the engineer is more familiar.

Operations (Operational) Research and Systems Engineering

Whereas Systems Engineering has its origins in the design of Engineering Systems, Operations Research is said to

have been born in the Battle of Britain which led to the, by now, legendary studies into the optimal size of convoys. Operations Research is defined by the British Operational Research Society as "The application of the methods of science to complex problems arising in the direction and management of large systems of men, machines, materials and money in industry, business, government, and defence. The distinctive approach is to develop a scientific model of the system, incorporating measurements of factors such as chance and risk, with which to predict and compare the outcomes of alternative decisions, strategies or controls. The purpose is to help management determine its policy and actions scientifically." Hence, it is clear that Operations Research and Systems Engineering have much in common. In fact, during an article in a book entitled "Operations Research and Systems Engineering", Roy [13] states that "in a certain sense, operations research and systems engineering *are* the same". However, in the same breath he goes on to say that "The operations research team is more likely to be concerned with operations *in being* rather than with operations *in prospect*" and "systems engineers are more likely to be engaged in the design of systems yet to be, rather than in the operation of systems in being". This supposed difference has also been suggested by several other people, including Hall [19]. However, it is a false and artificial distinction since Systems Engineering is just as much concerned with redesigning existing systems as in designing new ones. In fact, designing a new system is usually the most satisfactory of situations since a fresh start can be made. However, the majority of systems have just evolved in a haphazard way without any clear objectives, or if there were clear objectives originally, these have now changed without any consequent change in the system. In such a situation, the application of systems engineering is as valuable, or even more valuable, as when a fresh start can be made.

To a certain extent it is true that, in its early days, Systems Engineering was more concerned with the design of what may be called Technical Systems, such as military and space systems, new plants, the improvement of existing plants and systems engineering studies leading to the installation of on-line computers on plants. (These are areas which involve the development of new technology and as such lie outside the field of practice of operational research workers.) However, in recent years, this activity has been extended considerably and the systems approach is now being applied, for example, to such wide ranging problems as the design of integrated production–distribution planning and control systems, corporate planning systems, transportation systems and to improving the efficiency of departments in a city administration.

The writer cannot speak for Operational Research but can only repeat that Systems Engineering is concerned with placing a big emphasis on the design of the total system and not individual sub-systems. It is difficult to escape the conclusion that if Operational Research is really concerned with the overall design of complex human-machine systems, the subject has a rather unfortunate title and that many of its exponents are nevertheless content to tinker with the sub-systems.

Systems Analysis and Systems Engineering

The word Systems Analysis has been used, for example by the RAND Corporation [30] and the Systems Development Corporation [31] to describe the application of the systems approach to the wider "non-hardware" systems mentioned earlier. It is unfortunate perhaps that, in their attempts to emphasize that Systems Analysis is concerned with the design of much wider systems than "engineering" or "hardware" systems, the users of this word have only told part of the story. This is because systems synthesis is an equally important step as systems analysis in the design of systems. However, the word "engineering" covers the processes of analysis and synthesis and it is for this reason that the Department of Systems Engineering at the University of Lancaster has been so named. The word "engineer" has been used in the general sense of the man who designs or engineers systems whether they be composed of hardware or software or just people.

Clearly, semantic discussions resolve nothing. However, since Operational Research, Systems Analysis and Systems Engineering have a great deal in common, then the systems approach would suggest that there is need for better communication between them.

B. Stages in the application of Systems Engineering

This section gives some general guide lines as to how a systems engineer would tackle any problem. The various stages to be described represent a breakdown and amplification of the four steps

1. Systems Analysis,
2. Systems Design,
3. Implementation,
4. Operation,

mentioned earlier and are summarized in the flow diagram of Figure 8.5. It is *not* suggested that all systems projects will proceed along the following lines. Rather, the stages are intended as rough guide lines to aid clear thinking and to emphasize above all that *Systems Engineering is an orderly and well-disciplined way of getting things done.*

1. SYSTEMS ANALYSIS

1.1. Formulation of the problem
1.2. Organization of the project
1.3. Definition of the system
1.4. Definition of the wider system
1.5. Objectives of the wider system
1.6. Objectives of the system
1.7. Definition of overall economic criterion
1.8. Information and data collection
↓
2. SYSTEMS DESIGN

2.1. Forecasting
2.2. Model building and simulation
2.3. Optimization
2.4. Control
2.5. Reliability
↓
3. IMPLEMENTATION

3.1. Documentation and Sanction Approval
3.2. Construction
↓
4. OPERATION

4.1. Initial operation
4.2. Retrospective appraisal
4.3. Improved operation

Figure 8.5   Detailed stages in a Systems Approach to problems.

B.1. Systems Analysis

The first step in Systems Engineering is Systems Analysis. This involves the following stages:

1.1. Recognition and formulation of the problem.
1.2. Organization of the systems project.
1.3. Definition of the system.
1.4. Definition of the wider system of which the system being studied forms part.
1.5. Definition of the objectives of the wider system.
1.6. Definition of the objectives of the system being studied.
1.7. Definition of the overall economic criterion.
1.8. Information and data collection.

1.1. *Recognition and formulation of the problem*

Firms and organizations do not exist to provide employment for systems engineers! Rather, they have problems which arise in the day-to-day running of their organizations, the solution of which would lead to improved efficiency and profitability. The job of the systems engineer is to provide effective solutions to those problems.

A problem arises because some manager needs *help* – he may have noticed that something is going wrong or he may need help to make a planning decision or to implement a planning decision made higher up. He may then decide to consult the systems engineer as an individual accustomed to taking an overall point of view towards solving problems. In these circumstances the systems engineer should interrogate the manager very thoroughly and also all other persons within the organization who are likely to be able to help. In particular he should ask

(1) How did the problem arise?

(2) Who are the people who believe it to be a problem?

(3) If it involves implementing a planning decision made higher up, what is the chain of argument leading to the making of the decision?

(4) Why is the solution important? How much money might it save?

(5) Is it the right problem anyway? Might it not be just a manifestation of a much deeper problem? Would greater benefits accrue if that problem were solved rather than the one posed by the manager?

(6) Inevitably, the resources available to the firm are limited. On the evidence available at this stage, does it seem that there would be a reasonable return on systems effort if applied to the project or would this effort be better employed in tackling a different problem?

As a result of this dialogue, a clearer picture should now begin to emerge about the scope of the problem and the likely benefits which would result from its solution.

1.2. *Organization of the project*

1. *Composition of the systems team.* Once the scope of the problem has been defined, the way in which it is to be tackled should be mapped out. Systems Engineering is a team activity not an individual activity and an *ad hoc* systems team should now be set up. Ideally this should be able to draw some of its members from a small central systems department within the company. In addition, it will be necessary to supplement these systems men by people, drawn from various departments within the company, whose specialist knowledge can be brought to bear upon the problem.

Many companies do not have a central systems organization nor a great deal of systems experience. This does not mean that a systems team cannot be formed. The best resources available within the organization for tackling the problem should be brought together and, with efficient leadership, they can develop into a systems team very quickly.

A typical systems team would contain some or all of the following:

(*a*) *Team leader* – ideally an experienced systems engineer, or alternatively, someone with a keen intellect and a great deal of knowledge of the problem which is to be tackled.

(*b*) *User* – a representative of the team which will operate the engineered system. For example, if the problem is to design and build a chemical plant, production department should be represented, preferably by the plant manager designate.

(*c*) *Model builders* – to take part in the model building itself and also to liaise with and stimulate those specialist functional departments (such as research, process development and sales departments) which will be able to provide information for the sub-systems models.

(*d*) *Designers* – if the system involves the building of hardware, representatives of the engineering team who will be responsible for the design of this hardware to meet the system specification. Similarly, if the system involves software, representatives of the team which will design this software, for example computer programmers, data processing and computer experts.

(*e*) *Computer Programmers/Mathematicians* – to programme the systems models and to help with the optimization of the design.

(*f*) *An economist or accountant* – to provide information on the general economic environment of the problem which will help in defining the overall economic criterion, and to assist in obtaining cost information for the model.

(*g*) *Systems engineers* – these may contribute to a greater or lesser extent in the model building, programming, optimization, economic evaluation, etc. In some situations, they may have to do most of this work themselves. Above all, however, they should be taking an overall view of the development of the project.

2. *Terms of reference.* The systems team should take steps to ensure that they are given the widest possible terms of reference and are given access to any information or

person. In other words, they should be given the maximum opportunity to stand back and take a fresh look at the problem.

3. *Scheduling the project*. The systems engineering team should apply the systems approach to the conduct of its own activities to ensure that the work is carried out logically and systematically and that the implementation of the systems study can take place by an allotted time. Thus a decision network should be constructed (for example a critical path schedule), targets set and duties allocated. In this way, maximum effort can be concentrated in areas which are most important. The systems team will then ensure, by its critical approach to its own method of working, that problems are tackled in their correct order of importance.

1.3. *Definition of the system*

The next task of the systems engineering team is to define in precise terms the system which is to be studied. This is a process of *analysis* in which the system has to be broken down into its important sub-systems and the interactions between these sub-systems indicated by drawing a *flow-block diagram*. The subsequent task of the systems engineer is one of *synthesis*, that is to design or engineer the individual sub-systems so that they work together towards achieving an overall objective. As indicated in Section A.1, the flows typically appearing in a flow-block diagram represent money, energy, materials, information and decisions. In constructing a flow diagram, it is sometimes helpful to use a different flow convention for these different types of flow, or alternatively, the flows should be clearly labelled.

The extent to which the system needs to be broken down into sub-systems may not be known initially. For example, certain processing units in a chemical plant may usefully be lumped together and considered as one unit for the purpose of building a model to establish the overall system requirements. To avoid making the system description too complex, it is usually better to work with a simple representation of the system first and then elaborate later if necessary. If the system already exists, as for example in a process improvement study of an existing plant, the simplicity of the system diagram, and its description, is justified if the resulting model is able to describe those areas which are sensitive to cost. Even when nothing very much is known about the system, as in the initial stages of the design of a new plant, there is a great deal to be said for making the system description simple to start with and then examining the consequences of gradual elaboration later.

A related question to the simplicity of the system description is that the systems design process must be sufficiently *flexible*, so that this description can be changed as further knowledge and experience is accumulated during the course of the project. This is especially important in the design of a new system when there may be very inadequate knowledge at the start of a project. As the project proceeds, the system description will become clearer as the process of *innovation* develops. Indeed, there may have to be several iterations of the design process before a satisfactory solution can be found.

1.4. *Definition of the wider system which contains the system being studied*

To define the objectives of the system, it is necessary to display very clearly the role which the system plays in the wider system of which it forms part. A separate flow-block diagram should be constructed to display this role very clearly. By contrast to the flow-block diagram of the system itself, the flow-block diagram of the system as part of a wider system should include as much detail as is available. Invariably, it happens that the relationship of the system to the wider system is hazy and unclear to most people at the beginning. Hence a great deal of clear thinking will be necessary to fill in sufficient detail on this flow-block diagram so that proper account is taken of the interactions between the system and the wider system when formulating objectives. The flow diagram of the wider system provides an excellent tool for clarifying this thinking.

1.5. *Definition of the objectives of the wider system*

The block diagrams of the system and of the wider system provide invaluable tools for analysing and then formulating objectives. Because systems form part of a hierarchy of systems, it is impossible to dissociate the objectives of the system being studied from those of the wider system of which it forms part. In fact, it is the objectives of the wider system which are the crucial ones since they determine the *environment* within which the system has to function. If this environment changes, then so will the objectives of the system change. To take a very simple example, the objectives of a single chemical plant must fit into the overall production plan of the company. At different times the company plan may stipulate one of several objectives.

For example,

(1) the plant must make a fixed tonnage of the right quality product at minimum cost per ton. This is commonly referred to as a *production limited* situation, or

(2) the plant must make as much product as possible while satisfying the same or possibly less stringent quality constraints than in (1), or

(3) the plant must make a fixed tonnage at minimum cost per ton but using a cheaper, less pure, raw material, and so on.

Therefore, in a process improvement exercise, there may not be one unique objective but rather a *catalogue* of possible objectives, each resulting in a different way of operating the plant. Thus the relevant objective at any given instant must be dictated by the needs of the wider system. Definition of the objectives of the wider system brings several advantages:

(1) It focuses attention on the fact that systems must be designed so that:

> (*a*) junior systems in a hierarchy should play their designed role in achieving the objectives of more senior systems in the hierarchy,
>
> (*b*) senior systems in the hierarchy should make a clear, unambiguous statement of what the junior systems are expected to contribute.

Without such clearly defined responsibilities a system may operate very inefficiently, or if the objectives are very vague, anarchy may result.

(2) We have seen that the objectives of systems at the same level in the hierarchy are usually in conflict – such systems are usefully described as *interlocking* or *competitive* systems. Thus, defining the objectives of the wider system is essential so that the objectives of the competitive systems can be formulated in such a way that they contribute effectively to the objectives of the wider system instead of pulling in different directions. For example, two plant managers can very easily operate their own plants in such a way that they optimize their performance individually but at the expense of not meeting the company's objectives efficiently. Such conflicts are of frequent occurrence in industry and in other walks of life and stem from a failure to define objectives clearly.

(3) Facing up to the objectives of the senior systems in the hierarchy will counteract the tendency to omit these systems altogether. There will always be a tendency to omit the systems at the top because they seem too vague, or more importantly, *too difficult* to formulate. In fact, the systems at the top should not be omitted until the consequence of doing so on the system being studied have been carefully ascertained and shown to be of no consequence. For example, it might be sensible to omit the influence of the British Economy in deciding how to operate a plant but to omit the influence of raw material availability within the company might be very short sighted.

(4) By defining the objectives of the senior systems in the hierarchy, the system under study can be designed so that it is capable of *adapting itself to change* quickly. For example, by knowing that the production system of a company may make changing demands on an individual plant, the operation of that plant can be planned so that it is able to react quickly to the changes when they occur. This can be achieved, for example, by tabulating the best operating conditions for different values of the throughput.

(5) The performance of junior systems in the hierarchy may improve, especially the performance of the people involved. By communicating the objectives of the higher systems to those involved in the junior systems, their sense of involvement is increased, with a consequent increase in efficiency. Sometimes immediate and worthwhile benefits can result by communicating objectives of the senior systems since it can pin-point areas where conflicts are leading to a deterioration in efficiency.

1.6. *Definition of the objectives of the system*

The end product of any definition of objectives is the formulation of the criterion, usually an economic one, which measures the efficiency with which the system is achieving its objective. The formulation of the economic criterion may require a careful study in its own right. However, in the early stages it is better to define the objectives in broad terms.

There will usually be conflicting objectives and at the start of a systems study it is essential to make a *comprehensive list* of all possible objectives in *their anticipated order of importance*. One, or possibly a few, objectives might then be singled out as being the most important ones. What weight to give these conflicting objectives in the formulation of the overall economic criterion will have to be considered later.

At this important stage of any systems study, much questioning will have to be done and many different points of view listened to. In the end the systems engineer must make up his own mind about the correct objectives, then get agreement with all concerned and finally communicate his findings to everybody so that their future cooperation can be relied upon.

Important points to be borne in mind at this stage are:

(1) The systems engineer may meet resistance when he tries to define objectives. People who have got along quite well in the past with vague objectives may object to the influx of new ideas. However, the systems engineer must persist because no system can be designed properly unless it is clearly known what it is trying to achieve.

(2) He may be frustrated because the objectives are not clear. If after persistent attempts, objectives are still not satisfactorily defined, this must be faced up to. This means that the resulting system will have to be acknowledged to be imperfect and improved later if more precise information becomes available. His motto should be "It ain't much but it's all I've got" rather than "I'm sorry mate but I don't know enough to start!"

(3) Where possible, objectives should be *simple and direct*. If simple quantitative objectives are not possible, they should be replaced by simple subjective objectives. Failure to quantify objectives should be recorded and brought to the attention of people so that attempts can be made at some future stage to improve precision. In other words, the systems engineer can make a big contribution by being objective about subjective matters!

1.7. *Definition of the overall economic criterion*

Once the objectives have been agreed, the next step is to define, in as precise terms as possible, a criterion which measures the efficiency with which the system can achieve its objective. Usually, but not invariably, this criterion will be an economic one, for example a company may measure performance by its rate of return on capital, or the performance of a chemical plant may be measured by the cost per ton of manufacturing the main product. The more precise the objectives, the easier it is to set up quantitative criteria. Conversely, if the overall objectives are not precise, then there will have to be some subjective criterion of performance.

An overall economic criterion should be:

(1) *Related to objectives* – care should be taken to avoid a precise mathematical criterion which does not embrace all the objectives.

(2) *Simple and direct* – if possible, both objectives and performance criterion should be expressed as concisely and simply as possible.

(3) *Clearly agreed and accepted, even if qualitative* – in practice confusion often arises because of the application of contradictory criteria. For example, one manager may decide that a certain course of action is desirable because

it is based on a certain criterion, whereas another manager in the same company may reach the opposite decision because his criterion is different. It is very important that criteria of performance be agreed by everyone, notified to everyone and applied by everyone in the same way – otherwise confusion results and efficiency is impaired.

Resolution of conflicting objectives. To formulate an economic criterion, it is necessary to decide on the compromises which have to be achieved between the conflicting objectives of a system. There are two basic ways in practice in which conflicting objectives can be met.

(1) By *weighting* alternative objectives in the overall criterion.

(2) By imposing *constraints* (sometimes objective, sometimes subjective) on certain variables which enter into the economic criterion.

These two methods are now discussed briefly.

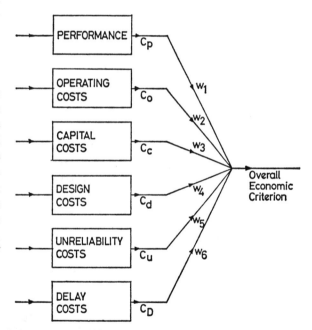

Figure 8.6 Conflicting objectives in the design of a system.

1. *Weighting of objectives.* Figure 8.6 summarizes typical conflicting objectives which have to be met by any system. This shows that the overall economic criterion has to be obtained by attaching weights $w_1, w_2, \ldots, w_6$ to:

1. The performance of the system.
2. Operating and production costs.

3. Capital costs.
4. Design costs.
5. Unreliability costs.
6. "Delay to build" costs.

Very often these weights will not be known exactly and it may be necessary to make *value judgements* of what the real weights are. This does not detract from the exercise but on the contrary forces designers to think more clearly about the subjective judgements that they have to make. For example, in the case of a plant design study, the influence of these costs on total cash flow as the project develops is illustrated in Figure 8.7. Thus the time and money spent on each of the four stages – research, development, construction and start-up – can have a considerable effect on the profitability of the project.

Most plant design studies nowadays try to balance capital against operating costs. Unfortunately, insufficient attention seems to be paid to unreliability and "delay to build" costs. Bad judgement of these costs can result in poor performance during the early years of a plant and convert what would otherwise have been a highly profitable project into one whose profitability is unacceptably low.

Figure 8.6 gives the impression that the weighting of objectives is *static*. However, in most systems design, the weighting must be *dynamic* so that the contribution of the various costs to project profitability can be discounted over the life time of the project. Discussion of the various forms of discounted cash flow criteria now being used to weight conflicting objectives lies outside the scope of the present paper. However, all criteria are based on the fact that a predicted net cash flow of £a_i for the project in year i is worth £$a_i/(1 + r)^i$ now, where r is the interest rate one

could reasonably expect to earn by investing one's money in other projects inside the company, or possibly outside. For example, the *net present worth* (N.P.W.) of a project is defined by

$$\text{N.P.W.} = \sum_{i=1}^{n} a_i/(1 + r)^i,$$

where n is the expected life time of the project. Again, from the point of view of systems design, such criteria should not be used in a mechanical fashion. In practice, it is necessary to look at the individual predicted cash flows and their *uncertainty* in greater detail because two projects with widely different cash flows can give rise to the same net present worth. Therefore, it is usually necessary to compare the *risks* associated with two projects before a decision in favour of one or the other can be made.

2. *Constraints*. It is not always possible to achieve a compromise between conflicting objectives by weighting alone. In addition, the conflicts may have to be resolved by imposing certain constraints on the design of the system. These constraints are usually of two kinds:

(*a*) physical constraints,

(*b*) constraints which are a recognition of the fact that *it is sometimes difficult to quantify.*

Once again, this is illustrated by considering the design of a chemical process. Under (*a*) come constraints on quality and physical properties imposed by customers and by equipment performance, etc. Under (*b*) come, for example, factors associated with the safe running of the process at conditions as near as possible to the inflammable or explosive limits or other process constraints. If an explosion happens, there may be a loss of human life and the plant may be shut down for long periods.

Figure 8.7 Cash flow as a function of time for a typical project.

To allow for such factors in a quantitative way would be too difficult or too complex. As mentioned earlier, much is to be gained by making the overall economic criterion simple. In other words, one should try to build in those main economic features which are well understood and then impose certain constraints on the freedom of choice of certain variables in the design to allow for factors which are much more difficult to quantify, such as the loss in customers due to bad quality and to shutdowns due to explosions, the loss of lives, etc.

This illustrates the general point made about objectives earlier, namely that a detailed analysis of the economics of a situation may reveal areas which are difficult to quantify. As with objectives, it is better to bring to the foreground these subjective elements rather than bury one's head in the sand and to pretend that one is making progress by using a criterion which is easy to quantify but *irrelevant* to the real-life situation. The fact that subjective elements are present does not mean that nothing can be done. On the contrary, it means that subjective economic judgements have to be made and these are usually best expressed in the form of constraints imposed on the design. Indeed, once this is done, the possibility arises of varying the constraints to see what effect they have on the economic performance of the system.

1.8. *Information and data collection*

The final, and probably most extensive, stage in Systems Analysis is the gathering of data and information which will form the basis of any future modelling of the system. If the system is not in existence, then the fact finding will have to be based on new research and development and on other similar systems if they exist. Data will be required not only to provide information about the operation of the system but also to make *forecasts* of the *environment* in which the system will have to operate in future.

Efficient information and data collection requires

(i) *Clear thinking* about the problem so that relevant sources of information can be tapped.

(ii) *Ability to communicate* in speech and in writing so that people are stimulated into parting with information and into volunteering new information.

(iii) *A grasp of statistical techniques* so that the significance of the data can be appreciated and used in subsequent model building and decision making.

B.2. Systems Design (or Synthesis)

The systems analysis stage should have opened up the problem, enabled objectives to be defined and initiated fact finding. Based on these foundations, the Systems Design stage can then be tackled with confidence. It is convenient to discuss the design stage under the five headings

2.1. Forecasting,
2.2. Model Building and Simulation,
2.3. Optimization,
2.4. Control,
2.5. Reliability.

2.1. *Forecasting*

Forecasting is the first important step in the design of any system. For example, in the design of a production control or production planning system, forecasts of demand may be needed for each fortnight or month for up to a year ahead (short term forecasting). Similarly, to design a plant, forecasts of demand will be needed for a period of several years ahead (medium term forecasting) and to design a Corporate Plan for a company, forecasts of the firm's activities and environment will be needed for up to 15 or even 20 years ahead (long term forecasting, technological forecasting).

Accurate forecasts are essential for the efficient design of any system. By contrast, if the forecasts are inaccurate, they can not be compensated for by sophisticated model building and optimization at a later stage. Indeed such sophistication at a later stage may then turn out to be a complete waste of time.

Forecasts of future values are not of much use on their own. In addition, it is essential to obtain estimates of their *accuracy*, so that this can be allowed for in assessing the *risk* associated with the design of the system.

2.2. *Model building and simulation*

To compute the costs associated with different ways of running a system, it is necessary to predict the performance of the system over a wide range of operational conditions. To do this, a *model* of the system needs to be built. By a model is meant a *quantitative* description of the behaviour of the system which can be used to predict performance over a relevant range of operating conditions and real life environments. In its crudest form, a model could consist of a set of tables or graphs; at a more sophisticated level it might be written in mathematical form, namely as a set of algebraic or differential equations.

Model building is not a straightforward, but rather, a highly creative activity. It is of necessity an *iterative* or *adaptive* process in which one moves from a state of little knowledge to one of greater knowledge – in other words, it is a process of hauling oneself up by one's bootstraps. To design a system, many different types of model may need to be developed. Experience and good judgement are needed to decide which type of model should be used for any particular situation, so that the system can then be designed as efficiently as possible with the minimum expenditure of time and money.

Quantitative models useful in Systems Engineering may be classified into four types:

(i) *Descriptive* models, which provide a qualitative description and insight, as compared with *predictive* models, which should be able to give predictions of the economic performance of a system to a required degree of accuracy.

(ii) *Mechanistic* models, which are based on a mechanism by the way that the system behaves, as compared with *empirical* or *statistical* models, obtained by fitting data obtained from the system.

(iii) *Steady state* models, which are based on average performance, as compared with *dynamic* models which allow for the way that performance fluctuates with time.

(iv) *Local* models, which describe the behaviour of sub-systems, as compared with *global* models which tie together the sub-system models into a model for the overall system.

Model building is the cornerstone of any scientific activity and, as such, plays a very important role in systems engineering – as mentioned on p. 152, a model replaces guesses by facts. However, there are important differences between the approach required for model building in systems engineering compared with that required for other scientific subjects. For example, in physics and chemistry, model building is almost an end in itself since the objective is to subsume as many facts as possible under the umbrella of a single model. In Systems Engineering, on the other hand, the end objective is to *optimize* the performance of a system and hence model building must be subservient to this objective. Thus a Systems Engineering team must:

(1) Ensure that model building is carried out *with a sense of purpose*, that is to enable a system to be designed as cheaply and efficiently as possible.

(2) *Tie together* the various specializations that may be needed for building models of the sub-systems. In particular, the systems team will always be emphasizing to the specialist model builders that the important thing is to model those areas to which the overall economic criterion is sensitive.

(3) *Ensure that work is concentrated where it is most needed*. Because it takes an overall view, the systems team will be in a much better position to pin-point those areas which are cost sensitive and, if necessary, to ask for more work to be done in those areas. Conversely, it will be in a better position to stop activity in those areas which are not cost sensitive. For example, in a plant design project an over-enthusiastic chemist may believe that it is necessary to predict a certain physical property to say within 1%, whereas from a systems viewpoint it may only be necessary to predict it to within 5% or even 10%. *As a general rule, models should be kept as simple as possible.*

(4) *Decide when the model is adequate* for the purposes for which it is needed, namely to predict overall system performance to a sufficient degree of accuracy. Model building is a fascinating activity and people, if left to their own initiative, tend to be carried away, tend to become emotionally involved and tend to waste time and money by over-elaborating the model. By contrast, the systems approach requires discipline to ensure that when the model is adequate, model building is terminated and the optimization stage begun as soon as possible.

(5) If the model is to be used for planning, see that an *effective dialogue* is conducted between the systems team and the managers who will use the model. Experience suggests that in such areas as production, investment and corporate planning, that this *dialogue must start whilst the model is being built* and not when the model is handed over. This is because models must be thoroughly understood by management if they are to be used effectively and moreover, because it is management that makes the decisions, their involvement at an early stage can often lead to suggestions resulting in substantial improvements and simplifications in the models themselves.

Simulation. Once a model of the overall system has been built, the model has to be converted from a *passive* device (a set of graphs or equations) into an *active* device which can then be used to *simulate* the behaviour of the system when subjected to:

(a) realistic inputs typical of those which the operational system will have to meet in practice,

(b) realistic disturbances, which will cause the behaviour of the system to fluctuate from its average or steady state performance.

Hence a simulation is a *working* or *operational* model of the system which should be able to reproduce the actual behaviour of the real system to an accepted degree of accuracy. If the simulation is accurate, data generated from the simulation should agree closely with data from the operational system. In other words, from the point of view of systems design, we can treat the simulation *as if it were* the actual system and make changes to the parameters in the simulation to see how to optimize the system.

The inputs or disturbances, in the simulation may be:

   (i) deterministic, or
   (ii) statistical,

and correspondingly, the simulation is said to be *deterministic* or *statistical*. An example of a deterministic simulation is provided by a model of a chemical plant which is set up in such a way that it can be fed with average values of process inputs and used to calculate the corresponding values of the average outputs. An example of a statistical simulation is provided by a model which describes the random times of arrival of tankers at a port with a view to optimizing the berthing facilities.

In a statistical simulation, it may be possible to collect enough data relating to the statistically fluctuating variables directly from an operating system. However, it often happens that insufficient data are available to simulate the behaviour of the system over a sufficiently long period for the results to have meaning. In these cases, a statistical analysis will be needed to analyse the data so that a statistical (probability) model can be set up to describe the data. Armed with a statistical model, unlimited amounts of hypothetical data can then be generated so that the system can be simulated over a sufficiently long period of time.

In recent years, powerful computer simulation languages have been developed to speed up the simulation stage of a systems design. As with modelling, the systems engineer will emphasize that a simulation should be made as simple as possible so that optimization can go ahead with minimum delay.

2.3. *Optimization*

The next step after simulation is to optimize the system. Armed with a model which can predict performance, it is then possible to compute the value of the economic criterion corresponding to different modes of operating the system. For example, when designing an industrial plant, it enables the rate of return on capital to be calculated for different sizes of equipment and operating conditions, and so on. Choosing the system which results in the most favourable value of the economic criterion is what is meant by optimization. It is at this point that the importance of defining the overall objectives should become apparent. If the system

and its objectives are too narrow, then the most profitable mode of operation for this narrow system will almost certainly be in conflict with the most profitable conditions for the wider system which has been overlooked. This is usually referred to as *sub-optimization*.* One of the most important jobs of the systems engineer is to ensure that sub-optimization does not take place. He will constantly need to emphasize that the optimization of each sub-system independently will not in general lead to a system optimum. More strongly, he will have to emphasize that improvement to a particular sub-system *may actually worsen* the overall system.

During the last fifteen years, the need to optimize systems has stimulated the development of a number of mathematical techniques called *optimization techniques*.†

Although these mathematical techniques are very important, from a systems engineering point of view, optimization involves a great deal more than a mathematical problem. Assuming that the problem is one of maximization, optimization is equivalent to climbing a multi-dimensional hill. Very often one is debarred from climbing to the top because of the constraints on the design variables. However, in systems engineering work, one is not only interested in getting to the highest point possible on the hill and then planting the Union Jack at the summit! In the design of a system, three other much more important considerations have to be investigated, namely:

(1) The sensitivity of the economic criterion to changes in the parameters near the "optimum".

---

* It is stated [25] that the word "sub-optimize" was first used by C. J. Hitch [32]. In his analysis of the wartime problem where it was shown that convoys should be made as large as possible, he points out that although the final answer reached was approximately correct, it was arrived at for the wrong reasons. He argues that the reasons were wrong because too much emphasis was placed on a sub-system, namely a skirmish between a convoy and a submarine pack, rather than on the wider system, that is winning the Battle of the Atlantic or more importantly still, optimizing an even wider system, namely winning the war.

† From a mathematical point of view, the problem of optimization is one of maximizing or minimizing an overall economic criterion

$$f(x_1, x_2, \ldots, x_n)$$

which depends on various design parameters $x_1, x_2, \ldots, x_n$, (e.g. operating conditions, sizes of equipment, when designing a plant) and is subject to certain inequality constraints

$$g_i(x, x_{21}, \ldots, x_n) \leqslant c, i = 1, 2, \ldots, l$$

and certain equality constraints

$$h_j(x_1, x_2, \ldots, x_n) = d_j, j = 1, 2, \ldots, m.$$

(2) The sensitivity of the economic criterion to various assumptions made in the design.

(3) The effect of uncertainty in the forecasts of the environment in which the system will have to operate.

(1) In many optimization studies, there are usually more design variables to choose from than one usually can, or wants to, work with. As a first approach, one can choose those variables which appear to be the most important on intuitive grounds and optimize with respect to these. It is useful then to plot the economic criterion as a function of each variable, holding the others fixed at their best values – in this way one can identify the variables to which the value of the economic criteria is sensitive. Those variables to which it is insensitive can be left out and further optimization runs made with these insensitive variables replaced by new variables.

When all the sensitive variables have been discovered, the end point of any optimization study should be:

(a) to quote the best values of all variables.

(b) to give plots of the economic criterion with respect to each variable, holding all other variables at their best values.

(c) if possible, to give contour plots for certain pairs of variables, holding all other variables at their best values. This type of exercise can be very useful in discovering how one can "trade-off" one parameter against another in achieving a given cost or performance.

When (a), (b) and (c) are completed, it should be possible to obtain a clear picture of how the system is sensitive to cost.

Thus, if the overall economic criterion is smooth with respect to changes in the design parameters, then this information tells us that a wide range of systems is acceptable, each with a value of the economic criterion that is roughly the same as that of the "best" system.

Figure 8.8 Sensitivity of a design to the design parameters.

This constitutes a good design, as indicated in Figure 8.8. On the other hand, if the economic criterion is steep and pointed, small changes in the design of the system will produce very marked changes in its profitability. Such sensitivity to small changes in the design parameters is undesirable and leads to a bad design since one cannot be absolutely certain that the assumptions, on which the design was based, are valid. If the assumptions are wrong, there might be a high probability that the realized economic performance will occur in the foothills of the surface rather than near the top.

(2) This brings us to a very important part of the optimization stage, namely that it is essential that changes should be made in the assumptions on which the design is based and an examination made of the effects which these changes have on the system. If the changes produce markedly different systems, then one will have to think again. On the other hand, if they produce systems having the same general features, then one can feel more assured about recommending the design. The system can then be said to be *robust* with respect to the underlying assumptions.

(3) Not only must sensitivity to assumptions about performance of sub-systems be investigated but also sensitivity to the uncertainty in the forecasts of the environment within which the system will have to operate. For example, in designing a plant, if the sales forecasts are very uncertain, it has to be faced up to that the most pessimistic forecasts might be the ones that actually occur, and hence that low profitability may result. However, one should clearly not design in the expectation that the most pessimistic forecasts will be realized. A *risk analysis* is then very important in helping to assess the most reasonable approach to the design problem. For example, this form of analysis can be especially helpful if a multi-product complex is being designed when the sales forecasts for each product are subject to different degrees of uncertainty. The size of these uncertainties can have an appreciable effect on the way in which the complex is designed.

To summarize, at the optimization stage the systems engineer should pay particular attention to the following:

(1) He should be aware of the dangers of sub-optimization and indeed of *leaving out altogether* certain important variables.

(2) After locating the optimum design conditions, he should examine very carefully the economic criterion surface to see which parameters are cost sensitive.

(3) He should guard against "very sharp optima" since a system which is very cost sensitive may be highly dependent on the assumption made in the design.

(4) He should make a *sensitivity analysis* to see whether changes in the assumptions lead to systems with the same general features. If not, he should think again.

(5) Finally, he should be very conscious of the fact that, when optimization is complete, a *very costly decision* may have to be made to allow the optimized design to be built. Therefore, at the optimization stage, he should be guided by certain techniques for making decisions in the presence of uncertainty, such as risk analysis.

2.4. *Control*

When a system has been optimized, a control system must be set up so that the most profitable design conditions can be realized when the system is operated in a real life environment. Control is necessary because unpredictable *disturbances* enter a system which cause its *actual* performance to deviate from its *predicted* performance. For example, local control devices will need to be installed on a chemical plant to regulate automatically the flow of materials, the levels of liquids in tanks and the temperatures and pressures required to achieve the most profitable operating conditions. Similarly, a management control system is needed to control a company production plan. This means that when a company production plan has been formulated, it must be backed up by an accounting system which feeds information to senior managers indicating whether the plan is being "kept on target". Management can then be helped to take corrective action to compensate for deviations from the plan. As argued elsewhere [4]:

(1) Control should be thought of as an integral part of the design of the system and not an afterthought, as often happens for example in the design of an industrial plant.

(2) A systems approach takes away the undue attention that is sometimes given to the mechanics of the control of local loops and focuses attention on the wider questions of where should control be exercised, how sophisticated should it be, what equipment is needed, whether an on-line computer is justifiable, and so on.

(3) A systems approach focuses attention on the economic benefits, both tangible and intangible, which result from control and demands that the cost should be justified as part of the design of the overall system.

(4) Most important of all, the advantages of local control within a firm can only be realized effectively when it

plays its planned role within a hierarchy of technical and financial control systems within the company.

2.5. *Reliability*

The importance of system reliability has already been mentioned in the section dealing with the definition of the economic criterion (stage 1.7). A good control system will go part of the way towards ensuring good reliability. For example, if there are process constraints which must not be isolated in the operation of a plant, the control system will have to be both efficient and reliable to keep clear of these constraints. However, systems reliability involves looking at aspects other than control by considering the overall effect of *uncertainty* on the design of the system. Uncertainty in forecasting environmental factors has already been discussed on p. 157. Other sources of unreliability are, for example, breakdown of equipment, non-availability of resources in the form of raw materials and men to perform operating and maintenance tasks. To cope with such unpredictable events requires redundant or stand-by equipment, extra storage and capacity, extra manpower and so on. This inevitably leads to higher capital and operating costs so that reliability questions must be considered as an integral part of the overall optimization of the design. The singling out of systems reliability as a separate stage in this paper is a reflection of the fact that reliability questions are all too often regarded as an *after thought*, invariably resulting in disastrous effects on performance and profitability. It is hoped to prepare a paper for a later issue of this journal to illustrate how neglect of reliability problems had serious consequences on the profitability of a large petrochemical complex.

Another reason for separating out reliability from optimization is that extensive simulation and modelling may be needed after the optimization stage to check that system unreliability has been reduced to an acceptable level.

B.3. Implementation

No systems study, however well carried out, is of much use unless it leads to positive action and is properly implemented. The important steps in this stage are:

3.1. Documentation and sanction approval.
3.2. Construction.

3.1. *Documentation and sanction approval*

The end product of a systems engineering study is a report (or reports) which should highlight proposals for ACTION.

Failure of *communication* at this very important stage can sometimes ruin what is otherwise a perfectly good systems study. To avoid this happening,

(1) *before issue*, the form and content of the final reports should be discussed and agreed with those senior managers whose backing will be needed to implement the results of the study, and not planted on their desks as a "fait accompli" before any discussion has taken place.

(2) the report should be simple, direct and logical. A three tier report is recommended for work of this kind.

(i) (*a*) A brief statement of the problem,
(*b*) a summary of the main conclusions and benefits of the study,
(*c*) a summary of the recommendations, including an overall figure for the savings and the cost of implementing them.

Many senior managers will only have time to read this part of the report so that it should make the maximum impact in the smallest amount of space.

(ii) A middle section where the main substance of the recommendations and benefits are argued so that any intelligent manager can understand them.
(iii) A final, more detailed, section containing the technical details of the study.

(3) a separate document will usually be needed within the organization to highlight the recommendations and to draw up a time-table or critical path schedule for their implementation. Such a sanctioning document may need to go to higher management to obtain approval for the project to proceed.

This is the most critical stage of any systems study since a *decision* has now to be reached as to whether to go ahead and build the system. Clearly, this decision should be made in an objective way and no attempt should be made to "dress up" the sanction proposal. On the other hand, the systems engineer should avoid the all-too-common mistake of putting forward bad arguments for a good case. In this way, not only does he not do justice to himself and his team but will have turned out to be a bad systems engineer.

3.2. *Construction*

Some projects may require the building of special hardware and software before implementation is possible. For example, if a plant is to be built, site works must be con-

structed and equipment ordered, delivered and installed on site. Similarly, if an on-line computer is to be installed on a plant, hardware in the form of instrumentation, control equipment and the computer itself must be ordered, delivered and installed. In addition, software in the form of computer programmes must be designed to implement the control and optimization algorithms.

The majority of the systems team may have moved on to other work by this stage. However, it is important to realize that the construction stage is still a part of the overall systems design. Thus, bad planning at the construction stage can have a big effect on the profitability of a project by holding up its start-up date. A systems approach at this stage would ensure that

(i) the systems team has specified the system in a clear and unambiguous way down to the minutest detail of all subsidiary sub-systems.
(ii) by the continued involvement of the systems team, the builders of the system are kept constantly in touch with the philosophy underlying the design and the way that it is to be implemented when in operation,
(iii) the project is well planned, duties allocated and targets met on time. Critical path scheduling emerges as the important technique in this area. One of the big advantages of C.P.S. is that it forces planners to concentrate attention on those areas which are critical for completion of the project.

B.4. Operation

After the system has been designed, built and installed in its working environment, then follow the steps:

4.1. *Initial Operation* of the system.
4.2. *Retrospective Appraisal* of the system in the light of operational experience, and if necessary,
4.3. *Improved Operation* of the system.

4.1. *Initial operation*

Effective liaison between the systems team and the users of the system is essential if the full benefits of the systems study are to be realized. In the writer's experience, this is the part of the exercise which is least well done in practice. The process of handing over is helped if:

(1) adequate documentation and training have been provided in advance,
(2) one of the users of the operational system has been involved as a member of the systems team, so that he is fully conversant with the design philosophy,

(3) adequate communication is maintained between the systems team and the users so that any defects and misunderstandings can be cleared up without delay.

Difficulties can usually be expected at the *start-up* of the system. However, good systems thinking will ensure that these upsets are minimized and that the operation works smoothly according to plan.

4.2. *Retrospective appraisal of the project*

After the new system has been operating for a sufficiently long period, the systems team should collaborate with the users of the system in making a retrospective appraisal of system performance. If the system is shown to be working according to plan, or better, everyone will be happy and the original systems thinking will have been vindicated. On the other hand, if system performance is not up to expectation, a postmortem will be needed. Nothing but harm, both to himself and to the systems approach, will be achieved if the systems engineer regards his job as finished when the original systems study has been completed. He must be prepared to accept full responsibility for the successful operation of the system and to identify himself with its success or failure. The retrospective appraisal may show that

(1) the original system study has overlooked certain factors, or
(2) the system has had to operate in an environment which is different from that for which it was designed. For example, a chemical plant may have had to switch to feedstocks of different quality, or the plant may have to operate at throughput in excess of design, and so on.

In either of the situations (1) or (2), a certain amount of reoptimization will be inevitable, however painful this may turn out to be. In the retrospective appraisal, a splendid opportunity arises of checking the economic assessment that was made at the design stage and hence to check the systems thinking. For example, in a computer control scheme, a list should be made of all the benefits, both tangible and intangible, which have been achieved. This is usually a very worthwhile exercise despite the fact that some of the benefits may be difficult to assess.

4.3. *Improved operation*

Improved operation of the system may be needed

(i) if the retrospective appraisal of the system shows that actual performance is falling short of plan, or

(ii) in certain cases, because certain parameters can only be optimized when operational experience has been obtained.

The system must then be "tuned" to its environment, leading to improved operation. If the retrospective appraisal shows that reoptimization is necessary, the systems engineering work at the design stage may have to be re-examined and modified. If the original systems study was conducted in an orderly way and well documented, this should not prove difficult. However, if this was not well done and people have left the company in the meantime, chaos may result – Joe Bloggs will have disappeared into thin air taking away in his head all the details of the system!

Finally, if redesign or retuning of the system is necessary, a decision will have to be made as to whether the improved system performance is acceptable.

Summary of stages in the application of Systems Engineering

The various stages in a Systems Approach are summarized below in the form of certain key questions which need to be answered.

1. Systems Analysis

1.1. *Formulation of the problem.* What is the problem? How did it arise? Who believes it to be important? Why is it important? Is it the right problem anyway? Will it save money? Is there the prospect of a reasonable rate of return on systems effort to justify tackling it as compared with some other problem?

1.2. *Organization of project.* What is the best composition for the systems team? Are its terms of reference sufficiently wide? When is the project to be completed? Has a preliminary project schedule been constructed? Have duties been allocated so that a more detailed critical path schedule can be set up?

1.3. *Definition of the system.* What is the precise nature of the system being studied? How is it best broken down into convenient sub-systems? What are the interactions between these sub-systems? Has a flow-block diagram been constructed?

1.4. *Definition of the wider system.* What is the environment (commercial, social, political) in which the system will have to operate? How does the system fit into the flow-block diagram of the wider system?

1.5. *Definition of the objectives of the wider system.* Have *competitive* and *senior* systems been properly taken into account? How do they influence the objectives of the system being studied? Is there a danger of sub-optimization?

1.6. *Definition of the objectives of the system.* Has a list of objectives in order of importance been drawn up? Have the constraints been listed? Are the objectives simple and direct? Are there some subjective features which are difficult to quantify? Have the objectives been agreed? Have they been communicated to all concerned with the design of the system?

1.7. *Precise definition of economic criterion.* Have conflicting objectives been properly weighted? Are the constraints reasonable? Are both criterion and constraints simple and direct? Have they been clearly agreed and accepted, even if qualitative?

1.8. *Information and data collection.* Have all important persons and sources of data been interrogated? Has all relevant data been assembled and presented in the best way?

2. Systems Design

2.1. *Forecasting.* Has all relevant data been used to forecast system environments? How accurate are these forecasts?

2.2. *Model building and simulation.* What type of model is best suited to the purposes at hand? Is the model building concentrated where it is most needed? Does the simulation performance agree sufficiently well with actual or conjectured performance for optimization to proceed?

2.3. *Optimization.* What optimization technique should be used? Have the performance sensitive variables been isolated? Have plots of the economic criterion with respect to the main variables been prepared? Has the sensitivity of the design to assumptions been checked? Would a risk analysis help?

2.4. *Control.* How can the optimized conditions be realized most economically as part of the overall design by installing a control system? Where should control be exercised and what instrumentation is needed? What type of control is required? How sophisticated should it be?

2.5. *Reliability.* Has the effect of uncertainty on system reliability been properly taken into account? Has the unreliability been reduced to an acceptable level?

3. Implementation

3.1. *Documentation and sanction approval.* Have the conclusions been agreed? Is the report well written so as to make the maximum impact? Has a time-table been prepared for implementation? Have the users of the system been fully involved and briefed?

3.2. *Construction.* Is the hardware and/or software fully integrated into the system specification? Have the users of the system been kept in touch with the philosophy underlying the design? Has a critical path schedule been drawn up for building and installation?

4. Operation

4.1. *Initial operation.* Have adequate plans been made for start up? Is there effective liaison with the users so that the system can be handed over? Have all the operational snags been ironed out?

4.2. *Retrospective appraisal.* Is the actual performance as predicted at the design stage? If not, why not? Has the retrospective appraisal been adequately documented?

4.3. *Improved operation.* Does the system need reoptimizing either by retraining or redesign? How is this best achieved? Finally, is the resulting improved operation now adequate?

Role of the Systems Engineer

A great deal of the work described above will involve people other than systems engineers. In this interdisciplinary approach, it is useful to highlight the *key roles* played by the systems engineer.

(1) He tries to distinguish the wood from the trees – what's it all about?

(2) He stimulates discussion about objectives – obtains agreement about objectives.

(3) He communicates the finally agreed objectives to all concerned so that their co-operation can be relied upon.

(4) He always takes an overall view of the project and sees that techniques are used sensibly.

(5) By his overall approach, he ties together the various specializations needed for model building.

(6) He decides carefully when an activity stops.

(7) He asks for more work to be done in areas which are sensitive to cost.

(8) He challenges the assumptions on which the optimization is based.

(9) He sees that the project is planned to a schedule, that priorities are decided, tasks allocated, and above all that the project is finished on time.

(10) He takes great pains to explain carefully what the systems project has achieved, and presents a well-argued and well-documented case for implementation.

(11) He ensures that the users of the operational system are properly briefed and well trained.

(12) He makes a thorough retrospective analysis of system performance.

References

[1] Jenkins, G. M. (1967) "Systems and their Optimisation", Inaugural lecture, University of Lancaster publication.

[2] Andrew, S. M. (1969) "Computer Modelling and Optimisation in the Design of a Complete Chemical Process", *Trans. Inst. Chem. Eng.* **47** (4), T79–T84.

[3] Jenkins, G. M. and Youle, P. V. (1968) "A Systems Approach to Management", *Opl. Res. Quart.* **19**, 5.

[4] Jenkins, G. M. (1968) "Control as Part of a Wider Systems Philosophy", *Meas. and Contr.* **1**, 105.

[5] Stephenson, G. G. (1965) "Production Optimisation at I.C.I.'s Complex at Wilton", *Chem. Proc.* **11**, 48.

[6] Taylor, A. W. and Youle, P. V. (1969) "The Optimisation of a Large Petrochemical Complex", *Jour. Syst. Eng.* **1**, 55.

[7] Jenkins, G. M. (1969) "A Systems Study of a Petrochemical Plant", *Jour. Syst. Eng.* **1**, 99.

[8] Schlager, K. J. (1956) "Systems Engineering – Key to Modern Development", *IRE Trans., Prof. Group Eng. Man.* **3**, 64.

[9] Schlager, K. J. (1957) "Organisation for Effective Systems Engineering", *Problems and Practices in Engineering Management*, Amer. Man. Assoc. Special Report **24**, 115.

[10] Goode, H. H. and Machol, R. E. (1959) *Systems Engineering*, McGraw-Hill, New York.

[11] Engstrom, E. W. (1957) "Systems Engineering – A Growing Concept", *Elec. Eng.* **76**, 113.

[12] Morton, J. A. (1959) "Integration of Systems Engineering with Component Development", *Elec. Man.* **64**, 85.

[13] Flagle, C. D., Huggins, W. H. and Roy, R. H. (eds.) (1960) *Operations Research and Systems Engineering*, Johns Hopkins Press, Baltimore.

[14] Williams, T. J. (1961) *Systems Engineering in the Process Industries*, McGraw-Hill, New York.

[15] Williams, T. J. (1962) "Systems Engineering a Large Chemical Plant Complex", *Elec. Eng.*, **82**, 590, August.

[16] Levine, S. and Buegler, R. J. (1962) "Large-Scale Systems Engineering for Airline Reservations", *Elec. Eng.*, **82**, 604, August.

[17] Chadwick, W. L. (1962) "Systems Engineering for Automation of a Large Power Station", *Elec. Eng.*, **82**, 598, August.

[18] Dommasch, D. O. and Landeman, C. W. (1962) *Principles Underlying Systems Engineering*, Pitman Publish. Corp., New York.

[19] Hall, A. D. (1962) *A Methodology for Systems Engineering*, Van Nostrand, Princeton, N.J.

[20] Feigenbaum, D. S. (1963) "Systems Engineering – A Major New Technology", *Ind. Qual. Con.* **20**, 9.

[21] Johnson, R. A., Kast, F. E. and Rosenzweig, J. E. (1963) *The Theory and Management of Systems*, McGraw-Hill, New York.

[22] Affel, H. A. (1964) "Systems Engineering", *Intern. Sci. Technol.* **35**, 18.

[23] Rosenstein, A. B. (1964) "Systems Engineering and Modern Engineering Design", *Amer. Ceram. Soc. Symposium Proc.* (Chicago, Ill., April 19), Miscellaneous Publication 267, Nat. Bur. Stand., Washington, D.C.

[24] Chestnut, H. (1965) *Systems Engineering Tools*, John Wiley, New York.

[25] Machol, R. E. (1965) *Systems Engineering Handbook*, McGraw-Hill, New York.

[26] Savas, E. S. (1965) *Computer Control of Industrial Processes*, McGraw-Hill.

[27] Chestnut, H. (1967) *Systems Engineering Methods*, John Wiley, New York.

[28] Jeffreys, T. O. (1967) "Nuclear Power and the Systems Engineer", Inaugural Lecture, University of Swansea Publication.

[29] Kline, M. B. and Lifson, M. W. (1968) "Systems Engineering", Chapter 2 of *Cost Effectiveness*, J. M. English (ed.), John Wiley, New York.

[30] Kahn, H. and Mann, I. (1957) *Techniques of Systems Analysis*, R. M. – 1829 – 1, The Rand Corporation.

[31] Adelson, M. (1966) "The System Approach – a Perspective", *Systems Development Corporation Magazine*, **9** (10), 1.

[32] Hitch, C. (1953) "Sub-optimisation in Operations Problems", *Jour. Op. Res. Soc. Am.* **1**, 87.

[33] Anthony, R. N. (1965) *Planning and Control Systems: A Framework for Analysis*, Harvard Grad. School of Bus. Admin., Boston, Mass.

[34] Schoderbek P. (ed.) (1967) *Management Systems*, John Wiley, New York.

Appendix

Techniques useful in Systems Engineering

The following table lists, alongside the various stages in the development of a system project, the techniques which are most relevant at each stage. The final column in the table gives a selected list of references which describe these techniques – note that the numbering refers to a selected

1. *Systems Analysis*

1.1. Formulation of the problem	Critical Examination	1, 2
1.2. Organization of the project	Critical path scheduling	3, 4, 5
1.3. Definition of the system		
1.4. Definition of the wider system		
1.5. Objectives of the wider system ⎱	Corporate Planning	6, 7, 8
1.6. Objectives of the system ⎰	Management by Objectives	9
1.7. Definition of overall economic criterion	Financial Practice and Economic Modelling	10
	Discounted cash flow techniques	11, 12
1.8. Information and data collection	Statistical techniques	13

2. *Systems Design*

2.1. Forecasting	Short and medium term forecasting	14
	Technological forecasting	15, 16
2.2. Model Building	Empirical – steady state models	17, 18, 19
	Empirical – dynamic models	14
	Mechanistic – steady state models	20, 21
	Mechanistic – dynamic models	22
	Probabilistic models	23
	Economic Modelling	10
	Numerical Mathematics	24
Simulation	Statistical (Monte Carlo) Simulation	25, 26, 27, 28
	Deterministic Simulation	29
	Analogue Computer Simulation	30
2.3. Optimization	Linear Programming	31, 32
	Hill climbing	33, 34
	Variational methods (Dynamic programming)	35, 36
	Risk Analysis	37
	Decision Theory	38
2.4. Control	Technical Control	39
	Computer Control	40
	Statistical Control	14
	Production Control	41, 42
	Management Control	43, 44
2.5. Reliability	Reliability Techniques	45

3. *Implementation*

3.1. Documentation and Sanction Approval	Report Writing	46
3.2. Construction	Critical path scheduling	3, 4, 5

4. *Operation*

4.1. Initial operation ⎱	Systems Analysis	
4.2. Retrospective appraisal ⎰	Techniques	
4.3. Improved operation	Systems Design Techniques	

bibliography of techniques given at the end of this appendix and is quite distinct from the reference numbering used in the main body of the paper. Most of the references are to books, but in some cases, recent papers are included.

Finally, there is a brief reference to the literature on Operational Research, including a very valuable survey by P. G. Moore.

Selected Bibliography of Techniques

1 Currie, R. M. (1963) Chapter 7 of *Work Study*, Pitman, London (2nd ed.).

2 Whitmore, D. A. (1968) Chapter 5 of *Work Study and Related Management Sciences*, Heinemann, London.

3 Lambourne, S. (1967) *Network Analysis in Project Management*, Industrial and Commercial Techniques, Ltd. Handbook.

4 Battersby, A. (1964) *Network Analysis for Planning and Scheduling*, Macmillan, London.

5 Archibald, R. D. and Villoria, R. L. (1967) *Network based Management Systems (PERT/CPM)*, John Wiley, New York.

6 Argenti, J. (1968) *Corporate Planning*, George Allen and Unwin, London.

7 Jackson, A. S., Stephenson, G. G. and Townsend, E. C. (1968) "Financial Planning with a Corporate Financial Mode", *The Accountant*, Jan. 27th–Feb. 17th.

8 Spencer, R. S. (1966) "Modelling strategies for corporate growth. Paper presented at the Society for General Systems Research session at the conference of the American Association for the Advancement of Science, Washington, D.C., Dec. 27th.

9 Odiorne, G. S. (1965) *Management by Objectives*, Pitman, London.

10 Baumol, W. J. (1965) *Economic Theory and Operations Analysis*, Prentice-Hall, Englewood Cliffs, N.J. (2nd ed.).

11 Merrett, A. J. and Sykes, A. (1963) *The Finance and Analysis of Capital Projects*, Longmans, London.

12 English, J. M. (ed.) (1968) *Cost-Effectiveness, The Economic Evaluation of Engineered Systems*, John Wiley, New York.

13 Lowe, C. W. (1968) *Industrial Statistics, Vol. 1*, Business Books, London.

14 Box, G. E. P. and Jenkins, G. M. (in the press) *Time Series Analysis, Forecasting and Control*, Holden-Day, San Francisco.

15 Jantsch, E. (1967) *Technological Forecasting in Perspective*, O.E.C.D. Publication, Paris.

16 Quinn, J. B. (1967) "Technological Forecasting", *Harvard Bus. Rev.* **45**, 89.

17 Draper, N. R. and Smith H. (1966) *Applied Regression Analysis*, John Wiley, New York.

18 Davis, O. L. (ed.) (1963) *The Design and Analysis of Industrial Experiments*, Oliver and Boyd, Edinburgh (2nd ed.).

19 Box, G. E. P. and Draper, N. R. (1969) *Evolutionary Operation*, John Wiley.

20 Himmelblan, D. M. and Bischoff, K. B. (1968) *Process Analysis and Simulation*, John Wiley, New York.

21 Hunter, W. G., Kittrell, J. R. and Mezaki, R. (1967) "Experimental Strategies for Mechanistic Model Building", *Trans. Inst. Chem. Eng.* **45**, 146.

22 Campbell, D. P. (1958) *Process Dynamics*, John Wiley, New York.

23 Feller, W. (1966) *Probability Theory and its Applications*, John Wiley, New York, Vol. 1, 1950, Vol. 2.

24 Conte, S. D. (1965) *Elementary Numerical Analysis*, McGraw-Hill, New York.

25 Tocher, K. D. (1964) *The Art of Simulation*, English Universities Press, London.

26 Naylor, T. H. *et al.* (1966) *Computer Simulation Techniques*, John Wiley, New York.

27 *Bibliography on Simulation*, I.B.M. publication (Form 320-0924-0), White Plains, New York.

28 Lee, A. M. (1966) *Applied Queuing Theory*, Macmillan, London.

29 Sargent, R. W. H. (1968) "Developments in Computer Aided Process Design", *Chem. Eng. Prog.* **64** (4), 39.

30 Rogers, A. E. and Connolly, T. W. (1960) *Analogue Computers in Engineering Design*, McGraw-Hill, New York.

31 Beale, E. M. L. (1968) *Mathematical Programming in Practice*, Pitman, London.

32 Gass, S. I. (1958) *Linear Programming*, McGraw-Hill, New York.

33 Box, M. J., Davies, D., Swann, W. H. (1969) *Non-Linear Optimisation Techniques*, I.C.I. Monographs in Mathematics and Statistics, No. 5, Oliver and Boyd, Edinburgh.

34 Wilde, D. and Beightler, C. (1966) *Foundations of Optimisation*, Prentice-Hall.

35 Jacobs, O. L. R. (1967) *An Introduction to Dynamic Programming*, Chapman and Hall, London.

36 Rosenbrock, H. H. and Storey, C. (1966) *Computational Techniques for Chemical Engineers*, Pergamon, London.

37 Adelson, R. M. (1965) "Criteria for Capital Investment: An Approach Through Decision Theory", *Opl. Res. Quart.*, **16**, 19 .

38 Morris, W. T. (1964) *The Analysis of Management Decisions*, Irwin, Homewood, Ill.

39 Kuo, B. C. (1962) *Automatic Control Systems*, Prentice-Hall, Englewood Cliffs.

40 Savas, E. S. (1965) *Computer Control of Industrial Processes*, McGraw-Hill, New York.

41 Magee, J. F. (1967) *Production Planning and Inventory Control*, McGraw-Hill, New York, 1958 2nd ed. J. F. Magee and D. Boodman, McGraw-Hill, New York.

42 Forrester, J. W. (1961) *Industrial Dynamics*, M.I.T. Press, Cambridge, Mass. (and see Article 18).

43 Boyce, R. O. (1967) *Integrated Managerial Control*, Longmans, London.

44 Anthony, R. N. (1965) *Planning and Control Systems: A Framework for Analysis*, Harvard Grad. School of Bus. Admin., Boston, Mass.

45 Sandler, G. H. (1963) *Systems Reliability Engineering*, Prentice-Hall, Englewood Cliffs, N.J.

46 Cooper, B. M. (1969) *Writing Technical Reports*, Penguin Books Ltd., Harmondsworth.

Bibliography of Operations Research

1 *Philosophy*

(a) Rivett, B. H. P. and Ackoff, R. L. (1963) *The Manager's Guide to Operational Research*, John Wiley, New York.

(b) Rivett, B. H. P. (1968) *Concepts of Operational Research*, C. A. Watts, London.

2 *Techniques*

Sasieni, M., Yaspan, A. and Friedman, L (1959) *Operational Research – Methods and Problems*, John Wiley, New York.

3 *Survey*

Moore, P. G. (1966) "A Survey of Operational Research", *Jour. Roy. Stat. Soc. A*, **129**, 399.

Reprinted from Jenkins, G. M. (1969) "The Systems Approach", *Journal of Systems Engineering*, **1**, 1.

Section III

Introduction

Considerable emphasis has been placed on the application and development of systems ideas in modern human systems. The results have not always been successful in their application or acknowledged as a contribution to their subject area. Both articles in this section are much cited and have stood the test of time. It is perhaps not without significance that neither has been replaced by more recent thinking or developments. Emery and Trist, in their 1960 article on *sociotechnical systems*, present the findings of several studies of human work groups including their own reorganizations based on the systems concepts outlined.

The concept of organizations, nations and societies as systems has been developed and used to try to explain their behaviour and changes which occur in their structures. Buckley develops a systems approach to the study of society well beyond the earlier attempts in the area of the functionalists (see Article 3 by Kast and Rosenzweig). Buckley argues that rather than thinking of societies as organisms, it is fruitful to think of them as complex adaptive systems, i.e., open systems in close contact with an environment which is rapidly changing. The view of these complex systems is essentially holistic and relies heavily on the consideration of control, communication and information.

Associated reading

Martin Lockett and Roger Spear have produced a companion volume to this one: *Organisations as Systems* (Open University Press, 1980).

Emery has produced two books of readings which contain many articles on systems in organisations: *Systems Thinking Vols. I and II* (Penguin Books, 1981) and, with Russ Ackoff, a book entitled *On Purposeful Systems* (Tavistock, 1972). In *Sociology and Modern System Theory* (Prentice-Hall, 1967) Buckley presents his general ideas in much more detail.

Systems and organizations have received considerable attention in the Open University, including whole courses on Systems Management (T242, 1974) and Systems Organisation: The Management of Complexity (T243, 1980). Most relevant and recent single books are *Organisations* (T243, Block 3) (Open University Press, 1980) and *Industrial Social Systems* (T241, units 5/6, 1982).

Emergence Tavistic view.

① Open systems can maintain steady state by constant exchange with their environment.

② There are two component sub-systems – technical & social.

③ There are choices in the social sub-system – "two contrasting social systems can effectively operate the same technology"

④ Implicit in the whole idea is the concept that the technical subsystem too must contain options – there too one can exercise choice.

9 Sociotechnical systems

by F. E. Emery and E. L. Trist

The analysis of the characteristics of enterprises as systems would appear to have strategic significance for furthering our understanding of a great number of specific industrial problems. The more we know about these systems the more we are able to identify what is relevant to a particular problem and to detect problems that tend to be missed by the conventional framework of problem analysis.

The value of studying enterprises as systems has been demonstrated in the empirical studies of Blau (1955), Gouldner (1955), Jaques (1951), Selznick (1949) and Warner and Low (1947). Many of these studies have been informed by a broadly conceived concept of bureaucracy, derived from Weber and influenced by Parsons and Merton:

> They have found their main business to be in the analysis of a specific bureaucracy as a complex social system, concerned less with the individual differences of the actors than with the situationally shaped roles they perform. (Drucker, 1952)

Granted the importance of system analysis there remains the important question of whether an enterprise should be construed as a "closed" or an "open system", i.e., relatively "closed" or "open" with respect to its external environment. Von Bertalanffy (1950) first introduced this general distinction in contrasting biological and physical phenomena. In the realm of social theory, however, there has been something of a tendency to continue thinking in terms of a "closed" system, that is, to regard the enterprise as sufficiently independent to allow most of its problems to be analyzed with reference to its internal structure and without reference to its external environment. Early exceptions were Rice and Trist (1952) in the field of labour turnover and Herbst (1954) in the analysis of social flow systems. As a first step, closed-system thinking has been fruitful, in psychology and industrial sociology, in directing attention to the existence of structural similarities, relational determination and subordination of part to whole. However, it has tended to be misleading on

problems of growth and the conditions for maintaining a "steady state". The formal physical models of "closed systems" postulate that, as in the second law of thermodynamics, the inherent tendency of such systems is to grow towards maximum homogeneity of the parts and that a steady state can only be achieved by the cessation of all activity. In practice, the system theorists in social science (and these include such key anthropologists as Radcliffe-Brown) refused to recognize these implications but instead, by the same token, did "*tend* to focus on the statics of social structure and to neglect the study of structural change" (Merton, 1949).

In an attempt to overcome this bias, Merton (1949) suggested that "the concept of dysfunction, which implies the concept of strain, stress and tension on the structural level, provides an analytical approach to the study of dynamics and change". This concept has been widely accepted by system theorists, but while it draws attention to sources of imbalance within an organization, it does not conceptually reflect the mutual permeation of an organization and its environment that is the cause of such imbalance. It still retains the limiting perspectives of "closed-system" theorizing. In the administrative field the same limitations may be seen in the otherwise invaluable contributions of Barnard (1948) and related writers.

The alternative conception of "open systems" carries the logical implications that such systems may spontaneously reorganize towards states of greater heterogeneity and complexity and that they achieve a "steady state" at a level where they can still do work. Enterprises appear to possess at least these characteristics of "open systems". They grow by processes of internal elaboration (Herbst, 1954) and manage to achieve a steady state while doing work, i.e., achieve a quasi-stationary equilibrium in which the enterprise as a whole remains constant, with a continuous "*throughput*", despite a considerable range of external changes (Lewin, 1951; Rice and Trist, 1952).

The appropriateness of the concept of "open system" can be settled, however, only by examining in some detail what is involved in an enterprise achieving a steady state. The continued existence of any enterprise presupposes some regular commerce in products or services with other enterprises, institutions and persons in its external social environment. If it is going to be useful to speak of steady states in an enterprise, they must be states in which this commerce is going on. The conditions for regularizing this commerce lie both within and without the enterprise. On the one hand, this presupposes that an enterprise has at its immediate disposal the necessary material supports for its activities – a workplace, materials, tools and machines – and a workforce able and willing to make the necessary modifications in the material "throughput" or provide the requisite services. It must also be able, efficiently, to utilize its material supports and to organize the actions of its human agents in a rational and predictable manner. On the other hand, the regularity of commerce with the environment may be influenced by a broad range of independent external changes affecting markets for products and inputs of labour, materials and technology. If we examine the factors influencing the ability of an enterprise to maintain a steady state in the face of these broader environmental influences, we find that:

1 The variation in the output markets that can be tolerated without structural change is a function of the flexibility of the technical productive apparatus – its ability to vary its rate, its end-product or the mixture of its products. Variation in the output markets may itself be considerably reduced by the display of distinctive competence. Thus the output markets will be more attached to a given enterprise if it has, relative to other producers, a distinctive competence – a distinctive ability to deliver the right product to the right place at the right time.

2 The tolerable variation in the "input" markets is likewise dependent upon the technological component. Thus some enterprises are enabled by their particular technical organization to tolerate considerable variation in the type and amount of labour they can recruit. Others can tolerate little.

The two significant features of this state of affairs are:

1 That there is no simple one-to-one relation between variations in inputs and outputs. Depending upon the technological system, different combinations of inputs may be handled to yield similar outputs and different "product mixes" may be produced from similar inputs. As far as possible an enterprise will tend to do these things rather than make structural changes in its organization. It is one of the additional characteristics of "open systems" that while they are in constant commerce with the environment they are selective and, within limits, self-regulating.

2 That the technological component, in converting inputs into outputs, plays a major role in determining the self-regulating properties of an enterprise. It functions as one of the major boundary conditions of the social system of the enterprise in thus mediating between the ends of an enterprise and the external environment. Because of this the materials, machines and territory that go to making up the technological component are usually defined, in any modern society, as "belonging" to an enterprise and excluded from similar control by other enterprises. They represent, as it were, an "internalized environment".

Thus the mediating boundary conditions must be represented among "the open system constants" (von Bertalanffy, 1950) that define the conditions under which a steady state can be achieved. The technological component has been found to play a key mediating role and hence it follows that the open-system concept must be referred to the sociotechnical system, not simply to the social system of an enterprise.

It might be justifiable to exclude the technological component from the system concept if it were true, as many writers imply, that it plays only a passive and intermittent role. However, it cannot be dismissed as simply a set of limits that exerts an influence at the initial stage of building an enterprise and only at such subsequent times as these limits are overstepped. There is, on the contrary, an almost constant accommodation of stresses arising from changes in the external environment; the technological component not only sets limits upon what can be done, but also in the process of accommodation creates demands that must be reflected in the internal organization and ends of an enterprise.

Study of a productive system therefore requires detailed attention to both the technological and the social components. It is not possible to understand these systems in terms of some arbitrarily selected single aspect of the technology such as the repetitive nature of the work, the coerciveness of the assembly conveyor or the piecemeal nature of the task. However, this is what is usually attempted by students of the enterprise. In fact:

It has been fashionable of late, particularly in the "human relations" school, to assume that the actual job, its technology, and its mechanical and physical requirements are relatively unimportant compared to the social and psychological situation of men at work. (Drucker 1952)

Even when there has been a detailed study of the technology this has not been systematically related to the social system but has been treated as background information (Warner and Low, 1947).

In our earliest study of production systems in coal mining it became apparent that "so close is the relationship between the various aspects that the social and the psychological can be understood only in terms of the detailed engineering facts and of the way the technological system as a whole behaves in the environment of the underground situation" (Trist and Bamforth, 1951).

An analysis of a technological system in these terms can produce a systematic picture of the tasks and task interrelations required by a technological system. However, between these requirements and the social system there is not a strictly determined one-to-one relation but what is logically referred to as a correlative relation.

In a very simple operation such as manually moving and stacking railway sleepers ("ties") there may well be only a single suitable work relationship structure, namely, a cooperating pair with each man taking an end of the sleeper and lifting, supporting, walking and throwing in close coordination with the other man. The ordinary production process is much more complex and there it is unusual to find that only one particular work relationship structure can be fitted to these tasks.

This element of choice and the mutual influence of technology and the social system may both be illustrated from our studies, made over several years, of work organization in British deep-seam coal mining. The following data are adapted from Trist and Murray (1948).

Thus Table 9.1 indicates the main features of two very different forms of organization that have both been operated economically within the same seam and with identical technology.

The conventional system combines a complex formal structure with simple work roles; the composite system combines a simple formal structure with complex work roles. In the former the miner has a commitment to only a

Table 9.1 Same technology, same coal seam, different social systems

	A conventional cutting longwall mining system	A composite cutting longwall mining system
Number of men	41	41
Number of completely segregated task groups	14	1
Mean job variation for members:		
Task groups worked with	1·0	5·5
Main tasks worked	1·0	3·6
Different shifts worked	2·0	2·9

Table 9.2 Production and costs for different forms of work organization with same technology

	'Conventional'	'Composite'
Productive achievement*	78	95
Ancillary work at face (hours per man-shift)	1·32	0·03
Average reinforcement of labour (percent of total face force)	6	—
Percent of shifts with cycle lag	69	5
Number of consecutive weeks without losing a cycle	12	65

* Average percent of coal won from each daily cut, corrected for differences in seam transport.

single part task and enters into only a very limited number of unvarying social relations that are sharply divided between those within his particular task group and those who are outside. With those "outside" he shares no sense of belongingness and he recognizes no responsibility to them for the consequences of his actions. In the composite system the miner has a commitment to the whole group task and consequently finds himself drawn into a variety of tasks in cooperation with different members of the total group; he may be drawn into any task on the coal-face with any member of the total group.

That two such contrasting social systems can effectively operate the same technology is clear enough evidence that there exists an element of choice in designing a work organization.

However, it is not a matter of indifference which form of organization is selected. As has already been stated, the technological system sets certain requirements of its social system and the effectiveness of the total production system will depend upon the adequacy with which the social system is able to cope with these requirements. Although alternative social systems may survive in that they are both accepted as "good enough" (Simon, 1957), this does not preclude the possibility that they may differ in effectiveness.

In this case the composite systems consistently showed a superiority over the conventional in terms of production and costs.

This superiority reflects, in the first instance, the more adequate coping in the composite system with the task requirements. The constantly changing underground conditions require that the already complex sequence of mining tasks undergoes frequent changes in the relative magnitudes and even the order of these tasks. These conditions optimally require the internal flexibility possessed in varying degrees by the composite systems. It is difficult to meet variable task requirements with any organization built on a rigid division of labour. The only justification for a rigid division of labour is a technology which demands specialized non-substitute skills and which is, moreover, sufficiently superior, as a technology, to offset the losses due to rigidity. The conventional longwall cutting system has no such technical superiority over the composite to offset its relative rigidity – its characteristic inability to cope with changing conditions other than by increasing the stress placed on its members, sacrificing smooth cycle progress or drawing heavily upon the negligible labour reserves of the pit.

The superiority of the composite system does not rest alone in more adequate coping with the tasks. It also makes better provision to the personal requirements of the miners. Mutually supportive relations between task groups are the exception in the conventional system and the rule in the composite. In consequence, the conventional miner more frequently finds himself without support from his fellows when the strain or size of his task requires it. Crises are more likely to set him against his fellows and hence worsen the situation.

Similarly, the distribution of rewards and statuses in the conventional system reflects the relative bargaining power of different roles and task groups as much as any true differences in skill and effort. Under these conditions of disparity between effort and reward any demands for increased effort are likely to create undue stress.

Table 9.3 indicates the differences in stress experienced by miners in the two systems.

These findings were replicated by experimental studies in textile mills in the radically different setting of Ahmedabad, India (Rice, 1958).

However, two possible sources of misunderstanding need to be considered:

1 Our findings do not suggest that work group autonomy should be maximized in all productive settings. There is an optimum level of grouping which can be determined only by analysis of the requirements of the technological system. Neither does there appear to be any simple relation between level of mechanization and level of grouping. In one mining study we found that in moving from a hand-filling to a machine-filling technology, the appropriate organization shifted from an undifferentiated composite system to one based on a number of partially segregated task groups with more stable differences in internal statuses.

2 Nor does it appear that the basic psychological needs being met by grouping are workers' needs for friendship on the job, as is frequently postulated by advocates of better "human relations" in industry. Grouping produces its main psychological effects when it leads to a system of work roles such that the workers are primarily related to each other by way of the requirements of task performance and task interdependence. When this task orientation is established the worker should find that he has an adequate range of mutually supportive roles (mutually supportive with respect to performance and to carrying stress that arises from the task). As the role system becomes more mature and integrated, it becomes easier for a worker to understand and appreciate his relation to the group. Thus in the comparison of different composite mining groups it was found that the differences in productivity and in coping with stress were not primarily related to differences in the level of friendship in the groups. The critical prerequisites for a composite system are an adequate supply of the required special skills among members of the group and conditions for developing an appropriate system of roles. Where these prerequisites have not been fully met, the composite system has broken down or established itself at a less than optimum level. The development of friendship and particularly of mutual respect occurs in the composite systems but the friendship tends to be limited by the requirements of the system and not assume unlimited disruptive forms such as were observed in conventional systems and were reported by Adams (1953) to occur in certain types of bomber crews.

The textile studies (Rice, 1958) yielded the additional finding that *supervisory roles* are best designed on the basis of the same type of sociotechnical analysis. It is not enough simply to allocate to the supervisor a list of responsibilities for specific tasks and perhaps insist upon a particular style of handling men. The supervisory roles arise from the need to control and coordinate an incomplete system of men–task relations. Supervisory responsibility for the specific parts of such a system is not easily reconcilable

Table 9.3 Stress indices for different social systems

	'Conventional'	'Composite'
Absenteeism (percent of possible shifts)		
Without reason	4·3	0·4
Sickness or other	8·9	4·6
Accidents	6·8	3·2
Total	20·0	8·2

with responsibility for overall aspects. The supervisor who continually intervenes to do some part of the productive work may be proving his willingness to work but is also likely to be neglecting his main task of controlling and coordinating the system so that the operators are able to get on with their jobs with the least possible disturbance.

Definition of a supervisory role presupposes analysis of the system's requirements for control and coordination and provision of conditions that will enable the supervisor readily to perceive what is needed of him and to take appropriate measures. As his control will in large measure rest on his control of the boundary conditions of the system, i.e., those activities relating to a larger system, it will be desirable to create "unified commands" so that the boundary conditions will be correspondingly easy to detect and manage. If the unified commands correspond to natural task groupings, it will also be possible to maximize the autonomous responsibility of the work group for internal control and coordination, thus freeing the supervisor for his primary task. A graphic illustration of the differences in a supervisory role following a sociotechnical reorganization of an automatic loom shed (Rice, 1958) can be seen in Figures 9.1 and 9.2. Figure 9.1 represents the situation before and Figure 9.2 represents the situation after change.

This reorganization was reflected in a significant and sustained improvement in mean percentage efficiency and a decrease in mean percentage damage.

The significance of the difference between these two organizational diagrams does not rest only in the relative simplicity of the latter (although this does reflect less confusion of responsibilities) but also in the emergence of clearly distinct areas of command which contain within themselves a relatively independent set of work roles together with the skills necessary to govern their task boundaries. In like manner the induction and training of new members was recognized as a boundary condition for the entire shed and located directly under shed management instead of being scattered throughout subordinate commands. Whereas the former organization had been maintained in a steady state only by the constant and arduous efforts of management, the new one proved to be inherently stable and self-correcting, and consequently freed management to give more time to their primary task and also to manage a third shift.

Similarly, the primary task in managing the enterprise as a whole is to relate the total system to its environment and is not in internal regulation per se. This does not mean that managers will not be involved in internal problems but that such involvement will be oriented consciously or unconsciously to certain assumptions about the external relations of the enterprise.

This contrasts with the common postulate of the structural–functional theories that "the basic need of all empirical systems is the maintenance of the integrity and continuity of the system itself" (Selznick, 1948). It

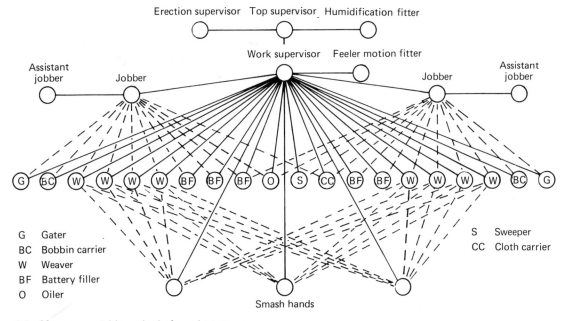

Figure 9.1 Management hierarchy before change.

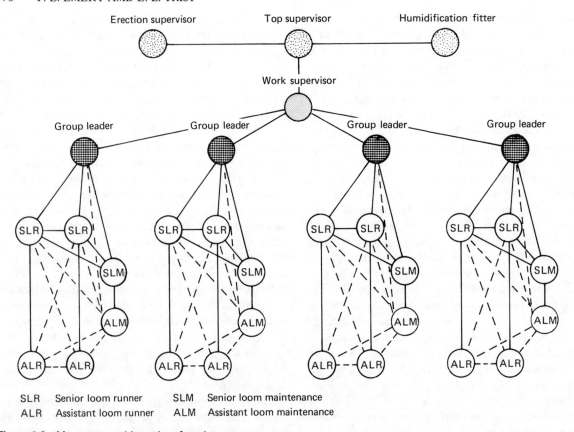

SLR   Senior loom runner   SLM   Senior loom maintenance
ALR   Assistant loom runner   ALM   Assistant loom maintenance

Figure 9.2 Management hierarchy after change.

contrasts also with an important implication of this postulate, namely, that the primary task of management is "continuous attention to the possibilities of encroachment and to the forestalling of threatened aggressions or deleterious consequences from the actions of others" (Selznick, 1948). In industry this represents the special and limiting case of a management that takes for granted a previously established definition of its primary task and assumes that all they have to do, or can do, is sit tight and defend their market position. This is, however, the common case in statutorily established bodies and it is on such bodies that recent studies of bureaucracy have been largely carried out.

In general the leadership of an enterprise must be willing to break down an old integrity or create profound discontinuity if such steps are required to take advantage of changes in technology and markets. The very survival of an enterprise may be threatened by its inability to face up to such demands as, for instance, switching the main effort from production of processed goods to marketing or from production of heavy industrial goods to consumer goods. Similarly, the leadership may need to pay "continuous"

attention to the possibilities of making their own encroachments rather than be obsessed with the possible encroachments of others.

Considering enterprises as "open sociotechnical systems" helps to provide a more realistic picture of how they are both influenced by and able to act back on their environment. It points in particular to the various ways in which enterprises are enabled by their structural and functional characteristics ("system constants") to cope with the "lacks" and "gluts" in their available environment. Unlike mechanical and other inanimate systems they possess the property of "equifinality"; they may achieve a steady state from differing initial conditions and in differing ways (von Bertalanffy, 1950). Thus in coping by internal changes they are not limited to simple quantitative change and increased uniformity but may, and usually do, elaborate new structures and take on new functions. The cumulative effect of coping mainly by *internal* elaboration and differentiation is generally to make the system independent of an increasing range of the predictable fluctuations in its supplies and outlets. At the same time, however, this process ties down in specific ways more and more of its capital, skill and energies and renders it less able to cope with newly emergent and unpredicted changes that challenge the primary ends of the enterprise. This process has been traced out in a great many empirical studies of bureaucracies (Blau, 1955; Merton, 1949; Selznick, 1949).

However, there are available to an enterprise other aggressive strategies that seek to achieve a steady state by transforming the environment. Thus an enterprise has some possibilities for moving into new markets or inducing changes in the old, for choosing differently from among the range of personnel, resources and technologies offered by its environment or training and making new ones, and for developing new consumer needs or stimulating old ones.

Thus, arising from the nature of the enterprise as an open system, management is concerned with "managing" both an internal system and an external environment. To regard an enterprise as a closed system and concentrate upon management of the "internal enterprise" would be to expose the enterprise to the full impact of the vagaries of the environment.

If management is to control internal growth and development it must in the first instance control the "boundary conditions" – the forms of exchange between the enterprise and its environment. As we have seen most enterprises are confronted with a multitude of actual and possible exchanges. If resources are not to be dissipated the management must select from the alternatives a course of action. The casual texture of competitive environments is such that it is extremely difficult to survive on a simple strategy of selecting the best from among the alternatives immediately offering. Some that offer immediate gain lead nowhere, others lead to greater loss; some alternatives that offer loss are avoidable, others are unavoidable if long-term gains are to be made. The relative size of the immediate loss or gain is no sure guide as to what follows. Since also the actions of an enterprise can improve the alternatives that are presented to it, the optimum course is more likely to rest in selecting a strategic objective to be achieved in the long run. The strategic objective should be to place the enterprise in a position in its environment where it has some assured conditions for growth; unlike war the best position is not necessarily that of unchallenged monopoly. Achieving this position would be the *primary task* or overriding mission of the enterprise.

In selecting the primary task of an enterprise, it needs to be borne in mind that the relations with the environment may vary with: (1) the productive efforts of the enterprise in meeting environmental requirements, (2) changes in the environment that may be induced by the enterprise and (3) changes independently taking place in the environment. These will be of differing importance for different enterprises and for the same enterprises at different times. Managerial control will usually be greatest if the primary task can be based on productive activity. If this is not possible, as in commerce, the primary task will give more control if it is based on marketing than simply on foreknowledge of the independent environmental changes. Managerial control will be further enhanced if the primary task, at whatever level it is selected, is such as to enable the enterprise to achieve vis-à-vis its competitors, a *distinctive competence*. Conversely, in our experience, an enterprise which has long occupied a favoured position because of distinctive productive competence may have grave difficulty in recognizing when it is losing control owing to environmental changes beyond its control.

As Selznick (1957) has pointed out, an appropriately defined primary task offers stability and direction to an enterprise, protecting it from adventurism or costly drifting. These advantages, however, as he illustrates, may be no more than potential unless the top management group of the organization achieves solidarity about the new primary task. If the vision of the task is locked up in a single man or is the subject of dissension in top management it will be subject to great risk of distortion and susceptible to violent fluctuations. Similarly, the enterprise as a whole needs to be reoriented and reintegrated about this primary task. Thus, if the primary task shifts from heavy industrial goods to durable consumer goods it would be necessary to ensure that there is a corresponding shift in values that are embodied in such sections as the sales force and design department.

References

Adams, S. (1953) "Status congruency as a variable in small group performance", *Social Forces* **32**, 16–22.

Barnard, C. I. (1948) *The Functions of the Executive,* Harvard University Press, Cambridge, Mass.

von Bertalanffy, L. (1950) "The theory of open systems in physics and biology", *Science* **111**, 23–29.

Blau, P. (1955) *The Dynamics of Bureaucratic Structure: A Study of Interpersonal Relations in Two Government Agencies",* University of Chicago Press, Chicago.

Drucker, P. F. (1952) "The employee society", *American Sociological Review* **58**, 358–363.

Gouldner, A. W. (1955) *Patterns of Industrial Bureaucracy,* Routledge & Kegan Paul, London.

Herbst, P. G. (1954) "The analysis of social flow systems", *Human Relations* **7**, 327–336.

Jaques, E. (1951) *The Changing Culture of a Factory,* Tavistock, London.

Lewin, K. (1951) *Field Theory in Social Science,* Harper, New York.

Merton, R. K. (1949) *Social Theory and Social Structure,* Free Press, Chicago.

Rice, A. K. and Trist, E. L. (1952) "Institutional and sub-institutional determinants of change in labour turnover (The Glacier Project – VIII)", *Human Relations* 5, 347–372.

Rice, A. K. (1958) *Productivity and Social Organization: The Ahmedabad Experiment,* Tavistock, London.

Schutzenberger, M. P. (1954) "A tentative classification of goal-seeking behaviours", *Journal of Mental Science* 100, 97–102.

Selznick, P. (1948) "Foundations of the theory of organization", *American Sociological Review* 13, 25–35.

Selznick, P. (1949) *TVA and the Grass Roots,* University of California Press, Berkeley, Calif.

Selznick, P. (1957) *Leadership in Administration,* Row-Peterson, Evanston, Ill.

Simon, H. A. (1957) *Models of Man,* Wiley, New York.

Tolman, E. C. and Brunswik, E. (1935) "The organism and the causal texture of the environment", *Psychological Review* 42, 43–77.

Trist, E. L. and Bamforth, K. W. (1951) "Some social and psychological consequences of the longwall method of coal-getting", *Human Relations* 4.

Trist, E. L. and Murray, H. (1948) "Work organization at the coal face: a comparative study of mining systems", *Tavistock Institute of Human Relations*, Doc. no. 506.

Warner, W. L. and Low, J. O. (1947) *The Social System of the Modern Factory,* Yale University Press, New Haven, Conn.

Reprinted from C. W. Churchman and M. Verhulst (eds.) (1960) *Management Science, Modes and Techniques,* Pergamon Press, vol. 2.

Main Conclusions :-

(a) Open systems may spontaneously reorganise themselves so that they become more heterogeneous and complex. They can achieve a steady state, not moving to entropy (disorder) as closed systems do.

(b) Open sy. maintains continuous throughput despite continual changes.

(c) Open sy in constant commerce with environment and self regulating.

(d) Technological component forms link between enterprise and environment. – So study of production system requires detailed attention to both technological and social components.

(e) Main management task to relate total system to environment – not just internal regulatory. It must not just react defensively but must control boundary conditions

(f) Open sy. have equifinality – achieve a steady state from different initial conditions and via different paths.

10 Society as a complex adaptive system
by Walter Buckley

We have argued at some length in another place[1] that the mechanical equilibrium model and the organismic homeostasis models of society that have underlain most modern sociological theory have outlived their usefulness. A more viable model, one much more faithful to the *kind* of system that society is more and more recognized to be, is in process of developing out of, or is in keeping with, the modern systems perspective (which we use loosely here to refer to general systems research, cybernetics, information and communication theory, and related fields). Society, or the sociocultural system, is not, then, principally an equilibrium system or a homeostatic system, but what we shall simply refer to as a complex adaptive system.

To summarize the argument in overly simplified form: Equilibrial systems are relatively *closed* and *entropic*. In going to equilibrium they typically *lose structure* and have a *minimum of free energy*; they are affected only by external "disturbances" and have *no internal or endogenous sources of change*; their component elements are *relatively simple* and *linked directly via energy exchange* (rather than information interchange); and since they are relatively closed they have no feedback or other systematic self-regulating or adaptive capabilities. The homeostatic system (for example, the organism, apart from higher cortical functioning) is open and negentropic, maintaining a moderate energy level within controlled limits. But for our purposes here, the system's main characteristic is its functioning to *maintain the given structure of the system* within pre-established limits. It involves feedback loops with its environment, and possibly information as well as pure energy interchanges, but these are geared principally to *self-regulation* (structure maintenance) rather than adaptation (*change* of system structure). The complex adaptive systems (species, psychological and sociocultural systems) are also open and negentropic. But they are *open "internally"* as well as *externally* in that the interchanges among their components may result in *significant changes in the nature of the components themselves* with important consequences for the system as a whole. And the energy level that may be mobilized by the system is subject to relatively wide fluctuation.

Internal as well as external interchanges are mediated characteristically by *information flows* (via chemical, cortical, or cultural encoding and decoding), although pure energy interchange occurs also. True feedback control loops make possible not only self-regulation, but self-direction or at least adaptation to a changing environment, such that the system may *change or elaborate its structure* as a condition of survival or viability.

We argue, then, that the sociocultural system is fundamentally of the latter type, and requires for analysis a theoretical model or perspective built on the kinds of characteristics mentioned. In what follows we draw on many of the concepts and principles presented throughout this source-book to sketch out aspects of a complex adaptive system model or analytical framework for the sociocultural system. It is further argued that a number of recent sociological and social psychological theories and theoretical orientations articulate well with this modern systems perspective, and we outline some of these to suggest in addition that modern systems research is not as remote from the social scientists' interests and endeavors as many appear to believe.

Complex adaptive systems: a paradigm

A feature of current general systems research is the gradual development of a general paradigm of the basic mechanisms underlying the evolution of complex adaptive systems. The terminology of this paradigm derives particularly from information theory and cybernetics. We shall review these concepts briefly. The *environment*, however else it may be characterized, can be seen at bottom as a set or ensemble of more or less distinguishable elements, states, or events, whether the discriminations are made in terms of spatial or temporal relations, or properties. Such distinguishable differences in an ensemble may be most generally referred to as "*variety*". The relatively stable "causal", spatial and/or temporal relations between these distinguishable elements or events may be generally referred to as "*constraint*". If the elements are so "loosely" related that there is equal probability of any element or state being associated with any other, we speak of "chaos" or complete randomness, and hence, lack of "constraint". But our more typical natural environment is characterized by a relatively high degree of constraint, without which the development and elaboration of adaptive systems (as well as "science") would not have been possible. When the internal organization of an adaptive system acquires features that permit it to discriminate, act upon, and respond to aspects of the environmental variety and its constraints, we might generally say that the system has "*mapped*" parts of the environmental variety and constraints into its organization as structure and/or "information". Thus, a subset of the ensemble of constrained variety in the environment is coded and transmitted in some way via various channels to result in a change in the structure of the receiving system which is isomorphic in certain respects to the original variety. The system thus becomes selectively matched to its environment both physiologically and psychologically. It should be added that two or more adaptive systems, as well as an adaptive system and its natural environment, may be said to be selectively interrelated by a mapping process in the same terms. This becomes especially important for the evolution of social systems.

In these terms, then, the paradigm underlying the evolution of more and more complex adaptive systems begins with the fact of a potentially changing environment characterized by variety with constraints, and an existing adaptive system or organization whose persistence and elaboration to higher levels depends upon a successful mapping of some of the environmental variety and constraints into its own organization on at least a semi-permanent basis. This means that our adaptive system – whether on the biological, psychological, or sociocultural level – must manifest (1) some degree of "*plasticity*" and "*irritability*" vis-à-vis its environment such that it carries on a constant interchange with environmental events, acting on and reacting to it; (2) some source or mechanism for *variety*, to act as a potential pool of adaptive variability to meet the problem of mapping new or more detailed variety and constraints in a changeable environment; (3) a set of *selective* criteria or mechanisms against which the "variety pool" may be sifted into those variations in the organization or system that more closely map the environment and those that do not; and (4) an arrangement for *preserving and/or propagating* these "successful" mappings.[2]

It should be noted, as suggested above, that this is a *relational* perspective, and the question of "substance" is quite secondary here. (We might also note that it is this kind of thinking that gives such great significance to the rapidly developing relational logic that is becoming more and more important as a technical tool of analysis.) Also, as suggested, this formulation corresponds closely with the current conception of "information" viewed as the process of selection – from an ensemble of variety – of a subset which, to have "meaning", must match another subset taken from a similar ensemble.[3] Communication is the process by which this constrained variety is transmitted in one form or another between such ensembles, and involves coding and decoding such that the original variety and its constraints remains relatively invariant at the receiving end. If the source of the "communication" is the causally constrained variety of the natural environment, and the destination is the biological adaptive system, we refer to the Darwinian process of natural selection whereby the information encoded in the chromosomal material (for example the DNA) reflects or is a mapping of the environmental variety, and makes possible a continuous and more or less successful adaptation of the former system to the latter. If the adaptive system in question is a (relatively high-level) psychological or cortical system, we refer to "learning", whereby the significant environmental variety is transmitted via sensory and perceptual channels and decodings to the cortical centers where, by selective criteria (for example, "reward" and "punishment") related to physiological and/or other "needs" or "drives", relevant parts of it are encoded and preserved as "experience" for varying periods of time and may promote adaptation. Or, on the level of the symbol-based sociocultural adaptive system, where the more or less patterned actions of persons and groups are as crucial a part of the environment of other persons and groups as the non-social environment, the gestural variety and its more or less normatively defined constraints is encoded, transmitted, and decoded at the receiving end by way of the various familiar channels with varying degrees of fidelity. Over time, and again by a selective process – now much more complex, tentative, and less easily specified – there is a selective elaboration and more or less temporary preservation of some of this complex social as well as non-social constrained variety in the form of "culture", "social organization", and "personality structure".

On the basis of such a continuum of evolving, elaborating levels of adaptive system (and we have only pointed to three points along this continuum), we could add to and refine our typology of systems. Thus, we note that as adaptive systems develop from the lower biological levels through the higher psychological and sociocultural levels we can distinguish: (1) the *varying time span* required for exemplars of the adaptive system to map or encode within themselves changes in the variety and constraints of the environment; phylogenetic time scales for organic systems and for tropistic or instinctual neural systems; ontogenetic time scales for higher psychological or cortical systems; and, in the sociocultural case, the time span may be very short – days – or very long, but complicated by the fact that the relevant environment includes both intra- and inter-societal variety and constraints as well as natural environment variety (the latter becoming progressively less determinant); (2) the greatly *varying degrees of fidelity of mapping* of the environment into the adaptive system, from the lower unicellular organisms with a very simple repertoire of actions on and reactions to the environment, through the complex of instinctual and learned repertoire, to the ever-proliferating more refined and veridical accumulations of a sociocultural system; (3) the progressively greater separation and independence of the more refined "stored information" from purely biological processes as genetic information is gradually augmented by cortically imprinted information, and finally by entirely extrasomatic cultural depositories. The implications of these shifts, and others that could be included, are obviously far-reaching.

One point that will require more discussion may be briefly mentioned here. This is the *relative* discontinuity we note in the transition from the non-human adaptive system to the sociocultural system. (The insect society and the rudimentary higher animal society make for much less than a complete discontinuity.) As we progress from lower to higher biological adaptive systems we note, as a general rule, the gradually increasing role of other biological units of the same as well as different species making up part of the significant environment. The variety and constraints represented by the behavior of these units must be mapped along with that of the physical environment. With the transition represented by the higher primate social organization through to full-blown human, symbolically mediated, sociocultural adaptive systems, the mapping of the variety and constraints characterizing the subtle behaviors, gestures and intentions of the individuals and groups making up the effective social organization become increasingly central, and eventually equal if not overshadow the requirements for mapping the physical environment.[4]

It was these newly demanding requirements of coordination, anticipation, expectation and the like within a more and more complex *social* environment of interacting and interdependent others – where genetic mappings were absent or inadequate – that prompted the fairly rapid elaboration of relatively new system features. These included, of course: the ever-greater conventionalizing of gestures into true symbols; the resulting development of a "self", self-awareness, or self-consciousness out of the symbolically mediated, continuous mirroring and mapping of each unit's behaviors and gesturings in those of ever-present others (a process well described by Dewey, Mead, Cooley, and others); and the resulting ability to deal in the present with future as well as past mappings and hence to manifest goal-seeking, evaluating, self-other relating, norm-referring behavior. In cybernetic terminology, this higher level sociocultural system became possible through the development of higher order feedbacks such that the component individual subsystems became able to map, store, and selectively act toward, not only the external variety and constraints of the social and non-social environment, but also their own internal states. To speak of self-consciousness, internalization, expectations, choice, certainty and uncertainty, and the like, is to elaborate this basic point. This transition, then, gave rise to the newest adaptive system level we refer to as socio-cultural. As we argued earlier, this higher level adaptive organization thus manifests features that warrant its scientific study in terms as distinct from a purely biological system as the analytical terms of the latter are from physical systems.

The sociocultural adaptive system

From the perspective sketched above, the following principles underlying the sociocultural adaptive system can be derived:

1. The principle of the "irritability of protoplasm" carries through to all the higher level adaptive systems. "Tension" in the broad sense – in which stress and strain are manifestations under conditions of felt blockage – is ever-present in one form or another throughout the sociocultural system – how as diffuse, socially unstructured strivings, frustrations, enthusiasms, aggressions, neurotic or psychotic or normative deviation; sometimes as clustered and minimally structured crowd or quasi-group processes, normatively supportive as well as destructive; and now as socioculturally structured creativity and production, conflict and competition, or upheaval and destruction. As Thelen and colleagues put it:

1. Man is always trying to live beyond his means. Life is a sequence of reactions to stress: Man is continually meeting situations with which he cannot quite cope.
2. In stress situations, energy is mobilized and a state of tension is produced.

3. The state of tensions tends to be disturbing, and Man seeks to reduce the tension.

4. He has direct impulses to take action. . . .[5]

2. Only closed systems running down to their most probable states, that is, losing organization and available energy, can be profitably treated in equilibrium terms. Outside this context the concept of equilibrium would seem quite inappropriate and only deceptively helpful. On the other side, only open, tensionful, adaptive systems can elaborate and proliferate organization. Cannon coined the term "homeostasis" for biological systems to avoid the connotations of equilibrium, and to bring out the dynamic, processual, potential-maintaining properties of *basically unstable* physiological systems.[6] In dealing with the sociocultural system, however, we need yet a new concept to express not only the *structure-maintaining* feature, but also the *structure-elaborating and changing* feature of the inherently unstable system. The notion of "steady state", now often used, approaches the meaning we seek if it is understood that the "state" that tends to remain "steady" is *not to be identified with the particular structure* of the system. That is, as we shall argue in a moment, in order to maintain a steady state the system may change its particular structure. For this reason, the term "morphogenesis" is more descriptive.[7] C. A. Mace recognizes this distinction in arguing for an extension of the concept of homeostasis:

The first extension would cover the case in which what is maintained or restored is not so much an internal state of the organism as some relation of the organism to its environment. This would take care of the facts of adaptation and adjustment, including adjustment to the social environment . . . the second extension would cover the case in which the goal and/or norm is some state or relation which has never previously been experienced. There is clearly no reason to suppose that every process of the homeostatic type consists in the maintenance or restoration of a norm.[8]

3. We define a system in general as a complex of elements or components directly or indirectly related in a causal network, such that at least some of the components are related to some others in a more or less stable way *at any one time*. The interrelations may be mutual or unidirectional, linear, non-linear or intermittent, and varying in degrees of causal efficacy or priority. The particular kinds of more or less stable interrelationships of components that become established at any time constitute the particular *structure* of the system at that time.

Thus, the complex, adaptive system as a continuing entity is not to be confused with the structure which that system may manifest at any time. Making this distinction allows us to state a fundamental principle of open, adaptive systems: *Persistence or continuity of an adaptive system may require, as a necessary condition, change in its structure*, the degree of change being a complex function of the internal state of the system, the state of its relevant environment, and the nature of the interchange between the two. Thus, animal species develop and persist or are continuously transformed (or become extinct) in terms of a change (or failure of change) of structure – sometimes extremely slow, sometimes very rapid. The higher individual organism capable of learning by experience maintains itself as a viable system vis-à-vis its environment by a change of structure – in this case the neural structure of the cortex. It is through this principle that we can say that the "higher" organism represents a "higher" level of adaptive system capable, ontogenetically, of *mapping the environment more rapidly and extensively* and with *greater refinement and fidelity*, as compared to the tropistic or instinct-based adaptive system which can change its structure only phylogenetically. The highest level adaptive system – the sociocultural – is capable of an even more rapid and refined mapping of the environment (including the social and non-social environment, as well as at least some aspects of its own internal state) since sociocultural structures are partially independent of both ontogenetic and phylogenetic structures, and the mappings of many individuals are selectively pooled and stored extrasomatically and made available to the system units as they enter and develop within the system.

Such a perspective suggests that, instead of saying, as some do, that a prime requisite for persistence of a social system is "pattern maintenance", we can say, after Sommerhof and Ashby,[9] that persistence of an adaptive system requires as a necessary condition the maintenance of the system's "essential variables" within certain limits. Such essential variables and their limits may perhaps be specified in terms of what some have referred to as the "functional prerequisites" of any social system (for example, a minimal level organismal sustenance, of reproduction, of patterned interactive relations, etc.). But the maintenance of the system's essential variables, we are emphasizing, may hinge on (as history and ethnography clearly show) *pattern reorganization or change*. It is true, but hardly helpful, to say that *some* minimal patterning or stability of relations, or integration of components, is necessary – by the very definition of "system" or adaptive organization. Nor can we be satisfied, with the statement that persistence, continuity, or social "order" is promoted by the "institutionalization" of interactive relations via norms and values, simply because we can say with equal validity that discontinuity or social "disorder" is *also* promoted by certain kinds of "institutionalization".

To avoid the many difficulties of a one-sided perspective it would seem essential to keep before us as a basic principle that the persistence and/or development of the complex sociocultural system depends upon structuring, destructuring, and restructuring – processes occurring at widely varying rates and degrees as a function of the external social and non-social environment. Jules Henry, among others, has made this point:

> ... the lack of specificity of man's genetic mechanisms has placed him in the situation of constantly having to revise his social structures because of their frequent failure to guide inter-personal relations without tensions felt as burdensome even in the society in which they originate ... thus man has been presented with a unique evolutionary task: because his mechanisms for determining inter-personal relations lack specificity, he must attempt to maximize social adaptation through constant conscious and unconscious revision and experimentation, searching constantly for social structures, patterns of inter-personal relations, that will be more adaptive, as he feels them. Man's evolutionary path is thus set for him by his constant tendency to alter his modes of social adaptation.[10]

More generally, we recall that Karl W. Deutsch has seen restructuring as a basic feature distinguishing society from an organism or machine. Speaking of "the critical property which makes a given learning net into a *society*", he says:

> A learning net functions as a society, in this view, *to the extent* that its constituent physical parts are capable of regrouping themselves into new patterns of activity in response to changes in the net's surroundings, or in response to the internally accumulating results of their own or the net's past.
>
> The twin tests by machine we can tell a society from an organism or a machine, on this showing, would be the freedom of its parts to regroup themselves; and the nature of the regroupings which must imply new coherent patterns of activity – in contrast to the mere wearing out of a machine or the aging of an organism, which are marked by relatively few degrees of freedom and by the gradual disappearance of coherent patterns of activity. . . .

This in turn may rest on specific properties of their members: *their capacity for readjustment to new configurations, with renewed complementarity and sustained or renewed communication.*[11]

4. The cybernetic perspective of control or self-regulation of adaptive systems emphasizes the crucial role of "deviation", seen in both negative and positive aspects. On the negative side, certain kinds of deviations of aspects of the system from its given structural state may be seen as "mismatch" or "negative feedback" signals *interpreted by certain organizing centers* as a failure of the system's operating processes or structures relative to a goal state sought, permitting – under certain conditions of adaptive structuring – a change of those operating processes or structures toward goal-optimization. (Thus, one facet of the "political" process of sociocultural systems may be interpreted in this light, with the more "democratic" type of social organization providing the more extended and accurate assessment of the mismatch between goal-attainment on the one hand, and current policy and existing social structuring on the other.)

On the positive side, the cybernetic perspective brings out the absolute necessity of deviation – or, more generally, "variety" – in providing a pool of potential new transformations of process or structure that the adaptive systems might adopt in responding to goal-mismatch. On the lower, biological levels we recognize here the principle of genetic variety and the role of gene pools in the process of adaptive response to organismic mismatch with a changed environment. (And in regard to the other major facet of the "political" process, the more democratic type of social organization makes available a broader range of variety, or "deviation", from which to select new orientations.) Ashby, in developing his very general theory of the adaptive or self-regulating system, suggests the "law of requisite variety", which states that the variety within a system must be at least as great as the environmental variety against which it is attempting to regulate itself. Put more succinctly, only variety can regulate variety. Although such a general principle is a long way from informing more concrete analysis of particular cases, it should help provide a needed corrective to balance (not replace) the current emphasis in social science on conformity, the "control" (as against the cultivation) of "deviants", and "re-equilibration" of a given structure.

Thus, the concept of requisite deviation needs to be proffered as a high-level principle that can lead us to theorize: A requisite of sociocultural systems is the development and maintenance of a significant level of non-pathological deviance manifest as a pool of alternate ideas and behaviors with respect to the traditional, institutionalized ideologies and role behaviors. Rigidification of any given institutional structure must eventually lead to disruption or dissolution of the society by way of internal upheaval or ineffectiveness against external challenge. The student of society must thus pose the question – What "mechanisms" of non-pathological deviance production and maintenance can be found in any society, and what "mechanisms" of conformity operate to counteract these and possibly lessen the viability of the system?

Attempts to analyze a society from such a perspective make possible a more balanced analysis of such processes as socialization, education, mass communication, and economic and political conflict and debate. We are then encouraged to build squarely into our theory and research designs the full sociological significance of such informally well-recognized conceptions as socialization for "self-reliance" and relative "autonomy", education for "creativity", ideational flexibility and the "open mind", communications presenting the "full spectrum" of viewpoints, etc., instead of smuggling them in unsystematically as if they were only residual considerations or ill-concealed value judgments.

5. Given the necessary presence of variety or deviance in an adaptive system, the general systems model then poses the problem of the *selection* and more or less permanent *preservation* or systemic structuring of some of this variety. On the biological level, we have the process of "natural selection" of some of the genetic variety existing within the interfertile species and sub-species gene pool, and the preservation for various lengths of time of this variety through the reproductive process. On the level of higher order psychological adaptive systems, we have trial-and-error selection, by way of the so-called "law of effect", from the variety of environmental events and the potential behavioral repertoire to form learned and remembered experience and motor skills more or less permanently preserved by way of cortical structuring.[12] As symbolic mapping or decoding and encoding of the environment and one's self becomes possible,[13] the selection criteria lean less heavily on direct and simple physiological reward and more heavily on "meanings" or "significance" as manifested in existing self-group structural relations. In the process, selection from the full range of available variety becomes more and more refined and often more restricted, and emerges as one or another kind of "personality" system or "group character" structure. On the sociocultural level,

social selection and relative stabilization or institutionalization of normatively interpreted role relations and value patterns occurs through the variety of processes usually studied under the headings of conflict, competition, accommodation, and such; power, authority and compliance; and "collective behavior", from mob behavior through opinion formation processes and social movements to organized war. More strictly "rational" processes are of course involved, but often seem to play a relatively minor role as far as larger total outcomes are concerned.

It is clearly in the area of "social selection" that we meet the knottiest problems. For the sociocultural system, as for the biological adaptive system, analysis must focus on both the potentialities of the system's structure at a given time, and the environmental changes that might occur and put particular demands on whatever structure has evolved. In both areas the complexities are compounded for the sociocultural system. In developing a typology of systems and their internal linkages we have noted that, as we proceed from the mechanical or physical through the biological, psychic and sociocultural, the system becomes "looser", the interrelations among parts more tenuous, less rigid, and especially less directly tied to physical events as energy relations and transformations are overshadowed by symbolic relations and information transfers. Feedback loops between operating sociocultural structures and the surrounding reality are often long and tortuous, so much so that knowledge of results or goal-mismatch, when forthcoming at all, may easily be interpreted in non-veridical ways (as the history of magic, superstition, and ideologies from primitive to present amply indicate). The higher adaptive systems have not been attained without paying their price, as the widespread existence of illusion and delusions on the personality and cultural levels attest. On the biological level, the component parts have relatively few degrees of freedom, and changes in the environment are relatively directly and inexorably reacted to by selective structural changes in the species.

Sociocultural systems are capable of persisting within a wide range of degrees of freedom of the components, and are often able to "muddle through" environmental changes that are not too demanding. But of course this is part of the genius of this level of adaptive system: it is capable of temporary shifts in structure to meet exigencies. The matter is greatly complicated for the social scientist, however, by this system's outstanding ability to act on and partially control the environment of which a major determining part is made up of other equally loose-knit, more or less flexible, illusion-ridden, sociocultural adaptive systems. Thus, although the minimal integration required for a viable system does set limits on the kinds of structures that can persist, these limits seem relatively broad compared to a biological system.[14] And given the relatively greater degrees of freedom of internal structuring (structural alternatives, as some call them) and the *potentially* great speed with which restructuring may occur under certain conditions, it becomes difficult to predict the reactions of such a system to environmental changes or internal elaboration. Considering the full complexities of the problem we must wonder at the facility with which the functionalist sociologist has pronounced upon the ultimate functions of social structures, especially when – as seems so often the case – very little consideration is given either to the often feedback-starved social selective processes that have led to the given structures, or to the environmental conditions under which they may be presumed to be functional.

Although the problem is difficult, something can be said about more ultimate adaptive criteria against which sociocultural structures can be assessed. Consideration of the grand trends of evolution provides clues to very general criteria. These trends point in the direction of: (1) greater and greater flexibility of structure, as error-controlled mechanisms (cybernetic processes of control) replace more rigid, traditionalistic means of meeting problems and seeking goals; (2) ever more refined, accurate, and systematic mapping, decoding and encoding of the external environment and the system's own internal milieu (via science), along with greater independence from the physical environment; (3) and thereby a greater elaboration of self-regulating substructures in order – not merely to restore a given equilibrium or homeostatic level – but to purposefully restructure the system without tearing up the lawn in the process.[15]

With these and perhaps other general criteria, we might then drop to lower levels of generality by asking what restrictions these place on a sociocultural adaptive system if it is to remain optimally viable in these terms. It is possible that this might provide a value-free basis for discussing the important roles, for example, of a vigorous and independent science in all fields; the broad and deep dissemination of its codified findings; the absence of significant or long-lasting subcultural cleavages, power centers and vested interests, whether on a class or ethnic basis, to break or hinder the flow of information or feedback concerning the internal states of the system; and the promotion of a large "variety pool" by maintaining a certain number of

degrees of freedom in the relations of the component parts – for example, providing a number of real choices of behaviors and goals. Thus we can at least entertain the feasibility of developing an objective rationale for the sociocultural "democracy" we shy from discussing in value terms.

6. Further discussion of the intricacies of the problem of *sociocultural selection processes* leading to more or less stable system *structures* may best be incorporated into the frame of discussion of the problem of *"structure versus process"*. This is another of those perennial issues of the social (and other) sciences, which the modern systems perspective may illuminate.

Our argument may be outlined as follows:

– Much of modern sociology has analyzed society in terms of largely structural concepts: institutions, culture, norms, roles, groups, etc. These are often reified, and make for a rather static, overly deterministic, and elliptical view of societal workings.

– But for the sociocultural system, "structure" is only a relative stability of underlying, ongoing micro-processes. Only when we focus on these can we begin to get at the selection process whereby certain interactive relationships become relatively and temporarily stabilized into social and cultural structures.

– The unit of dynamic analysis thus becomes the systemic *matrix* of interacting, goal-seeking, deciding individuals and subgroups – whether this matrix is part of a formal organization or only a loose collectivity. Seen in this light, society becomes a continuous morphogenic process, through which we may come to understand in a unified conceptual manner the development of structures, their maintenance, and their change. And it is important to recognize that out of this matrix is generated, not only *social* structure, but also *personality* structure, and *meaning* structure. All, of course, are intimately interrelated in the morphogenic process, and are only analytically separable.

Structure, process, and decision theory

Though the problem calls for a lengthy methodological discussion, we shall here simply recall the viewpoint that sees the sociocultural system in comparative perspective against lower-level mechanical, organic and other types of systems. As we proceed upward along such a typology we noted that the ties linking components become less and less rigid and concrete, less direct, simple and stable within themselves. Translation of energy along unchanging and physically continuous links gives way in importance to transmission of information via internally varying, discontinuous components with many more degrees of freedom. Thus for mechanical systems, and parts of organic systems, the "structure" has a representation that is concrete and directly observable – such that when the system ceases to operate much of the structure remains directly observable for a time. For the sociocultural system, "structure" becomes a theoretical construct whose referent is only indirectly observable (or only inferable) by way of series of events along a time dimension; when the system ceases to operate, the links maintaining the sociocultural structure are no longer observable.[16] "Process", then, points to the actions and interactions of the components of an ongoing system, in which varying degrees of structuring arise, persist, dissolve, or change. (Thus "process" should not be made synonymous simply with "change", as it tended to be for many earlier sociologists.)

More than a half century ago, Albion W. Small argued that, "The central line in the path of methodological progress in sociology is marked by the gradual shifting of effort from analogical representation of social structures to real analysis of social processes."[17] This was an important viewpoint for many social thinkers earlier in this century, possibly as part of the trend in physical science and philosophy toward a process view of reality developing from the work of such people as Whitehead, Einstein, Dewey, and Bentley. Such views have apparently had little impact on those of recent decades who had developed the more dominant structure-oriented models of current sociology, but it seems clear that – with or without the aid of the essentially process-conscious general systems approach – a more even balance of process with structure in the analysis of sociocultural systems is gradually regaining lost ground.

C. H. Cooley, in his *Social Process*, focused on the "tentative process", involving inherent energy and growth as the dynamic agents, with ongoing "selective development" set in motion by the interaction of "active tendencies" and surrounding "conditions". He argued that for the social process, "that grows which works" is a better phrase than "natural selection" or "survival of the fittest", since "it is not so likely to let us rest in mechanical or biological conceptions".[18] R. E. Park, with his recognition of the central importance of communication, kept the notion of process in the foreground whether developing the forms of interaction or the foundations of social ecology. We should also recall the leaders of the so-called "formal" school: Whereas Simmel focused on "forms of interaction", the emphasis was always on the "interaction" as

process rather than simply on the "forms"; and though the Wiese–Becker systematics developed in great detail a classification of action *patterns*, it gave equal attention to *action* patterns. For W. I. Thomas, all social becoming is viewed as a product of continual interaction of individual consciousness and objective social reality. (F. Znaniecki more recently reinforced this point of view.[19]) And at least one unbroken thread in this vein continuing from the early part of the century is the Dewey–Mead perspective referred to as social interactionism (which, we have noted, has established a strong base especially congenial to the modern cybernetic approach).[20] A reviewer of a recent collection of social interactionist essays was "reminded throughout of the continuous character of socialization, of the complexity and fluidity of interaction when it is viewed as a process rather than as the mere enactment of social forms . . .".[21]

We can take only brief note of a few of the more recent arguments for the process viewpoint. The anthropologists, for example, have become acutely concerned in the last few years with this issue. G. P. Murdock seems to be echoing Small when he says, 'All in all, the static view of social structure which seeks explanations exclusively within the existing framework of a social system on the highly dubious assumption of cultural stability and nearly perfect functional integration seems clearly to be giving way, in this country at least, to a dynamic orientation which focuses attention on the processes by which such systems come into being and succeed one another over time."[22] At about the same time, Raymond Firth was stating: "The air of enchantment which for the last two decades has surrounded the 'structuralist' point of view has now begun to be dispelled. Now that this is so, the basic value of the concept of social structure as an heuristic tool rather than a substantial social entity has come to be more clearly recognized."[23]

Soon after appeared the late S. F. Nadel's penetrating work, *The Theory of Social Structure*, which was preceded by his article on "Social Control and Self Regulation". This perspective is used effectively in *The Theory of Social Structure* as a basis for a critique of the current rather one-sided equilibrium model emphasizing the "complementarity of expectations" to the relative neglect of the several other crucial types of associative *and* dissociative social interrelationships considered equally important in earlier sociology.

Parsons' model has to do with "the conditions of relatively stable interaction in social systems", implying defined value "standards" and "institutionalized role expectations": any willful disagreement with them simply falls outside the stipulated stability and the model based on it.

I would argue that this is not necessarily so and that our model must allow for such disagreements. Even "relatively stable" social systems do not exclude them, or include them only in the form of purely fortuitous contingencies. Far from being fortuitous or idiosyncratic, the rejection of the sanctioning potentialities of other roles may itself be anchored in the existing institutions, reflecting the presence of diverse but equally legitimate "value patterns", ideologies or schools of thought, that is, that plurality of norms we spoke of before.[24]

Nadel's book as a whole explores the thesis that structural analysis is not, and should not be treated as, static analysis: "Social structure as Fortes once put it, must be 'visualized' as 'a sum of processes in time'. As I would phrase it, social structure is implicitly an event-structure. . . . "[25] And in concluding he reiterates his argument that

... it seems impossible to speak of social structure in the singular. Analysis in terms of structure is incapable of presenting whole societies; nor, which means the same, can any society be said to exhibit an embracing, coherent structure as we understand the term. There are always cleavages, dissociations, enclaves, so that any description alleged to present a single structure will in fact present only a fragmentary or one-sided picture.[26]

As a final example in anthropology, we should mention the cogent argument of Evon Z. Vogt that the two concepts of structure and process must be integrated into a general theoretical model. As with Nadel, structure is seen as falsely conceived as static, with change pathological. Rather, Vogt feels, must we pose the primacy of change, considering structure the way in which moving reality is translated, for the observer, into an instantaneous and artificial observation: social and cultural structures are only the intersections in time and space of process in course of change and development.[27]

Among sociologists, a perennial critic of the overly-structural conception of the group is Herbert Blumer. Blumer has argued that it is from the process of ongoing interaction itself that group life gets its main features, which cannot be adequately analyzed in terms of fixed attitudes, "culture", or social structure – nor can it be conceptualized in terms of mechanical structure, the functioning of an organism, or a system seeking equilibrium, ". . . in view of

the formative and explorative character of interaction as the participants *judge* each other and *guide* their own acts by that judgment."

The human being is not swept along as a neutral and indifferent unit by the operation of a system. As an organism capable of self-interaction he forges his actions out of a process of definition involving *choice*, *appraisal*, and *decision*. . . . Cultural norms, status positions and role relationships are only *frameworks* inside of which that process [of formative transaction] goes on.[28]

Highly structured human association is relatively infrequent and cannot be taken as a prototype of a human group life. In sum, institutionalized patterns constitute only one conceptual aspect of society, and they point to only a part of the ongoing process (and, we might add, they must be seen to include deviant and disfunctional patterns: for conceptual clarity and empirical relevance, "institutionalization" cannot be taken to imply only "legitimacy", "consent", and ultimately adaptive values).

Finally, it should be noted that Gordon Allport, viewing personality as an open-system, stresses a very similar point concerning the organization of personality:

... the best hope for discovering coherence would seem to lie in approaching personality as a total functioning structure, i.e., as a *system*. To be sure, it is an incomplete system, manifesting varying degrees of order and disorder. It has structure but also unstructure, function but also malfunction. As Murphy says, "all normal people have many loose ends". And yet personality is well enough knit to qualify as a system – which is defined merely as *a complex of elements in mutual interaction*.[29]

In the light of such views, we need only recall the many critiques pointing to the incapacity or awkwardness of the conventional type of framework before the facts of process, "becoming", and the great range of "collective behavior".[30]

Statements such as Blumer's, a continuation of the perspective of many neglected earlier sociologists and social psychologists, would seem to constitute a perspective that is now pursued by many under new rubrics such as "decision theory". For earlier antecedents it should be enough to mention W. I. Thomas's "definition of the situation", Znaniecki's "humanistic coefficient", Weber's "verstehen", Becker's "interpretation", and MacIver's "dynamic assessment".[31] Much of the current structural, consensus theory represents a break from this focus. As Philip Selznick has argued,

A true theory of social action would say something about goal-oriented or problem-solving behavior, isolating some of its distinctive attributes, stating the likely outcomes of determinate transformations. . . . In Parsons' writing there is no true embrace of the idea that structure is being continuously opened up and reconstructed by the problem-solving behavior of individuals responding to concrete situations. This is a point of view we associate with John Dewey and G. H. Mead, for whom, indeed, it had significant intellectual consequences. For them and for their intellectual heirs, social structure is something to be taken account of in action; cognition is not merely an empty category but a natural process involving dynamic assessments of the self and the other.[32]

It can be argued, then, that a refocusing is occurring via "decision theory", whether elaborated in terms of "role-strain" theory; theories of cognitive dissonance, congruence, balance, or concept formation; exchange, bargaining, or conflict theories, or the mathematical theory of games. The basic problem is the same: How do interacting personalities and groups define, assess, interpret, "verstehen", and act on the situation? Or, from the broader perspective of our earlier discussion, how do the processes of "social selection" operate in the "struggle" for socio-cultural structure? Instead of asking how structure affects, determines, channels actions and interactions, we ask how structure is created, maintained, and recreated.

Thus we move down from structure to social interrelations and from social relations to social actions and interaction processes – to a matrix of "dynamic assessments" and intercommunication of meanings, to evaluating, emoting, deciding and choosing. To avoid anthropomorphism and gain the advantages of a broader and more rigorously specified conceptual system, we arrive at the language of modern systems theory.

Basic ingredients of the decision-making focus include, then: (1) a *process* approach; (2) a conception of *tension* as inherent in the process; and (3) a renewed concern with the role and workings of man's enlarged cortex seen as a complex adaptive subsystem operating within an *interaction matrix* characterized by *uncertainty, conflict*, and other dissociative (as well as associative) processes *underlying the structuring and restructuring of the larger psycho-social system.*

Process focus

The process focus points to information-processing individuals and groups linked by different types of communication nets to form varying types of interaction matrices that may be characterized by "competition", "cooperation", "conflict", and the like. Newer analytical tools being explored to handle such processes include treatment of the interaction matrix over time as a succession of states described in terms of transition probabilities, Markoff chains, or stochastic processes in general. The Dewey–Mead "transactions" are now discussed in terms of information and codings and decodings, with the essential "reflexivity" of behavior now treated in terms of negative and positive feedback loops linking via the communication process the intrapersonal, interpersonal and intergroup subsystems and making possible varying degrees of matching and mismatching of Mead's "self and others", the elaboration of Boulding's "Image",[33] and the execution of Miller's "Plans". And herein we find the great significance for sociology of many of the conceptual tools (though not, at least as yet, the mathematics) of information and communication theory, cybernetics, or general systems research, along with the rapidly developing techniques of *relational* mathematics such as the several branches of set theory – topology, group theory, graphy theory, symbolic logic, etc.

Conception of tension

Tension is seen as an inherent and essential feature of complex adaptive systems; it provides the "go" of the system, the "force" behind the elaboration and maintenance of structure. There is no "law of social inertia" operating here, nor can we count on "automatic" re-equilibrating forces counteracting system "disturbances" or "deviance", for, whereas we do find deviance-reducing negative feedback loops in operation we *also* find deviance-maintaining and deviance-amplifying *positive* feedback processes often referred to as the vicious circle or spiral, or "escalation".[34] It is not at all certain whether the resultant will maintain, change, or destroy the given system or its particular structure. The concepts of "stress" or "strain" we take to refer only to the greater mobilization of normal tension under conditions of more than usual blockage. And instead of a system's seeking to manage *tension*, it would seem more apt to speak of a system's seeking to manage *situations* interpreted as responsible for the production of greater than normal tension.

The "role strain" theory of William J. Goode is an illustrative attack on assumptions of the widely current structural approach, using a process and tension emphasis and contributing to the decision-theory approach. Goode analyzes social structure or institutions into role relations, and role relations into role transactions. "Role relations are seen as a sequence of 'role bargains' and as a continuing process of selection among alternative role behaviors, in which each individual seeks to reduce his role strain."[35] Contrary to the current stability view, which sees social system continuity as based primarily on normative consensus and normative integration, Goode thus sees "dissensus, nonconformity, and conflicts among norms and roles as the usual state of affairs. . . . The individual cannot satisfy fully all demands, and must move through a continuous sequence of role decision and bargains . . . in which he seeks to reduce his role strain, his felt difficulty in carrying out his obligations."[36] Goode also recognizes that there is no "law of social inertia" automatically maintaining a given structure.

> Like any structure or organized pattern, the role pattern is held in place by both internal and external forces – in this case, the role pressures from other individuals. Therefore, not only is role strain a normal experience for the individual, but since the individual processes of reducing role strain determine the total allocation of role performances to the social institutions, the total balances and imbalances of role strains create whatever stability the social structure possesses.[37]

It should be noted, however, that Goode accepts unnecessarily a vestige of the equilibrium or stability model when he states, "The total role structure functions so as to reduce role strain."[38] He is thus led to reiterate a proposition that – when matched against our knowledge of the empirical world – is patently false. Or, more precisely, not false, but a half-truth: it recognizes deviance-reducing negative feedback processes, but not deviance-amplifying positive feedback processes. Such a proposition appears reasonable only if we "hold everything else constant", that is, take it as a closed system. However, the proposition is unnecessary to his argument and, in fact, clashes with the rest of his formulation: ". . . though the sum of role performances ordinarily maintains a society it may also change the society or fail to keep it going. There is no necessary harmony among all role performances. . . . But whether the resulting societal pattern is 'harmonious' or integrated or whether it is even effective in maintaining that society, are separate empirical questions."[39]

Study of cognitive processes
A more concerted study of cognitive processes, especially under conditions of *uncertainty* and *conflict*, goes hand in hand, of course, with a focus on decision-making and role transactions. Despite the evolutionary implications of man's enlarged cortex, much social (and psychological) theory seems predicted on the assumption that men are decorticated. Cognitive processes, as they are coming to be viewed today, are not to be simply equated with the traditional, ill-defined, concept of the "rational". That the data-processing system – whether socio-psychological or electro-mechanical – is seen as inherently "rational" tells us little about its outputs in concrete cases. Depending on the adequacy and accuracy of the effectively available information, the total internal organization or "Image", the character of the "Plans" or program, and the nature of the significant environment, the output of either "machine" may be sense or nonsense, symbolic logic or psychologic, goal-attainment or oscillation.

Beyond giving us a deeper perspective on the concept of the "rational", current theories of cognitive processes give promise of transcending the hoary trichotomy of the cognitive, the conative, and the moral as analytical tools. Whether this amounts to a rejection of the distinction, or simply an insistence that what was analytically rent asunder must now be reunified, the ferment appears significant. We refer here, not only to the many neurological and schematic studies of the brain, or the processes by which it solves problems and attains concepts, but especially to the several theories of cognitive "dissonance" or "congruence" or "balance" represented in the works of Heider, Cartwright and Harary, Osgood and Tannenbaum, Festinger, and others, as well as the symbol-processing and interpersonal communication perspectives represented by the "psycho-linguistics" of Osgood, the "communicative acts" of Newcomb, and the "two factor" theory of Mowrer.

The intricate meeting of the cognitive, the affective and evaluative (or attitudinal), and the semantic or symbolic in such theories is well illustrated in Osgood's treatment of "cognitive dynamics". Equating "cognitive elements" with the *meanings* of signs, Osgood proposes that "congruity exists when the evaluative meanings of interacting signs are equally polarized or intense – either in the same or opposite evaluative directions . . .".[40] In contrast to the theories of Heider and Festinger, this theory "*assigns affective or attitudinal values to the cognitive elements themselves*, and not to their relations . . .".[41] And in discussing the "process of inference through psycho-logic", Osgood says:

> Much of what is communicated attitudinally by messages and by behavior is based on such inferences; . . . The syntax of language and of behavior provides a structural framework within which meaningful contents

are put; the structure indicates what is related to what, and how, but only when the meaningful values are added does the combination of structure and content determine psycho-logical congruence or incongruence.[42]

Despite the incorporation of aspects of these several elements into their theories, however, the psychologically oriented theorist usually leaves the sociologist something to be desired, namely, something that transcends "the individual" and "his" attempts to minimize inconsistency or dissonance and maintain stability, and which views the group situation as inadequately characterized in terms of "myriad decisions in individual nervous systems". Thus Osgood hypothesizes that

laws governing the thinking and behaving of individuals also govern the "thinking" and "behaving" of groups . . . with nothing but communication to bind us together, it is clear that "decisions" and "behaviors" of nations must come down to myriad decisions in individual nervous systems and myriad behaviors of individual human organisms.[43]

We are reminded here of Robert R. Sears' complaint that "psychologists think monadically. That is, they choose the behavior of one person as their scientific subject matter. For them, the universe is composed of individuals . . . the universal laws sought by the psychologist almost always relate to a single body."[44] Arguing for the desirability of combining individual and social behavior into a common framework, Sears noted that, "Whether the group's behavior is dealt with as antecedent and the individual's as consequent, or vice versa, the two kinds of event are so commonly mixed in causal relationships that it is impractical to conceptualize them separately."[45]

Fortunately, however, there are recent statements that rally to the side of the sociological interactionist theorists, whose perspective continues to be ignored or little understood by so many personality theorists who are nevertheless gradually rediscovering and duplicating its basic principles. A good beginning to a truly interpersonal approach to personality theory and the problem of stability and change in behavior is the statement of Paul F. Secord and Carl W. Backman, which remarkably parallels Goode's theory of stability and change in social systems discussed earlier. Pointing to the assumptions of several personality theorists that when stability of behavior occurs it is solely a function of stability in personality structure, and that this latter structure has, inherently, a strong resistance to change except when special change-inducing

forces occur, Secord and Backman see as consequences the same kinds of theoretical inadequacies we found for the stability view of social systems:

The first is that continuity in individual behavior is not a problem to be solved; it is simply a natural outcome of the formation of stable structure. The second is that either behavioral change is not given systematic attention, or change is explained independently of stability. Whereas behavioral stability is explained by constancy of structure, change tends to be explained by environmental forces and fortuitous circumstances.[46]

Their own theoretical view abandons these assumptions and "places the locus of stability and change in the interaction process rather than in intrapersonal structures." Recognizing the traditional two classes of behavioral determinants, the cultural-normative and the intrapersonal, their conceptualization

attempts to identify a third class of determinants, which have their locus neither in the individual nor the culture, but in the interaction process itself. In a general sense this third class may be characterized as the tendencies of the individual and the persons with whom he interacts to shape the interaction process according to certain requirements, i.e., they strive to produce certain patterned relations. As will be seen, the principles governing this activity are truly interpersonal; they require as much attention to the behavior of the other as they do to the behavior of the individual, and it cannot be said that one or the other is the sole locus of cause.[47]

They go on to analyze the "interpersonal matrix" into three components: an aspect of the self-concept of a person, his interpretation of those elements of his behavior related to that aspect, and his perception of related aspects of the other with whom he is interacting. "An interpersonal matrix is a recurring functional relation between these three components."

In these terms, Secord and Backman attempt to specify the conditions and forces leading to or threatening congruency or incongruency, and hence stability or change, in the matrix. Thus, four types of incongruency, and two general classes of resolution of incongruency, are discussed. One of these latter classes

results in restoration of the original matrix, leaving self and behavior unchanged (although cognitive distortions may occur), and the other leads to a new matrix in which self or behavior are changed.[48]

In sum, contrary to previous approaches, theirs emphasizes

that "the individual strives to maintain interpersonal relations characterized by congruent matrices, rather than to maintain a self, habits, or traits".

> Maintenance of intrapersonal structure occurs only when such maintenance is consistent with an ongoing interaction process which is in a state of congruency. That most individuals do maintain intrapersonal structure is a function of the fact that the behavior of others toward the individuals in question is normally overwhelmingly consistent with such maintenance.[49]

And this conception also, as most approaches do not (or do inadequately), predicts or accounts for the fact that, should the interpersonal environment cease to be stable and familiar, undergoing great change such that others behave uniformly toward the individual in new ways, the individual "would rapidly modify his own behavior and internal structure to produce a new set of congruent matrices. As a result, he would be a radically changed person."[50]

As we have said, the Secord and Backman theory and Goode's role-strain theory may be seen as closely complementary views. The former argues that *personality* structure is generated in, and continues to have its seat in, the social interactive matrix; the latter argues that *social* structure is generated in, and continues to have its seat in, the social interactive matrix. Since it is the latter that we are focusing on here, we shall conclude with additional examples of current theory and research that explore further the mechanisms underlying the genesis or elaboration of social structure out of the dynamics, especially the role dynamics, of the symbolic interaction process.

Further examples

Ralph Turner has addressed himself to the elaboration of this perspective in that conceptual area fundamental to the analysis of institutions – roles and role-taking.[51] The many valid criticisms of the more static and overdetermining conception of roles is due, he believes, to the dominance of the Linton view of role and the use of an over-simplified model of role functioning. Viewing role-playing and role-taking, however, as a process (as implied in Meadian theory), Turner shows that there is more to it than just "an extension of normative or cultural deterministic theory" and that a process view of role adds novel elements to the notion of social interaction.

The morphogenic nature of role behavior is emphasized at the start in the concept of *"role-making"*. Instead of postulating the initial existence of distinct, identifiable roles, Turner posits "a tendency to create and modify conceptions of self- and other-roles" as the interactive orienting process. Since actors behave *as if* there were roles, although the latter actually exist only in varying degrees of definitiveness and consistency, the actors attempt to define them and make them explicit – thereby in effect creating and modifying them as they proceed. The key to role-taking, then, is the morphogenic propensity "to shape the phenomenal world into roles"; formal organizational regulation restricting this process is not to be taken as the prototype, but rather as a "distorted instance" of the wider class of role-taking phenomena. To the extent that the bureaucratic setting blocks the role-making process, organization is maximal, "variety" or alternatives of action minimal, actors are cogs in a rigid machine, and the morphogenic process underlying the viability of complex adaptive systems is frustrated.

Role interaction is a tentative process of reciprocal responding of self and other, challenging or reinforcing one's conception of the role of the other, and consequently stabilizing or modifying one's own role as a product of this essentially feedback-testing transaction. The conventional view of role emphasizing a prescribed complementarity of expectations thus gives way to a view of role-taking as a process of "devising a performance on the basis of an imputed other-role", with an important part being played by cognitive processes of inference testing. In a manner consistent with models of the basic interaction process suggested by Goode and by Secord and Backman, Turner views as a central feature of role-taking "the process of discovering and creating 'consistent' wholes out of behavior", of "devising a pattern" that will both cope effectively with various types of relevant others and meet some recognizable criteria of consistency. Such a conception generates empirically testable hypotheses of relevance of our concern here with institutional morphogenesis, such as: "Whenever the social structure is such that many individuals characteristically act from the perspective of two given roles simultaneously, there tends to emerge a single role which encompasses the action."[52]

Turning directly to the implications for formal, institutional role-playing, Turner argues that the formal role is primarily a "skeleton" of rules which evoke and set into motion the fuller roles built-up and more or less consensually validated in the above ways. Role behavior becomes relatively fixed only while it provides a perceived consistency and stable framework for interaction, but it undergoes cumulative revision in the role-taking process of accommodation and compromise with the simple conformity demanded by formal prescriptions.

The purposes and sentiments of actors constitute a unifying element in role genesis and maintenance, and hence role-taking must be seen to involve a great deal of selective perception of other-behavior and relative emphasis in the elaboration of the role pattern. This selection process operates on the great variety of elements in the situation of relevant objects and other-behaviors which could become recognized components in a consistent role pattern. Not all combinations of behavior and object relations can be classed into a single role; there must be criteria by which actors come to "verify" or "validate" the construction of a number of elements into a consistent role. This verification stems from two sources: "internal validation" of the interaction itself, and "external validation" deriving from "the generalized other" of Mead. The former hinges on successful prediction or anticipation of relevant other-behavior in the total role-set, and hence on the existence of role patterns whereby coherent selection of behaviors judged to constitute a consistent role can be made. But the notion of fixed role prescriptions is not thereby implied, since, first, roles – like norms – often or usually provide a *range of alternative* ways of dealing with any other-role, or, as is most common, the small segment of it activated at any one time, and secondly, the coherence and predictability of a role must be assessed and seen as "validated", not in terms of any one other-role, but in terms of the Gestalt of all the accommodative and adjusted requirements set by the number of other-roles in the actor's role-set and generated in the ongoing role-making process.

An example is provided by the study by Gross *et al.* of the school superintendent role. It is found that incumbency in this role (1) actually involved a great deal of choice behavior in selecting among the alternative interpretations and behaviors deemed possible and appropriate, and that (2) consistency and coherence of an incumbent's behavior could be seen only in terms of the total role as an accommodation with correlative other-roles of school board member, teacher, and parent, with which the superintendent was required to interact simultaneously. As Gross puts it, a "system model" as against a "position-centric" model involves an important addition by including the inter-relations among the counter positions. "A position can be completely described only by describing the total system of positions and relationships of which it is a part. In other words, in a system of interdependent parts, a change in any relationship will have an effect on all other relationships, and the positions can be described only by the relationships."[53]

Thus Turner sees the internal criterion of role validation as insuring a constant modification, creation, or rejection of the content of specific roles occurring in the interplay between the always somewhat vague and incomplete ideal role conceptions and the experience of their concrete implications by the interpreting, purposive, selectively evaluating and testing self and others.

The basis of "external validation" of a role is the judgment of the behavior to constitute a role by others felt to have a claim to correctness of legitimacy. Criteria here include: discovery of a name in common use for the role, support of major norms or values, anchorage in the membership of recognized groups, occupancy of formalized positions, and experience of key individuals as role models acting out customary attitudes, goals and specific actions.

Under the "normal loose operation of society" these various internal and external criteria of validation are at best only partially conveyant and consistent in identifying the same units and content as roles. The resulting inevitable discrepancies between formal, institutional rules and roles, and the goals, sentiments and selective interpretations arising from the experience of actually trying to play them out, make role conceptions "creative compromises", and insure "that the framework of roles will operate as a hazily conceived ideal framework for behavior rather than as an unequivocal set of formulas".[54]

In sum, "institutions" may provide a normative framework prescribing roles to be played and thus assuring the required division of labor and minimizing the costs of general exploratory role-setting behavior, but the actual role transactions that occur generate a more or less coherent and stable working compromise between ideal set prescriptions and a flexible role-making process, between the structured demands of others and the requirements of one's own purposes and sentiments. This conception of role relations as "fully interactive", rather than merely conforming, contributes to the recent trends "to subordinate normative to functional processes in accounting for societal integration"[55] by emphasizing the complex adaptive interdependence of actors and actions in what we see as an essentially morphogenic process – as against a merely equilibrial or homeostatic process.

Organization as a negotiated order

Next we shall look at a recently reported empirical study of a formal organization that concretely illustrates many facets of the above conceptualization of Turner and contributes further to our thesis. In their study of the hospital and its interactive order, Anselm Strauss and colleagues develop a model of organizational process that bears directly on the basic sociological problem of "how a measure of order is maintained in the face of inevitable changes (derivable from sources both external and internal to the organization)".[56] Rejecting an overly structural view, it is assumed that social order is not simply normatively specified and automatically maintained but is something that must be "worked at", continually reconstituted. Shared agreements, underlying orderliness, are not binding and shared indefinitely but involve a temporal dimension implying eventual review, and consequent renewal or rejection. On the basis of such considerations, Strauss and colleagues develop their conception of organizational order as a "negotiated order".

The hospital, like any organization, can be visualized as a hierarchy of status and power, of rules, roles and organizational goals. But it is also a locale for an ongoing complex of transactions among differentiated types of actors: professionals such as psychiatrists, residents, nurses and nursing students, psychologists, occupational therapists and social workers; and non-professionals such as various levels of staff, the patients themselves, and their families. The individuals involved are at various stages in their careers, have their own particular goals, sentiments, reference groups, and ideologies, command various degrees of prestige, esteem and power, and invest the hospital situation with differential significance.

The rules supposed to govern the actions of the professionals were found to be far from extensive, clearly stated, or binding; hardly anyone knew all the extant rules or the applicable situations and sanctions. Some rules previously administered would fall into disuse, receive administrative reiteration, or be created anew in a crisis situation. As in any organization, rules were selectively evoked, broken, and/or ignored to suit the defined needs of personnel. Upper administrative levels especially avoided periodic attempts to have the rules codified and formalized, for fear of restricting the innovation and improvisation believed necessary to the care of patients. Also, the multiplicity of professional ideologies, theories and purposes would never tolerate such rigidification.

In sum, the area of action covered by clearly defined rules was very small, constituting a few general "house rules" based on long-standing shared understandings. The basis of organizational order was the generalized mandate, the single ambiguous goal, of returning patients to the outside world in better condition. Beyond this, the rules ordering actions to this end were the subject of continual negotiations – being argued, stretched, ignored, or lowered as the occasion seemed to demand. As elsewhere, rules failed to act as universal prescriptions, but required judgment as to their applicability to the specific case.

The ambiguities and disagreements necessitating negotiation are seen by the researchers to be patterned. The various grounds leading to negotiation include: disagreement and tension over the proper ward placement of a patient to maximize his chances of improvement; the mode of treatment selected by the physician, which is closely related to his own psychiatric ideology and training; the multiplicity of purposes and temporal ends of each of the professional groups as they maneuver to elicit the required cooperation of their fellow workers; the element of medical uncertainty involved in treating the patient as a unique, "individual case", and the consequent large area of contingency lying of necessity beyond specific role prescription; and, finally, the inevitable changes forced upon the hospital and its staff by external forces and the unforeseen consequences of internal policies and the round of negotiations themselves. What is concretely observed, then, in researching the organizational order of the hospital, is negotiation between the neurologically trained and the psychotherapeutically oriented physician, between the nurses and the administrative staff, between the nonprofessional floor staff and the physician, between the patient and each of the others.

The negotiation process itself was found to have patterned and temporal features. Thus, different physicians institute their own particular programs of treatment and patient care and in the process develop fairly stable understandings with certain nurses or other institutional gatekeepers such as to effectuate an efficient order of behaviors with a minimum of communication and special instructions. Such arrangements are not called for by any organizational role prescriptions; nevertheless, they represent a concrete part of the actual organization generated in the morphogenic process of negotiation (or role-making and -taking, in Turner's terms). Thus, agreements do not occur by chance but are patterned in terms of "who contracts with whom, about what, as well as when . . .".[57] There is an important temporal aspect, also, such as the specification of a termination period often written into an agreement – as when a physician bargains with a head nurse to leave his patient in the specific ward for "two more days" to see if things will work themselves out satisfactorily.

In a final section of their paper, Strauss and his colleagues bring out the full implications of their negotiation model in dealing with genuine organizational change. The model presents a picture of the hospital – and perhaps most other institutionalized spheres of social life – as a transactional milieu where numerous agreements are "continually being established, renewed, reviewed, revoked, revised". But this raises the question of the relation between this process and the more stable structure of norms, statuses, and the like. The authors see a close systemic relation between the two. The daily negotiations periodically call for a reappraisal and reconstitution of the organizational order into a "new order, not the reestablishment of an old, as reinstituting of a previous equilibrium". And, we would add, it contributes nothing to refer to this as a "moving equilibrium" in the scientifically established sense of the term. The daily negotiative process not only allows the day-by-day work to get done, but feeds back upon the more formalized, stable structure of rules and policies by way of "a periodic appraisal process" to modify it – sometimes slowly and crescively, sometimes rapidly and convulsively. And, as a reading of history suggests, virtually every formal structure extant can be traced, at least in principle, from its beginnings to its present apparently timeless state through just such a morphogenic process – a process characteristic of what we have called the complex adaptive system.

The school superintendent and his role

We turn to the study by Gross and his associates of the role system of the school superintendent and his counter-role partners, the school board member, the teacher, and the parent. A major burden of this empirical study is to demonstrate the research sterility of the Lintonian conception of role, and structural theories built on it, due principally to the postulate of consensus on role definition. The study showed a majority of significant differences in the definitions of their own roles by a sample of incumbents of the same social position and by incumbents of different but interrelated counter positions. This fact led Gross and his associates to the demonstration of a number of important theoretical consequences derived from rejection of the postulate of role consensus. It is often assumed, for example, that the socialization process by which roles are "acquired" provides for a set of clearly defined and agreed-upon expectations associated with any particular position. But the empirically discovered fact of differential *degrees of consensus* seriously challenged this assumption. From our systems model viewpoint, recognition of degrees of consensus is tantamount to the recognition of a continuous source of "variety" in the role system, as defined earlier, which leads us to seek the various *selective*, choice processes occurring in the role transactions. At least for the occupational positions studied, it was found that the assumption of socialization on the basis of prior consensus on role

definitions was untenable, and deserved "to be challenged in most formulations of role acquisition, including even those concerned with the socialization of the child".[58]

Secondly, the research showed that, instead of assuming role consensus and explaining variations of behavior of incumbents of the same position in terms of personality variables, one would better explain them in terms of the varying role expectations and definitions – which may be unrelated to psychological differences.

The implications are also great for a theory of social control. Instead of a model assuming that the application or threat of negative sanctions leads to conformity to agreed-upon norms, the research pointed to the numerous situations in which, due to variant or ambiguous role definitions, the same behavior resulted in negative sanctions by some role partners and positive sanctions by others, or failure to apply sanctions because of perceived ambiguity – or nonconformity to perceived expectations of another despite negative sanctions because other expectations were defined as more legitimate.

Another Lintonian postulate challenged by this research is that though an actor may occupy many positions, even simultaneously, he activates each role singly with the others remaining "latent". It is found, however, that individuals often perceive and act toward role partners as if simultaneous multiple roles were being activated. For example, one may hold different expectations regarding a teacher who is male, young and unmarried as against one who is female, older and married. In other words, standards and expectations are applied to the whole person as a result, in part, of the complex of positions the person is perceived as occupying at that time. A related consideration involves the time dimension over which two or more individuals interact; other positions they occupy enter progressively into their perception of each other and consequently modify evaluations and expectations. Thus the authors generalize their point to a broader theory of social interaction by suggesting that evaluative standards shift over time from those applied as appropriate to the incumbent of a particular position to those applied to a total person with particular personality features and capacities as the incumbent of multiple positions.

Finally, their rejection of the consensus model led these researchers to find a process of role-strain or role-conflict generation and resolution similar in principle to that conceptualized by others discussed above. Having defined the role set they were studying as a true *complex system* of interrelated components, and having then uncovered and analyzed the *variety* continuously introduced into the system by way of variant, ambiguous or changing role definitions, they then focused on the *selection process* whereby this variety was sifted and sorted in the give and take of role transactions. Thus, given the situation in which a role incumbent was faced with incompatible expectations on the part of two of his counter-role partners, a theory was constructed to answer the question of how the actor may choose from among four alternatives in resolving the role conflict. From our present perspective, the theoretical scheme suggested constitutes another important contribution to the forging of a conceptual link between the dynamics of the role transaction and the more stable surrounding social structure – a link that is too often skipped over by the consensus theorist's identification of social structure and consensual role playing.

This linkage is made in terms of the concepts of perceived *legitimacy* of the conflicting expectations, an assessment of the *sanctions* that might be applied, and predispositions to give primacy to a *moral* orientation, an *expedient* orientation, or a balance of the two. We face once again the reciprocal question of how role transactions are conditioned by the surrounding social structure and how that structure is generated and regenerated as a product of the complex of role transactions.

The four alternatives that Gross and colleagues see open to an actor to choose in attempting to resolve a role conflict between incompatible expectations A and B are: (1) conformity to expectation A; (2) conformity to expectation B; (3) compromise in an attempt to conform in part to both expectations; or (4) attempt to avoid conforming to either expectation. The first criterion that the theory postulates to underlie the particular alternative chosen is the actors' definition of the legitimacy of the expectations. Thus the prediction of behavior on this criterion is that, when only one expectation is perceived as legitimate the actor will conform to that one; when both are defined as legitimate he will compromise; and when neither is seen as legitimate he will engage in avoidance behavior. The second criterion is the actor's perception of the sanctions that would be applied for nonconformity, which would create pressures to conform if strong negative sanctions are foreseen otherwise. This predicts for three of the four combinations of two sets of expectations, but not for the case of both expectations being perceived as leading to weak or no negative sanctions.

It is assumed that for any role conflict situation an actor would perceive both of these dimensions and make his decision accordingly. Predictions on the basis of the theory so far provide for determinate resolutions of conflict in

seven of the sixteen combinations of the four types of legitimacy and the four types of sanctions situations, but the other nine are left indeterminate with only the two criteria. This is because the criteria predispose in different directions, and at least a third criterion is needed to determine the outcome. The authors thus appeal to the actor's predisposition to give primacy to either the legitimacy or to the sanctions dimension, or to balance the two, thus leading to the postulation of three types of predisposing orientations to expectations as listed above – the *moral*, the *expedient*, and the balanced *moral-expedient*. All the combinations of situations now become predictive.

The accuracy of the predictions was tested empirically with the data from the superintendent-role study for four "incompatible expectation situations", and the evidence supported the theory, though with some incorrect predictions.

The implications of this conceptualization and empirical analysis are far-reaching, as already suggested, for general sociological theory. The study is concerned with what must be considered "institutional" organization and process, and supports a model of that structure and process that is quite different from the more traditional models. As the authors point out, one strong advantage of the theory is its conceptualization of institutional role behavior in terms of "expectations", whether legitimate or illegitimate, rather than in terms of "obligations" (legitimate expectations) as is assumed in consensus theory. The theory thus allows for the possibility that illegitimate expectations constitute a significant part of institutional role behavior, and underlie much of the conflict occurring – as we feel intuitively to be the case – within the institutional process. It follows, further, that deviance – nonconformity to expectations – is a more intimate and normal element in institutional behavior than conformity theory would permit. And it also permits theoretical recognition of the possibility that, as Etzioni has suggested,[59] a great deal of organizational behavior is based, not on internalized norms and values, but on an expedient calculation of self-interests and of possible rewards and punishments. This, in turn, leaves open the theoretical possibility that non-legitimized power, as well as legitimized authority, may often be a controlling factor in institutional behavior.

Role conflict and change among the Kanuri

The final empirical study we shall sketch is explicitly based on an understanding of the modern systems approach, focusing as it does on a theory of "self-generating internal change". Ronald Cohen, an anthropologist, reports a theoretically well-organized analysis of his field study of role conflict and change among the Kanuri of Nigeria.[60] The study focuses on "goal ambiguity" and "conflicting standards" within a facet of the joint native–colonial political administrative hierarchy, particularly on the pivotal position of native "district head" which had come to combine the quite diverse cultural orientations of the colonial British and the Kanuri. This diversity between, as well as within, the two cultures made for inconsistencies, ambiguity, and conflict in political goals and in role standards and performances, which were continuously exacerbated by the variety of pressures put on district heads by the central native administration, the colonial administration, and the colonial technical departments.

The consequences of this situation for the political system are analyzed in terms of A. G. Frank's theory of organizational process and change.[61] Given the conditions of ambiguity and conflict of standards and goals, it is postulated that a process of *selective performance* and *selective enforcement* of standards will occur, with subordinates being forced to decide on which expectations to meet, and superiors required to selectively evaluate performances and hence selectively enforce some standards over others. This postulate leads to a number of predictions that Cohen proceeded to test. In essence, a continuous process is set up that appears, though in more exaggerated form, much like the "role strain", "role-making", "negotiated order" situations we met earlier. Role players fail to meet, or feign meeting some standards, and differentially select those they will meet. As a result, the role system is postulated to exhibit a strain toward substantive rationality (in Weber's sense), shifting standards for members, widespread role innovation or "deviance", ready adaptation to environmental changes, and an active and widespread circulation of information about standards and goals by "intermediary dealers in information" and by members seeking to reduce the ambiguity and conflict concerning these standards and goals.

The process is thus a circular, feedback loop whereby superiors continuously modify their standards or expectations as definitions of political objectives change, and subordinates adapt their decisions and performances to these changing expectations and surrounding circumstances, which in turn changes the states of the situation toward which superiors are acting. The role system, then, is seen as continuously receptive and responsive to external and internal pressures which demand some kind of workable "mapping" of the abundantly available situational "variety", which in turn makes possible – though does not

guarantee – the evolution of more or less adaptive, institutionalized internal system procedures.

Applying this theory to the Kanuri, Cohen found the predictions to be borne out to a substantial degree. We leave the detailed description of these phenomena to the original study, which drew the general practical conclusion that – in spite of its apparent conservative, anti-progressive traditionalism – the Kanuri political role system showed greater compliance to the varied pressures of superiors and situational exigencies than to the tenets of tradition and thereby proved to be a self-generating system containing mechanisms for its own transformation. The implications of this for policy relating to "developing countries" are of obvious importance.

On the theoretical side, Cohen clearly recognizes the implications of his mode of analysis for a genetic model of sociocultural evolution.

This model depends basically on two conditions. First, the evolving phenomenon must be shown to be *variable* in terms of its constituent units, and second, there must be analytically distinct *selective factors* which operate on the variation within the phenomenon to produce a constantly adapting and thus an evolving history of development. Although there are more or less stable orientations of tradition present in Bornu, conflicts in the political organization produce a variability of response by the actors upon which selective pressures exerted by superiors in the political hierarchy may operate to bring about innovations and changes that are incremental in their nature, i.e., evolutionary rather than revolutionary.[62]

We opened our discussion of the decision-making, process approach to complex adaptive systems with a turn-of-the-century prognosis of Albion Small. We might remind ourselves further of important ties with the past by closing with the early fundamental insight of Edward Sapir:

While we often speak of society as though it were a static structure defined by tradition, it is, in the more intimate sense, nothing of the kind, but a highly intricate network of partial or complete understandings between the members of organizational units of every degree of size and complexity. . . . It is only apparently a static sum of social institutions; actually it is being reanimated or creatively reaffirmed from day to day by particular acts of a communicative nature which obtain among individuals participating in it.[63]

Conclusion

We have suggested that much current thinking represents the coming to fruition of earlier conceptions of which Sapir's and Small's statements are harbingers. Although a science should not hesitate to forget its founders, it would do well to remain aware of their basic thought.

We have argued that a promising general framework for organizing these valuable insights of the past and present may be derived from the recent general systems perspective, embracing a holistic conception of complex adaptive systems viewed centrally in terms of information and communication process and the significance of the way these are structured for self-regulation and self-direction. We have clearly arrived at a point in the development of the "behavioral" sciences at which synthesis or conceptual unification of subdisciplines concerned with social life is challenging simple analysis or categorization. Not only is there growing demand that the "cognitive", "affective" and "evaluative" be conceptually integrated, but that the free-handed parceling out of aspects of the sociocultural adaptive system among the various disciplines (e.g., "culture" to anthropology, the "social system" to sociology, and "personality" to psychology) be reneged, or at least ignored. The potential of the newer system theory is especially strong in this regard.[64] By way of conclusion we recapitulate the main arguments.

1. The advance of science has driven it away from concern with "substance" and toward a focus on *relations* between components of whatever kind. Hence the concern with complex organization or systems, generally defined in terms of the transactions, often mutual and usually intricate, among a number of components such that some kind of more or less stable structure – often tenuous and only statistically delineated – arises (that is, *some* of the relations between components show *some* degree of stability or repetitiveness *some* of the time). Extremely fruitful advances have been taking place, especially since the rapid scientific progress made during World War II, in specifying basic features common to substantively different kinds of complex adaptive systems, as well as delineating their differences. In contrast to some of the general systems theorists themselves as well as their critics, we have argued that this is not simply analogizing but generalizing or abstracting as well (although the former is important, and scientifically legitimate also, when performed with due caution). To say that physiological, psychological, and sociocultural processes of control all involve the basic cybernetic principles of information flow along feedback loops is no more a mere analogy than to say that the trajectories of a falling apple, an artificial satellite, or a planet all involve the basic principle of gravitational attraction.

2. Complex adaptive systems are open systems in intimate interchange with an environment characterized by a great deal of shifting variety ("booming, buzzing confusion") and its constraints (its structure of causal interrelations). The concept of equilibrium developed for closed physical systems is quite inappropriate and usually inapplicable to such a dynamic situation. Rather, a characteristic resultant is the elaboration of organization in the direction of the less probable and the less inherently stable.

Features common to substantively different complex adaptive systems can be conceptualized in terms of the perspective of information and control theory. "Information" in its most general sense is seen, not as a thing that can be transported, but as a selective interrelation or mapping between two or more subsets of constrained variety selected from larger ensembles. Information is thus transmitted or communicated as invariant constraint or structure in some kind of variety, such that subsystems with the appropriate matched internal ensembles, reacting to and acting upon the information, do so in a situation of decreased uncertainty and potentially more effective adaptation to the variety that is mapped. Unless mapping (encoding, decoding, correlating, understanding, etc.) occurs between two or more ensembles we do not have "information", only raw variety or noise.

In these terms, adaptive systems, by a continuous selective feedback interchange with the variety of the environment, come to make and preserve mappings on various substantive bases, which may be transmitted generationally or contemporaneously to other similar units. By means of such mappings (for example, via genes, instincts, learned events, culture patterns) the adaptive system may, if the mappings are adequate, continue to remain viable before a shifting environment. The transmission and accumulation of such information among contemporaneous adaptive systems (individuals) becomes more and more important at higher levels until it becomes the prime basis of linkage of components for the highest level sociocultural system.

Some of the more important differences between complex adaptive systems include the substantive nature of the components, the types of linkage of the components, the kinds and levels of feedback between system and environment, the degree of internal feedback of a system's own state (for example, "self-awareness"), the methods of transmission of information between subsystems and along generations, the degree of refinement and fidelity of mapping and information transfer, the degree and rapidity with which the system can restructure itself or the environmental variety, etc.

3. Such a perspective provides a general framework which meets the major criticisms leveled against much of current sociological theory: lack of time and process perspective, overemphasis on stability and maintenance of given structure, and on consensus and cooperative relations, to the relative neglect – or unsystematic treatment – of deviance, conflict and other dissociative relations underlying system destructuring and restructuring.

4. Thus, the concept of the system itself cannot be identified with the more or less stable structure it may take on at any particular time. As a fundamental principle, it can be stated that a condition for maintenance of a viable adaptive system may be a change in its particular structure. Both stability and change are a function of the same set of variables, which must include both the internal state of the system and the state of its significant environment, along with the nature of the interchange between the two.

5. A time perspective is inherent in this kind of analysis – not merely historical but evolutionary. (It can probably be said that the time was ripe by 1959 for a Darwinian centennial ramifying well beyond the purely biological.) This perspective calls for a balance and integration of structural and processual analysis. As others have pointed out, the Linnean system of classification of structures became alive only after Darwin and others discovered the processes of variation, selection and recombination that gave them theoretical significance, though these discoveries leaned heavily in turn on the classification of systematically varying structures.

And among the important processes for the sociocultural system are not only cooperation and conformity to norms, but conflict, competition and deviation which may help create (or destroy) the essential variety pool, and which constitute part of the process of selection from it, such that a more or less viable system structure may be created and maintained (or destroyed).

6. In sociological terms, the "complementarity of expectations" model is an ideal type constituting only one pole of a continuum of equally basic associative and dissociative processes characterizing real societies – although the particular "mix" and intensities of the various types may differ widely with different structural arrangements. Further, the systemic analysis of a sociocultural system is not exhausted by analysis of its institutionalized patterns. By focusing on process, we are more prepared to

include all facets of system operation – from the minimally structured end of the collective behavior continuum through the various degrees and kinds of structuring to the institutional pole. The particular characteristics of the process, especially the degrees and kinds of mappings and mismatchings of the interacting units, tell us whether we are in fact dealing with certain degrees of structuring and the dynamics underlying this structuring: de facto patterning may be anchored in coercive, normative, or utilitarian compliance, making for very different kinds of system.

7. "Institutionalized" patterns are not to be construed as thereby "legitimized" or as embracing only "conformity" patterns – at least for the sake of conceptual clarity and empirical adequacy. Processes of all degrees and kinds of structuring may be seen in terms of deviant as well as conformity patterns – relative to the point of reference selected by the observer. One may select certain institutional patterns and values (to be clearly specified) as an arbitrary reference point to match against *other* institutional patterns and values, along with less structured behaviors. The concept of *the* institutionalized common value system smuggles in an empirically dubious, or unverified, proposition – at least for complex modern societies.

8. The complex adaptive system's organization *is* the "control", the characteristics of which will change as the organization changes. The problem is complicated by the fact that we are dealing directly with two levels of adaptive system and thus two levels of structure, the higher level (sociocultural) structure being largely a shifting statistical or probability structure (or ensemble of constraints) expressing over time the transactional processes occurring among the lower level (personality) structures. We do not have a sociocultural system *and* personality systems, but only a sociocultural system *of* constrained interactions among personality systems.

We can only speak elliptically of "ideas" or "information" or "meanings" in the head of a particular individual: all we have is an ensemble of constrained variety embodied in a neurological net. "Meaning" or "information" is generated only in the process of interaction with other ensembles of similarly mapped or constrained variety (whether embodied in other neurological nets or as the ensemble of causally constrained variety of the physical environment), whereby ensemble is mapped or matched against ensemble via communication links, and action is carried out, the patterning of which is a resultant of the degree of successful mapping that occurred. (Of course, "meaning" on the symbolic level can be regenerated over a long period by the isolated individual through an internal interchange or "conversation" of the person with his "self", made possible by previous socially induced mappings of one's own internal state that we call "self-awareness". But in some respects, part of the world literally loses its meaning for such a person.)

If the ensembles of variety of two interacting units, or one unit and its physical environment, have no or little isomorphic structuring, little or no meaning can be generated to channel ongoing mutual activity; or in more common terms, there is no "common ground", no "meeting of minds" and thus no meaning or information exchange – only raw variety, uncertainty, lack of "order" or organization.

Unless "social control" is taken as simply the more or less intentional techniques for maintaining a given institutional structure by groupings with vested interests, it must refer to the above transactional processes as they operate – now to develop new sociocultural structures, now to reinforce existing ones, now to destructure or restructure older ones. Thus, we cannot hope to develop our understanding much further by speaking of one "structure" determining, "affecting", or acting upon another "structure". We shall have to get down to the difficult but essential task of (a) specifying much more adequately the distribution of essential features of the component subsystems' internal mappings, including both self-mappings and their mappings of their effective environment, (b) specifying more extensively the structure of the transactions among these units at a given time, the degree and stability of the given structuring seen as varying with the degree and depth of common meanings that are generated in the transaction process, and (c) assessing, with the help of techniques now developing, the ongoing process of transitions from a given state of the system to the next in terms of the deviation-reducing and deviation-generating feedback loops relating the tensionful, goal-seeking, decision-making subunits via the communication nets partly specified by (b). Some behavior patterns will be found to be anchored in a close matching of component psychic structures (for example, legitimized authority or normative compliance); others, in threats of goal-blockage, where there is minimal matching (for example, power or coercive compliance); still others, anchored in a partial matching, primarily in terms of environmental mappings of autonomous subunits and minimally in terms of collective mappings (for example, opportunism or utilitarian compliance). As the distribution of mappings shifts in the system (which normally occurs for a number of reasons), so will the transaction processes and communication nets, and thus will the sociocultural structure tend to shift as gradients of misunderstanding, goal-blockage, and tensions develop.

9. Finally, we have tried to show how this perspective bears on, and may help to integrate conceptually, the currently developing area of "decision theory" which recognizes individual components as creative nodes in an interactive matrix. In the complex process of transactions occurring within a matrix of information flows, the resulting cognitive mappings and mismappings undergo various stresses and strains as component units assess and reassess with varying degrees of fidelity and refinement their internal states and the shifting and partially uncertain, and often goal-blocking environment. Out of this process, as more or less temporary adjustments, arises the more certain, more expected, more codified sequences of events that we call sociocultural structure. In the words of Norbert Wiener, "By its ability to make decisions" the system "can produce around it a local zone of organization in a world whose general tendency is to run down".[65] Whether that structure proves viable or adaptive for the total system is the kind of question that cannot be reliably answered in the present state of our discipline. It most certainly demands the kind of predictive power that comes with the later rather than the earlier stages of development of a science. And later stages can arrive only at some sacrifice of ideas of earlier stages.

References

1 *Sociology and Modern Systems Theory* (Englewood Cliffs, N.J.: Prentice-Hall, 1967).

2 See Campbell, Donald T. (1959) "Methodological Suggestions from a Comparative Psychology of Knowledge Processes", *Inquiry*, **2**, 152–67.

3 See, for example, Rapoport and MacKay, Chapters 16 and 24 of *Modern Systems Research for the Behavioral Scientist*.

4 For an excellent recent overview of this transition, see Hallowell, A. Irving, "Personality, Culture, and Society in Behavioral Evolution", in Koch, Sigmund (ed.), *Psychology: A Study of a Science*, Volume 6: Investigations of Man as Socius (New York: McGraw-Hill, 1963), 429–509.

5 Thelen, Herbert A. (1956) "Emotionality and Work in Groups", in Leonard D. White (ed.), *The State of the Social Sciences* (Chicago: University of Chicago Press), pp. 184–6.

6 See Cannon, Article 11, p. 205.

7 Or perhaps we might take Cadwallader's suggestion and use Ashby's term "ultrastability". I dislike, how-

ever, the connotative overemphasis on "stability", which is sure to be misunderstood by many.

I prefer the term "morphogenesis" as best expressing the characteristic feature of the adaptive system. Thus, we might say that physical systems are typically equilibrial, physiological systems are typically homeostatic, and psychological, sociocultural, or ecological systems are typically morphogenic. From this view, our paradigm of the mechanisms underlying the complex system becomes a basic paradigm of the morphogenic process, perhaps embracing as special cases even the structuring process below the complex adaptive system level.

8 Mace, C. A. (1953) "Homeostasis, Needs and Values", *British Journal of Psychology*, **44**, 204–5. Gordon Allport reinforces this view for personality (but note his terminology): "Some theories correctly emphasize the tendency of human personality to go beyond steady states and to elaborate their internal order, even at the cost of disequilibrium. Theories of changing energies . . . and of functional autonomy . . . do so. These conceptions allow for a continual increase of men's purposes in life and for their morphogenic effect upon the system as a whole. Although homeostasis is a useful conception for short-run 'target orientation', it is totally inadequate to account for the integrating tonus involved in 'goal orientation'. . . . Although these formulations differ among themselves, they all find the 'go' of personality in some dynamic thrust that exceeds the pale function of homeostatic balance. They recognize increasing order over time, and view change within personality as a recentering, but not as abatement, of tension." – Allport, Gordon W. (1961) *Pattern and Growth in Personality* (New York: Holt, Rinehart & Winston), p. 569.

9 See Chapters 34 and 35 of *Modern Systems Research for the Behavioral Scientist*.

10 Henry, Jules (1959) "Culture, Personality, and Evolution", *American Anthropologist*, **61**, 221–2.

11 Deutsch, Karl W. (1948–9) "Some Notes on Research on The Role of Models in Natural and Social Science", *Synthese*, pp. 532–3.

12 See Campbell, *op. cit.*

13 See Osgood, Charles E., "Psycholinguistics", in Koch, S. (ed.), *Psychology*, *loc. cit.*, pp. 244–316; Mowrer, O. Hobart (1960) *Learning Theory and the Symbolic Processes* (New York: John Wiley), esp. Chapter 7: "Learning Theory, Cybernetics, and the Concept of

Consciousness." For less behavioristic and more genetic and emergent views, see, for example, Mead, George H. (1934) *Mind, Self and Society* (Chicago: University of Chicago Press), and more recently, Werner, Heinz and Kaplan, Bernard (1963) *Symbol Formation* (New York: John Wiley).

14 See, for example, Sahlins, Marshall D. (1964) "Culture and Environment: The Study of Cultural Ecology", in Sol Tax (ed.), *Horizons of Anthropology* (Chicago: Aldine), pp. 132–47.

15 See the selections from Nett (Chapter 48), Deutsch (Chapter 46), Hardin (Chapter 55), and Vickers (Chapter 56) in *Modern Systems Research for the Behavioral Scientist*.

16 However, we should not deemphasize the important structuring role of concrete artifacts, for example, the structure of physical communication nets, road nets, cities, interior layouts of buildings, etc., as limiting and channeling factors for sociocultural action and interaction.

17 Small, Albion W. (1905) *General Sociology* (Chicago: University of Chicago Press), p. ix.

18 Cooley, Charles H. (1918) *Social Process* (New York: Scribner's).

19 Znaniecki, Florian (1952) *Cultural Sciences* (Urbana: University of Illinois Press).

20 Consider the explicit "feedback" and "self-regulation" conceptions in the following statements of G. H. Mead in *Mind, Self and Society*: ". . . the central nervous system has an almost infinite number of elements in it, and they can be organized not only in spatial connection with each other, but also from a temporal standpoint. In virtue of this last fact, our conduct is made up of a series of steps which follow each other, and the later steps may be already started and influence the earlier ones. The thing we are going to do is playing back on what we are doing now" (p. 71). "As we advance from one set of responses to another we find ourselves picking out the environment which answers to this next set of responses. To finish one response is to put ourselves in a position where we see other things. . . . Our world is definitely mapped out for us by the responses which are going to take place. . . . The structure of the environment is a mapping out of organic responses to nature; any environment, whether social or individual, is a mapping out of the logical structure of the act to which it answers, an act seeking overt expression" (pp. 128–9, and footnote 32, p. 129). "It

is through taking this role of the other that [the person] is able to come back on himself and so direct his own process of communication. This taking the role of the other, an expression I have so often used, is not simply of passing importance. It is not something that just happens as an incidental result of the gesture, but it is of importance in the development of cooperative activity. The immediate effect of such role-taking lies in the control which the individual is able to exercise over his own response. . . . From the standpoint of social evolution, it is this bringing of any given social act, or of the total social process in which that act is a constituent, directly and as an organized whole into the experience of each of the individual organisms implicated in that act, with reference to which he may consequently regulate and govern his individual conduct, that constitutes the peculiar value and significance of self-consciousness in those individual organisms" (p. 254, including part of footnote 7).

See also the extended discussion based on Mead's essentially cybernetic perspective in Shibutani, Chapter 39.

21 Seeman, Melvin, review of Rose, Arnold (ed.) *Human Behavior and Social Processes*, in *American Sociological Review*, **27** (August 1962), 557.

22 Murdock, George P. (1955) "Changing Emphasis in Social Structure", *Southwestern Journal of Anthropology*, **11**, 366.

23 Firth, Raymond (1955) "Some Principles of Social Organization", *Journal of the Royal Anthropological Institute*, **85**, 1.

24 Nadel, S. F. (1957) *The Theory of Social Structure* (New York: The Free Press of Glencoe), pp. 54-5.

25 *Ibid.*, p. 128.

26 *Ibid.*, p. 153.

27 Vogt, Evon Z. (1960) "On the Concept of Structure and Process in Cultural Anthropology", *American Anthropologist*, **62**, 18-33.

28 Blumer, Herbert (1953) "Psychological Import of the Human Group", in Sherif, Muzafer and Wilson, M. O. (eds.) *Group Relations at the Crossroads* (New York: Harper), pp. 199-201. Emphasis added.

29 Allport, Gordon W. (1961) *Pattern and Growth in Personality* (New York: Holt, Rinehart, & Winston), p. 567.

30 For example, see Gouldner, Alvin W. (1956) "Some Observations on Systematic Theory, 1945-55", in Zetterberg, Hans L. (ed.) *Sociology in the United States of America* (Paris: UNESCO), pp. 39-40. See also Moore, Jr., Barrington (1955) "Sociological Theory and Contemporary Politics", *American Journal of Sociology*, **61** (September), 111-15.

31 Recall, for example, the excellent treatment of "decision theory" in MacIver, Robert M. (1942) *Social Causation* (New York: Ginn & Co.), esp. pp. 291 ff.

32 Selznick, Philip (1961) "Review Article: The Social Theories of Talcott Parsons", *American Sociological Review*, **26** (December), 934.

33 Boulding, Kenneth E. (1956) *The Image* (Ann Arbor: University of Michigan Press).

34 Recall Maruyama's discussion in Chapter 36 of *Modern Systems Research for the Behavioral Scientist*.

35 Goode, William J. (1960) "A Theory of Role Strain", *American Sociological Review*, **25** (August), 483.

36 *Ibid.*, 495.

37 *Ibid.*

38 *Ibid.*, 487.

39 *Ibid.*, 494.

40 Osgood, Charles E. (1960) "Cognitive Dynamics in the Conduct of Human Affairs", *Public Opinion Quarterly*, **24**, 347.

41 *Ibid.*, 347-8.

42 *Ibid.*, 351.

43 *Ibid.*, 363.

44 Sears, Robert R. (1951) "A Theoretical Framework for Personality and Social Behavior", *American Psychologist*, **6**, 478-9.

45 *Ibid.*, 478.

46 Secord, Paul F. and Backman, Carl W. (1961) "Personality Theory and the Problem of Stability and Change in Individual Behavior: An Interpersonal Approach", *Psychological Review*, **68**, 22.

47 *Ibid.*

48 *Ibid.*, 26.

49 *Ibid.*, 28.

50 *Ibid.*

51 Turner, Ralph H. (1962) "Role-Taking: Process Versus Conformity", in Rose, Arnold M. (ed.) *Human Behavior and Social Processes* (Boston: Houghton Mifflin Co.), Chapter 2.

52 *Ibid.*, 26.

53 Gross, Neal, *et al.* (1958) *Explorations in Role Analysis* (New York: John Wiley), p. 53.

54 Turner, *loc. cit.*, p. 32.

55 *Ibid.*, p. 38.

56 Strauss, Anselm *et al.* (1963) "The Hospital and Its Negotiated Order", in Freidson, Eliot (ed.) *The*

Hospital in Modern Society (New York: The Free Press of Glencoe), p. 148.

57 *Ibid.*, p. 162.

58 Gross, Neal *et al.*, *op. cit.*, p. 321. Also see Kahn, Robert L. *et al.* (1964) *Organizational Stress: Studies in Role Conflict and Ambiguity* (New York: John Wiley).

59 Etzioni, Amitai (1961) *A Comparative Analysis of Complex Organizations* (New York: The Free Press of Glencoe).

60 Cohen, Ronald (1964) "Conflict and Change in a Northern Nigerian Emirate", in Zollschan, George K. and Hirsch, Walter (eds.) *Explorations in Social Change* (Boston: Houghton Mifflin Co.), Chapter 19.

61 Frank, A. G. (1959) "Goal Ambiguity and Conflicting Standards: An Approach to the Study of Organization", *Human Organization*, 17, 8–13.

62 *Op. cit.*, 519. Emphasis supplied.

63 Sapir, Edward (1931) "Social Communication", *Encyclopedia of the Social Sciences* (New York: Macmillan), Vol. 4, p. 78.

64 This still remains primarily a potential, however; perusal of the general systems literature shows treatment of the sociocultural level systems to be sparse compared to that of biological, psychological and other systems. Part of the reason for this is the failure of sociologists to participate and to make what could be significant contributions to a field rapidly leaving us behind.

65 Wiener, Norbert (1954) *The Human Use of Human Beings* (Garden City, N.Y.: Doubleday Anchor, 2nd ed., rev.), p. 34.

Reprinted from *Modern Systems Research for the Behavioral Scientist: A Sourcebook* edited by Walter Buckley (1968). Published by permission of Aldine Publishing Company, Chicago.

Section IV

Introduction

Whereas all the systems we have considered so far have been essentially human activity systems, we now move into the area of biological and ecological systems. Cannon's brief note about homeostasis, written as it was in the 1930s, shows the tentative emergence of the concept which, by the 1980s, Toates takes as given and explains in what is a teaching text rather than a research paper. The concepts of control as used by the engineer have been applied to biological systems with considerable success. Provided that it is possible to quantify the activities of the biological components and represent them as a set of simple engineering components, then realistic mathematical models can be developed to simulate different conditions. Unfortunately the complex and rich nature of these systems and hence their models provides limits to the modelling activity.

The article by Dale looks not at the internal physiological systems of man and animals but at the interrelation of plants, animals and their environment in ecosystems. Dale again starts by explaining systems analysis in his own terms and then details the techniques and methods involved.

Most of the ecological systems which are of interest are actually "managed" in some way by humans. They can therefore, for certain purposes, usefully be considered as human activity systems. In other words people can and do intervene to affect change in their behaviour, structures, processes, etc.

Associated reading

The major work on biological systems is J. G. Miller's *Living Systems* (McGraw-Hill, 1978).

Biological control systems have become of great interest to engineers in recent years, partly because engineering analysis can be hoped to reveal more of the functioning of important physiological systems and partly because engineers learn much from these extremely "well-engineered" systems. There are a number of fairly detailed books on control theory and systems ideas applied to biological systems. J. H. Milsum's *Biological Control Systems Analysis* (McGraw-Hill, 1966) is a comprehensive treatment; *The Application of Control Theory to Physiological Systems* by H. T. Milhorn (W. B. Saunders, London, 1966) is another. Work on the respiratory system is covered by J. H. Comroe in the physiology of respiration in his article "The lung" in *Scientific American* (February 1966). The respiratory system is also dealt with in Units 13 and 14 *The Human Respiratory System* of Systems Behaviour T241 (Open University Press).

Ecological systems are the topic of another module of the same course: *The Structure and Management of Ecosystems*. A whole course on food and food production systems is detailed on p. 8.

11 Self-regulation of the body
by Walter B. Cannon

I

Our bodies are made of extraordinarily unstable material. Pulses of energy, so minute that very delicate methods are required to measure them, course along our nerves. On reaching muscles they find there a substance so delicately sensitive to slight disturbance that, like an explosive touched off by a fuse, it may discharge in a powerful movement. Our sense organs are responsive to almost incredibly minute stimulations. Only recently have men been able to make apparatus which could even approach the sensitiveness of our organs of hearing. The sensory surface in the nose is affected by vanillin, 1 part by weight in 10,000,000 parts of air, and by mercaptan 1/23,000,000 of a milligram in a liter (approximately a quart) of air. And as for sight, there is evidence that the eye is sensitive to 5/1,000,000,000,000 erg, an amount of energy, according to Bayliss, which is 1/3,000 that required to affect the most rapid photograph plate.

The instability of bodily structure is shown also by its quick change when conditions are altered. For example, we are all aware of the sudden stoppage of action in parts of the brain, accompanied by fainting and loss of consciousness, that occurs when there is a momentary check in the blood flow through its vessels. We know that if the blood supply to the brain wholly ceases for so short a time as seven or eight minutes certain cells which are necessary for intelligent action are so seriously damaged that they do not recover. Indeed, the high degree of instability of the matter of which we are composed explains why drowning, gas poisoning, or electric shock promptly brings on death. Examination of the body after such an accident may reveal no perceptible injury that would adequately explain the total disappearance of all the usual activities. Pathetic hope may rise that this apparently normal and natural form could be stirred to life again. But there are subtle changes in the readily mutable stuff of the human organism which prevent, in these conditions, any return of vital processes.

When we consider the extreme instability of our bodily structure, its readiness of disturbance by the slightest application of external forces and the rapid onset of its decomposition as soon as favoring circumstances are withdrawn, its persistence through many decades seems almost miraculous. The wonder increases when we realize that the system is open, engaging in free exchange with the outer world, and that the structure itself is not permanent but is being continuously broken down by the wear and tear of action, and as continuously built up again by processes of repair.

II

The ability of living beings to maintain their own constancy has long impressed biologists. The idea that disease is cured by natural powers, by a *vis medicatrix naturae*, an idea which was held by Hippocrates (460–377 B.C.), implies the existence of agencies which are ready to operate correctively when the normal state of the organism is upset. More precise references to self-regulatory arrangements are found in the writings of modern physiologists. Thus the German physiologist, Pflüger, recognized the natural adjustments which lead toward the maintenance of a steady state of organisms when (1877) he laid down the dictum, "The cause of every need of a living being is also the cause of the satisfaction of the need." Similarly, the Belgian physiologist, Léon Fredericq, in 1885, declared, "The living being is an agency of such sort that each disturbing influence induces by itself the calling forth of compensatory activity to neutralize or repair the disturbance. The higher in the scale of living beings, the more numerous, the more perfect and the more complicated do these regulatory agencies become. They tend to free the organism completely from the unfavorable influences and changes occurring in the environment." Again, in 1900, the French physiologist, Charles Richet, emphasized the remarkable fact. "The living being is stable," he wrote. "It must be so in order not to be destroyed, dissolved or disintegrated by the colossal forces, often adverse, which surround it. By an apparent contradiction it maintains its stability only if it is excitable and capable of modifying itself according to external stimuli and adjusting its response to the stimulation. In a sense it is stable because it is modifiable – the slight instability is the necessary condition for the true stability of the organism."

Here, then, is a striking phenomenon. Organisms, composed of material which is characterized by the utmost inconstancy and unsteadiness, have somehow learned the methods of maintaining constancy and keeping steady in the presence of conditions which might reasonably be expected to prove profoundly disturbing. For a short time men may be exposed to dry heat at 115 to 128 degrees Centigrade (239 to 261 degrees Fahrenheit) without an increase of their body temperature above normal. On the other hand arctic mammals, when exposed to cold as low as 35 degrees Centigrade below freezing (31 degrees below zero Fahrenheit) do not manifest any noteworthy fall of body temperature. Furthermore, in regions where the air is extremely dry the inhabitants have little difficulty in retaining their body fluids. And in these days of high ventures in mountain climbing and in airplanes human beings may be surrounded by a greatly reduced pressure of oxygen in the air without showing serious effects of oxygen want.

Resistance to changes which might be induced by external circumstances is not the only evidence of adaptive stabilizing arrangements. There is also resistance to disturbances from within. For example, the heat produced in maximal muscular effort, continued for twenty minutes, would be so great that, if it were not promptly dissipated, it would cause some of the albuminous substances of the body to become stiff, like a hard-boiled egg. Again, continuous and extreme muscular exertion is accompanied by the production of so much lactic acid (the acid of sour milk) in the working muscles that within a short period it would neutralize all the alkali contained in the blood, if other agencies did not appear and prevent that disaster. In short, well-equipped organisms – for instance, mammalian forms – may be confronted by dangerous conditions in the outer world and by equally dangerous possibilities within the body, and yet they continue to live and carry on their functions with relatively little disturbance.

III

The statement was made above that somehow the unstable stuff of which we are composed had learned the trick of maintaining stability. As we shall see, the use of the word "learned" is not unwarranted. The perfection of the process of holding a stable state in spite of extensive shifts of outer circumstance is not a special gift bestowed upon the highest organisms but is the consequence of a gradual evolution. In the eons of time during which animals have developed on the earth probably many ways of protecting against the forces of the environment have been tried. Organisms have had large and varied experience in testing different devices for preserving stability in the face of agencies which are

potent to upset and destroy it. As the construction of these organisms has become more and more complex and more and more sensitively poised, the need for more efficient stabilizing arrangements has become more imperative. Lower animals, which have not yet achieved the degree of control of stabilization seen in the more highly evolved forms, are limited in their activities and handicapped in the struggle for existence. Thus the frog, as a representative amphibian, has not acquired the means of preventing free evaporation of water from his body, nor has he an effective regulation of his temperature. In consequence he soon dries up if he leaves his home pool, and when cold weather comes he must sink to its muddy bottom and spend the winter in sluggish numbness. The reptiles, slightly more highly evolved, have developed protection against rapid loss of water and are therefore not confined in their movements to the neighborhood of pools and streams; indeed, they may be found as inhabitants of arid deserts. But they, like the amphibians, are "cold-blooded" animals, that is, they have approximately the temperature of their surroundings, and therefore during the winter months they must surrender their active existence. Only among the higher vertebrates, the birds and mammals, has there been acquired that freedom from the limitations imposed by cold that permits activity even though the rigors of winter may be severe.

The constant conditions which are maintained in the body might be termed *equilibria*. That word, however, has come to have fairly exact meaning as applied to relatively simple physico-chemical states, in closed systems, where known forces are balanced. The coordinated physiological processes which maintain most of the steady states in the organism are so complex and so peculiar to living beings – involving, as they may, the brain and nerves, the heart, lungs, kidneys and spleen, all working cooperatively – that I have suggested a special designation for these states, *homeostasis*. The word does not imply something set and immobile, a stagnation. It means a condition – a condition which may vary, but which is relatively constant.

It seems not impossible that the means employed by the more highly evolved animals for preserving uniform and stable their internal economy (i.e., for preserving homeostasis) may present some general principles for the establishment, regulation and control of steady states, that would be suggestive for other kinds of organization – even social and industrial – which suffer from distressing perturbations. Perhaps a comparative study would show that every complex organization must have more or less effective self-righting adjustments in order to prevent a check on its functions or a rapid disintegration of its parts when it is subjected to stress. And it may be that an examination of the self-righting methods employed in the more complex living beings may offer hints for improving and perfecting the methods which still operate inefficiently and unsatisfactorily. At present these suggestions are necessarily vague and indefinite. They are offered here in order that the reader, as he continues into the concrete and detailed account of the modes of assuring steady states in our bodies, may be aware of the possibly useful nature of the examples which they offer. . . .

12 Homeostasis, regulation and control

by F. Toates

1 Introduction

A subject which forms an important part of this study is *homeostasis*. Although we will use it to introduce the discussion and it appears throughout the study, homeostasis will not be raised to the status of a panacea that can explain all our observations. We will show where homeostasis can illuminate aspects of behaviour, but also where additional but closely allied theoretical concepts are needed.

There are a number of situations where a living organism appears frail and vulnerable. Lack of oxygen in the brain for a few seconds leads to death. For the animal to stay alive body temperature can depart only a little from its normal value. Yet, what is so impressive is just how well the body maintains itself in the face of hostile environments. In the case of humans and many other species, body temperature does not depart far from 37°C despite enormous changes in environmental temperature. The body has evolved the ability to make adjustments such that its internal environment is relatively stable. In the case of fluid balance, although we constantly lose water by evaporation, urination, etc., we fairly accurately replace it. This stability of the body's interior was termed *homeostasis* by W. B. Cannon in his book *The Wisdom of the Body*, first published in 1932.* Homeostasis means that not only are bodily conditions relatively constant but, within bounds, whenever something threatens to shift conditions away from equilibrium corrective action is automatically taken so as to return to equilibrium. Homeostasis is one of the absolute fundamentals of physiology.

Each system has its effectors. For example, relative constancy of body fluids is crucial to survival; drinking and water excretion being the instruments of action. When body temperature falls or is in danger of falling we start to shiver. This generates heat and brings temperature back to normal. If temperature rises above normal then we sweat. This causes heat to be lost from the body at an increased rate until temperature comes down to normal.

* See Article 11.

At this point it is appropriate to introduce an analogy or model. We can take a system in engineering, and from examining how it works illustrate some features that it has in common with a biological system. It is important that we are prepared to modify our model. Analogies are useful up to a point but we should constantly challenge our analogy or model in the belief that it may give rise to a better one. The models which follow have undergone this evolutionary development.

We will consider the thermostatically controlled system which heats a room, a favourite example in this area. The occupant has set the temperature on the dial to, say, 20°C, and at the time of observation room temperature is indeed 20°C. The temperature outside is 0°C. The occupant opens a window for a few minutes and some heat escapes, taking the temperature down a few degrees. The temperature detector in the room perceives this, and the heating comes on automatically. Heat is generated until the temperature returns to 20°C, and then the heating is automatically switched off. We would explain what has happened in the following terms. The system is constructed to compare the actual temperature of the room with the temperature set on the dial. When actual temperature falls below set temperature then heating is switched on. When temperature returns to the set value heating is switched off. Suppose the occupant decides the room is not warm enough and moves the setting from 20°C to 22°C. Heating will come on for long enough to bring temperature to 22°C. Perhaps half an hour later temperature will fall sufficiently to switch the heating on again.

We can now introduce some control systems terminology. The temperature which the occupant sets on the dial is the *set-point* of the system. It may also be called the *input* to the system. "Input" is not to be confused with the energy input of the heater, though beginners usually do make that mistake. We are concerned with the information input on the temperature dial, not the energy input. The temperature of the room is the *output* or *actual value* of the control system. If everything is working satisfactorily and we do not make unreasonable demands then the output will closely match the input. But if we impose excessive demands this match may be unobtainable. If it is very cold and we ask for 26°C then even with heating on for 24 hours a day the room may never reach this value. In German, set-point is known as *Sollwert*, "should value", and output is known as *Ist-wert*, "is value". This perhaps conveys the meaning more vividly than the English equivalents, drawing the useful distinction between command and response.

Engineering science can often be extremely helpful in illuminating how living systems work. However, it can also be misleading, sometimes to an alarming degree, unless we are clear as to how far we can take any particular analogy. In the case of a set point in engineering, a human set it, an engineer designed it and a room occupant adjusts it. Now clearly a rather different set of circumstances lies behind any biological control system. Even so, it may be the case that features can be identified which are in some sense analogous to those of the engineering system. Often, though, the biologist tends to infer the existence of components in the biological domain simply because the behaviour of the biological system suggests that they might be present. It is precisely here that the kind of model that may prove to be more harm than help can start its gestation. I believe, though, that often even if a model ultimately proves to be highly inadequate it is better than no model at all. At least it provides a means for critical discussion. We will return to this subject after we consider a biological system.

To take a particular example, body water content is maintained at a fairly constant level. A hormone, known as antidiuretic hormone (ADH), controls the rate at which the body excretes water. As its name implies, the higher the concentration of ADH in the blood the lower is the excretion rate of water. If an organism in normal fluid balance is loaded with water the secretion of ADH is temporarily halted, and the body produces urine at a high rate. When the excess has been lost ADH secretion rate rises back to normal and consequently urine flow falls back to its normal value again. To consider the opposite disturbance, when the body has lost water through, for example, being exposed to heat, production of ADH is high and little urine is formed. Although, of course, this cannot provide water, it can at least ensure that only a minimum amount is lost from the body. In other words, when body water content departs from normal the ADH–kidney system automatically takes action to minimize the effect of the disturbance, which seems to bear a strong similarity to the room temperature control system. This is indeed the case

and the analogy has proven to be extremely valuable. There appear to be detectors of some aspects of body fluid volume. A detector in the blood signals that volume has increased following a water load and causes ADH secretion to be inhibited. A detector of the size of the cellular compartment will also signal an excess and contribute to excretion. Conversely if the body were to lose water these same detectors would cause ADH secretion to be increased and would also cause the animal to ingest water if it were available.

The essential features which the room temperature and body water systems have in common are as follows. The causal agents drinking and excretion are influenced by body fluid volume. They are influenced such that if body fluid volume is disturbed it tends to return to its original value. For a fixed setting on the dial, generation of heat bears the same relation to room temperature. For some purposes it may be convenient to call the normal value of body fluids the set point, and this is the subject to which we now direct attention.

2 Set-points

Body water volume is fairly constant from day to day. If it departs from normal, action is quickly taken to return it to normal. Why then should there be any harm if biologists use the expression "set-point" in such a case? After all, the similarity to room temperature control would seem very striking. At first "set-point" may be useful as a provisional term. But we may find ourselves stuck with the term after it outlives its usefulness. The point is that until we scrutinize the biological system we may find more than one different model that can appear to explain its behaviour.

Although total body water remains relatively constant, and indeed a single set-point system yields predictions entirely compatible with the behaviour of this biological system, we believe control to be exerted by detectors of cellular and extracellular components of body water. If we were to insist upon a total body fluid set-point just because it seemed to work in some situations we would miss the precise mode by which regulation is achieved. We might spend all of our time wondering how a single detector could measure total body water when in reality that is not how control is achieved.

The situation may be even worse than this. It can be illustrated by a familiar example. In England the amount of water in the village pond usually stays reasonably constant throughout the year (except during the freak drought of 1976). If it rains heavily the level rises a little, but soon water leaves the pond by ditches and the level drops to normal. If, because of low rainfall, little water enters the pond the level may fall slightly. However, as a result of this, ditches either slow down or halt their rate of removal of water so the fall is checked. In other words, water level is fairly constant and disturbances are checked, but would we want to call the normal level a set-point value? I think not, and even as a convenient fiction or metaphor it might be deceptive to employ the expression. Consider another village pond, a man-made one with a full-time attendant. A tap controls flow out and the attendant's hand controls the tap. When the level rises above a certain reading on a depth gauge the attendant opens the tap. When it falls below this level he closes the tap. Here we have what is, beyond dispute, a set-point controlled system in the traditional engineering sense, and yet, if all we do is observe water level and flow, its behaviour may be indistinguishable from the first pond we described. If we were simply to examine the performance characteristics of an ordinary village pond, we might start a fruitless search for a tap and human hand controlling it. In biology the moral is that a particular engineering model should never dominate our investigations. We must be cautious and consider each system on its

merits. Our model should be based upon observables and suggest possible alternative mechanisms but should not entirely colour our interpretation of the data. Sometimes the biological system may possibly be explained in terms of set-points, at other times a simpler mode of operation better fits the evidence.

How about our water excretion model? At present we do not have a perfectly clear picture of how control is exerted. Suppose it is as shown in Figure 12.1. When blood volume falls below value N then ADH secretion rate rises sharply, and when it goes above N then secretion is soon inhibited. "N" appears to take on the property of an engineering set-point, and some may wish to call it that. I would not do so, since the precise analogous component of a set-point in the engineering system is not present. I think it is analogous to the unattended village pond. We should simply describe the biological problem in the formal terms we have just used. There is no benefit to be served by calling N a set-point unless we can find some physiological signal which is directly analogous to its engineering equivalent. Engineering has served us well enough already in indicating that a displacement is self-correcting and showing us the essential performance characteristics.

3 Homeostasis and behaviour

So much for physiological homeostasis, but where do the particular interests of the experimental psychologist and ethologist lie? The organism is not self-sufficient, but only survives by its commerce with the environment. In response to water loss only behaviour can correct the physiological deficit. Feeding and drinking are aroused by the need for appropriate commodities, food and water. When body temperature is above normal the organism will take corrective physiological action, but behaviour is also involved: the rat spreads saliva on its skin, and both lizards and humans seek the shade. As students of behaviour we should be concerned with both physiological and behavioural aspects of regulation. At the time of water shortage the kidney and the mechanisms of thirst work in harmony to minimize loss and maximize gain of water. It is only through examination of this concerted effort that we can fully appreciate the result.

If a researcher deprives an animal of water for a period of time (s)he is working on the assumption that this will motivate the animal to drink when water is returned. Water is being lost from the body and, it is claimed, the resulting deficit sets up a state of thirst motivation or drive. When water is available the animal drinks, and so its behaviour forms part of a homeostatic system. If the ani-

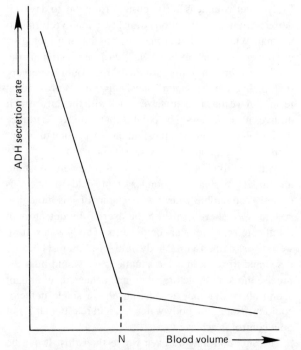

Figure 12.1 A suggested relationship between blood volume and anti-diuretic hormone (ADH) secretion rate. The normal volume of blood is N. A fall in blood volume below this value sharply increases ADH secretion rate, whereas a rise has a less powerful effect in decreasing secretion rate.

mal has learned to press a lever in a Skinner box for the reward of water it will exhibit this following water deprivation. According to a traditional school within psychology, motivation arises because of a physiological displacement, in this case a lower level of body fluid than normal. When the animal ceases to drink or work for water reward, it is said to be sated (or satiated), and the displacement assumed to exist no more. This is one aspect of homeostasis applied to motivation, and it has played an important role in the development of psychology. It is closely associated with the American psychologist Clark Hull, who based much of his theorizing on the fact that organisms seek to reduce drive levels and learn responses that are associated with drive reduction.

It is worth distinguishing "broad" and "narrow" homeostatic interpretations of behaviour. According to the broad view the drinking behaviour of an animal has evolved to serve a regulatory system and so almost every act of water ingestion, except possibly the most bizarre, is seen as homeostatic. The narrow homeostatic view would refer to homeostatic drinking only as that caused by an observable deficit in body fluids. The broad view stems from Cannon, who recognized that an organism may employ a variety of processes by which it achieves relative constancy (see discussion in Toates, 1979). For example, it may learn to drink and so avoid dehydration. The narrow view arises because regulation can so obviously and simply be understood in terms of responding to a disturbance so as to eliminate the disturbance. We should recognize that, important as this disturbance-actuated process is, it is only one amongst several that may be employed in the interests of constancy.

An aspect of the narrow homeostatic interpretation of behaviour is as follows. If we observe an animal in the presence of water *ad lib* it will take, say, 15 drinks per 24 hours. Some of these will be in association with meals, but let us just consider those drinks that occur in isolation. To explain such behaviour by means of narrow homeostatic interpretation one would argue that at the time of drinking the body water deficit has built up to a magnitude such as to trigger drinking. The animal then drinks until the deficit is eliminated. This view of motivation sees an otherwise passive organism being goaded into action only when the relevant physiological quantity had departed significantly from normal. Further, it sees the animal as being goaded for a sufficient period of time to return the body to physiological quiescence. The broader view would not deny that deficits can cause drinks, but would not inevitably assume that every drink was caused by a deficit.

4 Closed and open loops, positive and negative feedback

We have already discussed *feedback*, though we did not call it that. Here we will familiarize ourselves with this expression, as well as another having the same meaning – *closed loop*. Our thermostatically controlled room exhibits feedback, the actual temperature of the room is fed back and is instrumental in determining the heating effort. By contrast, if we had no thermostat but simply switched the heat on full in, say, October and left it on until April, irrespective of the consequences, we would have what is known as an *open-loop* system. In this case "open loop" means that although room temperature is dependent upon the output of energy by the heater, the activity of the heater is *not* dependent upon room temperature. The path of causality is open rather than closed. In thermostatically controlled heating not only is the temperature of the room dependent upon the heater but the heater is dependent upon room temperature. This is called a closed-loop system because the direction of causality forms a loop (open loop is something of a misnomer). Output (actual temperature) is fed back and compared with input (setting on the dial).

There are closed loops between volume and "flow out" in the case of the unattended pond and like the system of fluid balance it is also an example of *negative* feedback; deficits cause ingestion of an appropriate amount of water to *eliminate* the deficit. Feedback systems can also show *positive* feedback where displacement is not self-correcting but self-enlarging. Because we live in a finite world, positive feedback is usually short-lived. If the body loses a large amount of blood this diminishes the supply of blood to the heart itself, which weakens it. The heart therefore pumps less effectively, which in turn diminishes the amount of blood going to the heart still more, and so on. Death quickly follows, at which point of course the system, as such, is totally destroyed.

Positive feedback will probably be recognized by the reader as the more commonly expressed "vicious circle". It is not only in pathological states that biological systems exhibit positive feedback, but it is sometimes employed for specific purposes in the normal behaviour of an animal. Consider the effect of drinking on the tendency to continue drinking. In the long term, of course the effect is one of negative feedback; water serves to terminate further ingestion. However, in the case of the mouse, before this effect occurs the initial licks appear to potentiate the animal's drive as measured by lick intensity (Wiepkema, 1968).

5 Feedback, feedforward and homeostasis

As we have seen, homeostasis and homeostatic behaviour both take slightly different shades of meaning in the hands of different authors. To some, homeostasis refers simply to the relative constancy of the various body functions over time, without much concern for the exact mechanisms by which constancy is achieved. Others are concerned with a variety of mechanisms actively involved in homeostasis, such as memory, learning, anticipation of future states and negative feedback. To some, "homeostatic" strictly means a particular type of mechanism in which a departure from equilibrium causes quantitatively appropriate corrective action to be taken, i.e., negative feedback. In the latter terms, homeostatic drinking is that in response to a water deficit somewhere.

It is clear that the body fluid regulation system can be made to exhibit negative feedback, for example loss of blood, water deprivation and salt injection are all drinking stimuli. However, it is wrong to attribute the relative constancy of body fluids exclusively to its negative feedback aspect; constancy may be better attained by other mechanisms working in concert with it. An example is as follows. When food arrives in the gut, unless sufficient water is already present there, it attracts water by an osmotic process. In so doing, it dehydrates the blood. If the animal were simply to behave according to negative feedback it would drink in response to this dehydration, and some species may indeed do this and no more. However, in the case of the rat it drinks so quickly after feeding that, given the speed of movement of water between blood and gut, it is clear that by then the blood has not had sufficient time to be dehydrated (Oatley and Toates, 1969). In other words, rats take action before the disturbance even occurs and in so doing they avoid it. Clearly this serves homeostasis in that body fluid volume is well maintained, but this is not achieved by the organism simply reacting to a body fluid displacement.

By analogy, if it were known that, in a thermostatically controlled room, departures from the temperature set point would arise, then an additional mechanism would be needed for precise regulation. Suppose that we set 20°C on the dial, but find it necessary to open the window every 2 hours to get fresh air. In the past this has caused the temperature to fall to 17°C before corrective action is able to bring it back to 20°C. To pre-empt the disturbance, next time we open the window we could simultaneously switch on an additional source of heat for a few minutes, and experiment with its intensity until opening the window causes almost no error in room temperature.

A "trial and error" process may be at work in the evolution of the interaction from feeding to drinking. "Evolution" could be in the experience of an individual animal. It learns that unless action is taken in advance, meals are associated wih dehydration a little later. Alternatively, there could be an innate neural connection, in which case we literally mean evolution through the experience of the species. Either way the animal anticipates the deficit and drinks to avoid it, an example of *feedforward*. Feedback is response to a displacement, while feedforward is response in anticipation of a displacement that would otherwise occur.

Researchers in animal behaviour may have over-emphasized the role of feedback mechanisms and may have given insufficient weight to feedforward. There is no doubt that feedback may be very widely demonstrated in physiological/behavioural systems, but it is accompanied in many cases by feedforward processes.

6 The detector in the system – a likely site of misunderstanding

After making explicit the mechanism of control we can still be misled in our line of argument unless every move is critically questioned. For instance, it may be argued that when the size of the body's cellular fluid compartment is reduced below normal, by salt injection, drinking is aroused and a quantity of fluid is ingested to return cellular size to normal. A cell in the brain appears to act as a microcosm, representing the fluid state of all the cells of the body. Such an assumption allows us to speak of a single entity, cellular water, provided that the stimulus at the detector cell is representative of the whole cellular compartment. Under some circumstances it may not be so. If minute quantities of hypertonic saline are injected into the brain then this causes local cellular dehydration and the animal ingests massive quantities of water, but the cells of the body as a whole may be hardly dehydrated at all. By analogy, it is possible to disrupt room temperature by holding a cigarette-lighter near to the thermostat. The detector would get hot and switch off all the heating, while the occupants of the room would be cold. Conversely, if we were to pack ice cubes around the detector then it would pour out heat to a room having the correct temperature already.

Summary

Physiological functions such as body fluid volume, temperature and electrolyte concentration vary only slightly over long periods of time, despite a hostile environment. Homeostasis refers to this aspect of the organism's performance and to the mechanisms that ensure stability. One such mechanism is negative feedback. If we disturb the physiological function then detection of the disturbance instigates corrective action so as to eliminate the disturbance.

To some investigators "negative feedback" and "homeostatic" are synonymous; the organism is said to be responding homeostatically when the stimulus is an internal displacement. This was termed the narrow interpretation, not in any pejorative sense but merely to distinguish it from other interpretations. The broad view considers a variety of processes contributing to homeostasis such as avoidance of disturbances by anticipation, memory, etc. The negative feedback mode is seductive in that it so obviously can contribute to constancy; the thermostat analogy is intuitively appealing. Other processes working in concert with negative feedback are perhaps more subtle.

The negative feedback aspect of behaviour may be clearly shown; for example, the post-deprivation drinking behaviour of an animal or its response to salt injection. Biological negative feedback systems do not necessarily involve anything directly corresponding to an engineering set point. The "passive" regulation of the village pond may sometimes turn out to provide a suitable analogy.

References

Oatley, K. and Toates, F. M. (1969) "The passage of food through the gut of rats and its uptake of fluid", *Psychonomic Science* **16,** 225–226.

Toates, F. M. (1979) "Homeostasis and drinking", *The Behavioural and Brain Sciences* **2,** 95–139.

Wiepkema, P. R. (1968) "Positive feedbacks at work during feeding", *Behaviour* **39,** 266–273.

13 Systems analysis and ecology
by M. B. Dale

Systems analysis is defined as the use of scientific method with conscious regard for the complexity of the object of study. It has strong relationships with problem solving, in that the same four phases – lexical, parsing, modelling, and analysis – are identifiable in both. Examination of each of these phases reveals some of the problems involved in the use of systems methods in ecology. A model of the precipitation–evaporation system is presented as an example. Problems in experimenting with models of systems and with control, optimization, and comparison of such models are considered.

Introduction

Systems analysis has been presented as a desirable framework on which the investigation and comparison of ecosystems can be hung. This approach has been especially emphasized by the productivity subgroups of the International Biological Program (IBP). Claims of the importance of systems analysis are not restricted to ecology, for in other fields the results of employing these methods have been claimed to give additional insight and clarity (see e.g. Halmos and Vaughan 1950, Bush and Mosteller 1955, Glanzer and Glaser 1959, Orcutt 1960, Harary and Lipstein 1962, Keeney, Koenig and Zemach 1967). Examples of explicit use of systems methods in ecology are few (Olson 1963, Patten 1965, Holling 1966, Watt 1968), and it is by no means clear from these examples what systems analysis is, what it does, what restrictions it imposes, nor how the variety of ecology (or more precisely ecological methodology) can be attached to this framework. This paper attempts to clarify some of the questions an ecologist must answer and the problems he must resolve before using systems methods, and to introduce some of these methods in the context of a general systems approach. It does not provide the mathematical, statistical, and other details of the use of the methods, although it is hoped that sufficient references are included to enable the interested ecologist to obtain this information. Necessary definitions are provided and the general nature of systems considered. The relationship between systems analysis and problem solving is established, and the ecosystem is examined in the framework of the problem-solving processes. An example of a systems model is presented and the problems of investigating and manipulating systems and of organizing ecosystem descriptions are considered.

Systems analysis, systems, and ecosystems
Systems analysis

Systems analysis has rarely been defined when introduced into ecological studies. Watt (1968) suggests that it is the determination of those variables which are important in a system, and further adds that systems simulation, systems optimization, and systems measurement are other facets of the systems approach. Others, such as Priban (1968), view model building as the essence of the systems approach. Morton (1964) has suggested that systems analysis is no more nor less than scientific method itself, and that the distinguishing feature of the systems approach is the conscious application of scientific method to complex organizations in order that no important factor be overlooked, a view expressed by Pascal as "error comes from exclusion". These viewpoints are not necessarily mutually exclusive. Systems analysis is the application of scientific method to complex problems, and this application is further distinguished by the use of advanced mathematical and statistical techniques and by the use of computers. The computers are used as "number-crunching" calculating machines and as convenient tools for modelling systems too complex for analytic solutions to be presently possible. This modelling function is of great importance in studies of complex natural systems, for, provided the model can be treated as representing the real system for the purposes of the investigation, experiments can be performed on the model with a consequent gain in control and rapidity of response. A good model will obviously contain the important variables, so Watt's comments are pertinent. Equally, if natural systems are complex then the modelling phase of the systems analysis will be emphasized and Priban's emphasis accepted. Morton's more general view, since it includes both the others, seems the most acceptable since it does not presuppose some a priori emphasis on certain parts of the analysis.

Systems

A system is a collection of interacting entities, or alternatively it is a collection of parts, together with statements on the relationships, of some kind, between these parts. The interpretation to be given to the entities is the choice of the investigator, but the entities need not, and in general are not, in one-to-one correspondence with "real" things. They can represent classes of things, or classes of processes if this seems necessary. The state of the system at some point in space and time is described by the values of properties of the entities, and all properties used to so describe the system are termed endogenous. Variables which affect the interrelationships between entities, but which are not included in the state description, are called exogenous and form the environment in which the system acts. If endogenous properties are interchanged with other systems outside the defined one, then the system is said to be "open" for these properties. If there is no import or export, the system is closed. Representations of systems can take a variety of forms. Perhaps the commonest is as a network (Ford and Fulkerson 1962, Harary, Norman, and Cartwright 1965) or as a matrix derived from such a network. An alternative mathematical representation is given by Rosen (1958), and an ecological example is the structural description diagrams of Dansereau, Buell, and Dagon (1966). Such general descriptions permit discussions about systems, but a computer program modelling a system is equally a representation of that particular system.

Any system is composed of subsystems defined for subsets of the entities. Each of these subsystems can be treated as a system in its own right, so that the definition of a system is recursive.* An open system, that is, one open for at least one property, can be considered as a subsystem of some "higher" order system (Cooper 1969), and since each subsystem can be decomposed into sub-subsystems, a hierarchy of systems is produced. A familiar example of such a hierarchy is . . . –organism–organ–tissue–cell–organelle– . . . Obviously some means is required to prevent infinite regress, and in practical work this termination depends on the fidelity of the model of the system to the "real" system. This fidelity requirement will be discussed later.

Finally, it is necessary to define an ecosystem. An ecosystem is a system open for at least one property, in which at least one of the entities is classed as living. This definition

---

* A simple example of recursive definition is the factorial of an integer number written $n!$. This can be calculated as follows:

$$n! = n \times (n - 1) \times (n - 2) \times (n - 3)$$
$$\times \ldots \times 3 \times 2 \times 1$$

Equally the value can be calculated from the following rule.

$$n! = if\ n = 1\ then\ 1\ else\ n \times (n - 1)!$$

is very broad, but restrictions imposed by ecologists to limit this definition for particular studies have not received much consideration. It must be remembered that an ecosystem is a special case of the general system and will possess all properties of the general system. Thus there is no restriction on the number of properties which may be used to describe the system, although many ecologists have so restricted themselves, with the consequent introduction of difficulties with an excessively large number of exogenous variables. There is certainly no restriction to studies of productivity or energy transfer, although many applications of systems analysis in ecology have been on these problems. Population models are systems models and so is the physiognomic description of vegetation. However, since the preponderance of systems studies in ecology have been studies of productivity, it will be convenient to phrase examples in these terms.

Systems and problem solving

The recursive hierarchical nature of systems is closely paralleled in some theories of human problem solving (e.g., Simon and Newall 1962, Feigenbaum and Feldman 1963). Here an attempt is made to decompose insoluble problems into sub-problems. Any subproblems remaining insoluble are further decomposed, until hopefully all subproblems and their derivatives are soluble, when an attempt is made to reintegrate the solutions into a single solution of the original problem. The parallel between problem solving and systems can be drawn more closely, however. Ross (1967) distinguishes four phases in problem solving: (i) lexical, (ii) parsing, (iii) modelling, and (iv) analysis (see also Morton 1964). In systems analysis these same four phases can also be identified: (i) delimination of the entities or parts; (ii) the choice of relationships between entities which are of interest; (iii) the specification of the mechanism by which these interrelationships take place; and (iv) validation of the model of the system so produced and investigation of its properties.

Ross points out that the rules under which these phases are carried out must be agreed upon a priori, which is not a simple task. An obvious example of changing rules is given by the diversity of human language, which has an additional complication due to the possible existence of several scripts for one spoken language. Some of the phytosociological arguments on vegetation description appear to be arguments regarding rules of procedure, although the situation is complicated here because it is not clear that each system is intended to contain the same information. Ecologists must therefore agree on the rules to be used, otherwise comparison of systems will not be possible. Much of the difficulty lies in the choice of entities, and this will be discussed later.

The four phases of problem solving and systems analysis are used in the following sections as a framework in which to discuss problems in systems analysis.

The lexical phase

One of the most neglected problems in systems studies is the choice of the entities or parts which compose the system. It is commonly assumed that these are self-evident; yet the arguments which have taken place in areas such as the classification of organisms or vegetation concerning sampling, description, and measures of similarity suggest that this is not true. In taxonomy a hierarchy similar to the systems hierarchy is apparent – family, genus, species, etc., and taxonomists have agreed that while studies at any level are possible, the species level is in some way more important. It is by no means clear that the species level is a consistent level: the occurrence of "difficult" genera such as *Hieracium, Rubus*, or *Quercus*, and the varied degree of subtlety in characters used to describe and distinguish species in different families such as the Umbelliferae and the Magnoliaceae, attests some inconsistency. Yet the taxonomist has a distinct advantage over the ecologist in that there exists a generating system (Williams 1967), the genetic system, which constrains the possible variation, so that the lexical phase in taxonomy rests on the interpretation of genetic event patterns; that much of the genetic information available is not at the species level but within it is a practical problem though an unfortunate one. The ecologist has no such system presently available, and in the opinion of some ecologists there is no such system.

The choice of entities for the ecosystem is in part determined by the parsing phase, that is, by the nature of the relationships with which the system is concerned. The commonest choices have been between taxonomic, structural, and functional entities. Taxonomic is a convenient adjective to describe entities based on individual organisms, populations, and the commoner taxonomic categories of species, genera, and so on. Structural entities are based on life-form criteria, trees, shrubs, herbs, and bryoids providing a simple botanical example. Life-form criteria are in general more responsive to local environmental fluctuations than taxonomic criteria, since these latter employ characters selected to be invariant within taxa, wherever possible. Functional entities have perhaps received more attention in animal ecology, e.g., herbivore,

carnivore, omnivore, although a variety of similar units exists in plant ecology, though less precisely defined, e.g., xerophyte, halophyte, and saprophyte. The definition of entities is not of course concerned with the ease of identification of these parts, although it may well be essential to provide common means of identifying the entities if different systems are to be compared. Of more consequence is the possibility of conversion from one set of entities to another. If one description employs structural categories and another taxonomic categories, how can the two be compared? *Liriodendron tulipifera* is a taxon which could certainly fall into the categories of shrub or tree, and on some definitions the seedlings would be classed as herbs. Even restriction to species as entities fails to resolve the problem, for this ignores all ecotypic and ontogenetic variation and the inconsistencies in the species level noted above.

It may be true that some ecosystems can only be compared at gross levels such as autotroph and heterotroph, for example marine and terrestrial systems. Yet because the United Kingdom has some 1,700 species of vascular plants, 900 bryoids, and various numbers of lichens and fungi, whereas Oak Ridge, Tennessee, has some 2,000 species of vascular plants alone, does not imply that comparisons of the two areas are only possible at some very gross level, even though the species complements are widely different. To demand that comparisons be possible with both very similar and very different ecosystems places severe restrictions on the possible choices of entities which can be employed to describe the systems. It may also be possible to describe systems in terms of a few simple ratios, such as the efficiencies which have been proposed, but this could equally reflect the well-known half-truth that biologists, when given two numbers, divide one by the other.

Functional entities do not resolve the problems of choice any more than structural or taxonomic entities. Omnivores, for example, are both herbivorous and carnivorous, while insectivorous plants are both autotrophic and heterotrophic. Nonliving materials within the ecosystem are less well served with possibilities, while still having problems of ontogeny and chemical equilibrium, such as that between the various forms of nitrogen in the soil. Perhaps a distinction between solid, liquid, and gaseous phases is possible, but is this all?

Since the first phase of a systems analysis is the choice of entities, it is very necessary that an ecologist give considered thought to these problems. In a study of a single system, the problems may well be less acute than when comparison of systems is necessary. But the choice of entities is the ecologists' task and must not be given to the systems analysts by default.

The parsing phase

The second phase is concerned with the definition of the relationships between the selected entities. These relationships can be of any kind and need not be restricted to materials. It has been common practice in ecology to assume that the relationships are those relating to material which the system can reorder or reallocate among its parts. The relationships can, however, be spatial or temporal and need not concern materials at all. Such relationships are important in physiognomic description of vegetation. In view of the present great interest in productivity, however, attention will be concentrated on ecosystems models produced by such studies, and the properties relevant to them. These properties include energy, biomass, carbon, mineral nutrients, populations, individuals, water, and possibly information (in the form of genetic material). It does not include diversity in the sense in which this has been commonly used in ecology (Margalef 1947), which is a measure of the distribution of some property or properties over the entities, or some subset of them, in a single state description. Changes in diversity can provide useful indices of changes in this distribution caused by exogenous variables.

There is no restriction in the definition of the ecosystem given earlier on the use of several properties to describe the state of the system. The description can be multivariate. The importance of interaction between properties in such a multivariate system can be seen in work on mineral nutrient interactions and their effects on yield (Figure 13.1). Such interactions are not of course limited to these particular variables. The difficulties of modelling and experimenting with multivariate systems do impose practical constraints on the investigator (Jacoby and Harrison 1962). The problem can be reduced to a univariate one by treating other properties as exogenous, although this increases the experimentation required. In comparing two systems which have been made univariate, it is essential to ensure that differences between systems do not become confounded with differences in treatment of the relocated exogenous variables.

In the context of the International Biological Program the property most favored has been energy fixed as carbon, usually as total biomass. This implies a preference against edible, palatable, or otherwise desirable biomass such as protein, which preference may not always be desirable. Thus wool growth in sheep may well be related to amounts of sulfur-containing protein rather than total biomass

Figure 13.1 Dry weight response of *Atriplex inflata* after 8 weeks in relation to days of withholding water and the ratio (Na + K)/(Ca + Mg).

consumed. This is not to deny the importance of energy transfer as measured by total biomass, but merely to indicate that it alone will be but a partial representation of the "real" system and may not always be the most desirable. Other choices have been made including mineral nutrients, water, radioactive contaminants, and, with growing emphasis in the United States, pollutants in general. In all these cases, however, the possibility that a multivariate system might be more useful than the univariate one must be accepted and consideration given to the requirements of such a system model.

Modelling

Fidelity. Having fixed the entities and the properties, the next phase is the specification of the mechanisms by which changes in the system, that is in the distribution of the properties across the entities, take place. In choosing these processes, an attempt is made to make the model of the system "mimic" the real system, either to increase understanding of the system or to attain control of the system over some range of states. This difference in possible objective is characterized by differing degrees of fidelity.

High fidelity implies that the model resembles the real system for a wide range of states and changes in state and as a corollary, that this similitude is obtained by designing the model to follow presumed or known processes of the real system. The range of property values, for a given range of values of exogenous variables and for some entities, are called the outputs of the system, these being the particular values of interest. Knowledge of the sensitivity of the system to changes in some processes would be used to gain greater understanding of the mechanism of action of the system, and hence higher fidelity.

However, high fidelity is not always required. Provided that the model mimics the real system over some restricted range, that is, that the model outputs and the real system outputs are highly correlated, then the processes used in the model need not reflect the real system at all. As an example, in the description of spatial distributions of plants, several mathematical expressions may fit the data equally well, for example, Thomas' double poisson and the negative binomial distribution (Archibald 1948, Greig-Smith 1964). The mathematical expressions may well imply different models of the underlying real system, which may in fact agree with neither model, yet the results may be adequate. The simplest and most common ecosystem model is

Input–Ecosystem–Output

where the system itself is treated as a closed "black" box. This has been widely used in ecology (Van Dyne, Wright, and Dollar 1968), since it is the basis of univariate multiple regression. The attainment of high fidelity is expensive in time and in the effort required to obtain the precise and accurate data on which to build and validate the model. An analogy with sound reproduction is reasonably drawn. Telephone voice communication neither requires nor uses equipment necessary for the high-quality reproduction of music.* The complexity of model required to attain high fidelity must be matched by the quality of the data. To continue the sound-reproduction analogy, a scratched recording is still scratched on the best equipment. The collection of adequate and relevant data in studies of ecosystems will often be difficult if not impossible. For example, in studies of the interaction of radiant energy and a plant canopy, account must be taken of the spatial distribution of the stems and leaves. The collection of precise and detailed information on this feature is extremely difficult.

* In statistics the problem of fidelity appears in the use of one distribution to provide an approximation to another. One example is the use of the normal distribution to approximate others such as the binomial, poisson, or Mann-Whitney U (see Siegel 1956).

The processes to be defined must obviously depend on the choice of properties and entities. Changes in state of plant entities, for example, will require processes defining fixation of energy, carbon, nitrogen, and water, and other processes defining the reallocation of these properties among the entities. Some of the processes operate in sequence, the results of one forming an input to the next. They may also of course operate in parallel, that is, over the same time interval. This parallelism can be troublesome in some methods of investigating systems, such as simulation on digital computers which are essentially serial in operation. Special processing techniques (including special languages such as the SIMULA extension to ALGOL (Dahl and Nygaard 1966)) may be required.

The processes only change endogenous variables although they may employ both previous values of endogenous variables and exogenous variables in the calculation. It must also be realized that high fidelity in the definition of the processes does not guarantee high correlation between model and real outputs. The choice of exogenous variables also constrains the fidelity of the model. For example, consider two models of photosynthesis, one using mean day length to predict amount of carbon dioxide fixed, the other being more sophisticated and employing temperature, carbon dioxide, humidity, and radiation fluxes, together with data on spatial distribution of leaves to estimate the same value. The second might be expected to be of higher fidelity, yet by introducing appropriate stochastic variation into the first model it might be possible to make it of higher fidelity. This prediction requires less data, but the selection of the appropriate stochastic inputs would be troublesome. This emphasizes the importance of considering data-collection techniques when choosing the form of the processes (Watanabe and Abraham 1960). More than this, however, it reinforces the comment made earlier that the definition of the system is the ecologists' problem and is the result of interaction between available, or potentially available, information and the purposes for which the model is required. The modelling process may suggest areas where data-collection techniques might be improved so that a more faithful model becomes possible. One indication can be gleaned from economic models. The choice of interesting and practical models appears to be those models with 30–300 variables, with the experienced worker reducing the number (Forrester, *personal communication*).

Practical considerations. – Watt (1968) has presented a variety of approaches to the problem of defining processes; these by no means exhaust the possibilities. A very simple model of an ecosystem can be constructed consisting of four

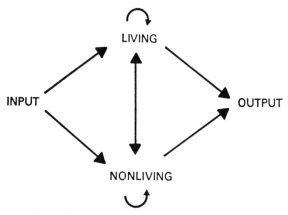

Figure 13.2 The primitive model.

	INPUT	LIVING	NONLIVING	OUTPUT
INPUT	0	a_{IL}	a_{IP}	0
LIVING	0	a_{LL}	a_{LP}	a_{LO}
NONLIVING	0	a_{PL}	a_{PP}	a_{PO}
OUTPUT	0	0	0	0

Figure 13.3 Transition matrix for the primitive model.

entities each of which represents a class and the properties and processes remain unspecified (Figure 13.2). The same system can be presented in the form of a transition matrix, where each a_{jk} represents the probability of transfer of a property between the jth and k^{th} entity (Figure 13.3). Similar matrices could be constructed for all properties, so that the entries can be interpreted as arrays of coefficients. To each of these there must be attached a corresponding process giving the next value of the a_{jk} in terms of the present and previous values of the whole matrix and any additional exogenous variables. The nature of these functions is, of course, of great interest to ecologists. The model does not include some features of human information transfer where questions of the value, reliability, and credibility of information are involved. It would include demographic or population models which form the bulk of ecological work on systems (see Kerner 1957, 1959, Whittle 1962, Bellman, Kagiwada, and Kalaba 1966, Garfinkel 1967a, b, Watt 1968, and others). Demographic models conveniently illustrate the duality between continuous and discrete models of systems. Many population models employ systems of differential equations which provide a continuous model of the system, including fractional values for the population total. But the population in most cases is discrete, being an integer number of individuals. Of the references given above only Whittle employs a discrete model (a discrete branching Markov process), probably because of the extra effort involved in the mathematics if restriction to integer solutions is imposed.

While demographic models can certainly be included in the ecosystem concept, it is also common to restrict the definition of ecosystem to models of the movement of materials or energy (e.g., Golley 1960, Olson 1963, Witherspoon, Auerbach, and Olson 1964, Patten 1965). If this restriction is accepted, then a slightly more complex model, as shown in Figure 13.4, hopefully would improve in fidelity over the primitive model of Figure 13.2. Autotroph in this model includes both energy and chemical fixation. Minor variants of this model in Figure 13.5 show its generality.

While the network representations of Figures 13.2, 13.4 and 13.5 are convenient visual models, mathematically the transition matrices corresponding to them are more easily handled. The meaning of such matrices can be considered geometrically. Consider a system with two entities and a single property. This can be represented as a point on a graph for any state. If the system changes due to change of an exogenous variable, then the point representing the system is displaced. A series of changes would trace a line, and the transition matrix contains the information describing this line. Of course in most models the graph is not in two dimensions, but the properties of the transition matrix still hold (see Keeney et al. 1967 for an extended description of this "state space" model).

The state of the system is a static description and the dynamics of changes in state are incorporated into the model by the processes. While some systems may only show changes in response to changes in exogenous variables, in many systems and certainly in ecosystems the changes in state are partly determined by the previous states of the system, that is, by its history, by means of "feedback" or "memory". This is of course also included in the processes by making these employ previous values of the endogenous variables in the calculations. If these processes themselves employ parameters which change with time, the system is evolutionary, whereas if the parameters do not change with time, the process is stationary. The difficulties introduced by considering evolutionary processes are such that the majority of models employ station-

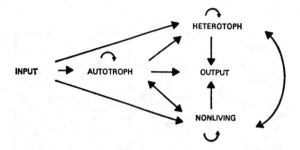

Figure 13.4 Developments of the model for non-demographic systems.

ary processes, although it is fairly clear that real ecosystems are strictly evolutionary. There is little work on the mathematics of evolutionary processes, and most of this is recent and at a somewhat advanced mathematical level. It would certainly be possible to permit evolutionary processes in simulation models, but this would involve a large increase in time and effort in an already time-consuming method, since the initial state of the system must be specified very carefully for evolutionary processes. For many practical purposes over moderate time intervals the assumption of stationarity may be justified, although, as with multivariate models, the possibility of increasing fidelity by employing evolutionary models must be considered.

Analysis

The final stage of the systems approach is the analysis proper. This involves the solution of the model, in some sense, and the validation of the model outputs by comparing them to the real system outputs. In a few simple cases the model may be solved analytically using standard mathematical techniques. Models employing linear differential equations, for example, may be soluble, and in this case the sensitivity of the model to small changes in parameter values can also be calculated (Wilkins 1966). In general, however, no analytic solution will be available, and recourse must be made to the somewhat time-consuming simulation approach.

The likelihood that high fidelity will be desired suggests that stochastic models, incorporating random processes, will be preferable to deterministic models. This is due to the more realistic incorporation of variability in stochastic models and to the availability of estimates of the expected variability of the outputs. As an example of the greater realism of stochastic models, consider the spread of an infection through a population. Deterministic models sug-

a. Perfect Autotroph Crop

b. Cavernicolous or Hypogean System

c. Isolated System or Spacecraft

Figure 13.5   Examples of restricted systems.

gest the existence of a critical population size at which there is a change from "no epidemic" to "epidemic" and the epidemic is of a fixed size. Stochastic models not only permit the epidemic to be variable in size, but also provide that, whatever the population size, there is an estimable chance of an epidemic occurring, and conversely of its not occurring (Bartlett 1960).

Simulation methods have been widely used both with analogue and with digital computers (Clymer and Graber 1964, International Business Machines Corporation 1966). Most of the ecological applications have used constant time increments, calculating the state of the model periodically. Less commonly event-orientated models have been attempted (Holling 1966). These essentially calculate the time interval between changes in state, so that periods when no change in state occurs require a constant computational effort independent of the length of the interval. Event orientation emphasizes the importance of recurrence intervals, which are ecologically important in determining survival times, where the event of "successful reproduction" and the event of "death" mark the intervals. Recurrence intervals are also important in migration and have been found useful in sampling vegetation (Williams, *personal communication*). Even if there are strongly periodic phenomena such as diurnal or annual cycles, an attempt to define events may force the modeller to consider his system in greater detail.

After a model of the system has been established and some means of investigating its responses has been provided, the crucial problem of the validation of the model remains. Validation may involve the functional form of the processes and the parameters supplied as constants to these processes, but primarily the interest lies in how well the model outputs mimic those of the real system, that is, in the fidelity of the model over the range of interest. If high fidelity is required there will usually be a process of successive approximation, with the model being progressively altered until the desired fidelity is obtained. This requires, of course, some measure of fidelity to assess the disparity between model and reality. Since the processes usually involve subsystems of the model, validating the processes is essentially also a process of measuring the fidelity of a system, in that the outputs of the subsystems to the complete system should presumably also be of high fidelity.

The difficulty of validating outputs depends on the features which it is desired to mimic. If only mean values must be estimated, the disparity can be measured by a test akin to Students' t, and various techniques are available to increase the precision of the comparison, mostly developed in Monte-Carlo studies (Hammersley and Morton 1956). These include such methods as Russian roulette, antithetic variables, and regression. If, however, the variance of the outputs or features of the transient response of outputs to particular changes in exogenous variables is required, the problem is more complex. The outputs form a correlated series of observations, and the comparison and investigation of such series present considerable statistical problems (see Quenouille 1957, Robinson 1967, Jenkins and Watt 1968). Rarely do ecological models specify which features of the output are to be reproduced by the model. Watt (1961) has provided examples of functions which produce outputs of given forms, and the use of least-squares surface fitting can also aid in the selection of possible functions to provide specific output forms. Perhaps the most general techniques are those of Wiener (1949), though these require a large amount of data.

Validation of the parameters of the processes involves searching the response surface of the model to obtain "best" estimates. A variety of techniques might be of use here,

including those due to Hooke and Jeeves (1961), Spang (1962), and Marquardt (1963). The general problem of estimation in simulation studies has received most attention in engineering and management studies (e.g., Burdick and Naylor 1966, Fishman 1967, Fishman and Kiviat 1967), but it must be remembered that even if the model is validated, extrapolation beyond the limits of such validation is the responsibility of the ecologist. It would be foolish to say that such extrapolation is never justified, but the justification is not mathematical or statistical.

An autotroph system

A diagrammatic representation of a precipitation–evapotranspiration (PET) system is used as an example of the models employed in systems analysis (Figure 13.6). This is not the only model of this system since both Crawford and Linsley (1966) and Hufschmidt and Fiering (1966) incorporate simple expressions in their larger models to represent the whole of the PET system. Equally, more detailed models might be built up from the equations describing the transfer of heat and water vapor between leaf and atmosphere, and corresponding detailed study of the distribution of stem and leaves. The fidelity of the model will depend on the specifications of the processes by which the transfers of the property, here water, between entities is to be made. Such specifications have been provided and the resulting model converted to a computer program. The diagram shows only the connections between entities which were considered in the modelling.

Two subsystems are easily identified, one modelling the entry of water into the soil, the other modelling its return to the atmosphere. These interact at two points, since changes in the amount of leaves (and their distribution) will affect interception, and changes in the amount of roots will affect water extraction from the soil by the plant. Conversely, both leaf and root growth will be dependent on water availability.

Three other systems are explicitly included. The photosynthetic system requires inputs from the leaves and will feedback to both leaves and roots. This feedback is accomplished by the growth system which is responsible for the partition of photosynthate between the parts of the plant. The atmospheric system provides the source of water and the radiation which finally controls the loss of water. A fourth system could easily be added to introduce the effects of topography on input and output of water as runoff to or from other areas, and possibly erosion effects of such runoff. All the systems here operate in parallel in that they all operate simultaneously.

Figure 13.6 The PET system.

An equal time model of this system would review the description of the entities, which in this case would be the water contents and size of plant parts, at periodic intervals recalculating when necessary. During these periods the state is assumed to be constant, but the interval can be arbitrarily small at the expense of more computation. Given the periodicity of instrumental recording this might be acceptable, but the existence of continuous recorders permits the event-orientated model to be investigated.

In the event-orientated model time is variable, but during the interval between events the processes are assumed to proceed in a determinate manner. The events here would mostly be effects on the rates of water movement and on the growth rates. The systems and subsystems need not operate synchronously, each having its own event timing. Thus the photosynthetic system would show no events during dark ness, and the growth system might show seasonal and ontogenetic effects. Dahl and Nygaard (1966) present a simple event model of an epidemic which illustrates the computer-programming techniques required. The event technique operates as if it followed small packages of water through the system and in this way transforms the parallel operation of the systems to a sequential operation. The choice between the two models, event or periodic time, will finally depend on the information available and the user's preferences. The PET system has in fact been programmed in both periodic and event-time forms (Cooper, *personal communication*), with the latter proving computationally more efficient.

With either approach to modelling the models may be deterministic or stochastic. The stochastic model effectively replaces certain constants in the deterministic model with random variables drawn from appropriate statistical distributions. This drawing need not in fact be strictly random since by careful manipulation of the technique of drawing, the precisions of comparisons between the performance of the model under varying conditions may be increased. The technique is related to stratified sampling. While the appropriate distributions to use are relatively specific to individual problems and, indeed, form one of the most difficult parts of model building, for very rare events it may be possible to make use of the fact that extreme values have only three possible distributions (Gumbel 1958). This might appear a marginal advantage as there remains some choice to be made. However, this particular problem is usually solved by an automatic choice of the exponential distribution probably because of its ease of computation, and without regard for the alternatives. The systems analyst may indeed accept the simple exponential distribution, but he should be aware of the alternatives.

One of the interesting possibilities of controlling the "random" numbers depends on the nonexistence of such numbers. Random numbers are, in fact, pseudorandom in that they pass some of the tests of randomness which are possible, but not all. The infinite number of such tests makes it impossible to know if any set of numbers is random. Provided that the numbers are random for the tests employed, nonrandomness can be incorporated to reduce the effects of unimportant sources of variation. Tocher (1963) considers the possibilities in some detail.

Experimentation control and optimization

The techniques and considerations of the previous sections will hopefully lead to a valid model of the ecosystem. We will now consider means of using such a model of a single system as a guide to the management of the real system. This will involve experimenting with the real and model systems, identifying the parameters of the system which will enable it to be controlled, choosing a value function by which the performance of the system is to be measured, selecting the route to some desired state, and maintaining the system at or near this desired point. The advantages of using the model system lie in the ease and rapidity with which experiments may be carried out, and the possibility of including experiments which might be totally destructive in the real system. The disadvantages lie in the restricted range of confirmed validity of the model and in its fidelity even within this range to the real system which it is desired to control.

Designing experiments for model systems will necessarily involve use of the techniques developed in statistics for efficient experimenting, though often in an unusual form. The output of the experiments forms a response surface, and special experimental designs have been developed for studying there (Box and Draper 1959, Cochran 1963, Draper and Lawrence 1965). Since the response is a correlated sequence of values, the "growth curve" techniques of Rao (1965) and Potthof and Roy (1964) may be of assistance (see also Whittle 1963, Phattaford 1965, Spent 1967). The response may of course be multivariate, and correspondingly so must the methods of analysis (see, e.g., Seal 1964), and may equally involve relaxation of assumptions of normality thus necessitating the use of non-parametric methods (Box and Watson 1962, Mood and Graybill 1963, Tiku 1964). Because the experiments are carried out on the model, efficiency and precision may be improved by restrictions imposed on the model which could not be imposed on the real system. One technique would be restrictions on the choice of "random" numbers as mentioned in the previous section, such as repeating the same sequence of "random" numbers both in the control and the experimental model solutions. A computer aid design may also be used in some cases (Kennard and Stone 1969).

The experiments lead towards control of the system, enabling a manager to manipulate the system towards some point and to maintain the system in the neighborhood of this point. Almost always there will be constraints on the actions available to the manager, such as avoiding certain states, restrictions on materials, and so on. General mathematical control principles are known (e.g., Pontryagin's continuous maximization principle, for which see Fan 1966), but these have proved difficult to apply in practice. Control implies the existence of a desired state and some means of assessing the importance and hence the size of any deviation from this state. Related to this is the need to measure the effects of any control operation. These subjects have been studied in detail in operations research (Bellman 1961, Muhzam 1963, Box and Tiao 1965). Maintenance of the system near the desired point means the control of variations in the outputs of the system. For example, management of a watershed to have flow proportional to demand would be ideal for hydroelectric power generation, where overproduction is worth little and underproduction is extremely costly. The quest for high fidelity models seems to result from the detailed control necessary, coupled with an assumption that the control of endogenous variables will be more selective, more efficient, and less expensive than control of exogenous variables. The truth of this assumption is debatable since the cost of obtaining the required detail in the model must also be considered. Both endogenous and exogenous variables can be manipulated in many systems.

Efficient control will usually imply the selection of important variables for which several techniques have been developed. Sensitivity analysis (Radanovic 1966, Wilkins 1966) is widely used to study the effects of small perturbations where the effects can be assumed to be nearly linear. Other approaches for isolating important variables exist, such as stepwise multiple regression, canonical correlation analysis (Kendall 1957), multiple predictive analysis, and two-parameter numerical taxonomy (Macnaughton-Smith 1965) or factor analysis (Lawley 1940, Harman 1966). Box and Jenkins (1962) have considered some statistical aspects of control.

The development of optimal control policies is one portion of the overall control process. The goal is provided by a "supersystem", and in this case the individual optimality of subsystems does not ensure the optimality of the system as a whole. An ecosystem might be evaluated in turn (in an appropriately organized society) by an administrative system, a political system, and a social system which employs a judicial system to enforce its control measures (Price 1965, Bulkley and McLaughlan 1966). The goals of all these evaluating systems must be defined and may often be conflicting. For the ecologist it is an evaluating function which is required rather than the goal itself, and this function may constrain the operation of the model and the operations of the managers. The existence of such an evaluating function is crucial, but two further problems are also apparent.

The first of these concerns the existence of "local" optima, which makes the search for the overall optimum more complex. Methods such as linear programming and its extensions to integer, quadratic, stochastic, and dynamic programming (Bellman 1957, Churchman, Ackoff, and Arnoff 1961, Wolfe, 1962, Dantzig 1963, Watt 1963) have proved useful initial guides even if the system models do not always precisely fit the mathematical specifications (see Serck-Hanssen 1963, Watt 1963, Petrini 1964, Heady and Egbert 1964). Other workers have used statistical decision theory in efforts to determine optimal policies for action (e.g., Dillon and Heady 1960, Findler 1966).

The second problem is that of moving from the present state to the optimal one. Here the techniques of network analysis as planning aids are useful, including critical path analysis, resource allocation scheduling, program evaluation, and review techniques and transportation methods (Hein 1967, Hasse 1960, Davis 1965, Martino 1965, Davis 1968). Since the majority of these methods require computer assistance with the calculation and the systems model itself will often be in the form of a computer program, it is interesting to speculate on what additional information is required to enable the computer to design its own experiments, and after analysis to report both the optimal point and the method of reaching it. Certainly cost functions, value functions, and constraints are required, but whether this is sufficient information is not known. As yet the evaluation of ecosystems is at a fairly gross level, and the ecologist is educating himself and others in the extent and degree of complexity inherent in ecosystem management, while avoiding the grosser catastrophes.

Comparison and organization of ecosystems

Some of the problems of comparing ecosystems will be considered briefly. Such comparisons are desirable partly because of the spatial and temporal variation between systems, and partly because as a "pure" science ecology will include the study of patterns in ecosystems.

While it would be possible to extend the description of a system to include those with which it interacts, this will often be impracticable. The pattern of ecosystems with respect to environmental factor, and the processes of successional change are both areas where the comparison of ecosystems is desirable. Such comparisons have for the most part been made by comparing the diversity of the systems as measured by a single property. In vegetation studies this has commonly meant comparison of species lists. The emphasis placed on functional entities by Lindeman (1942) and the increasing use of indicator species has not replaced the taxonomic comparisons, and the success of floristic methods such as those of Heikurainen (1964) suggests that there is strong relationship between functional and taxonomic classes. For some purposes it may be necessary to reconsider presently unfashionable entities, such as the synusiae of Lipmaa (1939).

The process of comparison and the organization of the resulting information to exhibit the patterns of ecosystem structuring is itself a systems process. Clowes (1967), in discussing similar problems in the computer processing of pictures, again distinguishes the four phases: the definition of parts, the provision of a grammar of parts (parsing phase), the representation of this part in relationship to structure in the machine (modelling), and the final analysis of the picture representation (analysis phase). A formal process of comparing ecosystems will itself involve these four phases, although the last analytic phase will be some numerical organization method such as classification, ordination, or spectral analysis (Robinson 1967, Jenkins and Watt 1968). The ecological difficulties all lie in the selection of the entities or parts and the selection of the relationships between the parts which are of interest in the particular study. Simple examples of relationships important in some areas of ecology are the concept of "epiphyte", which involves the relationship "growing on", and the concept of stratification of vegetation involving the spatial relationships "above" and "below". Selection of the appropriate relationships from the many available is a major ecological problem.

While the processing of the ecosystem description is possible, this is not the place to discuss the means available to represent ecosystems and the techniques necessary to compare the complex structures. The majority of the problems so far encountered in this area have been solved, in the sense that something can be done, although the ecological implications of the available solutions is not always clear.

Conclusion

The questions to be asked of this brief account of systems analysis fall into three categories. First, what additional knowledge must the ecologist acquire before he can use systems methods? Second, what ecological questions must be answered before he can apply the methods? Third, what can he hope to gain by using such methods? These will be considered in order.

It is apparent that systems analysis includes a wide variety of mathematical and statistical techniques and borders many areas, including computation, picture processing, language processing, and problem solving. The ecologist need not be fluent in all these areas, but some means of communicating between them seems desirable. The methods used in systems analysis are rarely phrased in ecological language, and the ecologist will certainly have to phrase his questions in non-ecological terms if the developers of the methods are to assist him.

The ecological questions rest on the need for this translation, for the ecologist defines the problems in which he is interested and must interpret them to the assisting workers. For systems he must specify the parts and the relationships and be prepared to modify these definitions in the light of data-collection problems and the fidelity requirement. If he is attempting to control or modify an ecosystem in the light of his models, he must have the desired objective stated, some means of evaluating departures from this state, and some idea of the external constraints imposed on the system and its managers. As an example where the objective function has been variously interpreted, consider the problem of controlling fire in forests. Australian foresters are at present recommending frequent controlled burning as a means of reducing fire hazards. Such a solution has one disadvantage, i.e., the frequency of burning increases due to the selection of rapidly recovering and fire-tolerant species. It also ignores the problems raised by loss of nutrients due to burning and the effects of such losses on the productivity of the trees, since the environment is already nutrient poor. As a solution to the problem of reducing fire risks immediately, controlled burning is probably acceptable, but this is in fact only part of the system.

The gains to be expected from a systems approach come from the precise statement of the problems and the discipline imposed by an ordered approach to the complexities of the real system. It is unlikely that an optimal solution to any problem will be attained directly, a process of successive approximation being likely. That the discipline is helpful can be seen from experience with one technique of management, the program evaluation and review technique (PERT, see Davis 1968). This technique has been credited with saving large sums of money, yet on closer inspection the method consists of little more than an explicit statement of what goes on and in what order! It should also be clear, however, that systems analysis is not a panacea, and its use will involve the ecologist in extending his knowledge, biological and other, before gaining much reward. Hopefully the use of systems methods will prevent ecologists from joining those "who saw the effect but not the cause".*

Acknowledgments

It is a great pleasure to acknowledge the advice and aid of Professor C. F. Cooper under whose auspices I worked at

* St Augustine Contra Pelagium IV 60.

the University of Michigan as a participant in a research project sponsored by Cooperative Research, U.S. Department of Agriculture. It is also a pleasure to record my thanks to Dr. J. Olson of Oak Ridge National Laboratory and other members of the discussion group on systems analysis. My thanks to Professor Cooper again for permission to use the PET model and to Dr. D. J. Anderson of the Australian National University for the response surface diagram.

Bibliography

Archibald, E. E. A. (1948) "Plant populations I. A new application Neyman's contagious distribution", *Ann. Bot.* (London) N.S. **12**, 221–35.

Bartlett, M. S. (1960) *Stochastic population models in ecology and epidemiology*, Methuen, London.

Bellman, R. (1957) *Dynamic programming*, Princeton Univ. Press, Princeton, N.J.

— (1961) *Adaptive control processes: a guided tour*, Princeton Univ. Press, Princeton, N.J.

Bellman, R., Kagiwada, H. and Kalaba, R. (1966) "Inverse problems in biology", *J. Theor. Biol.* **11**, 164–67.

Box, G. E. P., and Draper, N. R. (1959) "A basis for the selection of a response surface design", *J. Amer. Statist. Ass.* **54**, 622–54.

Box, G. E. P. and Jenkins, G. M. (1962) "Some statistical aspects of adaptive optimisation and control", *J. Roy. Statist. Soc., Ser. B*, **24**, 297–343.

Box, G. E. P., and Tiao, G. C. (1965) "A change in level of a nonstationary time series", *Biometrika* **52**, pp. 181–92.

Box, G. E. P., and Watson, G. S. (1968) "Robustness to non-normality of regression tests", *Biometrika* **49**, 93–106.

Bulkley, J. W., and McLaughlan, R. T. (1966) *Simulation of political interaction in multiple purpose river basin development*, Mass. Inst. Technol., Dep. Civil Eng. Hydrodyn. Lab. Rep. 100.

Burdick, D. S., and Naylor, T. H. (1966) "Design of computer simulation experiments for industrial systems", *Commun. Ass. Comput. Mach.* **9**, 329–39.

Bush, R. R., and Mosteller, F. (1955) *Stochastic models for learning*, John Wiley and Sons, Inc., New York.

Churchman, C. W., Ackoff, R. L. and Arnoff, E. L. (1961) *Introduction to operations research*, John Wiley and Sons, Inc., New York.

Clowes, M. B. (1967) "Perception, picture processing and computers". Collins, N. L. and Mitchie, D. (ed.) *Machine intelligence I*, Oliver and Boyd, Edinburgh & London.

Clymer, A. B. and Graber, G. F. (1964) "Trends in the development and applications of analog simulations in biomedical systems", *Simulation* **4**, 41–58.

Cochran, W. G. (1963) *Sampling techniques*, John Wiley and Sons, Inc., New York.

Cooper, C. F. (1969) "Ecosystem models in watershed management". Van Dyne, G. M. (ed.) *The ecosystem concept in natural resource management*. Academic Press, New York.

Crawford, N., and Linsley, R. (1966) *Digital simulation in hydrology. Stanford Watershed Model IV.* Stanford Univ., Dept. Civil Eng. Tech. Rep. 39.

Dahl, O. J., and Nygaard, K. (1966) "SIMULA: an ALGOL-based simulation language", *Commun. Ass. Comput. Mach.* **9**, 671–78.

Dansereau, P., Buell, P. F., and Dagon, R. (1966) "A universal system for recording vegetation", *Sarracenia* **10**, 1–64.

Dantzig, G. S. (1963) *Linear programming and extensions*, Princeton Univ. Press, Princeton, N.J.

Davis, E. W. (1965) "Resource allocation in project network models: a survey", *J. Ind. Eng.* **14**, 177–88.

David, J. B. (1968) "Why not PERT for your next resource management problem", *J. Forest* **66**, 405–8.

Dillon, J. L., and Heady, E. O. (1960) "Theories of choice in relation to farmer decision", *Iowa State Univ. Agr. Exp. Sta. Res. Bull.* **485**.

Draper, N. R., and Lawrence, W. E. (1965) "Designs which minimise model inaccuracies: cuboidal regions of interest", *Biometrika* **52**, 111–18.

Fan, Liang-Tseng (1966) *The continuous maximum principle*. John Wiley and Sons, Inc., New York.

Feigenbaum, E. A., and Feldman, J. (1963) *Computers and thought*, McGraw-Hill Book Co., Inc., New York.

Findler, N. V. (1966) "Human decision-making under uncertainty and risk: computer based experiments and a heuristic simulation program", *Proc. A.F.I.P.S. 1965 Fall Joint Computer Conf.*, **1**, 737–52.

Fishman, G. S. (1967) "Problems in the statistical analysis of simulation experiments: the comparison of means and the length of sample records", *Commun. Ass. Comput. Mach.* **10**, 94–9.

Fishman, G. S., and Kiviat, P. J. (1967) "The analysis of simulation generated time series", *Manag. Sci.* **13**, 525–57.

Ford, L. R., Jr., and Fulkerson, D. R. (1962) *Flows in networks*, Princeton Univ. Press, Princeton, N.J.

Garfinkel, D. A. (1967a) "A simulation study of the effects on simple ecological systems of making rate of increase of population density dependent'', *J. Theor. Biol.* **14**, 46–58.

—— (1967*b*) "Effect on stability of Lotka-Volterra ecological systems of imposing strict territorial limits on populations", *J. Theor. Biol.* **14**, 325–27.

Glanzer, M., and Glaser, R. (1959) "Techniques for the study of group structure and behaviour. 1. Analysis of structure", *Psychol. Bull.* **56**, 317–32.

Golley, F. B. (1960) "Energy dynamics of a food chain of an old field community", *Ecol. Monogr.* **30**, 187–206.

Greig-Smith, P. (1964) *Quantitative plant ecology*, Butterworth, London.

Gumbel, E. L. (1958) *Statistics of extremes*, Columbia Univ. Press, New York.

Halmos, P. R., and Vaughan, H. E. (1950) "The marriage problem", *Amer. J. Math.* **72**, 214–15.

Hammersely, J. M., and Morton, K. W. (1956) "A new Monte Carlo technique: antithetic variables", *Proc. Camb. Phil. Soc.* **52**, 449–75.

Harary, F., and Lipstein, P. (1962) "The dynamics of brand loyalty: a Markovian approach", *Oper. Res.* **10**, 19–40.

Harary, F., Norman, R. Z., and Cartwright, D. (1965) *Structural models: An introduction to the theory of directed graphs*, John Wiley and Sons, Inc., New York.

Harman, H. H. (1966) *Modern factor analysis*, 2nd ed. Univ. Chicago Press, Chicago.

Hasse, M. (1960) "Über die Behandlung Graphen theoretischer Probleme unter Verwendung der Matrizenrechnung", *Wiss. Z. Tech. Univ. Dresden* **10**, 1313–16.

Heady, E. O., and Egbert, A. C. (1964) "Regional programming of efficient agricultural patterns", *Econometrika* **32**, 374–86.

Heikurainen, L. (1964) *Suptyypien Ojituskelpoisus: metsänkasvatusta silmälläpitäen*, Kirjayhytyma, Helsinki.

Hein, L. W. (1967) *The quantitative approach to managerial decision*, Prentice-Hall, New York.

Holling, C. S. (1966) "The functional response of invertebrate predators to prey density", *Mem. Ent. Soc. Can.* **48**, 1–85.

Hooke, R., and Jeeves, T. A. (1961) "Direct search solutions of numerical statistical problems", *J. Ass. Comput. Mach.* **8**, 212–29.

Hufschmidt, M. M., and Fiering, M. B. (1966) *Simulation techniques for design of water resource systems*, Harvard Univ. Press, Cambridge, Mass.

International Business Machines Corporation (1966) *Bibliography on simulation*, Report 320-0926-0, White Plains, N.Y.

Jacoby, J. E., and Harrison, S. (1962) "Multivariable experimentation and simulation models", *Naval Res. Log. Quart.* **9**, 121–36.

Jenkins, G. M., and Watt, D. G. (1968) *Spectral analysis and its applications*, Holden Day, San Francisco, Calif.

Keeney, M. G., Koenig, H. E., and Zemach, R. (1967) *State space models of educational institutions*, Michigan State Univ. Div. of Engineering Research, East Lansing, Mich.

Kendall, M. G. (1957) *A course in multivariate analysis*, Griffin, London.

Kennard, R. W., and Stone, L. A. (1969) "Computer aided design of experiments", *Technometrics* **11**, 137–48.

Kerner, E. H. (1957) "A statistical mechanics of interacting biological species", *Bull. Math. Biophys.* **19**, 121–46.

—— (1959) "Further considerations on the statistical mechanics of biological association", *Bull. Math. Biophys.* **21**, 217–55.

Lawley, D. N. (1940) 'The estimation of factor loadings by the method of maximum likelihood", *Proc. Roy. Soc. Edinb.*, a, **60**, 64–82.

Lindeman, R. L. (1942) "The trophic dynamic aspect of ecology", *Ecology* **23**, 399–418.

Lippmaa, T. (1939) "The unistratal concept of plant communities', *Amer. Midland Natur.* **21**, 111–45.

Macnaughton-Smith, P. (1965) *Some statistical and other techniques for classifying individuals.* Home Office Res. Unit Rep. 6, H.M.S.O., London.

Margalef, D. R. (1947) "Information theory in ecology". *Mems. R. Acad. Barcelona* **23**, 373–440. (*Trans. in Gen. Systems* **3**, 36–71. 1958.)

Marquardt, D. W. (1963) "An algorithm for least squares estimation of nonlinear parameters", *J. Soc. Ind. Appl. Math.* **11**, 431–41.

Martino, R. L. (1965) "Advances in network techniques: an introduction to MAP", *Data Process.* **8**, 231–57.

Mood, A. M., and Graybill, F. A. (1963) *Introduction to the theory of statistics*, McGraw-Hill Book Co., Inc., New York.

Morton, J. A. (1964) "From research to industry", *Int. Sci. Technol.*, May 1964, 82–92, 105.

Muhzam, H. (1963) *On multivariate trends*, Paper presented to the 5th Int. Biometric Conf., Cambridge, England.

Olson, J. S. (1963) "Energy storage and the balance of producers and decomposers", *Ecology* **44**, 322–31.

Orcutt, G. H. (1960) "Simulation of economic systems", *Amer. Econ. Rev.* **50**, 893–907.

Patten, B. C. (1965) *Community organization and energy*

relationships in plankton. Oak Ridge Nat. Lab. Rep. ORNL-3634.

Petrini, P. (1964) "Competition between agriculture and forestry under Swedish conditions", *Lantbrukshägskolansannalar* **30**.

Phattaford, R. M. (1965) "Sequential analysis of dependent observations", *Biometrika* **52**, 157–65.

Potthof, R. F., and Roy, S. N. (1964) "A generalized multivariate analysis of variance model useful especially for growth curve problems", *Biometrika* **51**, 313–26.

Priban, I. P. (1968) "Forecasting failure of health", *Sci. Cult.* **34**, 232–5.

Price, D. K. (1965) *The scientific estate*, Harvard Univ. Press, Cambridge, Mass.

Quenouille, M. H. (1957) *Analysis of multiple time series*, Griffin, London.

Radanovic, L. (ed.) (1966) "Sensitivity methods in control theory", *Proc. Int. Symp. Dubrovnik, Yugoslavia*, Pergamon Press, New York.

Rao, C. R. (1965) "Theory of least squares when the parameters are stochastic and its application to the analysis of growth curves", *Biometrika* **52**, 447–58.

Robinson, E. A. (1967) *Multichannel time series analysis*, Holden Day, San Francisco, Calif.

Rosen, R. (1958) "The representation of biological systems from the standpoint of the theory of categories", *Bull. Math. Biophys.* **20**, 317–41.

Ross, D. T. (1967) "The AED approach to generalized computer-aided design", *Proc. Ass. Comput. Mach. National Meeting* **1967**, 367–85.

Seal, H. L. (1964) *Multivariate statistical analysis for biologists*, Methuen, London.

Serck-Hanssen, J. (1963) "A programming model for a fishing region in northern Norway", *Regional Science Association Papers* **12**, 107–18, Lund Congress.

Siegel, S. (1956) *Nonparametric statistics for the behavioural scientist*, John Wiley and Sons, Inc., New York.

Simon, H. A., and Newall, A. (1962) "Simulation of human thinking", 95–131, in M. Greenberger (ed.), *Computers and the world of the future*, Mass. Inst. Technol. Press, Cambridge, Mass.

Spang, H. A. (1962) "Review of minimization techniques for non-linear functions", *Soc. Ind. Appl. Math. Rev.* **4**, 363–5.

Spent, P. (1967) "Estimation of mean growth curves", *J. Theor. Biol.* **17**, 159–73.

Tiku, M. L. (1964) "Approximating the general non-normal variance ratio sampling distribution", *Biometrika* **51**, 83–95.

Tocher, K. D. (1963) *The art of simulation*, English Universities Press, London.

Van Dyne, G. M., Wright, R. G., and Dollar, J. F. (1968) *Influence of site factors on vegetation productivity*. ORNL-TM 1974 Contract No. W-7405-eng-26. Oak Ridge National Laboratory.

Watanabe, S., and Abraham, C. T. (1960) "Loss and recovery of information by coarse observation of stochastic chain", *Information and Control* **3**, 248–78.

Watt, K. E. F. (1961) "Mathematical models for use in insect pest control", *Can. Entomol. Suppl.* **19**, 1–62.

—— (1963) "Dynamic programming, 'Look Ahead' programming and the strategy of insect pest control", *Can. Entomol.* **95**, 525–36.

—— (1968) *Ecology and resource management: a quantitative approach*, McGraw-Hill Book Co., Inc., New York.

Whittle, P. (1962) "Topographic correlation, power-law covariance functions and diffusion", *Biometrika* **49**, 305–12.

—— (1963) *Prediction and regulation*, English Universities Press, London.

Wiener, N. (1962) *The extrapolation, interpolation and smoothing of stationary time series*, Mass. Inst. Technol. Press, Cambridge, Mass.

Wilkins, R. D. (1966) "General time varying systems error sensitivity analysis", *Commun. Ass. Comput. Mach.* **9**, 855–9.

Williams, W. T. (1967) "Numbers, taxonomy and judgement", *Bot. Rev.* **33**, 379–86.

Witherspoon, J. P., Auerbach, S. I., and Olson, J. S. (1964) "Cycling of caesium-134 in white oak trees", *Ecol. Monogr.* **34**, 403–20.

Wolfe, P. (1962) "Recent developments in non-linear programming", 156–87, in Alt, F. L., and Ruhinoff, M. (eds.), *Advances in computers* **3**.

Reprinted from Dale, M. B., *Systems Analysis and Ecology*. Reprinted by permission of the Publisher. Copyright 1970, Duke University Press, Durham, North Carolina.

Section V

Introduction

The study of ecosystems, included in the previous section, is considered to be the province of not only biologists/ecologists and systems people but also geographers. Geography, like systems, has its feet in many different camps; part of its background is in the natural sciences but its activities are often in the "softer" human area.

In the 1960s and 1970s geography was probably the area where systems ideas were being incorporated and developed the most rapidly. Much of the emphasis was on detailed mathematics and modelling techniques but the early papers in particular presented a conceptual framework too. In his article Haggett, one of the major figures in systems geography, quickly starts systems modelling. Geography and planning are allied topics in the applied social sciences and "systems planning" too has been very much in vogue in recent years. Friend and Jessop present a detailed examination of local government planning which leads into an article by Easton on systems and political science, an area which showed great promise when Easton's books first appeared but which has not radically changed the subjects of politics and government.

Associated reading

In the area of geography and ecology there are several books of which R. J. Bennet and R. J. Chorley, *Environmental Systems: Philosophy, analysis and control* (Methuen, 1978) is a most thorough synthesis of thinking in the area. Peter Haggett's books, particularly *Geography: A modern synthesis* (Harper and Row, 1972), are worth consulting as is the companion collection of readings *Fundamentals of Human Geography*, J. Blunden et al. (eds.) (Harper and Row, 1978).

Planning and systems are dealt with in the book by Friend and Jessop. A much more general and systems-based treatment is apparent throughout Sir Geoffrey Vickers' *Value Systems and Social Process* (Tavistock, 1968). At a considerably more technical level *Policy Analysis: A political and organisational perspective* by W. I. Jenkins (Martin Robertson, 1978) links planning, political science and systems.

Easton's two books, *A Framework for Political Analysis* (Prentice-Hall, 1961) and *A Systems Analysis for Political Life* (Wiley, 1965) develop much further the ideas which he presents in the article here.

14 On systems and models
by Peter Haggett

1 Human geography and general systems theory

During the last decade there has been a remarkable growth of interest in the biological and behavioural sciences in *general systems* theory (Bertalanffy, 1951). Some attempts have been made (notably by Chorley, 1962) to introduce its concepts into geomorphology and physical geography, and there seems no good reason why the concept of systems could not be further extended into geography. In this section we explore the possibilities.

a. Nature of systems. What is a system? One loose definition, cited by Chorley, describes it as ". . . a set of objects together with relationships between the objects and their attributes" (Hall and Fagen, 1956, p. 18). In everyday plumbing parlance we speak of a "hot-water system" in which the set of objects (stove, pipes, cylinders, etc.) are related through circulating water with inputs of energy in the form of heat. In geomorphology we may speak of an "erosional system" in which the set of objects (watersheds, slopes, streams) are related through the circulation of water and sediment with inputs of energy in the form of rainstorms.

In human geography, our nearest equivalent is probably the nodal region in which the set of objects (towns, villages, farms, etc.) are related through circulating movements (money, migrants, freight, etc.) and the energy inputs come through the biological and social needs of the community. This idea is implicit in most central-place theory, though in only a few statements (notably that of Vining, 1953, and Curry, 1964-B) is the description couched in "system" terms.

Clearly then, systems are arbitrarily demarcated sections of the real world which have some common functional connections. Von Bertalanffy (1950) distinguishes two separate frameworks: the *closed system* and the *open system*. Closed systems have definable boundaries across which no exchange of energy occurs, but since they are likely, by this definition, to be rather rare in geographical studies (except in the limiting case of a world-wide study) they are not considered here.

b. Nodal regions as open systems. The view taken in the first half of this book* is that we may regard nodal regions as open systems (Philbrick, 1957; Nystuen and Dacey, 1961). Indeed the organization of the chapters (Chaps. 2–6) shows the build-up of such a system; viz., the study of *movements* (Chap. 2) leads on to a consideration of the channels along which movement occurs, the *network* (Chap. 3), to the *nodes* on that network (Chap. 4) and their organization as a *hierarchy* (Chap. 5), with a final integration of the interstitial zones viewed as *surfaces* (Chap. 6). This progression, from energy flows to recognizable landforms, may be seen more clearly from Figure 14.1, in which more familiar geographical forms may be substituted for their abstract geometrical equivalents, i.e. roads, settlements, the urban hierarchy, and land-use zones. If the sceptic still regards the nodal region as a purely mental construct, then Dickinson (1964, pp. 227–434) has provided a detailed review of city-regions within the United States and western Europe, while Caesar (1955; 1964) has shown strong nodal organization within regions as unlike in scale as the communist block in eastern Europe and northeast England.

If we wish to view nodal regions as open systems we must first look at the typical characteristics of such systems and check their existence in the regional system. Chorley (1962, pp. 3–8) suggests that open systems have some of the following six characteristics: (i) the need for an energy supply for the system's maintenance and preservation, together with, the capacity to (ii) attain a "steady-state" in which the import and export of energy and material is met by form adjustments, (iii) regulate itself by homeostatic adjustments, (iv) maintain optimum magnitudes over periods of time; (v) maintain its organization and form over time rather than tending (as do closed systems) towards maximum entropy, and (vi) behave "equifinally", in the sense that different initial conditions may lead to similar end results.

In our regional systems we certainly find some of these six characteristics. Regional organization needs a constant

* *Locational Analysis in Human Geography* by Peter Haggett.

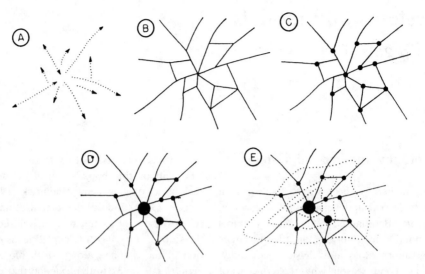

Figure 14.1   Stages in the analysis of regional systems. *A* Movements, *B* Networks. *C* Nodes. *D* Hierarchies. *E* Surfaces.

movement of people, goods, money, information to main-tain it; an excess of inward movements may be met by form changes (city expansion and urban sprawl) just as decreased movement may lead to contraction and ghost cities. The first two conditions are clearly met. Similarly, on the third condition the urban region follows Le Châtelier's Principle in that its hinterland may expand or contract to meet increased or decreased flows. Berry and Garrison (1958-c) would also suggest that it meets the fourth and fifth requirements in that the form of the urban rank-size relationships tends to be relatively constant over both space and time. Finally, the growing convergence of the form of the major cities in different continents suggests that the urban open system is capable of behaving equi-finally.

The advantages of viewing the region as an open system are that it directs our attention towards the links between process and form, and places human geography alongside other biological and social sciences that are organizing their thinking in this manner. Exchanges be-tween students of "ecosystems" at all scale levels should prove rewarding (e.g. Thomas, 1956, pp. 677–806).

2 Model building in human geography

In everyday language the term "model" has at least three different usages. As a noun, model implies a representa-tion; as an adjective, model implies ideal; as a verb, to model means to demonstrate. We are aware that when we refer to a model railway or a model husband we use the term in different senses. In scientific usage Ackoff (Ackoff, Gupta, and Minas, 1962) has suggested that we incorporate part of all three meanings; in model building we create an idealized representation of reality in order to demonstrate certain of its properties.

Models are made necessary by the complexity of reality. They are a conceptual prop to our understanding and as such provide for the teacher a simplified and apparently rational picture for the classroom, and for the researcher a source of working hypotheses to test against reality. Models convey not the whole truth but a useful and comprehensible part of it (Society for Experimental Biology, 1960).

a. Types of models. A simple three-stage breakdown has been suggested by Ackoff (Ackoff *et al.*, 1962) into *iconic, analogue,* and *symbolic* models, in which each stage represents a higher degree of abstraction than the last. Iconic models represent properties at a different scale; analogue models represent one property by another; symbolic models represent properties by symbols. A very simple analogy is with the road system of a region where air photographs might represent the first stage of abstrac-tion (iconic); maps, with roads on the ground represented by lines of different width and colour on the map, represent the second stage of abstraction (analogue); a mathematical expression, road density, represents the third stage of abstraction (symbolic). At each stage information is lost and the model becomes more abstract but more general.

Chorley (1964) carried this classification process further and created a "model of models" (Figure 14.2), illustrating

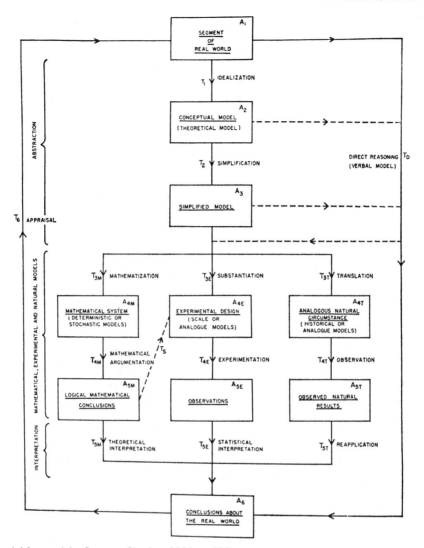

Figure 14.2   A model for models. Source: Chorley, 1964, p. 129.

it with examples from both physical and human geography. His model consists of a flow diagram in which a series of *steps* (A_1 to A_6) are linked by *transformations* (T_1 to T_6). Each step contains some aspect of the real world, model, observation or conclusion; each transformation connects these by some process (idealization, mathematical argument, statistical interpretation, etc.) which advances or checks on the reasoning process.

The first section of Figure 14.2 is concerned with the "abstraction" process in which the complexities of the real world are so simplified that they may become more comprehensible. Chorley argues that this process is difficult largely because as huge amounts of information

are lost, extraneous "noise" is introduced; a Cézanne painting represents an abstracted model of a landscape in which the noise level (brush-marks, etc.) is high, while a Van Ruysdael is less simplified but considerably less noisy (Chorley, 1964, p. 132). Successful models are those which manage a considerable amount of simplification without introducing extraneous noise.

The second section of Figure 14.2 breaks into the three main stems of mathematical, experimental, and natural models. *Mathematical models* might be represented in human geography by Isard's distance-inputs equations (Isard, 1956) or Beckmann's "equation of continuity" (Beckmann, 1952) in which features of the system being studied are replaced by abstract symbols and subjected to mathematical argument. *Experimental models* might be represented by Hotelling's use of a heat-flow analogue in migration theory (Hotelling, 1921; cited by Bunge, 1962, p. 115) or Weber's weight and pulley machine in industrial location (Weber, 1909) where tangible structures are used to simulate certain aspects of reality. Finally *natural models* might be represented by the Garrison ice-cap analogy of city growth (cited by Chorley, 1964, p. 136), where some analogous natural circumstance which is believed to be simpler or more readily available is substituted for reality. The problem in each case is to translate the circumstances being studied into some analogous form in which it is either simpler, or more accessible, or more easily controlled and measured; to study it in this analogue or model form; and to reapply the results of this study to the original system. Models then represent idealized parts of systems, just as systems represent an arbitrarily separated segment of the real world.

b. Approaches to model building. In economic geography, model building has proceeded along two distinct and complementary paths. In the first, the builder has "sneaked up" on a problem by beginning with very simple postulates and gradually introducing more complexity, all the time getting recognizably nearer to real life. This was the approach of Thünen (1875) in his model of land use in *Der Isolierte Staat*. In this "isolated state" he begins by assuming a single city, a flat uniform plain, a single transport media, and like simplicities and in this simple situation is able to derive simple rent gradients which yield a satisfying alternation of land-use "rings". But Thünen then disturbs this picture by reintroducing the very things that he originally assumed inert and brings back soil differences, alternative markets and different transport media. With their introduction, the annular symmetry of the original pattern gives way to an irregular mosaic far more like the pattern we observe in our land-use surveys. Nevertheless, Thünen's model has served its point; in Ackoff's terminology it has "demonstrated certain properties" of the economic landscape.

The second method is to "move down" from reality by making a series of simplifying generalizations. This is the approach of Taaffe (Taaffe, Morrill and Gould, 1963) in his model of route development. The study begins with a detailed empirical account of the development of routes in Ghana over the period of colonial exploitation. From the Ghanaian pattern a series of successive stages is recognized. In the first, a scatter of unconnected coastal trading posts; in the last, an interconnected phase with both high-priority

and general links established. This Ghanaian sequence is finally formalized as a four-stage sequence, common to other developing countries like Nigeria, East Africa, Malaya, and Brazil.

Not all such models have developed inductively from observations within geography. Some of the most successful have come from borrowing ideas from related fields, especially the field of physics. Thus Zipf (1949) attempted to extend Newton's "divine elastic" of gravitation to social phenomena and his $P_i P_j / d_{ij}$ formula for the interaction between two cities of "mass" P_i and P_j at a distance d_{ij} is a direct extension of Newtonian physics. When modified by Isard's refined concept of distance (Isard, 1960) and Stouffer's addition of intervening opportunity (Stouffer, 1962) it has proved a very powerful predictive tool in the study of traffic generation between points. A less widely known borrowing was used by Lösch (1954, p. 184). He has related the "bending" of transport routes across landscapes of varying resistance and profitability to the sine formula for the refraction of light and sound. While such borrowing may have its dangers, it is a most fruitful source of hypotheses that can be soberly tested for their relevance to the problems of economic geography. A book like D'Arcy Thompson's *On growth and form* (1917) illustrates how many subjects find common ground in the study of morphology; there is inspiration still to be found in his treatment of crystal structures or honeycomb formation as Bunge (1964) has illustrated. These models are treated at length in Part One of this book and in Chorley and Haggett (*in press*).

c. Role of models. In his *Novum Organum*, Bacon describes scientific theory as consisting of "anticipations, rash and premature". Certainly we might argue that most of the models put forward in the first half of this book fit this description admirably: all are crude, all full of exceptions, all easier to refute than to defend. Why then, we must ask, do we bother to create models rather than study directly the "facts" of human geography? The answer lies in the inevitability, the economy, and the stimulation of model building:

(i) Model building is inevitable because there is no fixed dividing line between facts and beliefs; in Skilling's terms ". . . belief in a universe of real things is merely a belief . . . a belief with high probability certainly, but a belief none the less" (1964, p. 394A). Models are theories, laws, equations, or hunches which state our beliefs about the universe we think we see.

(ii) Model building is economical because it allows us to pass on generalized information in a highly compressed form. Like rules for the plurals of French adjectives there may be exceptions but the rule is none the less an important ladder in learning the language. This use of models as teaching aids is discussed by Chorley and Haggett (1965–A, pp. 360–364).

(iii) Model building is stimulating in that, through its very over-generalizations, it makes clear those areas where improvement is necessary. The building and testing of models is as important to geography as aeronautics; the test flight of a hypothesis, no less exciting, nor much less dangerous, than the test flight of a prototype "Comet". Each leads on to further research and modifications.

In short the role of models in geography is to codify what has gone before and excite fresh inquiry. To be sure the present stock of models may be unprepossessing enough, but as Lösch asked ". . . does not the path of science include many precarious emergency bridges over which we have all been willing to pass provided they would help us forward on our road"; certainly his hope that his work on regions would open ". . . a path into a rich but almost unknown country" (Lösch, 1954, p. 100) has been richly fulfilled.

References

Ackoff, R. L., Gupta, S. K. and Minas, J. S., (1962). *Scientific method: optimizing applied research decisions.* New York.

Beckmann, M. J. (1952). A continuous model of transportation. *Econometrica,* **20,** 643–660.

Berry, B. J. L. and Garrison, W. L. (1958–C). Alternate explanations of urban rank size relationships. *Annals of the Association of American Geographers,* **48,** 83–91.

Bertalanffy, L. von (1951). An outline of general system theory. *British Journal of the Philosophy of Science,* **1,** 134–165.

Bunge, W. (1964). Patterns of location. *Michigan Inter-University Community of Mathematical Geographers, Discussion Papers,* **3.**

Caesar, A. A. L. (1955). On the economic organization of eastern Europe. *Geographical Journal,* **121,** 451–469.

Caesar, A. A. L. (1964). Planning and the geography of Great Britain. *Advancement of Science,* **21,** 230–240.

Chorley, R. J. (1962). Geomorphology and general systems theory. *United States, Geological Survey, Professional Paper,* **500–B.**

Chorley, R. J. and Haggett, P., editors (1965–A). *Frontiers in geographical teaching: the Madingley lectures for 1963.* London.

Curry, L. (1964–B). Landscape as system. *Geographical Review,* **54,** 121–124.

Dickinson, R. E. (1964). *City and region: a geographical interpretation.* London.

Hall, A. D. and Fagen, R. E. (1956). Definition of system. *General Systems Yearbook,* **1,** 18–28.

Hotelling, H. (1921). A mathematical theory of migration. *University of Washington, M.A. Thesis.*

Isard, W. (1956). *Location and space-economy: a general theory relating to industrial location, market areas, land use, trade and urban structure.* New York.

Lösch, A. (1954). *The economics of location.* New Haven.

Nystuen, J. D. and Dacey, M. F. (1961). A graph theory interpretation of nodal regions. *Regional Science Association, Papers and Proceedings,* **7,** 29–42.

Philbrick, A. K. (1957). Principles of areal functional organization in regional human geography. *Economic Geography,* **33,** 299–336.

Skilling, H. (1964). An operational view. *American Scientist,* **52,** 388A–396A.

Stouffer, S. A. (1962). *Social research to test ideas.* New York.

Taaffe, E. J., Morrill, R. L. and Gould, P. R. (1963). Transport expansion in underdeveloped countries: a comparative analysis. *Geographical Review,* **53,** 503–529.

Thomas, W. L., Jr., editor (1956). *Man's role in changing the face of the earth.* Chicago.

Thünen, J. H. von (1875). *Der Isolierte Staat in Beziehung auf Landwirtschaft und Nationalökonomie.* Hamburg.

Vining, R. (1953). Delimitation of economic areas: statistical conceptions in the study of the spatial structure of an economic system. *Journal of the American Statistical Association,* **18,** 44–64.

Weber, A. (1909). *Uber den Standort der Industrien.* Tübingen.

Zipf, G. K. (1949). *Human behaviour and the principle of least effort.* Cambridge.

Reprinted from *Locational Analysis in Human Geography* by Peter Haggett (1965). Used with permission of Edward Arnold (Publishers) Ltd.

15 The nature of planning
by J. K. Friend and W. N. Jessop

A systems approach

In relation to the community it serves, a local authority is both a regulator and a provider. On the one hand, it regulates certain aspects of behaviour and development within the community; on the other hand, it procures and uses resources, powers and information in order to provide a variety of services for the members of that community. This description is, of course, equally applicable to the activities of central government and indeed to the whole network of governmental agencies at international, national, regional and local levels.

Because we believe that our analysis of the public planning process has some validity at each of these levels, we will develop it in the most general possible terms, and will take as our basic framework the idea of a continuing dialogue between a *governmental system* and a *community system*. The former may include several distinct public authorities which jointly provide for and regulate the latter. The precise boundary between the two systems may not always be easy to define; but this need not deter us provided the basic concept of two interacting systems provides an adequate framework for our analysis. Perhaps one of the most satisfactory ways of differentiating the two systems is that suggested by Sir Geoffrey Vickers (1965), when he draws a distinction between the realm of "market choice" (in which people make choices on their own behalf) and the realm of "political choice" (in which people make choices on behalf of others). Such a distinction may, if anything, lead to an unduly broad definition of what should be included within the "governmental system"; however, it does relate to the popular view of "us" (the people) and "them" (the "authorities"). Also, a distinction based on contrasting fields of *choice* is highly relevant to our own view of planning as a process of strategic choice.

In using the word "system" our intention is to embrace all the many perspectives from which government and community can be viewed. In writing about the governmental system, we have in mind that its reality extends beyond its formal and legal aspects, and can only be described adequately through a combination of social, political, economic, functional and many other frames of references; likewise, in writing about the community system we will have in mind a rich network of relationships between people and the environment in which they live. Families, individuals and organizations may participate in the community system in many different capacities; for instance, Mr Smith may participate as a local resident, as a shopper, as a car-driver and as an employee of a local industrial firm. Perhaps, of course, his employers may be the local authority itself, or he may be an elected member of the local council; in which case he participates both in the realm of "market choice" and in that of "political choice", and may therefore be said to "belong" to both the governmental and the community systems at the same time.

The "dialogue" model

The first of our diagrammatic models, which appears as Figure 15.1, concerns a "dialogue" between these two systems consisting of a continuing interchange of information and influence across the interface between them. Each "round" of the dialogue is shown as beginning with a *situation* arising within the community system; this may be in the nature of a clear-cut demand, such as a request by Mrs Brown for provision of home help because of a physical disability, or an application from a local sports club for development of land under current town planning legislation. On the other hand, it may be something a good deal less explicit, such as a persistent state of congestion at some road junction, or a progressive deterioration of housing in some neighbourhood, which might lead somebody to perceive, perhaps gradually over time, that "something ought to be done". Situations requiring action within the governmental system may therefore be detected not only through the receipt of specific demands, but also through a sensitivity to more diffuse and continuous forms of pressure.

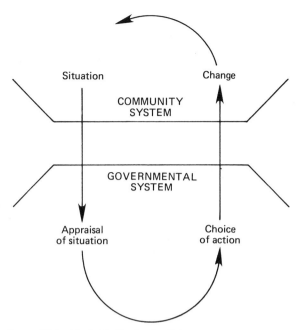

Figure 15.1 Model 1: the basic dialogue.

In Figure 15.1, we show the appraisal of situations as leading to a choice of actions within the governmental system, each resulting in some form of change within the community system (unless of course the "action" selected is one of doing nothing for the time being). The original situation then becomes modified, so completing what we may call an "action circuit". The continuing dialogue between government and community can be visualized in terms of a rich variety of such "action circuits", cutting across the interface between the two systems in many different ways.

The existence of many different channels of communication inevitably leads to the growth of many different perspectives of the governmental system within the community system, and many different perspectives of the community system within the governmental system; it is only through a bringing together of several such perspectives that the richness and complexity of interaction between the two systems can be appreciated in any degree of depth.

The selection of response

We will now take that part of the "action circuit" which lies within the boundaries of the governmental system and examine it more closely from the point of view of the *operations* required. Here we are using the word "operation" in the sense defined by Ackoff (1961) when he says:

An operation is a *set* of acts *required* for the accomplishment of a desired outcome; that is, it is not a single act but a complex of interrelated acts performed simultaneously or in sequence, which leads to the accomplishment of some desired outcome.

The operation with which we are here concerned is that of the *selection of response* by the governmental system to a situation which is seen to arise within the community; the desired outcome in this case is the achievement of an *intervention* in the community system which is believed to be in some way "right" or "appropriate" to the situation in hand.

In Figure 15.2 we extend our original picture by identifying three successive stages in the operation of selecting an appropriate response. The first stage involves a "perception of the decision field", by which we mean the initial understanding of what kind of problem it is that the situation creates for the governmental system. The question at this stage is one of appreciating what *kind* of response is called for, rather than what particular courses of action might be feasible. Perception of the decision field may sometimes be obvious, as in the case of Mrs Brown's application for home-help service, but there may be other cases where it is open to some doubt; for instance, a local situation created by a severe traffic hold-up might be seen by the police as requiring a decision on some kind of immediate emergency action, but be seen by the district traffic engineers as requiring a decision on whether there should be any permanent change in the traffic control arrangements for the area concerned.

The initial perception of the decision field is depicted in Figure 15.2 as leading to a process of formulation and comparison of alternative actions within that decision field. No clear separation has been shown between the activities of formulation and of comparison, because they may not always take place in strict sequence; perhaps, after certain initial possibilities for action have been compared and some of them discarded, a need to formulate further possibilities will be diagnosed before the final step of selecting a preferred course of action is taken. Sometimes, the process of formulating and comparing alternative solutions will cause the original perception of the decision field to be modified; this is a possibility we will explore more fully later in this chapter.

Sooner or later, the formulation and comparison of possible actions leads to choice of one particular course of action; a formal commitment is then generated through an assignment of resources or a public statement of intent, and the stage of intervention in the community system

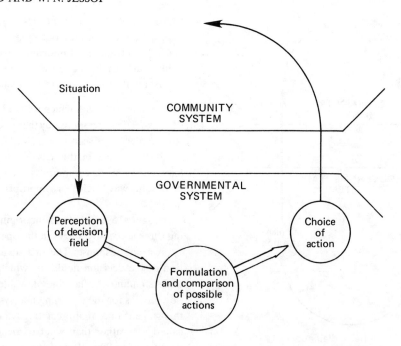

Figure 15.2 Model 2: the selection of response.

begins. This is the stage of decision *taking* as opposed to the wider process of decision *making* which can be said to embrace all three stages of the total operation shown in Figure 15.2.

The context of operations

The model of Figure 15.2 is sufficiently general to apply to all situations from the most trivial to the most complex. At a complex level – for instance, in the choice of response to a situation created by the closure of a major industrial enterprise on which much of the life of a town depends – there may be a few guidelines or precedents to be followed. The level of discretion is high and selection of a preferred set of responses may require a good deal of thought and discussion. At the other extreme, a clerk dealing with applications for renewal of vehicle licences may require little discretion and his response may be virtually instantaneous.

Operations which allow little discretion of response tend to arise in any setting where situations arise with high frequency in the form of explicit demands, so that classes of similar situations can be recognized and responses can be determined by rules of procedure or conventions based on whatever classifying features are agreed to be most relevant. This means that the decision-making process of Figure 15.2 follows a course which is essentially determined by a *generic* viewpoint, whether this is made explicit through

the laying-down of formal regulations, or is implied in the growth of conventions which reflect the perspectives and experience of those concerned. We will use the term *operational policies* to refer to any such generically determined forms of response, whether or not they are embodied in any formal rules of procedure.

Whenever a situation cannot easily be related to existing operational policies, then the choice of a response may be shaped partly by the personal and group objectives of those concerned, and partly by their appreciation of the constraints which may inhibit the attainment of those objectives; such constraints may apply in particular to their ability to mobilize the resources for certain desired courses of action. All these factors – the operational policies themselves, the local objectives and the appreciation of external constraints – contribute towards the general view of the way in which appropriate actions should be selected. We will refer to this general view as the *context of operations,* and Figure 15.3 attempts to show its influence on the continuing decision process.

Here we represent the current context of operations by use of broken lines, so as to distinguish the idea of *context* from the idea of *process* as represented by the "action circuit" with its origins in a given situation. The context is shown as influencing all three stages of the ongoing decision process; and also as itself continually undergoing mod-

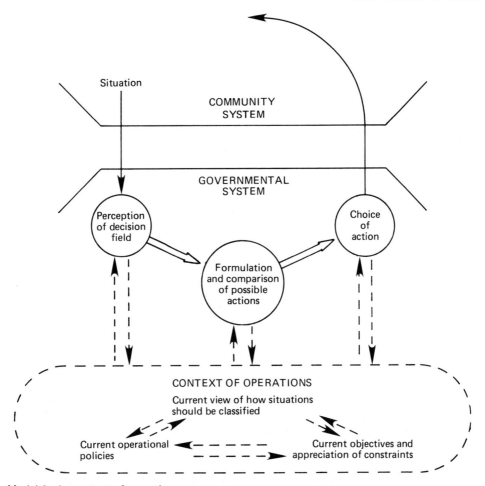

Figure 15.3 Model 3: the context of operations.

ification as situations arise within the community which cannot easily be dealt with within the existing context. The extent to which the context of operations changes will depend on the governmental system's capacity to *learn* about the changing pressures and relationships of the community system. Through such a learning process, the appreciation of factors relevant to decision making may gradually change, so that the range of situations covered by operational policies will either extend or diminish over time; meanwhile, objectives may gradually become modified and the ability to mobilize resources become either more or less constrained.

In the remainder of this chapter, we will explore further the implications of situations where it is found difficult to select a response within the current context of operations.

The perception of uncertainties

At this point, it becomes possible to link the concept of the changing context of operations to the concepts of *uncertainty*. There are three fundamental causes of difficulty in making a selection between alternative courses of action, which we define as uncertainties in knowledge of the external environment (UE), uncertainties as to future intentions in related fields of choice (UR) and uncertainties as to appropriate value judgements (UV). A perception of uncertainties of the first kind can lead to demands for further gathering and interpreting of information about the present and future state of the community or its physical setting (sometimes expressed in the form of demands for "more research"); while a perception of uncertainties of the second kind can lead to demands for a widening of the field of decision (often expressed as a demand for "more coordination"); and a perception of uncertainties of the third kind can lead to demands for "more policy guidance". These all represent demands for a change of some kind in the context of decision for the situation now being

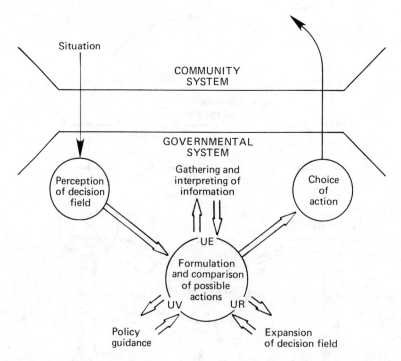

Figure 15.4 Model 4: responses to uncertainty.

considered. We can express these different opportunities for modifying the context of decision by superimposing our basic model of these three kinds of uncertainty onto the "process" model of Figure 15.2. The result is shown in Figure 15.4.

A perception of significant uncertainties in any one of the three directions UE, UR and UV is here shown as creating a pressure for a particular kind of change in the context of operations. However, whether or not such pressures affect the choice of action in this particular situation will depend on an appreciation of the pressures for early decision which arise from within the community. To adopt a physical analogy, it is possible to think of a driving force which operates throughout the action circuit and has its origin in the community system, pressing all the time for commitment; this has to contend with three kinds of frictional force associated with the UE, UR and UV components of uncertainty respectively, all coming into operation at the stage labelled "formulation and comparison of possible actions" so as to create a resistance which the driving force may or may not immediately be able to overcome.

The nature of the uncertainties which may exist in any of the three directions is unlikely to be fully perceived by any one individual or specialist group within the governmental system; and it is only to be expected that any local varia-

tions in perceptions of uncertainty may influence both the speed with which a decision is reached and also the particular course of action which is ultimately chosen. We will call any element of uncertainty which is relevant to a particular choice, but which is not perceived by those responsible, a *latent uncertainty* in relation to the choice concerned.

The need to plan

It is through a perception of our second kind of uncertainty – uncertainty as to intentions in related fields of choice – that the process of decision first begins to become one of planning or *strategic* choice. If there is a belief that it is difficult to select actions in one decision field without at the same time considering possible actions (now or later) in other fields, then this creates a pressure for all the fields concerned to be brought together to form a single wider field of choice. This process is illustrated in Figure 15.5 for the case of one original decision field A and a single related decision field B; this model can, however, easily be extended to the more general case where there are several separate decision fields B, C, D, . . ., each of which is seen to be related in some way to the original decision field A.

In this extended model, the choice of action for A is shown as being deferred until possible solutions have been formulated and compared over a wider decision field AB;

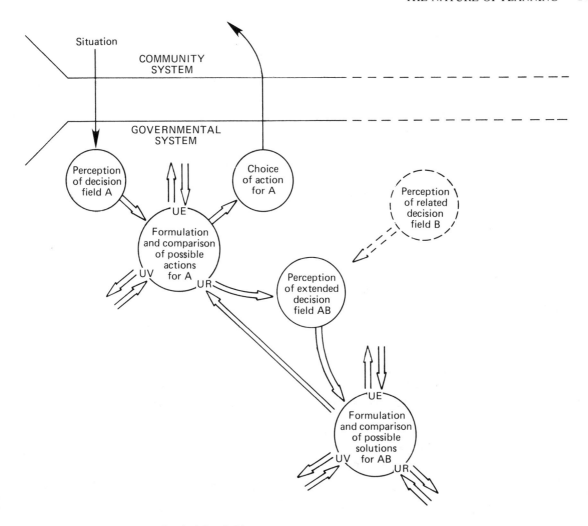

Figure 15.5 Model 5: expansion of a decision field.

the action circuit is in effect diverted into a subsidiary loop in order to reduce some of the uncertainties (of class UR) arising in the consideration of A alone. An example might be the situation where a decision on road design (decision field A) is deferred until it has been considered in relation to various possibilities for the future development of the public transport system (decision field B).

As Figure 15.5 shows, however, there may still be uncertainties of all three kinds in formulating and comparing possible solutions over the wider field AB (indeed in some organizational contexts the level of perceived uncertainty in the class UV may even be increased, because the bringing-together of the groups responsible for decision fields A and B may expose conflicts between their assumptions of value which hitherto had remained latent). Any awareness of uncertainties which may remain in the new context of the extended decision field may lead to a new set of pressures for gathering and interpreting of information, for policy guidance or for still further extensions to the decision field; eventually, therefore, the decision makers may be led to formulate and compare possible actions over a still wider field of choice embracing many other situations which seem to be related either to A or to B or perhaps to both.

In Figure 15.5 we have not shown a full action circuit for B to correspond to that for A, because the situation from which decision field B is seen to arise may be an *anticipated* one rather than one which has actually developed within the community. In this case, no immediate commitment to a specific course of action for B may be required; the concern may simply be to select a preferred *action* for A through a comparison of joint *solutions* for A and B together. In our example, the joint consideration of alternative road designs and public transport systems might lead to a clear choice in respect of the former but to the leaving open of a range of different options in respect of the latter; however, the road design selected might well be *different* from that which would have been selected if the decision field had not been extended by the consideration of possible future solutions to the public transport problem.

This state of affairs, in which A has a higher degree of urgency than B, is more typical than that in which A and B both require simultaneous commitment, because the process by which the community presents situations requiring intervention by government is essentially a continuous one: it is not like the presentation of a brief to an architect or engineer as a result of which some set of related choices must be made in order to produce a "finished" design by some particular point in time. In a process of continuous choice in a changing environment, it may be purely accidental if any two related situations requiring decisions both arise at the same time; a capacity for anticipation of future situations therefore becomes inevitable. This means that the governmental system must, whether consciously or otherwise, develop *predictive models* of the community system and the way its internal relationships can be expected to change and develop over future time. Of course, every decision maker has to develop some capability to make predictions, even if only so that he may assess the more long-term consequences of his *current* actions; but it is only when he also applies this predictive ability to appraise the consequences of certain possible *future* actions that he can be said to have become a planner.

Sometimes, of course, it may be only through the anticipation of future situations that the governmental system comes to recognize other current situations where more immediate initiatives might be taken. For instance, it may be only because of an anticipated future situation in which population growth will have outstripped the supply of dwellings that a local authority recognizes a need to consider immediate initiatives to reserve or acquire land, to recruit extra architectural staff or to approach neighbouring authorities with proposals to form a regional housing consortium. The anticipated decision field – relating to alternative ways in which a future housing shortage might be tackled – has in this case what Sir Geoffrey Vickers (1965) calls a "latent urgency" which induces the governmental system to consider carefully the choice of a response to certain current situations which would otherwise probably have been ignored. Certain fields of current choice in effect remain *latent* until another future decision field has been anticipated.

There may be many such fields of current choice, which only emerge through the existence of a forward planning activity; and not all of these may relate to choice of action across the interface between government and community. Some may concern choice of action within the boundaries of the governmental system itself: the allocation of existing staff to particular tasks, the initiation of different stages of design activity and other such acts of internal mobilization. Clearly, the basic theme of Figure 15.5, showing the relationship of a current decision field A to an anticipated decision field B, is capable of many variations. There may in fact be many As and many Bs, some of the As remaining latent until certain of the Bs have been identified; while some of the As may relate to purely internal actions within the governmental system, rather than interventions by government in the affairs of the community system.

We have now developed our basic model of the selection of response to a stage where it can provide some further insights into the nature of the governmental planning process. In particular, it enables us to appraise more clearly the operational definition of planning as a *process of strategic choice*.

We can now put forward the proposition that *any process of choice will become a process of planning* (or *strategic choice*) *if the selection of current actions is made only after a formulation and comparison of possible solutions over a wider field of decision relating to certain anticipated as well as current situations.*

Programmes, policies and plans

According to the above proposition, the significance of any planning activity – no matter how far into the future it may set out to look – will depend on the guidance that it can give in the selection of appropriate courses of action to deal with current circumstances. Sometimes, of course, it is possible to lose sight of the connection between a long-range planning activity and the more immediate operations of the governmental system; the process of visualizing possible designs for the long-term future of a community can easily acquire its own internal momentum, and the danger may then arise that it ceases to exert due influence on the solution of current problems.

In making this point, however, it is necessary to make a careful distinction between the 'planning process', in the sense of the activity of formulating and comparing possible solutions over a wide decision field, and the making public of "plans" or statements of future intent. Whenever a plan is made public, this means that knowledge of its content is seen as having a value not only to the governmental system but also to the community system, in providing a firmer basis for the selection of current actions by private individuals, families or institutions; in effect, it then becomes a framework not only for the processes of "political choice" but also for those of "market choice" on the opposite side of the government/community interface. In a sense, publication of any plan or policy can be seen as a form of response to direct or indirect pressures within the community for access to the future intentions of government; the act of publication must then itself be considered an intervention by government in the affairs of the community.

At this point, it is appropriate for us to put forward some operational definitions of words such as "programme", "policy" and "plan", which are liable to arise frequently in practice and are sometimes regarded as interchangeable. We will find it useful to distinguish a *programme* as a set of related future intentions in respect of certain *specific* situations which are anticipated in the future, and a *policy* as a set of future intentions in relation to certain *classes* of situation; this is consistent with our earlier definition of an *operational* policy, but allows a somewhat wider interpretation. The distinction can be expressed another way; a programme relates to intentions for future action *when* certain expected situations arise, while a policy relates to intentions for action *whenever* situations arise which are seen as belonging to certain defined classes. In putting forward these definitions, it is however necessary to note that 'policy' used as an adjective does not always carry the same generic connotations as 'policy' used as a noun. Sometimes, where a situation arises which does not appear to fit into any existing classification, it will be said that a 'policy decision' or 'policy guidance' is required. In this case, the generic implications are indirect; a precedent is set which may help to determine how similar situations should be classified in future, and the context of future operations is modified accordingly. There is a close parallel with the process by which the context of legal judgements may develop from a succession of case decisions over time.

The word "plan" we will use to describe any coordinated set of future intentions which includes elements of both a specific and a generic character, as in a development plan which may include a statement of both intended development projects and policies for development control. Occasionally, a plan may have aspects of a *contingency plan* in that it specifies certain alternative sets of intentions depending on whether certain specific future situations do or do not arise. The statements of intent may now include not only "when" and "whenever" clauses but also "if" clauses.

The concept of a contingency plan has much in common with the concept of a *strategy* as it is commonly used, for instance in relation to an armed conflict or a game of chess. This idea of a strategy has been given more formal definition in the theory of games (Luce and Raiffa, 1957), which relates to situations in which a decision maker wishes to anticipate a range of alternative actions either by some readily identifiable "opponent" or by other less clear-cut groups of forces operating within his environment, and to select his present and future responses accordingly.

Adaptive planning

In public planning, however, it is exceptionally difficult to formulate strategies in advance which are sufficient to cope with all conceivable contingencies; the complexity of the community system, and the imperfect understanding of it in the governmental system, combine to prevent any complete enumeration of the situations which the former might be expected to present. In these circumstances, planning must become in some degree an *adaptive* process. Although firm commitments may from time to time be required in particular sectors of a complex decision field, it may also become particularly important to retain an element of *flexibility* in other sectors in the expectation that, by the time commitment in these sectors becomes inevitable, the state of knowledge of the environment may be very different and the whole context of decision may have changed.

This does not necessarily mean that the process has reverted from one of planning to one of uncoordinated, short-term response; by adopting a *strategic approach*, involving formulation and comparison of possible solutions over a wide decision field embracing anticipated as well as current situations, the governmental system may find that it is led to select a very different set of immediate actions than would otherwise have been the case. For instance, the most immediately attractive solution to a problem of coping with increasing local demand for technical college or hospital facilities might be to extend an existing group of buildings; but this might limit the scope for further extensions in the future, and a strategic approach might reveal that a move to a new site would allow greater flexibility of future choice in response to changes in circumstances which cannot yet be clearly foreseen.

In the United Kingdom, a significant step towards a more adaptive philosophy of planning was taken by the Planning Advisory Group (1965) which was set up to produce recommendations on the future of development plans. The Group's report paved the way for legislation whereby the traditional idea of the "town map", incorporating specific commitments over a wide decision field relating to future land uses, was superseded by a system of "urban structure maps" and "district plans" allowing more flexible interpretation, to be augmented by more detailed "action area" plans wherever pressures for action and statements of intent were currently seen to be strongest. It was significant perhaps that publication of the new proposals gave rise to a good deal of public discussion as to how a proper balance between flexibility and commitment should be drawn; and concern was expressed in some quarters (Sharp, 1966) that the new proposals might in fact have moved too far in the direction of flexibility, at the expense of those members of the community whose interests might be most affected by the decisions of the local planning authority.

Improvement in the planning process

The formation of the Planning Advisory Group, and the legislative changes which followed, provide only one instance of a more widespread search for improvement in the mechanisms of public planning. In one particular local authority members and officers alike were much concerned with the problems of reconciling planning with democracy, of forming adequate bridges between the mechanisms of departmental and political choice and of striking a balance between commitment and adaptiveness.

During the four years of our research, dissatisfaction with existing mechanisms for public planning was equally evident at many other levels of the governmental system, and also within the community at large. In the United Kingdom, perhaps the outstanding example within this period concerned the siting of London's third airport. The main implication of the criticisms which eventually led to the re-examination of the Stansted decision was that too many uncertainties of value judgement, and of future intentions in related areas of choice, had been allowed to remain latent in the process by which the original decision was taken. Through basing many other decisions on the assumption that Stansted was the only acceptable site, the planners in effect found themselves caught in what might be called a "policy trap". Escape (or resolution) was then seen to lie in only one direction; and it was argued that, right or wrong, the Stansted decision would have to

remain. By the time the case for a full inquiry into possible alternatives had been conceded, a great deal of time had been lost, with far-reaching consequences for many sectors of the community and of government itself.

Many other examples could be quoted of this kind of breakdown in the credibility of established methods of strategic choice, at local, regional and national levels. However, it is of course much easier to agree that improvement is necessary than to agree how "improvement" should be defined, particularly in relation to a continually changing environment where "before" and "after" comparisons may be misleading and where many competing interests may be involved. Perhaps the only yardstick of a "better" planning process can be the degree to which it becomes generally accepted as increasing the capacity of government to make *intelligent* decisions on behalf of the community; in other words to choose what actions to take with a fuller awareness of what the consequences are likely to be.

This does not itself resolve all the practical problems of defining improvement, for in any governmental system there are many different groups whose aims may not always coincide, and an increase in the power of one group to make intelligent choices may sometimes only be achieved at the cost of a reduction in the power of another group. Neither can an absolute definition of "improvement" be constructed by relating it to some such abstraction as the "common interest" or the "general good of the community", whose interpretation is likely to differ from individual to individual and from group to group. In the last resort, the test of "improvement" can only be an empirical and to some extent a political one; whatever change is proposed in existing mechanisms of choice, it must be such as to gain acceptance in practice, by convincing a sufficient number of people that it offers them a better instrument for achieving the things they want to achieve.

References

Ackoff, R. L. (ed.) (1961) *Progress in Operations Research,* vol. 1, chap. 1, Wiley, New York.

Luce, R. D. and Raiffa, H. (1957) *Games and Decisions,* Wiley, New York.

Planning Advisory Group (1965) *The Future of Development Plans,* HMSO, London.

Sharp, T. (1966) "Planning planning", *Journal of the Town Planning Institute,* June.

Vickers, Sir Geoffrey (1965) *The Art of Judgement: A Study of Policy Making,* Chapman & Hall, London.

16 A systems analysis of political life
by David Easton

In *A Framework for Political Analysis*[1] I spelled out in considerable detail the assumptions and commitments that would be required in any attempt to utilize the concept "system" in a rigorous fashion. It would lead to the adoption of what I there described as a systems analysis of political life. Although it would certainly be redundant to retrace the same ground here, it is nonetheless necessary to review the kinds of basic conceptions and orientations imposed by this mode of analysis. In doing so, I shall be able to lay out the pattern of analysis that will inform and guide the present work.

Political life as an open and adaptive system

... The question that gives coherence and purpose to a rigorous analysis of political life as a system of behavior is as follows. How do any and all political systems manage to persist in a world of both stability and change? Ultimately the search for an answer will reveal what I have called the life processes of political systems – those fundamental functions without which no system could endure – together with the typical modes of response through which systems manage to sustain them. The analysis of these processes, and of the nature and conditions of the responses, I posit as a central problem of political theory.

Although I shall end by arguing that it is useful to interpret political life as a complex set of processes through which certain kinds of inputs are converted into the type of outputs we may call authoritative policies, decisions and implementing actions, at the outset it is useful to take a somewhat simpler approach. We may begin by viewing political life as a system of behavior imbedded in an environment to the influences of which the political system itself is exposed and in turn reacts. Several vital considerations are implicit in this interpretation and it is essential that we become aware of them.

First, such a point of departure for theoretical analysis assumes without further inquiry that political interactions in a society constitute a *system* of behavior. This proposition is, however, deceptive in its simplicity. The truth is that if the idea "system" is employed with the rigor it

permits and with the implications currently inherent in it, it provides a starting point that is already heavily freighted with consequences for a whole pattern of analysis.

Second, to the degree that we are successful in analytically isolating political life as a system, it is clear that it cannot usefully be interpreted as existing in a void. It must be seen as surrounded by physical, biological, social and psychological *environments*. Here again, the empirical transparency of the statement ought not to be allowed to distract us from its crucial theoretical significance. If we were to neglect what seems so obvious once it is asserted, it would be impossible to lay the groundwork for an analysis of how political systems manage to persist in a world of stability or change.

This brings us to a third point. What makes the identification of the environments useful and necessary is the further presupposition that political life forms an *open* system. By its very nature as a social system that has been analytically separated from other social systems, it must be interpreted as lying exposed to influences deriving from the other systems in which empirically it is imbedded. From them there flows a constant stream of events and influences that shape the conditions under which the members of the system must act.

Finally, the fact that some systems do survive, whatever the buffetings from the environments, awakens us to the fact that they must have the capacity to *respond* to disturbances and thereby to adapt to the conditions under which they find themselves. Once we are willing to assume that political systems may be adaptive and need not just react in a passive or sponge-like way to their environmental influences, we shall be able to break a new path through the complexities of theoretical analysis.

As I have elsewhere demonstrated, in its internal organization, a critical property that a political system shares with all other social systems is this extraordinarily variable capacity to respond to the conditions under which it functions. Indeed, we shall find that political systems accumulate large repertoires of mechanisms through which they may seek to cope with their environments. Through these they may regulate their own behavior, transform their internal structure, and even go so far as to remodel their fundamental goals. Few systems, other than social systems, have this potentiality. In practice, students of political life could not help but take this into account; no analysis could even begin to appeal to common sense if it did not do so. Nevertheless it is seldom built into a theoretical structure as a central component; certainly its implications for the internal behavior of political systems have never been set forth and explored.

Equilibrium analysis and its shortcomings

It is a major shortcoming of the one form of inquiry latent but prevalent in political research – equilibrium analysis – that it neglects such variable capacities for systems to cope with influences from their environment. The equilibrium approach is seldom explicitly elaborated, yet it infuses a good part of political research, especially group politics and international relations. Of necessity an analysis that conceives of a political system as seeking to maintain a state of equilibrium must assume the presence of environmental influences. It is these that displace the power relationships in a political system – such as a balance of power – from their presumed stable state. It is then customary, if only implicitly so, to analyze the system in terms of a tendency to return to a presumed pre-existing point of stability. If the system should fail to do so, it would be interpreted as moving on to a new state of equilibrium and this would need to be identified and described. A careful scrutiny of the language used reveals that equilibrium and stability are usually assumed to mean the same thing.

Numerous conceptual and empirical difficulties stand in the way of an effective use of the equilibrium idea for the analysis of political life. But among these there are two that are particularly relevant for my present purposes.

In the first place, the equilibrium approach leaves the impression that the members of a system are seized with only one basic goal as they seek to cope with change or disturbance, namely, to re-establish the old point of equilibrium or, at most, to move on to some new one. This is usually phrased, at least implicitly, as the search for stability as though this were sought above all else. In the second place, little if any attention is explicitly given to formulating the problems relating to the path that the system takes insofar as it does seek to return to this presumed point of equilibrium or to attain a fresh one. It is as though the pathways taken to manage the displacements were an incidental rather than a central theoretical consideration.

But it would be impossible to understand the processes underlying the capacity of some kind of political life to sustain itself in a society if either the objectives or the form of the responses are taken for granted. A system may well seek goals other than those of reaching one or another point of equilibrium. Even though this state were to be used only as a theoretical norm that is never achieved, it would offer a less useful theoretical approximation of reality than one that takes into account other possibilities. We would find it more helpful to devise a conceptual approach that recognized that at times members in a system may wish to take positive actions to destroy a previous equilibrium or even to achieve some new point of continuing disequilibrium. This is typically the case where the authorities may seek to keep themselves in power by fostering internal turmoil or external dangers.

Furthermore, with respect to these variable goals, it is a primary characteristic of all systems that they are able to adopt a wide range of actions of a positive, constructive and innovative sort for warding off or absorbing any forces of displacement. A system need not just react to a disturbance by oscillating in the neighborhood of a prior point of equilibrium or by shifting to a new one. It may cope with the disturbance by seeking to change the environment so that the exchanges between the environment and itself are no longer stressful; it may seek to insulate itself against any further influences from the environment; or the members of the system may even transform their own relationships fundamentally and modify their own goals and practices so as to improve their chances of handling the inputs from the environment. In these and other ways a system has the capacity for creative and constructive regulation of disturbances as we shall later see in detail.

It is clear that the adoption of equilibrium analysis, however latent it may be, obscures the presence of system goals that cannot be described as a state of equilibrium. It also virtually conceals the existence of varying pathways for attaining these alternative ends. For any social system, including the political, adaptation represents more than simple adjustments to the events in its life. It is made up of efforts, limited only by the variety of human skills, resources, and ingenuity, to control, modify or fundamentally change either the environment or the system itself, or both together. In the outcome the system may succeed in fending off or incorporating successfully any influences stressful for it.

Minimal concepts for a systems analysis

A systems analysis promises a more expansive, more inclusive, and more flexible theoretical structure than is available even in a thoroughly self-conscious and well-developed equilibrium approach. To do so successfully, however, it must establish its own theoretical imperatives. Although these were explored in detail in *A Framework for Political Analysis*, we may re-examine them briefly here, assuming, however, that where the present brevity leaves unavoidable ambiguities, the reader may wish to become more familiar with the underlying structure of ideas by consulting this earlier volume. In it, at the outset, a system was defined as any set of variables regardless of the degree of interrelationship among them. The reason for preferring this definition is that it frees us from the need to argue about whether a political system is or is not really a system. The only question of importance about a set selected as a system to be analyzed is whether this set constitutes an interesting one. Does it help us to understand and explain some aspect of human behavior of concern to us?

To be of maximum utility, I have argued, a *political* system can be designated as those interactions through which values are authoritatively allocated for a society; this is what distinguishes a political system from other systems that may be interpreted as lying in its environment. This environment itself may be divided into two parts, the intra-societal and the extra-societal. The first consists of those systems in the same society as the political system but excluded from the latter by our definition of the nature of political interactions. Intra-societal systems would include such sets of behavior, attitudes and ideas as we might call the economy, culture, social structure or personalities; they are functional segments of the society with respect to which

the political system at the focus of attention is itself a component. In a given society the systems other than the political system constitute a source of many influences that create and shape the conditions under which the political system itself must operate. In a world of newly emerging political systems we do not need to pause to illustrate the impact that a changing economy, culture, or social structure may have upon political life.

The second part of the environment, the extra-societal, includes all those systems that lie outside the given society itself. They are functional components of an international society or what we might describe as the supra-society, a supra-system of which any single society is part. The international political systems, the international economy, or the international cultural system would fall into the category of extra-societal systems.

Together, these two classes of systems, the intra- and extra-societal, that are conceived to lie outside of a political system may be designated as its total environment. From these sources arise influences that are of consequence for possible stress on the political system. The total environment is presented in Table 16.1 as reproduced from *A Framework for Political Analysis*, and the reader should turn to that volume for a full discussion of the various components of the environment as indicated on this table.

Disturbances is a concept that may be used to identify those influences from the total environment of a system that act upon it so that it is different after the stimulus from what it was before. Not all disturbances need strain the

Table 16.1 Components of the Total Environment of a Political System

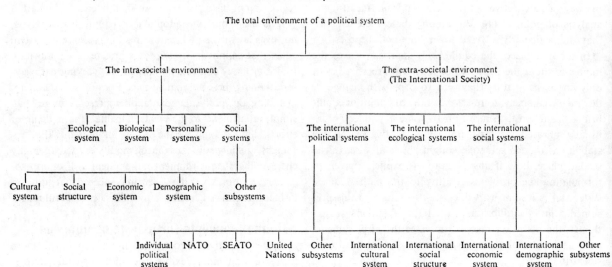

system. Some may be favorable with respect to the persistence of the system; others may be entirely neutral with respect to possible stress. But many can be expected to lead in the direction of stress.

When may we say that *stress* occurs? This involves us in a rather complex idea, one that has been treated at length. But since it does stand as a major pillar underpinning the analysis to be elaborated in the succeeding chapters, I must at least broadly sketch out its implications. It embodies several subsidiary notions. All political systems as such are distinguished by the fact that if we are to be able to describe them as persisting, we must attribute to them the successful fulfillment of two functions. They must be able to allocate values for a society; they must also manage to induce most members to accept these allocations as binding, at least most of the time. These are the two properties that help us to distinguish most succinctly political systems from other kinds of social systems.

By virtue of this very fact these two distinctive features – the allocations of values for a society and the relative frequency of compliance with them – are the *essential variables* of political life. But for their presence, we would not be able to say that a society has any political life. And we may here take it for granted that no society could exist without some kind of political system; elsewhere I have sought to demonstrate this in detail.

One of the important reasons for identifying these essential variables is that they give us a way of establishing when and how the disturbances acting upon a system threaten to stress it. Stress will be said to occur when there is a danger that the essential variables will be pushed beyond what we may designate as their *critical range*. What this means is that something may be happening in the environment – the system suffers total defeat at the hands of an enemy, or widespread disorganization in and disaffection from the system is aroused by a severe economic crisis. Let us say that as a result, the authorities are consistently unable to make decisions or if they strive to do so, the decisions are no longer regularly accepted as binding. Under these conditions, authoritative allocations of values are no longer possible and the society would collapse for want of a system of behavior to fulfill one of its vital functions.

Here we could not help but accept the interpretation that the political system had come under stress, so severe that any and every possibility for the persistence of a system for that society had disappeared. But frequently the disruption of a political system is not that complete; the stress is present even though the system continues to persist in some form. Severe as a crisis may be, it still may be possible for the authorities to be able to make some kinds of decisions and to get them accepted with at least minimal frequency so that some of the problems typically subjected to political settlements can be handled.

That is to say, it is not always a matter as to whether the essential variables are operating or have ceased to do so. It is possible that they may only be displaced to some extent as when the authorities are partially incapacitated for making decisions or from getting them accepted with complete regularity. Under these circumstances the essential variables will remain within some normal range of operation; they may be stressed but not in a sufficient degree to displace them beyond a determinable critical point. As long as the system does keep its essential variables operating within what I shall call their critical range, some kind of system can be said to persist.

As we have seen, one of the characteristic properties of every system is the fact that it has the capacity to cope with stress on its essential variables. Not that a system need take such action; it may collapse precisely because it has failed to take measures appropriate for handling the impending stress. But it is the existence of a capacity to respond to stress that is of paramount importance. The kind of response actually undertaken, if any, will help us to evaluate the probabilities of the system's being able to ward off the stress. In thus raising the question of the nature of the response to stress, it will become apparent, in due course, that the special objective and merit of a systems analysis of political life is that it permits us to interpret the behavior of the members in a system in the light of the consequences it has for alleviating or aggravating stress upon the essential variables.

The linkage variables between systems

But a fundamental problem remains. We could not begin the task of applying this kind of conceptualization if we did not first pose the following question. How do the potentially stressful conditions from the environment communicate themselves to a political system? After all, common sense alone tells us that there is an enormous variety of environmental influences at work on a system. Do we have to treat each change in the environment as a separate and unique disturbance, the specific effects of which for the political system have to be independently worked out?

If this were indeed the case, as I have shown in detail before, the problems of systematic analysis would be virtually insurmountable. But if we can devise a way for generalizing our method for handling the impact of the environment on the system, there would be some hope of reducing the enormous variety of influences into a relatively few, and therefore into a relatively manageable number of indicators. This is precisely what I have sought to effect through the use of the concepts "inputs" and "outputs".

How are we to describe these inputs and outputs? Because of the analytic distinction that I have been making between a political system and its parametric or environmental systems, it is useful to interpret the influences associated with the behavior of persons in the environment or from other conditions there as *exchanges* or *transactions* that cross the *boundaries* of the political system. Exchanges can be used when we wish to refer to the mutuality of the relationships, to the fact that the political system and those systems in the environmental have reciprocal effects on each other. Transactions may be employed when we wish to emphasize the movement of an effect in one direction, from an environmental system to the political system, or the reverse, without being concerned at the time about the reactive behavior of the other system.

To this point, there is little to dispute. Unless systems were coupled together in some way, all analytically identifiable aspects of behavior in society would stand independent of each other, a patently unlikely condition. What carries recognition of this coupling beyond a mere truism, however, is the proposal of a way to trace out the complex exchanges so that we can readily reduce their immense variety to theoretically and empirically manageable proportions.

To accomplish this, I have proposed that we condense the major and significant environmental influences into a few indicators. Through the examination of these we should be able to appraise and follow through the potential impact of environmental events on the system. With this objective in mind, I have designated the effects that are transmitted across the boundary of a system toward some other system as the *outputs* of the first system and hence, symmetrically, as the *inputs* of the second system, the one they influence. A transaction or an exchange between systems will therefore be viewed as a linkage between them in the form of an input–output relationship.

Demands and supports as input indicators

The value of inputs as a concept is that through their use we shall find it possible to capture the effect of the vast variety of events and conditions in the environment as they pertain to the persistence of a political system. Without the inputs it would be difficult to delineate the precise operational way in which the behavior in the various sectors of society affects what happens in the political sphere. In-

puts will serve as *summary variables* that concentrate and mirror everything in the environment that is relevant to political stress. Thereby this concept serves as a powerful tool.

The extent to which inputs can be used as summary variables will depend, however, upon how we define them. We might conceive of them in their broadest sense. In that case, we would interpret them as including any event external to the system that alters, modifies or affects the system in any and every possible way. But if we seriously considered using the concept in so broad a fashion, we would never be able to exhaust the list of inputs acting upon a system. Virtually every parametric event and condition would have some significance for the operations of a political system at the focus of attention; a concept so inclusive that it does not help us to organize and simplify reality would defeat its own purposes. We would be no better off than we are without it.

But as I have already intimated, we can greatly simplify the task of analyzing the impact of the environment if we restrict our attention to certain kinds of inputs that can be used as indicators to sum up the most important effects, in terms of their contributions to stress, that cross the boundary from the parametric to the political systems. In this way we would free ourselves from the need to deal with and trace out separately the consequences of every different type of environmental event.

As the theoretical tool for this purpose, it is helpful to view the major environmental influences as coming to a focus in two major inputs: demands and support. Through them a wide range of activities in the environment may be channeled, mirrored, and summarized and brought to bear upon political life, as I shall show in detail in the succeeding chapters. In this sense they are key indicators of the way in which environmental influences and conditions modify and shape the operations of the political system. If we wish, we may say that it is through fluctuations in the inputs of demands and support that we shall find the effects of the environmental systems transmitted to the political system.

Outputs and feedbacks

In a comparable way, the idea of outputs help us to organize the consequences flowing from the behavior of the members of the system rather than from actions in the environment. Our primary concern is, to be sure, with the functioning of the political system. In and of themselves, at least for understanding political phenomena, we would have no need to be concerned with the consequences that political actions have for the environmental system. This is a problem that can or should be handled better by theories seeking to explore the operations of the economy, culture, or any of the other parametric systems.

But the fact is that the activities of the members of the system may well have some importance with respect to their own subsequent actions or conditions. To the extent that this is so, we cannot entirely neglect those actions that do flow out of a system into the environment. As in the case of inputs, however, there is an immense amount of activities that take place within a political system. How are we to sort out the portion that has relevance for an understanding of the way in which systems manage to persist?

Later we shall see that a useful way of simplifying and organizing our perceptions of the behavior of the members of the system, as reflected in their demands and support, is in terms of the consequences of these inputs for what I shall call the political outputs. These are the decisions and actions of the authorities. Not that the complex political processes internal to a system, and that have been the subject of inquiry for so many decades in political science, will be considered in any way irrelevant. Who controls whom in the various decision-making processes will continue to be a vital concern since the pattern of power relationships helps to determine the nature of the outputs. But the formulation of a conceptual structure for this aspect of a political system would draw us into a different level of analysis. Here I am only seeking economical ways of summarizing the outcomes of these internal political processes – not of investigating them – and I am suggesting that they can be usefully conceptualized as the outputs of the authorities. Through them we shall be able to trace out the consequences of behavior within a political system for its environment.

There would be little point in taking the trouble to conceptualize the results of the internal behavior of the members in a system in this way unless we could so something with it. As we shall see, the significance of outputs is not only that they help to influence events in the broader society of which the system is a part; in doing so, they help to determine each succeeding round of inputs that finds its way into the political system. As we shall phrase it later, there is a *feedback loop* the identification of which will help us to explain the processes through which the authorities may cope with stress. This loop has a number of parts. It consists of the production of outputs by the authorities, a response on the part of the members of the society with respect to them, the communication of information about this response to the authorities, and finally, possible succeeding actions on the part of the authorities. Thereby a new round of outputs, response information feedback, and

reaction on the part of the authorities is set in motion and is part of a continuous never-ending flow. What happens in this feedback loop will turn out to have the deepest significance for the capacity of a system to cope with stress.

A flow model of the political system

It is clear from what has been said that this mode of analysis enables and indeed compels us to analyze a political system in dynamic terms. Not only do we see that it gets something done through its outputs but we are also sensitized to the fact that what it does may influence each successive stage of behavior. We appreciate the urgent need to interpret political processes as a continuous and interlinked flow of behavior.

If we apply this conceptualization in the construction of a rudimentary model of the relationships between a political system and its environment, we would have a figure of the kind illustrated in Figure 16.1. . . . In effect it conveys the idea that the political system looks like a vast and perpetual conversion process. It takes in demands and support as they are shaped in the environment and produces something out of them called outputs. But it does not let our interest in the outputs terminate at this point. We are alerted to the fact that the outputs influence the supportive sentiments that the members express toward the system and the kinds of demands they put in. In this way the outputs return to haunt the system, as it were. As depicted on the diagram, all this is still at a very crude level of formulation. It will be our task to refine these relationships as we proceed in our analysis.

But let us examine the model a little more closely since in effect this volume will do little more than to flesh out the skeleton presented there. In interpreting the diagram, we begin with the fact that it shows a political system surrounded by the two classes of environments that together form its total environment. The communications of the many events that occur here are represented by the solid lines connecting the environments with the political system. The arrowheads on the lines show the direction of flow into the system. But rather than attempting to discuss each disturbance in the environment uniquely or even in selected groups or classes of types, I use as an indicator of the impact that they have on the system, the way in which they shape two special kinds of inputs into the system, demands and support. This is why the effects from the environment are shown to flow into the box labelled "inputs". We must remember, however, that even though the desire for simplicity in presentation does not permit us to show it on

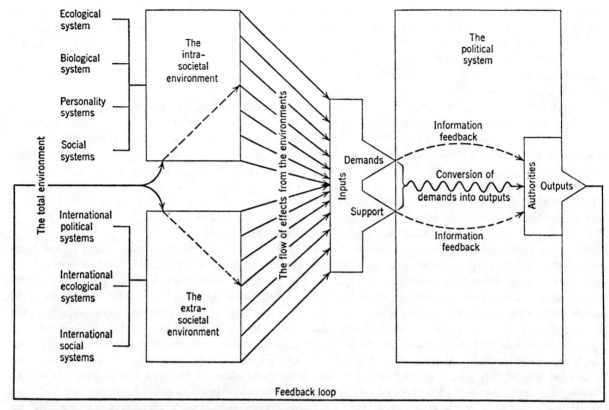

Figure 16.1 A Dynamic Response Model of a Political System.

the diagram, events occurring within a system may also have some share in influencing the nature of the inputs.

As is apparent, the inputs provide what we may call the raw materials on which the system acts so to produce something we are calling outputs. The way in which this is done will be described as a massive conversion process cavalierly represented on the diagram by the serpentine line within the political system. The conversion processes move toward the authorities since it is toward them that the demands are initially directed. As we shall see, demands spark the basic activities of a political system. By virtue of their status in all systems, authorities have special responsibilities for converting demands into outputs.

If we were to be content with what is basically a static picture of a political system, we might be inclined to stop at this point. Indeed much political research in effect does just this. It is concerned with exploring all those intricate subsidiary processes through which decisions are made and put into effect. This constitutes the vast corpus of political research today. Therefore, insofar as we were concerned with how influence is used in formulating and putting into effect various kinds of policies or decisions, the model to

this point would be an adequate if minimal first approximation.

But the critical question that confronts political theory is not just the development of a conceptual apparatus for understanding the factors that contribute to the kinds of decisions a system makes, that is, for formulating a theory of political allocations. As I have indicated, theory needs to know how it comes about that any kind of system can persist long enough to continue to make such decisions. We need a theory of systems persistence as well. How does a system manage to deal with the stress to which it may be subjected at any time? It is for this reason that we cannot accept outputs as the terminal point either of the political processes or of our interest in them. Thus it is important to note on the diagram, that the outputs of the conversion process have the characteristic of feeding back upon the system and shaping its subsequent behavior. Much later I shall seek to demonstrate that it is this feature together with the capacity of a system to take constructive actions that makes it possible for a system to seek to adapt or to cope with possible stress.

In the figure, this feedback is depicted by the line that

shows the effects of the outputs moving directly back to the environments. As the broken lines within the environmental boxes indicate, the effects may reshape the environment in some way; that is to say, they influence conditions and behavior there. In this way the outputs are able to modify the influences that continue to operate on the inputs and thereby the next round of inputs themselves.

But if the authorities are to be able to take the past effect of outputs into account for their own future behavior, they must in some way be apprised of what has taken place along the feedback loop. The broken lines in the box labeled "The political system" suggest that, through the return flow of demands and support, the authorities obtain information about these possible consequences of their previous behavior. This puts the authorities in a position to take advantage of the information that has been fed back and to correct or adjust their behavior for the achievement of their goals.

It is the fact that there can be such a continuous flow of effects and information between system and environment, we shall see, that ultimately accounts for the capacity of a political system to persist in a world even of violently fluctuating changes. Without feedback and the capacity to respond to it, no system could survive for long, except by accident.

In this brief overview, I have summarized the essential features of the analytic structure. . . . If we condensed the figure still further, we would have the diagram shown on Figure 16.2. It reduces to its bare essentials the fundamental processes at work in all systems and starkly reveals the source of a system's capacity to persist. It may well stand temporarily as the simplest image, to carry in our minds, of the processes we are about to discuss in detail.

To summarize the conceptualization being reviewed here, our analysis will rest on the idea of a system imbedded in an environment and subject to possible influences from it that threaten to drive the essential variables of the system beyond their critical range. To persist, the system must be capable of responding with measures that are successful in alleviating the stress so created. To respond, the authorities

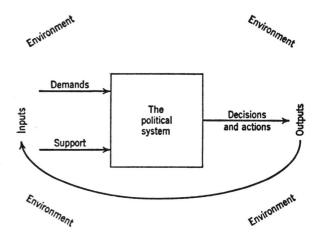

Figure 16.2 A simplified model of a political system.

at least must be in a position to obtain information about what is happening so that they may react insofar as they desire or are compelled to do so.

In *A Framework for Political Analysis* each of these concepts and interrelationships was attended to in varying degrees of detail . . . It will be my task to begin to apply them in an effort to construct a much more elaborate structure for the analysis of political systems.

In doing so, we shall find ourselves confronted with a series of major questions. What precisely are the nature of the influences acting upon a political system? How are they communicated to a system? In what ways, if any, have systems typically sought to cope with such stress? What kinds of processes will have to exist in any system if it is to acquire and exploit the potential for acting so as to ameliorate these conditions of stress? . . .

Reference

1 Easton, D. (1961) *A Framework for Political Analysis*, Prentice-Hall, Englewood Cliffs, N.J.

Section VI

Introduction

This section brings together articles on the application of systems ideas on the large scale – or at least the complex – and an article considering systems analysis from a critical standpoint.

Milsum looks at the application of systems concepts to the world and its environs. Forrester introduces systems dynamics, a modelling technique developed initially in an industrial context, and uses it to consider worldwide trends in key variables like population, pollution and natural resources. It was this work which led to the Club of Rome study *Limits to Growth*. What is of interest in this article is not just the possible developments which Forrester sees, but the fact that they are only the consequent behaviour of a system with the parameters and relationships assumed.

Peter Checkland's article details the soft-systems methodology which is referred to in his other article (Article 2) and which was developed as a result of the problems associated with applying the systems engineering methodology outlined in Gwilym Jenkins' paper (Article 8). This *soft*-systems method is applicable to situations where the "problem" and the associated objectives are either not definable and/or not agreeable. If it is generally accepted that the task in hand is to get a chemical plant working by a certain date to certain performance criteria and within various constraints, then a *hard*-systems engineering method may be in order. If, however, there are just symptoms and feelings about what is wrong in an organization, or what might be different, then a soft-systems method is implied. In real life it is often useful to see problem situations as soft-system ones initially, since one outcome from the application of a method like Checkland's can be a specification for a hard-systems project.

It is perhaps unfair to juxtapose the soft-systems methodology article with Ida Hoos' critique of engineers. However, although the examples she quotes are American, where the methods employed are different, and the practitioners are not like ourselves, the traps that she highlights are there for us all to fall into. The subject of systems has developed considerably even since the first edition of this book was published in 1972, but it will be some time before anything more than the most modest claims can be fully supported, and it is therefore fitting to end on a cautionary note.

Associated reading

Forrester's work and that of his colleagues is presented in several books. The original work on the method appears in *Industrial Dynamics* (1961) and *Urban Dynamics* (1969), both by J. W. Forrester (MIT Press). Later work is in *World Dynamics*, by Forrester (MIT Press, 1977), and *Limits to Growth*, by D. H. Meadows et al. (Earth Island, 1972).

An evaluation of system dynamics and world modelling is available in *World Models – Sense or Nonsense*, Unit 16 of Systems Modelling T341 (Open University Press).

Peter Checkland's book *Systems Thinking, Systems Practice* (Wiley, 1981) devotes considerable space to the soft-systems method, and the Open Systems Group has produced *The Checkland Methodology: A reader's guide*, which is a commentary on the article here.

There has been other critical work on systems in recent years, including Ida Hoos' book, *Systems Analysis in Public Policy* (University of California Press, 1972) and R. Lilienfeld, *The Rise of Systems Theory* (Wiley, 1978).

17 Technosphere, biosphere, and sociosphere: an approach to their systems modelling and optimization*

by J. H. Milsum

Introduction

In the last century, technology and the science underlying it have been primary agents forcing the vast changes that have occurred in the geosphere and sociosphere which we inhabit. The pace of this change has, in addition, accelerated fantastically in more recent years. Consider, for example, that in the lifetime of almost all here present, the following list represents only the most dramatic examples which have been invented, developed, and have reached mass-production with great social effects upon our lives: gas turbine (jet) engines (providing nearly instantaneous transport of people anywhere around the world at a cost that many can afford); rockets and nuclear energy (providing for space travel and potential "over-kill" capability against the whole human population, as well as other less dramatic, but probably more useful activities); radar, television, and solid-state electronics (providing instantaneous and reasonably economic world-wide communication); electronic computers (providing essentially instantaneous computational ability of such great power that we are only beginning to understand its vastly-pervading influence upon our lives).

While there has not been complete agreement in our society that these changes all represent improvement, nevertheless no groups of significant size ever seriously try to operate their societies without utilizing available technological advances. Thus it may be said that the technologist has had society's tacit support, even if he has not formally represented the ideal prototype for its citizens to aspire to. Unfortunately, it has been largely true that during this early technological period when the advantages of technological advances have generally been so obvious to society, in contrast to the disadvantages which tend to become obvious somewhat later and to cost money to avoid, then the technologist does not seem to have felt it his prime duty to anticipate and point out to society the concomitant disadvantages in comparison to the expected advantages. Nor indeed would it seem justified to consider him particularly culpable here, since society has not really encouraged consideration of the aesthetic and ethical aspects which might arise from technological advance if it were to involve larger cost. Consequently, a naïve technologist would seem superficially justified in being puzzled when he finds himself apt to be as much blamed as praised for new technological developments. Clearly this tendency for blame to be attached comes when societies are beginning to realize that things are not going quite according to plan, and yet are not really clear why. Certainly few would now agree with the philosopher, Dr. Pangloss of *Candide*, that "All is necessarily for the best in the best of all possible worlds". In fact, in spite of the invention, development, and widespread production of vast numbers of useful consumer goods and services, which have turned most Western societies into very affluent ones, it is clear that we perceive ourselves to have some very urgent and perplexing problems.

As regards tackling these problems, it now seems clear that the technologist must increasingly take a systems view which is broad enough to include the problems of social values, and that he must be prepared to take more of a lead in pointing out to his less technically-literate confreres in society how some of the different aspects, such as beautification and prevention of pollution, will trade off in the overall optimization of the system under consideration. Then, while it will remain true that simple answers cannot be expected to the complex problems which we are now producing for ourselves as a result of the vast interlocking of our systems, nevertheless society will be encouraged into the dialogue in helping establish how human values should be entered into the complicated systems equations.

Despite such optimization attempts, it will almost undoubtedly remain true that the affluence available through maximum use of technology will bring at the same time many new problems and will also place constraints upon us. Inasmuch as certain of such constraints may be con-

* Presidential address presented at the Annual Meeting of the Society for General Systems Research, New York, December 1967.

sidered unacceptable by societies at any given time, then it is probable that not every technological advance will be automatically accepted. On the other hand, societies are always adapting, if only slowly, and therefore it will seldom be possible to predict with certainty whether any given innovation will remain unacceptable. It is both refreshing and sobering to realize that in the late twenties Freud was very concerned about these same problems (*Civilization and Its Discontents*, Norton, 1929).

In this talk, I hope to make a few useful suggestions towards how we may bring a systems approach to bear on analyzing our problems in the broad areas of geosphere, biosphere, technosphere, and sociosphere, and hopefully towards optimizing them. It should be mentioned that these of course represent only my own opinions, arising from my own background of control engineering, systems research, and biomedical engineering.

Geosphere

Under this heading, we mention some of those vast natural processes in and upon the earth which do not either inherently or necessarily involve living processes. These physical systems involve such complicated interlocking dynamics that they are only now beginning to be understood, in the sense of adequate mathematical models being available.

Perhaps the most obvious dynamic phenomena in the geosphere are those cycles due to the varying exposure of the earth to the sun; namely the annual and daily cycles, and of course, although less noticeably, the lunar cycle. Thus genuine and fairly strict cycles exist in such atmospheric conditions as temperature and precipitation, which have in turn widespread influence upon our biosphere, technosphere, and sociosphere. Other major phenomena depend to a greater or lesser extent upon these cyclic-forcing inputs, in particular the circulation of water in the oceans, the circulation of air in the atmosphere, and the rainwater cycle itself. In turn, the latter is coupled to some extent with an electrical cycle which produces the familiar electrical discharges of lightning, among other things. Actually the word *circulation* may be much better than *cycle* to define these phenomena. The point here is that while a cycle may be traced, namely rain – surface and subsurface water flow – pooling in the seas (both ocean and landlocked) – evaporation – cloud formation – rainfall, the cycling is of given molecules between different phases; and that, from an information flow viewpoint, it is merely a relatively constant circulating flux rather than a true cycle. On the other hand, the circulation shows seasonal cyclicity at any one point on earth, of course; and furthermore, the large spatial coverage of many rain-water systems means that spatio-temporal effects couple-up inextricably.

In these cyclic or circulatory phenomena, some of the effects are unidirectional only, in the sense that what goes in one "direction" is not necessarily returned in the other. A specific important example arising in the rainfall circulation of water is that of erosion of the earth, and specifically of minerals into the sea. As one consequence, the sea cannot itself constitute a constant long-term environment for living species, which has evolutionary implications in the biosphere. It should be noted that the fact that some land also gets thrown back from the sea does not effectively cancel the erosion effect in this biological sense.

At another level of conceptualization, it could be commented that this washing of the land into the oceans is of course in accord with the second law of thermodynamics, namely that closed systems tend towards a state of uniform low order. In fact, the earth is not a closed system; but the geosphere cannot open itself to trap energy from the sun, not at least permanently nor to the same extent as the biosphere can. A further comment is that, in searching for the appropriate physical laws which govern the physical phenomena such as those described, the use of "minimal" principles has often proved important. Minimal principles usually concern conservation of certain properties, that of energy being most generally applicable and valuable, as in the Hamiltonian function.

Biosphere

Since all living organisms essentially exist close to the earth's surface, it is not surprising that many of the relevant major phenomena of the biosphere are closely coupled with those in the geosphere, such as already mentioned. Furthermore, some of the couplings in these combined systems is completely inextricable; for example, in circulatory cycles of such gases as oxygen and carbon dioxide, and indeed of many other materials, both solid and liquid. Again, there are also slow drifts in the sense that, while during the early stages of life on earth the earth may have been considered to provide a largely constant pool of basic materials, this is not necessarily true today when the biomass has become significantly large. Thus, as is obvious to us, the net result of these interactions is that the geosphere itself has been considerably modified from the relevant conditions which would otherwise exist were there no life on earth. In a parallel example to that of the increase of mineral concentrations in the sea of the geosphere, the carbon dioxide content of the atmosphere has increased as a result of life in general, and man's social system in particular. In turn, this is producing significant effects, both as to climate and net electromagnetic radiation conditions at the earth's surface.

The specific major new ability that living things have added over those exhibited in the non-living world is the ability of living organisms to trap high-energy electromagnetic radiations from the sun, on a relatively permanent basis in that the energy is transformed through photosynthesis into other forms useful in life, such as the so-called organic materials, cells, and high order organisms, and thus ultimately, our own societies.

Since apparently it has not proved practical to evolve organisms that live for an indefinitely extended period of time, then an essential feature of maintaining life has been the ability of these organisms to procreate. This ability provides the advantage that evolution can then operate through the competitive process of selection to allow refinement and improvement of the life forms. This expresses what is usually called the adaptive ability in systems theory, which is implemented in the form of some hill-climbing scheme. From a slightly different viewpoint, this ability of evolution to reject the worst results and retain the "best" may be considered a process which is of the positive-feedback, unstable type. Clearly this mechanism can potentially build up regimes of ever-increasing high order, rather than suffering the usual fate, as prescribed by the second law of thermodynamics, of degradation to uniform low order. The manifestly high-order regimes, which living forms have generated and continue to extend, therefore arises solely from the fact that living systems are able to "open" themselves to the high-energy source of the sun.

Inasmuch as the feeding patterns of living organisms represent a fantastically complicated predator–prey situation, a "balance of nature" is usually stated to express the phenomenon that there seems to be some sort of stability principle at work with regard to the populations to be found, both within species and their ecologies. Furthermore, and perhaps rather to the surprise of many, evidence is accumulating that a self-regulation of populations within species and groups exists, in order apparently to match the available food supplies with the size of the group concerned. Apparently this applies not only in the immediate sense of food supply available in a given short time period, but rather in the sense of the minimum amount available when statistical fluctuations are included over a much longer period. Social measures appear at least in part to be responsible for implementing this self-regulation in many different species, notably birds for example (see Wynn-

Edwards (1962) *Animal Dispersion in Relation to Social Behaviour*, Hafner).

Technosphere

Historically, it is hardly justifiable to consider that technology started only in the last one, or at most two, centuries. However, such is the nature of exponential growth processes that, for all practical purposes, it suffices to consider that the industrial age started with a small initial condition in the 18th century. Specifically, the so-called first industrial revolution of the 18th–19th century essentially relieved man of the requirement to obtain all his nicely controlled mechanical power through the use of either his own or animal muscles by providing, instead and in succession, steam power, electric power, hydrocarbon fuel power, and finally, nuclear power. This revolution has of course had tremendous social implications, which have been widely discussed, but nevertheless they probably provide only a small component cause in producing the difficult complex problems we face today. The major component arises from the more recent second industrial revolution, which in turn has relieved man of the need to perform all his own data processing by providing, instead, the tremendous capacity of modern electronic (and other) computing machines. This particular revolution has been extremely rapid, for within the course of about twenty-five years from the computer's inception, we now find ourselves affected in a wide spectrum of important ways by this new slave, both helpfully, disturbingly, and frustratingly. Part of the trouble lies in the fact that this slave does accurately and fast so many of the tasks society has found necessary, but which humans themselves have found tedious and therefore do not in fact perform well. Nevertheless, while their work may have generally been decried by these workers, at the same time it has constituted much of the basis for their self-respect. Hence it becomes necessary to define much more carefully what might be considered to constitute the essential characteristics of man, as opposed to a computing machine; in particular, what is necessary to man for him to feel enjoyment in life and to experience emotional and purposeful activity. It is generally presumed that these latter areas are not ones in which a computer excels, and yet, when one tries to define exactly where man does differ in a "superior" way from the computer, the matter becomes very perplexing.

Consequent upon these industrial revolutions, our technosphere now seems capable of providing, at least in principle, large integrated industrial processes which are both automated and computer controlled; as one example, we could cite the possibility of integrating the steel industry through from the mining of metal ores to the inventory control of finished products such as automobiles, almost without human intervention. In other words, given certain sensible and yet fairly unrestrictive constraints on any of man's material needs, he can now aspire to a society in which it is not necessary for the national production of material and information products to be tied essentially to the amount of man power available and its productivity. Theoretically, this should leave him free to develop the higher human qualities with which he believes himself specially endowed. The unfortunate fact that this does not seem to be working out, at present, probably and hopefully relates to the problems of the sociosphere, which at least we may be able to tackle if we can first define them.

Sociosphere

It has been noted that many of today's problems arise partly because the technological advances which have so greatly affected our social environment have occurred much faster than the normal rate at which adaptive changes in social behavior can accommodate to them. Stated slightly differently, the present time constants of technological change are probably at least one order of magnitude larger than that of social change. Some of these problems arise specifically because the result of technological change has been to call into question for needed re-evaluation certain relevant concepts and beliefs that were long thought either to have been handed down to the world by divine inspiration or else to have been adequately proven by long human experience. Indeed, for much of human history, the changes were of a sufficiently slow nature that they could be adapted to without doing great violence to traditional beliefs; that is, their evolution was possible rather than revolution. Today, however, we have seen reflected into society as a result of technological advancement such dramatic changes that it is clear to almost all that certain absurd situations are arising. Some outstanding examples in my view would seem to be:

1. The subject of *human population*, and the need for its rational control by the societies involved. Certainly there existed adequate justification throughout much of human history for attributing sacrosanct status to new human life, inasmuch as all population possible was desirable to offset the high wastage rate due to warfare and disease. Having now tampered very effectively with the death rate side of human population, sufficiently that a runaway condition is in progress, it would seem to represent elementary good

husbandry for us to consider some overall objectives for the size of human populations, so as to be able to work towards achieving such conditions before panic measures prove necessary. Relevant criteria in such considerations obviously must relate to matters such as family health, wealth, and security; adequacy of national food supply; natural resources, etc., and finally a satisfactory population density to avoid unsatisfactory, if as yet unknown, psychological pressures.

2. The matter of *work–leisure relations* in an affluent and automated society. A specific basic problem here concerns how we may accomplish change in the deeply-ingrained protestant ethic which makes it difficult for people to feel themselves fulfilled, and thus to maintain their necessary self-pride, if they cannot be working members of the community, no matter how unrewarding the work might seem to be at first glance. It should be noted that this difficulty seems largely independent of whether they are provided adequate sustenance by their society even when they do not work, in fact possibly even *because* they do not work. Again, therefore, the inheritance of a non-technological age, that unremitting toil is good and necessary, has now rapidly become inappropriate, but too rapidly for society to adopt happily to this condition.

3. The problem of *aggression and interpersonal fear* which lead especially to the problems of warfare and ethnic strife within a particular state.

4. The problem of unacceptably *large and probably increasing differences* between the affluence of the developed societies on the one hand, and the developing societies on the other. It should be noted that this is one of the inevitable effects when subsystems having positive feedback pathways are placed in competition with each other. The process is in fact an example of the general competitive exclusion aspect of evolution, and can lead to the same ruthless solutions unless we impose, as civilized societies, some higher performance criteria upon the overall system.

5. The problem of *participation* by the members of society in their society, in such a meaningful way that they are able to feel part of it and therefore to fulfill themselves. This problem is related to the work–leisure problem mentioned in 2 above. The word alienation has been used to describe the general absence of participation that people feel in large remotely-run and apparently inflexible societies.

Let us ask what may in some reasonable sense be considered the purpose of the people within their societies, and then even of their societies themselves. It seems clear that there are many needs which can already be described for individuals: to be closely involved in a "family", and in contributing to the generation and training of the new generation; to be valued by his neighbors for contributions he can make to his immediate community; to be able to call upon his community in times of need; to be able to develop himself in various intellectual, cultural, and other social ways; and finally, in a less well-defined way, to be able to contribute towards the development of his society at large towards some sort of inspiring long-term goal. It is important to notice in this latter regard that people do not need to be in a state of great affluence as a prerequisite to feeling that they are fulfilling themselves satisfactorily in a society, but rather that they are moving towards a better state by their effort. This fact seems again an illustration of the general biological phenomenon that the rate of change seems to be more important than the absolute value itself. A further point is that it is also necessary to have a basis for comparing performance with another outside standard in order to produce an "error signal" for deciding which action should be taken.

A pertinent question follows from these comments in that it is being implicitly suggested that societies can meaningfully be planned with some overall optimization in view. Unfortunately, of course, it is very hard to find successful evidence for this in history, especially since we are necessarily restricted to a history on which many stages of editing have been performed. Furthermore, since societies contain so much positive feedback, there is always the danger that prophecies may become self-fulfilling. Such conditions could considerably obscure the data obtained from historical studies. This emphasizes from another viewpoint that it is not for trivial reasons that the sociosphere is an area of the "soft sciences". However, while the problems are admittedly extremely complex, this fact alone would seem to emphasize how urgent it is that we as societies bring many of our best scientists to work upon the problems.

On the problems

Many of society's problems arise because change is necessary from some established conditions. The codification and implementation of these conditions has generally supported the development of a cadre of professionals, which then inherently tends to resist any changes suggested by its "lay electorate", even though the professionals themselves may generate amendments and even major changes in pursuing their maintenance task. In either case, it follows that changes, such as in amendments of laws, necessarily occur in discrete jumps and at discrete intervals of time, since each change must be brought about by "the pressure to reform" having reached a threshold level after which the resistance may crumble. It may be useful to think of this process as a form of relaxation oscillation, analogous, for example, to the stick-slip friction by which a bow produces a note on the violin string. Furthermore, it should be noted that the decaying of resistance, as the actual change process gathers momentum, is equivalent to positive feedback in the local circuit.

The tendency of the establishment to resist change is not in itself necessarily unhealthy since this procedure represents a reasonable way in which to filter out the high-frequency "noise" for which no change in the rules is really required. On the other hand, society's non-trivial problem in this respect is that of judging how to match the desirable time constant of the filter to the time constant of "DC" or permanent change in the process, so that substantial changes in the "signal" can be adjusted for as rapidly as desirable, while the high-frequency noise is filtered out. Note that use of the word desirable in this sense rather begs the question since, in order to predict this effectively, an observer of godly powers is required.

When changes are made they may fall into either of two general types. In the first type, change is of the amendment or evolutionary type in the sense that the general principles of operation remain the same, but the particular parameter values are changed. The second is of a more revolutionary type in that the whole structure is changed, and obviously therefore this will only occur at a greater threshold of change in the system variables. One classic example of the second type arises when a small one-man business prospers so well that in a relatively short time period it becomes restructured to include professional managers, accountants, salesmen, etc. A frequent by-product of such a change is that the original owner, while still being proud of his success superficially, finds himself increasingly frustrated in that the business is now no longer a simple direct extension of himself, with everything proceeding under his own control. This points to the fact that, during different phases of the life cycle of sociological organisms, staffs of different strengths and weaknesses are required for the different regimes of operation.

Most of man's sociological and industrial enterprises involving many staff have grown more or less successfully to their present stage in a groping manner. Indeed, when the enterprise has been almost entirely focused to achieve the objective of some particular individual, then this type of growth has usually been the most efficient. On the other hand, once its growth reaches the stage where it is essentially a "corporate" business, then it is common experience that the overt objectives of the enterprise can become distinctly modified by these strong but publicly unexpressed motivations of the staff, especially the managers. Thus it has been the well-documented experience of the systems analyst that, when he attempts analysis of such enterprises, this very attempt immediately requires that many questions as to corporate purpose and information-flow details be asked, and that this process itself seems surprisingly revolutionary. The typical consequence is that significant improvements can easily be made in the operation, largely as a result of certain critical questions having been asked for the first time because of the point of view taken by the systems analyst. Stated slightly differently, the first cream of the optimization process can often be gained without resorting to any major refinements. The second stage as a result of the systems study is usually to introduce complicated data processing and hence control schemes for the organization. As the operation becomes closer to optimal, the cost of the analyst and of the computing time necessary for the optimization studies becomes very significant, until finally the diminishing-returns stage is reached in which the cost of the analytical effort exceeds the economy gained as a result.

On the other hand, it should also be noted that the advantages of analytical optimization studies may be realized only after a considerable time delay so that in such cases an immediate economic loss is quite acceptable in view of the profit to be gained later by the experience acquired.

In performing any optimization study, one focal point of the analysis concerns establishing an appropriate performance criterion, also often called cost function or profit function. When the analyst is searching for background knowledge to establish this criterion, he often finds that he must ask questions for which answers are not readily available, while many of the correct answers which are available are unfortunately not answers to useful questions! In defining the performance criterion, one of the most difficult tasks relates to establishing quantitative values for the social aspects, an extreme example being the value of a person's life. In fact, some react with horror to the idea that such an evaluation can even be considered. Such reactions are clearly not rational, since in fact we place great reliance upon insurance schemes, which necessarily quantify such matters; but they do point out the deep-seated nature of reactions that must be considered in any realistic analysis.

The fact that we have accepted a position of such dependence upon our technological processes, in contrast to the condition of being subject only to natural accidents, means that we have to accept the responsibility for setting safety standards, etc., which in turn determine, at least statistically, the risk rate of accidental mortality. To emphasize the case by taking the absurd extreme, almost all new technological innovations would be too expensive for us to utilize if we insisted as a society that under no circumstances could these machines conceivably take or damage human life. As a concrete example, we all recognize that accidents can happen to airplanes, with heavy loss of life, but we go on flying; and furthermore it is doubtful whether we as a society would legislate for significantly lower risk rate, in view of the rapidly increasing cost which would probably be involved. In summary, there is some incompatibility between what might be called the public and private attitudes of society, or the conscious and unconscious attitudes, and all this is borne in mind by the managers of the various important undertakings of our society, for otherwise the society certainly could not function as relatively smoothly as it does.

This consideration suggests another problem concerning inquiries into social beliefs and behaviour, namely that there are strong feedback effects especially on the positive type. To amplify this point, recall that in the physical sciences it is usually possible to design instrumentation with sufficiently high input impedance that no significant power drain is placed upon the system being observed and therefore no significant changes caused upon it. Unfortunately, the position is much worse in the social field, in that it is almost impossible to ask any question of a human being without in some way either "loading the question" or the responder feeling that the question is loaded because of his own subjective reaction. In any case, he may not answer in an entirely frank way, and may even be quite dishonest. Of course, in view of the simultaneously-held, incompatible beliefs that any responder holds, it is probably begging the question to attach any value judgment to the word "dishonest" in this context.

On the phenomena

In this section are considered a number of the most important phenomena concerned in complex systems such as we have been discussing, as follows: growth and positive feedback; oscillations; unidirectionality; psychological and man–machine interactions; minimal principles; and extreme value statistics.

Growth and positive feedback

The expression "positive feedback" conveys some common meaning to most people in a qualitative way, but care must be taken before it is used in a quantitative way, especially if any value judgments are to be involved in the matter. For example, the term "vicious circles" is commonly used to connote that a chain of vicious effects circulates in an increasing way. On the other hand, positive feedback is fundamental to all growth processes, whether in living or non-living systems. In this growth, positive feedback is responsible for the rapid growth in the initial stages, although the subsequent decay of growth rate to zero so that some steady state value is reached is due to other feedbacks. Actually, it is very hard to see how social life, as we know it, could be continued without this initiating effect. A few examples are now mentioned from the several domains considered earlier:

Fire, an essential tool in our life, must necessarily start as a small initial condition and then grow rapidly until the equilibrium conditions are approached when a leveling out of growth occurs. Although perhaps trite, it seems worth pointing out that when fire gets out of hand, as in forest and house fire, etc., then the exponential growth stage has merely been able to continue somewhat further than is considered desirable from the viewpoint of our own particular social system. The basic process, however, is the same as that which we consider desirable when we contain the fire within our household grates, oil furnaces, or internal combustion engines to pleasant and/or useful levels.

Growth of organisms, journals, and capital

The very prototype of growth is that in which cells successively divide after relatively constant periods given adequate nutrition, and thus produce the classic exponential growth. To continue the classic picture, however, the usual later growth pattern is modeled reasonably well by the so-called logistic curve or S-curve, in that the decay of growth rate essentially follows a mirror image pattern to the initial increase of growth rate until a steady-state population is reached, typically under a constant nutrition condition (see for example *Positive Feedback*, J. H. Milsum, ed., Pergamon Press, 1968). At present, knowledge, journals, and information are in the stage of exponential explosion. De Solla Price points out that while specific subsets of such knowledge systems, for example, of universities, show more or less the classic S-curve of growth over defined periods, they often set off on a renewed growth curve after some dramatically new condition has appeared (*Science Since Babylon*, Yale University Press, 1961). As regards money, this obviously continues in principle to produce exponential growth if invested with compound interest at constant rate.

Bandwagons, fashions, and vicious cycles

All these terms are used to describe phenomena exhibiting positive feedback in the social domain, the following constituting a few random examples: growth of discussion about a new and important subject, once somebody has first raised the matter; the arousal of passion in mobs; the spread of fashion in such matters as clothing, usage of words, and beliefs.

Another important aspect of growth in complicated systems is that while positive feedback may stimulate the growth of a particular subsystem, there must often be present inhibition for other similar but less successful subsystems in the surrounding domain. For example, there develops a competition between the individual tiny trees in the initial stages of growth of a number of seedlings in the forest so that once some particular examples prevail strongly enough, for example by an appropriate advantage in height, etc., then they can continue to grow preferentially with regard to the others, which latter are effectively inhibited and die off. In turn, of course, further stages of competition arise as these saplings grow larger, until the end result is the few "mighty oaks" for each acre of mature forest. Similar growth examples exist for animal species; for example, in a colony of flour beetles in a jar of flour, the female beetles lay eggs almost continually in the tunnels, but there is an extremely high probability that these eggs will be subsequently eaten by other perambulating mature beetles. Thus, while chance may set the initial conditions by which certain eggs are overlooked, once these newly-hatched beetles have survived to a certain size their probability of survival becomes successively larger. At higher levels of social organization, such as in bee colonies and in political parties, the same initial stage of selecting the queen bee or leader occurs, usually followed by a rallying around or "climbing onto the bandwagon", then elimination of competitors, then a period of comparative stability and unchallenged leadership, until eventually sufficient decay in the leader's performance occurs that the competition starts up again. It is also interesting to note that in certain neuronal data processing, such as in the retina, there is a strong tendency to emphasize contrast and/or movement of perceived objects, which is analogous to the aspect already described of enhancing some central feature and inhibiting the surround.

A common feature, worth noting in this matter of accepting a leader and then inhibiting competition, is that the first important feature in the emergence is to provide a sufficiently superior initial condition for one object to excel over its competition. Once this superiority has been accepted by the surrounding competition, then the survivor essentially loses most of its competition for a period, and usually therefore survives even for some significant period after its performance has fallen below that threshold of superiority which was originally necessary. In our common jargon we say that habits, laws, beliefs, and systems tend to be carried along by their own momentum even after people start to become dissatisfied with them. When we view the matter, however, in terms of the "capital" invested in the system, whether emotional or financial, then such tolerance is not unreasonable. In any case, the result is typically that of the stick-slip friction model already discussed.

An interesting and relevant socio-technological example concerns the circumstances by which the gauge separating the two tracks of railroads became standardized. It provides a classic example of those growth situations in which the apparently unimportant detail decisions at the early stages in fact become inevitably frozen into the design of huge systems. Thus today's railroads apparently developed from their embryonic form of horse-drawn coal carts. In the 19th century these were first carried over wooden planks, and then on iron plateways, and then on crude rails after the invention of the flanged wheel. The essentials of the modern system then started in England at the beginning of the 19th century, and, as the typical explosion of railroad building occurred, there did not seem any compelling reason at any stage to change from the first gauge which had "just happened", namely 4 ft. 8 1/2 in. No compelling reason, that is, for the original inventor Stephenson and subsequently his son, who were responsible for building most of England's railroad trackage. However, there was competition, symbolized by the engineer, Brunel, who realized that this gauge was not technically optimum, and therefore decided to build the Great Western Railway on a gauge of 9 ft. Considerable rivalry grew up over this matter, and technical passions were raised; but ultimately it was resolved on the matter of total capital investment, rather than on technical merit alone. Thus, when it was resolved to standardize in England after many years, there was about 80% of the narrower gauge compared to the remainder of the wider gauge, so the result may have been considered inevitable.

A further pertinent aspect may be pointed out concerning this case history. England, as the originator of railroads, had been more or less strongly involved in developing railroads all over the world. Thus the decision concerning the gauge standardization affected all, but was made only by a few.

Oscillations

Oscillations occur in many systems, and in social systems especially in those where mutual interaction exists. Now, many ecologists consider that an ecology cannot be considered to have reached optimal conditions while considerable oscillation of more or less random patterns continues in the subpopulations of the system. Evidently as ecologies become more mature, then the magnitude of oscillatory behaviour decreases. This comment is probably pertinent for many of our own human social systems also. For example, as Boulding comments, we are no longer interested in merely understanding why our economic systems oscillate, because such oscillations produce profound human misery, but rather we wish to control these oscillations to a satisfactorily low level.

In contrast, it should be noted that, within animals, the perceptual mechanisms seem particularly designed for detection of changes, as characterized rather dramatically by the fact that in the absence of change in the stimuli most of the relevant receptors generally cease to be stimulated. Furthermore, it has been shown that if a large sensory loss is maintained for a considerable period of time, then the human psyche finds it very difficult to operate at all in a stable normal way.

The evidence is increasing that the normal condition of state variables within organisms such as man, animals, and even plants, is often one of continual cycling. This may be anywhere in the range from subcellular systems up to the level of the organism itself. In any one case, the oscillation is in relatively narrow spectral bands, typical examples being the approximately one-second heart cycle; a ten-second "engine" cycle at the capillary level of blood, as noted by Iberall; circadian cycles of temperature, metabolic activity, etc., of order one day; the three- to five-day water cycle; the monthly ovarian cycle; and finally, the various generational cycles of different species.

Most of the technological systems which have been designed to incorporate adaptive and optimizing aspects inherently require a more-or-less continuous cycling action. This is necessary both in theory and practice, because the performance criterion may be time varying, and the fact that the system had once adapted so as to reach maximum performance "on top of the hill" is not satisfactory in general, since the hill may subsequently have moved. A hill-climbing scheme is therefore necessary in which the relevant derivative must be measured so that direction and rate information can be provided for climbing again towards the optimal performance condition. It is therefore at least conceptually possible that much of the cycling found in living systems relates to the possibility of them continually optimizing themselves. However, there are other equally plausible explanations, for example, that the oscillation is difficult to filter out and in itself is not harmful, or that the oscillation may help implement the necessary sharing of materials which are competed for in such economies as those of cells.

Unidirectionality

Asymmetry is a particular form of non-linearity which arises widely in the operation of systems, but perhaps especially those of the biological and social type. It is noteworthy that the relative infrequency of non-linearity in technological systems merely reflects the purpose of the designers, is that there is at least a fairly coherent linear system theory, which unfortunately is not true for the non-linear domain. However, with the advent of more powerful theories, and of the computer, the engineer is increasingly beginning to design his systems to be non-linear, which often has advantages as far as optimization is concerned.

A major reason for asymmetry in many living systems is that negative quantities cannot exist for many variables. Examples are the concentrations of active chemicals such as hormones in the endocrine system; that the force which a muscle can exert is restricted to pulling, rather than pushing; that the firing frequency of neurons can only be at a positive rate, since negative frequencies are meaningless; that such behavioral variables as hostility can have only one polarity, unless an anti-hostility effect is definable; and that the strength of an army is only significant for positive quantities. In the detailed design of biological systems, this fundamental unidirectional nature of certain of the components is overcome by providing another parallel channel which utilizes the same operating principle, but is connected in the reverse sense so as to provide effectively a variable for the negative polarity requirement of the variable. Particularly obvious examples are agonist–antagonist pairs of muscles, and the stimulatory–inhibitory connections of neurons. Note that in obtaining efficient operation, reciprocal-type information networks must be provided so that the two energetically-expensive variables cannot fight each other for no net effect in the system. However, as often is the case in biological systems, more subtle uses can also be made of the system in which in fact such apparently useless action is implemented; for example, a pair of muscles will be provided with "tone" in order to maintain a certain desired stiffness in the system, and furthermore, when the muscles are required to shiver in order to produce heat for the thermoregulation system, then it is clearly necessary for both muscles to shiver at the same time.

The above comments have essentially concerned static unidirectionality, but some very interesting and advantageous system characteristics arise from dynamic unidirectionality of the type specially pursued by Clynes ("Rein Control, or Unidirectional Rate Sensitivity, A Fundamental Dynamic and Organizing Function in Biology", to be published in *Annals of the N.Y. Acad. of Sci.*, 1968). The general effect is that dynamic asymmetry tends to emphasize changes of condition, a process noted earlier as being ubiquitous in living systems. Further, it emerges that such dynamic unidirectionality provides especially good response characteristics at the high-frequency end of the spectrum, but unfortunately this cannot be pursued further here.

There is another steady-state effect of static unidirectionality that is worth mentioning, which is that, in systems exhibiting oscillation or statistical variation, the rectifying effect of unidirectionality can result in an irrevocable loss of system capacity. The prototype for this is perhaps the service capacity of a facility given a waiting line. In particular, when the vehicles arrive with some statistical variation or if the service time is similarly distributed, there is an irrevocable loss of service capacity as compared to the situation when both arrivals and servicings are regular. The classic result is that as the mean arrival time reduces until it approaches the mean service time, then the length of the waiting line extends theoretically to infinity. The physical basis for this result is that there is a basic asymmetry operating, in that whenever chance decrees that no vehicles are waiting for service, then this otherwise available service time is lost forever. This condition applies equally for a neuron which must cut off information flow at zero frequency. Of course, effective bidirectionality can be introduced by incorporating a high spontaneous level of neural firing for which the information transfer is zero, but such a technique is metabolically expensive.

Other similar examples arise wherever material is pooled in some capacitor but tends to escape when the pressure rises above a certain amount; for example, if a bathtub has an overflow system, then the result of a statistical variation in the height of water due to waves will be that the mean height will be less than this threshold value at which overflow can first occur.

Psychological and man–machine interactions

In man–machine systems, and indeed in any systems where the psychological characteristics of man contribute significantly, any satisfactory analysis depends upon obtaining good experimental data regarding the psychological aspects. This point is well illustrated by the study of how the flow of vehicles through a single-lane facility can be maximized. In the case of one of the New York tunnels, a well-defined curve was obtained relating the number of cars passing through the tunnel per hour to the steady-speed at which the cars were constrained to travel. To the untrained intuition, it may seem rather surprising that the maximum throughput rate occurred when the controlled speed was close to 20 mph, and that the hill characterizing the throughput was fairly steep sided. The explanation, why the throughput falls above the optimal speed, relates to the psychological considerations that, with very good reason, the driver is not prepared to remain as closely behind the car in front as he would at a lower speed. One base measure for his spacing would be if it increased as the square of the speed, therefore being proportional to kinetic energy, so that the driver would be assured of being able to brake to a full stop without an accident even if the car in front came to an instantaneous halt, such as could occur if he sustained a head-on collision. In practice, drivers can generally see conditions somewhat ahead of the car in front and, given certain other social pressures, the experienced driver then generally chooses some spacing relation intermediate between the quadratic type and a linear spacing with velocity, which in turn gives rise to the optimal condition already stated.

It should perhaps be pointed out that this particular optimal condition was not recognized as such until the appropriate experimental work had been done; indeed, most of the tunnels mentioned are frequently marked "maintain 40 mph". Furthermore, while the systems analyst can obtain such answers concerning optimality, it is most unlikely that any set of subsystems such as drivers themselves would ever arrive at this solution if left to their own resources. Indeed, as members of the social system, we have all experienced frustrating situations especially in traffic jams, of seeing the overall system degenerate to an obviously non-optimal condition in consequence of people operating individually and apparently in their own best interests; the resultant breakdown of the complete system, however, shows that this is not so; but on the other hand that the subsystems are equally powerless to do anything about it.

While man must necessarily set his own performance criteria, he may not necessarily be able to or even wish to reveal their nature to an experimenter. For example, if a person is asked to move a heavy weight with his arm as rapidly as possible across a smooth surface between two fixed points, then observation of the dynamic performance will reveal quite a lot about the subject's strategy. In fact, this does turn out to be generally similar to the "bang–bang" control which does produce the action in minimum time. However, the subject still has under his control the arbitrary choice of what strength of muscle force he shall utilize, and this never seems to be the very maximum that could be obtained. Furthermore, carefully detailed observation may reveal that the man does not in fact accept the verbally stated criterion as appropriate to him, in the light of his actual performance.

Minimal principles and optimality

A number of minimal principles, that is, equivalently optimality principles, are recognized in physics. A generalized verbal formulation of such principles may be given roughly as follows: The particular solution "selected" by a process in a physical system will be that one out of the possible family of solutions, all consistent with given constraints, which minimizes a certain "cost". Thus a ray of light moves through media of arbitrary refractive indices in least time (Fermat's Principle), while a mechanical system which conserves total energy moves along that path which minimizes the quantity defined as "action" (Maupertuis' Principle of Least Action). When slightly generalized to minimize "virtual displacement" rather than action, Maupertuis' principle becomes consistent with that most general minimal principle of physics called Hamilton's Principle. The major drawback to universal application is that only conservative systems can be so treated. Other minimal principles concern lines of minimum length joining points on a given surface, and generalizations of this. There are implications for the latter principle in biology, for example, concerning the deduction that thin films enclosing material should assume configurations which minimize surface area.

Minimal principles have been of considerable philosophical importance in physics, but have not become necessary working tools for normal problems, such as those of the atmospheric and oceanic circulation mentioned earlier. In part this is because the mechanical, hydrodynamic, electrical and other laws which are derivable from the above principle are already well known (and indeed were discovered first usually), but also importantly because the ubiquity of dissipative phenomena render them ineligible.

With the recent development of a comprehensive control theory (see, for example, Bellman, *Adaptive Control Pro-*

cesses: a Guided Tour, Princeton University Press, 1961) the Hamiltonian and its derivative Euler–Lagrange equations have become of renewed importance. In this case the Hamiltonian represents a function of the performance criterion, being in detail comprised not only of the cost function itself but also of the constraints on the system behaviour. This has significant implications for equally direct optimization in the general types of systems we have been considering, if and when it becomes possible to define quantitatively both the performance criteria and the constraints.

The situation in biology is somewhat different and more promising than in physics, as Rosen points out in his recent book (R. Rosen, Optimality Principles in Biology, Butterworths, 1967) ". . . it is possible to give at the outset a coherent, if qualitative, argument which will to some extent justify a search for such principles in biology, and help in their formulation. This argument is based on the phenomenon of natural selection, and the pressure which selection exerts on nearly every aspect of the structure, function, and performance of biological individuals. . . . It is now possible to make the fundamental hypothesis that biological structures, which are optimal in the context of natural selection, are also optimal in the sense that they minimize some cost functional derived from the engineering characteristics of the situation. This most natural assumption has been called the Principle of Optimal Design (N. Rashevsky, Mathematical Biophysics, 3rd edition, Dover, New York, 1960; see also D'Arcy Thompson, On Growth and Form, Macmillan, New York, 1945). . . . Usually, however, the appropriate cost functional is not immediately obvious; therein lies the art and difficulty of the entire subject." We might add furthermore that it is not indeed likely that most cost functionals will prove simple enough to allow this direct analytical attack even when they can be plausibly defined. It is of interest that Rosen then considers the vascular system and, by assuming a reasonable cost functional related to the metabolic cost of maintaining the system plus the hydrodynamic power loss in the system, is able to show that the results of an optimality analysis are consistent with those obtained for dogs as regards blood vessel size and the geometry of branching.

The last example illustrates a "design optimization" in the sense that this is achieved at the genetic and growth level, presumably just once for any organism. On the other hand, there is evidence for on-going "operating optimization" in the sense that many organ system functions such as respiration, locomotion, posture, and swimming in fishes seem to be optimized on an energy related criterion (J. H.

Milsum, Biological Control Systems Analysis, McGraw-Hill, 1966; also J. H. Milsum in Advances in Bio-Medical Engineering and Medical Physics, edited by S. N. Levine, Wiley-Interscience, 1967).

There is some first rather qualitative evidence that optimality principles apply also in social systems, where the interacting variables are probably more related to information flow than to energy flow (for example, G. K. Zipf, Human Behaviour and Principle of Least Effort, Harvard Univ. Press, 1949).

Extreme value statistics

Since nature's various populations and evolutionary experiments involve very large numbers, some of the small samples constituting our experimental research will inevitably differ from the mean by extremely large numbers of standard deviations, that is, falling into the area of extreme value statistics. For example, if the probability of an event such as a particular genetic combination is less than, say, ten to the minus nine, nevertheless such events may occur with reasonable regularity in some of nature's populations. In particular cases sufficient numbers of these extremely improbable events have happened, so that some form of evolution has even operated upon them. The simple animal hydra provides an example here in its evolution of unlikely methods of escaping either in space or time from unfavorable conditions such as by ballooning, etc. (see Slobodkin in Positive Feedback, J. H. Milsum, editor, Pergamon Press, 1968).

A trade-off situation is certainly involved in systems involving extreme value statistics, and some rather elementary examples will be considered; but in general it is certainly extremely difficult to attach quantitative values to the relevant variables. In these situations at least one new component is added to the performance criterion, representing the expected value or cost of the unlikely events. An expected value or cost equals the probability of the event multiplied by the value or cost of the event, should it happen. Numerically this value can be significant, and even comparable to other cost components of the performance criterion, even if the probability of the event is very small, provided that the cost attached to the event is large. Consider a simplified example of deciding what strength should be designed into buildings to combat the possibility of collapse due to earthquakes. If it is assumed that earthquakes are distributed in some reasonable and known statistical manner, then a probability value can be assigned concerning the occurrence of earthquakes of a given strength or larger during an appropriate period of time.

Clearly the construction cost will increase as the design strength against earthquakes is increased, and for an optimal design this must be traded off against the expected cost due to the finite possibility of building collapse. Thus, as design strength is increased, construction cost increases whereas the expected cost decreases because of the decreasing probability that a sufficiently strong earthquake will occur to cause building collapse. On the other hand, if construction strength is decreased, the latter cost is decreased whereas the expected cost of earthquake collapse is increased. It may be expected that an economic optimum point exists when mathematically the derivatives of the two costs, plotted as functions of construction strength, are equal in magnitude although opposite in sign.

Such an analysis forces us to confront the difficult issue of whether or not we are prepared to accept a possibility of building collapse "in cold blood". Clearly though, there is nothing wrong with the thinking of carrying out the analysis as long as we in society are prepared to say whether we are satisfied with the results, following upon incorporating into the performance criterion all values that concern us. Specifically, the difficult problem revolves about the cost of people's lives potentially lost in a collapse. This is certainly not an easy matter to resolve, but on the other hand, our society's nominal claim that we must not allow any risk of accidental death at all is clearly not carried out either individually or en masse in our normal affairs. As we increasingly generate new systems where such considerations will be forced upon us, as in universal systems of medical care, rational, but ethical guidelines will have to be developed. For example, in medical systems there is not only the problem of optimizing the system with regard both to the cost of medical care and the expected value of extended survival of life or mitigation of pain, but also whether or not the positive feedback dynamics of social pressures may allow any rational thinking about the value of prolonging life of individuals, and so on. Here the considerations move rapidly and increasingly confusingly into the technological, legal, ethical, moral, and religious domains.

On tampering and optimizing; some conclusions

It is a basic concept that systems comprise collections of subsystems, and that the problem in optimizing a social system is especially difficult in that it is as yet almost impossible to define quantitatively a relevant performance criterion. The difficulty resides especially in the fact that hard facts regarding costs of concrete, etc., have to be compared with "soft facts" concerning such social aspects as aesthetics and fulfillment. Furthermore, a satisfactory overall criterion must consist of a weighted collection of criteria which comprise the preferences of all the subsystems, namely ourselves who constitute the electorate for the overall systems planners and controllers, and therefore hopefully the ultimate controllers of the latter. It should be noted that the criteria we then choose will certainly be different from the ones we would otherwise be forced to choose if we were in a "dog-eat-dog" condition where each would have to optimize his own subsystem without regard to his neighbors. As Freud points out, in the work quoted, this is why societies have successively adopted the otherwise undesirable constraints of a civilized system. However, resulting from the energy and information revolutions, such constraints can become increasingly irksome while at the same time we enjoy the advantages, and therefore we must arrange that our legal and social structures, and our systems planning, are adequately flexible and fairly rapidly adaptable. In particular, they must try to anticipate the impact of technological change upon the social scene. This requires a vastly greater acceptance by the technologist and scientist of responsibility for reporting to society their intelligent predictions regarding social effects of technological change, and a vastly greater acceptance by the social scientists and humanists of their need to understand something not only of the general systems approach, but also of technological principles. Morison, in his book *Men, Machines, and Modern Times* (MIT Press, 1966) suggests that it is important for society to get into a mood of continuous, small-scale but ubiquitous experimentation, to be carried on by all intelligent members of society. This would encourage a sense of participation by individuals, would enable multiple-parallel experiments to be carried out on a small scale to predict effects of change rather in the same way that evolution operates, and would be a wonderfully fruitful way of realizing the dream of "intelligence amplification".

If such an experimental mood could be widely cultivated in society, then an atmosphere could be created for multidisciplinary systems analysis on a large number of large-scale technological projects with important social implications. For example, recent suggestions of this type include damming the Bering Straits, and widespread modifications of the North American fresh-water systems. A number of other vast projects are interestingly presented in *Engineer's Dreams* by Willy Ley (Viking, 1954).

Along with these new projects, society will also naturally tackle the pressing socio-technological problems such as that of air and water pollution due to pollutants of all types such as chemicals, noise, visual objects, and so on. A further aspect merging more towards the pure biological domain will be that of improving our attempts to control or eradicate what we conceive of as hostile species of animals, insects, etc., by use of the evolutionary process (by attracting and then sterilizing males, for example) rather than making it work continually against us, as in current pesticides. Furthermore, because of the huge and delicate balances of nature of the ecologies with which we tamper, we shall be forced to study the whole problem in a systems light. Finally, what can we say of man himself? We largely believe that we have provided the technological capability for fulfilling ourselves, but we have yet to define what this consists of, and how we must plan our society so as to be able to achieve it.

Reprinted from Milsum, J. H. (1968) "Technosphere, Biosphere and Sociosphere", *General Systems*, **13**.
Reprinted with permission of the Society for General Systems Research.

18 Understanding the counterintuitive behaviour of social systems*

by Jay W. Forrester

System dynamics has demonstrated how companies and how urban systems behave in ways that run against most of what man would do to correct their ills. Now the same obtuse behaviour can be assigned to the largest social issues which confront the world. Although this article is written with the United States in mind, the analytical techniques described and the conclusions derived from them can be applied to all industrialized countries.

This paper addresses several issues of broad concern in the United States: population trends; the quality of urban life; national policy for urban growth; and the unexpected, ineffective, or detrimental results often generated by government programmes in these areas.

The nation exhibits a growing sense of futility as it repeatedly attacks deficiencies in our social system while the symptoms continue to worsen. Legislation is debated and passed with great promise and hope. But many programmes prove to be ineffective. Results often seem unrelated to those expected when the programmes were planned. At times programmes cause exactly the reverse of desired results.

It is now possible to explain how such contrary results can happen. There are fundamental reasons why people misjudge the behaviour of social systems. There are orderly processes at work in the creation of human judgment and intuition that frequently lead people to wrong decisions when faced with complex and highly interacting systems. Until we come to a much better understanding of social systems, we should expect that attempts to develop corrective programmes will continue to disappoint us.

The purpose of this paper is to leave with its readers a sense of caution about continuing to depend on the same past approaches that have led to our present feeling of frustration and to suggest an approach which can eventually lead to a better understanding of our social systems and thereby to more effective policies for guiding the future.

A new approach to social systems

It is my basic theme that the human mind is not adapted to interpreting how social systems behave. Our social systems belong to the class called multiloop nonlinear

* This paper is based on testimony for the Subcommittee on Urban Growth of the Committee on Banking and Currency, US House of Representatives, on October 7, 1970.

feedback systems. In the long history of evolution it has not been necessary for man to understand these systems until very recent historical times. Evolutionary processes have not given us the mental skill needed to properly interpret the dynamic behaviour of the systems of which we have now become a part.

In addition, the social sciences have fallen into some mistaken "scientific" practices which compound man's natural shortcomings. Computers are often being used for what the computer does poorly and the human mind does well. At the same time the human mind is being used for what the human mind does poorly and the computer does well. Even worse, impossible tasks are attempted while achievable and important goals are ignored.

Until recently there has been no way to estimate the behaviour of social systems except by contemplation, discussion, argument, and guesswork. To point a way out of our present dilemma about social systems, I will sketch an approach that combines the strength of the human mind and the strength of today's computers. The approach is an outgrowth of developments over the last 40 years, in which much of the research has been at the Massachusetts Institute of Technology. The concepts of feedback system behaviour apply sweepingly from physical systems through social systems. The ideas were first developed and applied to engineering systems. They have now reached practical usefulness in major aspects of our social systems.

I am speaking of what has come to be called industrial dynamics. The name is a misnomer because the methods apply to complex systems regardless of the field in which they are located. A more appropriate name would be *system dynamics.* In our own work, applications have been made to corporate policy, to the dynamics of diabetes as a medical system, to the growth and stagnation of an urban area, and most recently to world dynamics representing the interactions of population, pollution, industrialization, natural resources, and food. System dynamics as an extension of the earlier design of physical systems, has been under development at MIT since 1956. The approach is easy to understand but difficult to practice. Few people have a high level of skill; but preliminary work is developing all over the world. Some European countries and especially Japan have begun centres of education and research.

Computer models of social systems

People would never attempt to send a space ship to the moon without first testing the equipment by constructing prototype models and by computer simulation of the anticipated space trajectories. No company would put a new kind of household appliance or electronic computer into production without first making laboratory tests. Such models and laboratory tests do not guarantee against failure, but they do identify many weaknesses which can then be corrected before they cause full-scale disasters.

Our social systems are far more complex and harder to understand than our technological systems. Why, then, do we not use the same approach of making models of social systems and conducting laboratory experiments on those models before we try new laws and government programmes in real life? The answer is often stated that our knowledge of social systems is insufficient for constructing useful models. But what justification can there be for the apparent assumption that we do not know enough to construct models but believe we do know enough to directly design new social systems by passing laws and starting new social programmes? I am suggesting that we now do know enough to make useful models of social systems. Conversely, we do not know enough to design the most effective social systems directly without first going through a model-building experimental phase. But I am confident, and substantial supporting evidence is beginning to accumulate, that the proper use of models of social systems can lead to far better systems, laws, and programmes.

It is now possible to construct in the laboratory realistic models of social systems. Such models are simplifications of the actual social system but can be far more comprehensive than the mental models that we otherwise use as the basis for debating governmental action.

Before going further, I should emphasize that there is nothing new in the use of models to represent social systems. Each of us uses models constantly. Every person in his private life and in his business life instinctively uses models for decision making. The mental image of the world around you which you carry in your head is a model. One does not have a city or a government or a country in his head. He has only selected concepts and relationships which he uses to represent the real system. A mental image is a model. All of our decisions are taken on the basis of models. All of our laws are based on the basis of models. All executive actions are taken on the basis of models. The question is not to use or ignore models. The question is only a choice among alternative models.

The mental model is fuzzy. It is incomplete. It is imprecisely stated. Furthermore, within one individual, a mental model changes with time and even during the flow of a single conversation. The human mind assembles a few relationships to fit the context of a discussion. As the subject shifts so does the model. When only a single topic is being discussed, each participant in a conversation employs a different mental model to interpret the subject. Fundamental assumptions differ but are never brought into the open. Goals are different and are left unstated. It is little wonder that compromise takes so long. And it is not surprising that consensus leads to laws and programmes that fail in their objectives or produce new difficulties greater than those that have been relieved.

For these reasons we stress the importance of being explicit about assumptions and interrelating them in a computer model. Any concept or assumption that can be clearly described in words can be incorporated in a computer model. When done, the ideas become clear. Assumptions are exposed so they may be discussed and debated.

But the most important difference between the properly conceived computer model and the mental model is in the ability to determine the dynamic consequences when the assumptions within the model interact with one another. The human mind is not adapted to sensing correctly the consequences of a mental model. The mental model may be correct in structure and assumptions but, even so, the human mind – either individually or as a group consensus – is most apt to draw the wrong conclusions. There is no doubt about the digital computer routinely and accurately tracing through the sequences of actions that result from following the statements of behaviour for individual points in the model system. This inability of the human mind to use its own mental models is clearly shown when a computer model is constructed to reproduce the assumptions held by a single person. In other words, the model is refined until it is fully agreeable in all its assumptions to the perceptions and ideas of a particular person. Then, it usually happens that the system that has been described does not act the way the person anticipated. Usually there is an internal contradiction in mental models between the assumed structure and the assumed future consequences. Ordinarily the assumptions about structure and internal motivations are more nearly correct than are the assumptions about the implied behaviour.

The kind of computer models that I am discussing are strikingly similar to mental models. They are derived from the same sources. They may be discussed in the same terms. But computer models differ from mental models in important ways. The computer models are stated explicitly. The "mathematical" notation that is used for describing the model is unambiguous. It is a language that is clearer, simpler, and more precise than such spoken languages as English or French. Its advantage is in the clarity of meaning and the simplicity of the language syntax. The language of a computer model can be understood by almost anyone, regardless of educational background. Furthermore, any concept and relationship that can be clearly stated in ordinary language can be translated into computer model language.

There are many approaches to computer models. Some are naïve. Some are conceptually and structurally inconsistent with the nature of actual systems. Some are based on methodologies for obtaining input data that commit the models to omitting major concepts and relationships in the psychological and human reaction areas that we all know to be crucial. With so much activity in computer models and with the same terminology having different meanings in the different approaches, the situation must be confusing to the casual observer. The key to success is not in having a computer; the important thing is how the computer is used. With respect to models, the key is not to computerize a model, but to have a model structure and relationships which properly represent the system that is being considered.

I am speaking here of a kind of computer model that is very different from the models that are now most common in the social sciences. Such a computer model is not derived statistically from time-series data. Instead, the kind of computer model I am discussing is a statement of system structure. It contains the assumptions being made about the system. The model is only as good as the expertise which lies behind its formulation. Great and correct theories in physics or in economics are few and far between. A great computer model is distinguished from a poor one by the degree to which it captures more of the essence of the social system that it presumes to represent. Many mathematical models are limited because they are formulated by techniques and according to a conceptual structure that will not accept the multiple-feedback-loop and nonlinear nature of real systems. Other models are defective because of lack of knowledge or deficiencies of perception on the part of the persons who have formulated them.

But a recently developed kind of computer modelling is now beginning to show the characteristics of behaviour of actual systems. These models explain why we are having the present difficulties with our actual social systems and furthermore explain why so many efforts to improve social systems have failed. In spite of their shortcomings, models can now be constructed that are far superior to the intuitive models in our heads on which we are now basing national social programmes.

This approach to the dynamics of social systems differs in two important ways from common practice in social sciences and government. There seems to be a common attitude that the major difficulty is shortage of information and data. Once data are collected, people then feel confident in interpreting the implications. I differ on both of these attitudes. The problem is not shortage of data but rather our inability to perceive the consequences of the information we already possess. The system dynamics approach starts with the concepts and information on which people are already acting. Generally these are sufficient. The available perceptions are then assembled in a computer model which can show the consequences of the well known and properly perceived parts of the system. Generally, the consequences are unexpected.

Counterintuitive nature of social systems

Our first insights into complex social systems came from our corporate work. Time after time we have gone into a corporation which is having severe and well-known difficulties. The difficulties can be major and obvious such as a falling market share, low profitability, or instability of employment. Such difficulties are known throughout the company and by anyone outside who reads the management press. One can enter such a company and discuss with people in key decision points what they are doing to solve the problem. Generally speaking we find that people perceive correctly their immediate environment. They know what they are trying to accomplish. They know the crises which will force certain actions. They are sensitive to the power structure of the organization, to traditions, and to their own personal goals and welfare. In general, when circumstances are conducive to frank disclosure, people can state what they are doing and can give rational reasons for their actions. In a troubled company, people are usually trying in good conscience and to the best of their abilities to solve the major difficulties. Policies are being followed at the various points in the organization on the presumption that they will alleviate the difficulties. One can combine these policies into a computer model to show the consequences of how the policies interact with one another. In many instances it then emerges that the known policies describe a system which actually causes the troubles. In other words, the known and intended practices of the organization are fully sufficient to create the difficulty, regardless of what happens outside the company or in the marketplace. In fact, a downward spiral develops in which the presumed solution makes the difficulty worse and thereby causes redoubling of the presumed solution.

The same downward spiral frequently develops in government. Judgment and debate lead to a programme that appears to be sound. Commitment increases to the apparent solution. If the presumed solution actually makes matters worse, the process by which this happens is not evident. So, when the troubles increase, the efforts are intensified that are actually worsening the problem.

Dynamics of urban systems

Our first major excursion outside of corporate policy began in February 1968, when John F. Collins, former mayor of Boston, became Professor of Urban Affairs at MIT. He and I discussed my work in industrial dynamics and his experience with urban difficulties. A close collaboration led to applying to the dynamics of the city the same methods that had been created for understanding the social and policy structure of the corporation. A model structure was developed to represent the fundamental urban processes. The proposed structure shows how industry, housing, and people interact with each other as a city grows and decays. The results are described in my book *Urban Dynamics*, and some were summarized in *Technology Review (April, 1969, pp. 21–31)*.

I had not previously been involved with urban behaviour or urban policies. But the emerging story was strikingly similar to what we had seen in the corporation. Actions taken to alleviate the difficulties of a city can actually make matters worse. We examined four common programmes for improving the depressed nature of the central city. One is the creation of jobs as by bussing the unemployed to the suburbs or through governmental jobs as employer of last resort. Second was a training programme to increase the skills of the lowest-income group. Third was financial aid to the depressed city as by federal subsidy. Fourth was the construction of low-cost housing. All of these are shown to lie between neutral and detrimental almost irrespective of the criteria used for judgment. They range from ineffective to harmful judged either by their effect on the economic health of the city or by their long-range effect on the low-income population of the city.

The results both confirm and explain much of what has been happening over the last several decades in our cities.

In fact, it emerges that the fundamental cause of depressed areas in the cities comes from *excess* housing in the low-income category rather than the commonly presumed housing shortage. The legal and tax structures have combined to give incentives for keeping old buildings in place. As industrial buildings age, the employment opportunities decline. As residential buildings age, they are used by lower-income groups who are forced to use them at a higher population density. Therefore, jobs decline and population rises while buildings age. Housing, at the higher population densities, accommodates more low-income urban population than can find jobs. A social trap is created where excess low-cost housing beckons low-income people inward because of the available housing. They continue coming to the city until their numbers so far exceed the available income opportunities that the standard of living declines far enough to stop further inflow. Income to the area is then too low to maintain all of the housing. Excess housing falls into disrepair and is abandoned. One can simultaneously have extreme crowding in those buildings that are occupied, while other buildings become excess and are abandoned because the economy of the area cannot support all of the residential structures. But the excess residential buildings threaten the area in two ways – they occupy the land so that it cannot be used for job-creating buildings, and they stand ready to accept a rise in population if the area should start to improve economically.

Any change which would otherwise raise the standard of living only takes off the economic pressure momentarily and causes the population to rise enough that the standard of living again falls to the barely tolerable level. A self-regulating system is thereby at work which drives the condition of the depressed area down far enough to stop the increase in people.

At any time, a near-equilibrium exists affecting population mobility between the different areas of the country. To the extent that there is disequilibrium, it means that some area is slightly more attractive than others and population begins to move in the direction of the more attractive area. This movement continues until the rising population drives the more attractive area down in attractiveness until the area is again in equilibrium with its surroundings. Other things being equal, an increase in population of a city crowds housing, overloads job opportunities, causes congestion, increases pollution, encourages crime, and reduces almost every component of the quality of life.

This powerful dynamic force to re-establish an equilibrium in total attractiveness means that any social programme must take into account the eventual shifts that will occur in the many components of *attractiveness*. As used here, attractiveness is the composite effect of all factors that cause population movement towards or away from an area. Most areas in a country have nearly equal attractiveness most of the time, with only sufficient disequilibrium in attractiveness to account for the shifts in population. But areas can have the same composite attractiveness with different mixes in the components of attractiveness. In one area component A could be high and B low, while the reverse could be true in another area that nevertheless had the same total composite attractiveness. If a programme makes some aspect of an area more attractive than its neighbour's, and thereby makes total attractiveness higher momentarily, population of that area rises until other components of attractiveness are driven down far enough to again establish an equilibrium. This means that efforts to improve the condition of our cities will result primarily in increasing the population of the cities and causing the population of the country to concentrate in the cities. The overall condition of urban life, for any particular economic class of population, cannot be appreciably better or worse than that of the remainder of the country to and from which people may come. Programmes aimed at improving the city can succeed only if they result in eventually raising the average quality of life for the country as a whole.

On raising the quality of life
But there is substantial doubt that our urban programmes have been contributing to the national quality of life. By concentrating total population, and especially low-income population, in urban locations, undermining the strength and cohesiveness of the community, and making government and bureaucracy so big that the individual feels powerless to influence the system within which he is increasingly constrained, the quality of life is being reduced. In fact, if they have any effect, our efforts to improve our urban areas will in the long run tend to delay the concern about rising total population and thereby contribute directly to the eventual overcrowding of the country and the world.

Any proposed programme must deal with both the quality of life and the factors affecting population. "Raising the quality of life" means releasing stress and pressures, reducing crowding, reducing pollution, alleviating hunger, and treating ill health. But these pressures are exactly the sources of concern and action aimed at controlling total population to keep it within the bounds of the fixed world within which we live. If the pressures are relaxed, so is the concern about how we impinge on the environment. Population will then rise further until the pressures reappear with an intensity that can no longer be relieved. To try to raise quality of life without intentionally creating compensating pressures to prevent a rise in population density will be self-defeating.

Consider the meaning of these interacting attractiveness components as they affect a depressed ghetto area of a city. First we must be clear on the way population density is, in fact, now being controlled. There is some set of forces determining that the density is not far higher or lower than it is. But there are many possible combinations of forces that an urban area can exert. The particular combination will determine the population mix of the area and the economic health of the city. I suggest that the depressed areas of most American cities are created by a combination of forces in which there is a job shortage and a housing excess. The availability of housing draws the lowest-income group until they so far exceed the opportunities of the area that the low standard of living, the frustration, and the crime rate counter-balance the housing availability. Until the pool of excess housing is reduced, little can be done to improve the economic condition of the city. A low-cost housing programme alone moves exactly in the wrong direction. It draws more low-income people. It makes the area differentially more attractive to the poor who need jobs and less attractive to those who create jobs. In the new population equilibrium that develops, some characteristic of the social system must compensate for the additional attractiveness created by the low-cost housing. The counterbalance is a further decline of the economic condition for the area. But as the area becomes more destitute, pressures rise for more low-cost housing. The consequence is a downward spiral that draws in the low-income population, depresses their condition, prevents escape, and reduces hope. All of this is done with the best of intentions.

My paper, "Systems Analysis as a Tool for Urban Planning" from a symposium in October 1969, at the National Academy of Engineering, suggests a reversal of present practice in order to simultaneously reduce the aging housing in our cities and allocate land to income-earning opportunities. The land shifted to industry permits the "balance of trade" of the area to be corrected by allowing labour to create and export a product to generate an income stream with which to buy the necessities of modern life from the outside. But the concurrent reduction of excess housing is absolutely essential. It supplies the land for new jobs. Equally important, the resulting housing shortage creates the population-stabilizing pressure that allows economic revival to proceed without being inundated by rising population. This can all be done without driving the present low-income residents out of the area. It can create *upward economic mobility* to convert the low-income population to a self-supporting basis.

The first reaction of many people to these ideas is to believe that they will never be accepted by elected officials or by residents of depressed urban areas. But some of our strongest support and encouragement is coming from those very groups who are closest to the problems, who see the symptoms first-hand, who have lived through the failures of the past, and who must live with the present conditions until enduring solutions are found.

Over the last several decades the country has slipped into a set of attitudes about our cities that are leading to actions that have become an integral part of the system that is generating greater troubles. If we were malicious and wanted to create urban slums, trap low-income people in ghetto areas, and increase the number of people on welfare, we could do little better than follow the present policies. The trend towards stressing income and sales taxes and away from the real estate tax encourages old buildings to remain in place and block self-renewal. The concessions in the income tax laws to encourage low-income housing will in the long run actually increase the total low-income population of the country. The highway expenditures and the government loans for suburban housing have made it easier for higher-income groups to abandon urban areas than to revive them. The pressures to expand the areas incorporated by urban government, in an effort to expand the revenue base, have been more than offset by lowered administrative efficiency, more citizen frustration, and the accelerated decline that is triggered in the annexed areas. The belief that more money will solve urban problems has taken attention away from correcting the underlying causes and has instead allowed the problems to grow to the limit of the available money, whatever that amount might be.

Characteristics of social systems

I turn now to some characteristics of social systems that mislead people. These have been identified in our work with corporate and urban systems and in more recent work that I will describe concerning the worldwide pressures that are now enveloping our planet.

First, social systems are inherently insensitive to most policy changes that people select in an effort to alter the behaviour of the system. In fact, a social system tends to draw our attention to the very points at which an attempt to intervene will fail. Our experience, which has been developed from contact with simple systems, leads us to look close to the symptoms of trouble for a cause. When we look, we discover that the social system presents us with an apparent cause that is plausible according to what we have learned from simple systems. But this apparent cause is usually a coincident occurrence that, like the trouble symptom itself, is being produced by the feedback-loop dynamics of a larger system. For example, as already discussed, we see human suffering in the cities; we observe that it is accompanied (some think caused) by inadequate housing. We increase the housing and the population rises to compensate for the effort. More people are drawn into and trapped in the depressed social system. As another example, the symptoms of excess population are beginning to overshadow the country. These symptoms appear as urban crowding and social pressure. Rather than face the population problem squarely we try to relieve the immediate pressure by planning industry in rural areas and by discussing new towns. If additional urban area is provided it will temporarily reduce the pressures and defer the need to face the underlying population question. The consequence, as it will be seen 25 years hence, will have been to contribute to increasing the population so much that even today's quality of life will be impossible.

A second characteristic of social systems is that all of them seem to have a few sensitive influence points through which the behaviour of the system can be changed. These influence points are not in the locations where most people expect. Furthermore, if one identifies in a model of a social system a sensitive point where influence can be exerted, the chances are still that a person guided by intuition and judgment will alter the system in the wrong direction. For example in the urban system, housing is a sensitive control point but, if one wishes to revive the economy of a city and make it a better place for low-income as well as other people, it appears that the amount of low-income housing must be reduced rather than increased. Another example is the world-wide problem of rising population and the disparity between the standards of living in the developed and the underdeveloped countries, an issue arising in the world system to be discussed in the following paragraphs. But it is beginning to appear that a sensitive control point is the rate of generation of capital investment.

And how should one change the rate of capital accumulation? The common answer has been to increase industrialization, but recent examination suggests that hope lies only in reducing the rate of industrialization. This may actually help raise quality of life and contribute to stabilizing population.

As a third characteristic of social systems, there is usually a fundamental conflict between the short-term and long-term consequences of a policy change. A policy which produces improvement in the short run, within five to ten years, is usually one which degrades the system in the long run, beyond 10 years. Likewise, those policies and programmes which produce long-run improvement may initially depress the behaviour of the system. This is especially treacherous. The short run is more visible and more compelling. It speaks loudly for immediate attention. But a series of actions all aimed at short-run improvement can eventually burden a system with long-run depressants so severe that even heroic short-run measures no longer suffice. Many of the problems which we face today are the eventual result of short-run measures taken as long as two or three decades ago.

A global perspective

I have mentioned social organizations at the corporate level and then touched on work which has been done on the dynamics of the city. Now we are beginning to examine issues of even broader scope.

In July 1970 we held a two-week international conference on world dynamics. It was a meeting organized for the Club of Rome, a private group of about 50 individuals drawn from many countries who have joined together to attempt a better understanding of social systems at the world level. Their interest lies in the same problems of population, resources, industrialization, pollution, and world-wide disparities of standard of living on which many groups now focus. But the Club of Rome is devoted to taking actions that will lead to a better understanding of world trends and to influencing world leaders and governments. The July meeting at MIT included the general theory and behaviour of complex systems and talks on the behaviour of specific social systems ranging from corporations through commodity markets to biological systems, drug addiction in the community, and growth and decline of a city. Especially prepared for this conference was a dynamic model of the interactions between world population, industrialization, depletion of natural resources,

agriculture, and pollution. A detailed discussion on this world system will soon appear in my book *World Dynamics*, and its further development is the purpose of the "Project on the Predicament of Mankind" being sponsored by the Club of Rome at MIT for a year under the guidance of Professor Dennis Meadows. The plan is to develop a research group of men from many countries who will eventually base their continuing efforts in a neutral country such as Switzerland. The immediate project will re-examine, verify, alter, and extend the preliminary dynamic study of the world system and will relate it to the present world-wide concern about trends in civilization.

The simple model of world interactions as thus far developed shows several different alternative futures depending on whether population growth is eventually suppressed by shortage of natural resources, by pollution, by crowding and consequent social strife, or by insufficient food. Malthus dealt only with the latter, but it is possible for civilization to encounter other controlling pressures before a food shortage occurs.

It is certain that resource shortage, pollution, crowding, food failure, or some other equally powerful force will limit population and industrialization if persuasion and psychological factors do not. Exponential growth cannot continue forever. Our greatest immediate challenge is how we guide the transition from growth to equilibrium. There are many possible mechanisms of growth suppression. That some one or combination will occur is inevitable. Unless we come to understand and to choose, the social system by its internal processes will choose for us. The natural mechanisms for terminating exponential growth appear to be the least desirable. Unless we understand and begin to act soon, we may be overwhelmed by a social and economic system we have created but can't control.

The diagram* shows the structure that has been assumed. It interrelates the mutual effects of population, capital investment, natural resources, pollution, and the fraction of capital devoted to agriculture. These five system "levels" are shown in the rectangles. Each level is caused to change by the rates of flow in and out, such as the birth rate and death rate that increase and decrease population. As shown by the dotted lines, the five system levels, through intermediate concepts shown at the circles, control the rates of flow. As an example, the death rate at Symbol 10 depends on population P and the "normal" lifetime as stated by death rate normal DRN. But death

* All figures are taken from *World Dynamics* by Jay W. Forrester, Wright–Allen Press, 238 Main Street, Cambridge, Mass. 02142.

Figure 18.1 Flow diagram of world. Levels are represented by rectangles; rates by valves; auxiliaries (significant components of rates) by circles; dotted lines indicate directions, shown by arrows.

rate depends also on conditions in other parts of the system. From Circle 12 comes the influence of pollution that here assumes death rate to double if pollution becomes 20 times as severe as in 1970; and, progressively, that death rate would increase by a factor of 10 if pollution became 60 times as much as now. Likewise from Circle 13 the effect of food per capita is to increase death rate as food becomes less available. The detailed definition of the model states how each rate of flow is assumed to depend on the levels of population, natural resources, capital investment, capital devoted to food, and pollution.

Individually the assumptions in the model are plausible, create little disagreement, and reflect common discussions and assertions about the individual responses within the world system. But each is explicit and can be subjected to scrutiny. From one viewpoint, the system of Figure 18.1 is very simplified. It focuses on a few major factors and omits most of the substructure of world social and economic activity. But from another viewpoint, Figure 18.1 is comprehensive and complex. The system is far more complete and the theory described by the accompanying computer model is much more explicit than the mental models

that are now being used as a basis for world and governmental planning. It incorporates dozens of nonlinear relationships. The world system shown here exhibits provocative and even frightening possibilities.

Transition from growth to equilibrium

With the model specified, a computer can be used to show how the system, as described for each of its parts, would behave. Given a set of beginning conditions, the computer can calculate and plot the results that unfold through time.

The world today seems to be entering a condition in which pressures are rising simultaneously from every one of the influences that can suppress growth – depleted resources, pollution, crowding, and insufficient food. It is still unclear which will dominate if mankind continues along the present path. Figure 18.2 shows the mode of behaviour of this world system given the assumption that population reaches a peak and then declines because industrialization is suppressed by falling natural resources. The model system starts with estimates of conditions in 1900. Adjustments have been made so that the generated paths pass through the conditions of 1970.

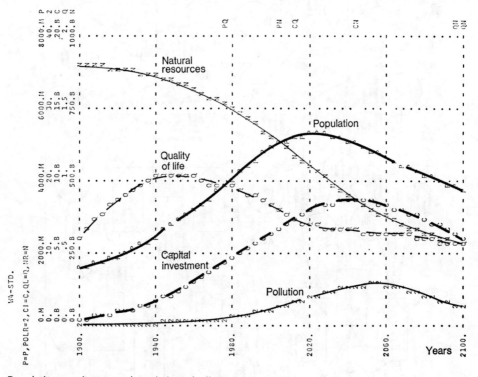

Figure 18.2 Population reaches a peak and then declines because industrialization is suppressed by falling natural resources.

In Figure 18.2 the quality of life peaks in the 1950's and by 2020 has fallen far enough to halt further rise in population. Declining resources and the consequent fall in capital investment then exert further pressure to gradually reduce world population.

But we may not be fortunate enough to run gradually out of natural resources. Science and technology may very well find ways to use the more plentiful metals and atomic energy so that resource depletion does not intervene. If so, the way then remains open for some other pressure to arise within the system. Figure 18.3 shows what happens within this system if the resource shortage is foreseen and avoided. Here the only change from Figure 18.2 is the usage rate of natural resources after the year 1970. In Figure 18.3 resources are used after 1970 at a rate 75 per cent less than assumed in Figure 18.2. In other words, the standard of living is sustained with a lower drain on the expendable and irreplaceable resources. But the picture is even less attractive! By not running out of resources, population and capital investment are allowed to rise until a pollution crisis is created. Pollution then acts directly to reduce birth rate, increase death rate, and to depress food production.

Population which, according to this simple model, peaks at the year 2030 has fallen to one-sixth of the peak population within an interval of 20 years – a world-wide catastrophe of a magnitude never before experienced. Should it occur, one can speculate on which sectors of the world population will suffer most. It is quite possible that the more industrialized countries (which are the ones which have caused such a disaster) would be the least able to survive such a disruption to environment and food supply. They might be the ones to take the brunt of the collapse.

Figure 18.3 shows how a technological success (reducing our dependence in natural resources) can merely save us from one fate only to fall victim to something worse (a pollution catastrophe). There is now developing throughout the world a strong undercurrent of doubt about technology as the saviour of mankind. There is a basis for such doubt. Of course, the source of trouble is not technology as such but is instead the management of the entire technological–human–political–economic–natural complex.

Figure 18.3 is a dramatic example of the general process

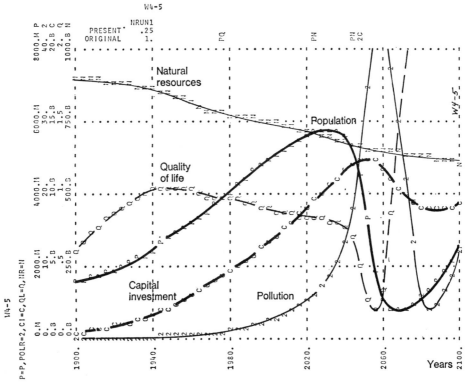

Figure 18.3   Resources are used after 1970 at a rate 75 per cent less than assumed in Fig. 18.2.

discussed earlier wherein a programme aimed at one trouble symptom results in creating a new set of troubles in some other part of the system. Here the success in alleviating a natural resource shortage throws the system over into the mode of stopping population caused by industrialization which has been freed from natural resource restraint. This process of a solution creating a new problem has defeated many of our past governmental programmes and will continue to do so unless we devote more effort to understanding the dynamic behaviour of our social systems.

Alternatives to decline or catastrophe

Suppose in the basic world system of Figures 18.1 and 18.2 we ask how to sustain the quality of life which is beginning to decline after 1950. One way to attempt this, and it is the way the world is now choosing, might be to increase the rate of industrialization by raising the rate of capital investment. Models of the kind we are here using make such hypothetical questions answerable

in a few minutes and at negligible cost. Figure 18.4 shows what happens if the "normal" rate of capital accumulation is increased by 20 per cent in 1970. The pollution crisis reappears. This time the cause is not the more efficient use of natural resources but the upsurge of industrialization which overtaxes the environment before resource depletion has a chance to depress industrialization. Again, an "obvious" desirable change in policy has caused troubles worse than the ones that were originally being corrected.

This is important, not only for its own message but because it demonstrates how an apparently desirable change in a social system can have unexpected and even disastrous results.

Figure 18.4 should make us cautious about rushing into programmes on the basis of short-term humanitarian impulses. The eventual result can be anti-humanitarian. Emotionally inspired efforts often fall into one of three traps set for us by the nature of social systems: The programmes are apt to address symptoms rather than

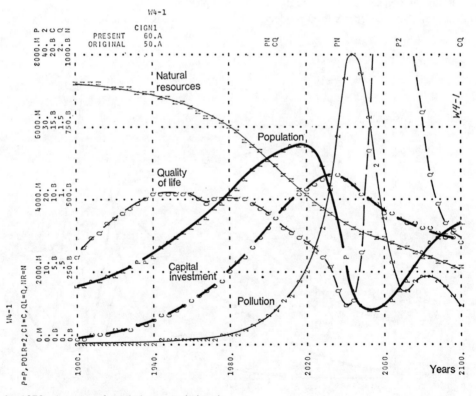

Figure 18.4 In 1970, the rate of capital accumulation is increased by 20 per cent in an effort to reverse the beginning decline in quality of life. The pollution crisis occurs before natural resources are depleted.

causes and attempt to operate through points in the system that have little leverage for change; the characteristic of systems whereby a policy change has the opposite effect in the short run from the effect in the long run can eventually cause deepening difficulties after a sequence of short-term actions; and the effect of a programme can be along an entirely different direction than was originally expected, so that suppressing one symptom only causes trouble to burst forth at another point.

Figure 18.5 retains the 20 per cent additional capital investment rate after 1970 from Figure 18.4 but in addition explores birth reduction as a way of avoiding crisis. Here the "normal" birth rate has been cut in half in 1970. (Changes in normal rates refer to coefficients which have the specified effect if all other things remain the same. But other things in the system change and also exert their effect on the actual system rates.) The result shows interesting behaviour. Quality of life surges upward for 30 years for

the reasons that are customarily asserted. Food-per-capita grows, material standard of living rises, and crowding does not become as great. But the more affluent world population continues to use natural resources and to accumulate capital plant at about the same rate as in Figure 18.4. Load on the environment is more closely related to industrialization than to population and the pollution crisis occurs at about the same point in time as in Figure 18.4.

Figure 18.5 shows that the 50 per cent reduction in "normal" birth rate in 1970 was sufficient to start a decline in total population. But the rising quality of life and the reduction of pressures act to start the population curve upward again. This is especially evident in other computer runs where the reduction in "normal" birth rate is not so drastic. Serious questions are raised by this investigation about the effectiveness of birth control as a means of controlling population. The secondary consequence of starting

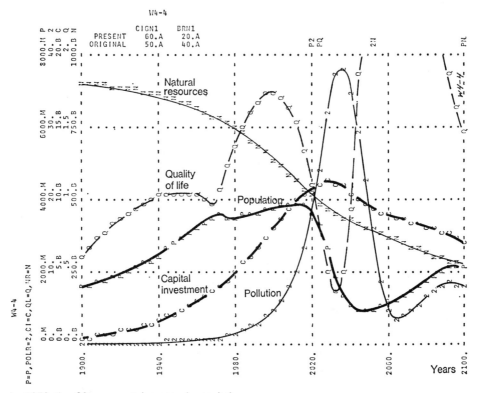

Figure 18.5 In 1970 the 20 per cent increase in capital accumulation from Fig. 18.4 is retained and "normal" birth rate is reduced 50 per cent. Capital investment continues to grow until the pollution crisis develops. After an initial decline, population is again pushed up by a rapid rise in quality of life that precedes the collapse.

a birth control programme will be to increase the influences that raise birth rate and reduce the apparent pressures that require population control. A birth control programme which would be effective, all other things being equal, may largely fail because other things will not remain equal. Its very incipient success can set in motion forces to defeat the programme.

Figure 18.6 combines the reduced resource usage rate and the increased capital investment rate of Figures 18.3 and 18.4. The result is to make the population collapse occur slightly sooner and more severely. Based on the modified system of Figure 18.6, Figure 18.7 then examines the result if technology finds ways to reduce the pollution generated by a given degree of industrialization. Here in Figure 18.7, the pollution rate, other things being the same, is reduced by 50 per cent from that in Figure 18.6. The result is to postpone the day of reckoning by 20 years and to allow the world population to grow 25 per cent greater before the population collapse occurs. The "solution" of reduced pollution has, in effect, caused more people to suffer the eventual consequences. Again we see the dangers of partial solutions. Actions at one point in a system that attempt to relieve one kind of distress produce an unexpected result in some other part of the system. If the interactions are not sufficiently understood, the consequences can be as bad or worse than those that led to the initial action.

There are no utopias in our social systems. There appear to be no sustainable modes of behaviour that are free of pressures and stresses. But there are many possible modes and some are more desirable than others. Usually, the more attractive kinds of behaviour in our social systems seem to be possible only if we have a good understanding of the system dynamics and are willing to endure the self-discipline and pressures that must accompany the desirable mode. The world system of Figure 18.1 can exhibit modes that are more hopeful than the crises of Figures 18.2 through 18.7. But to develop the more promising modes will require restraint and dedication to a long-range future that man may not be capable of sustaining.

Figure 18.8 shows the world system if several policy changes are adopted together in the year 1970. Population

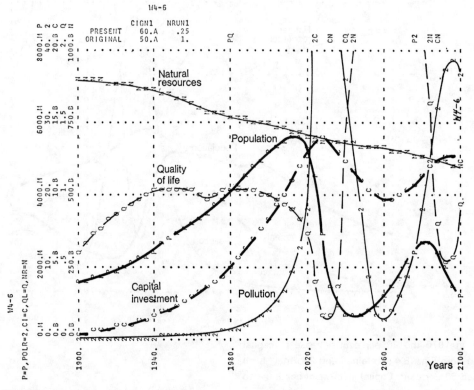

Figure 18.6 The 20 per cent increase of capital investment from Fig. 18.4 and the 75 per cent reduction of natural resource usage from Fig. 18.3 are combined.

is stabilized. Quality of life rises about 50 per cent. Pollution remains at about the 1970 level. Would such a world be accepted? It implies an end to population and economic growth.

In Figure 18.8 the normal rate of capital accumulation is *reduced* 40 per cent from its previous value. The "normal" birth rate is reduced 50 per cent from its earlier value. The "normal" pollution generation is reduced 50 per cent from the value before 1970. The "normal" rate of food production is *reduced* 20 per cent from its previous value. (These changes in "normal" values are the changes for a specific set of system conditions. Actual system rates continue to be affected by the varying conditions of the system.) But reduction in investment rate and reduction in agricultural emphasis are counterintuitive and not likely to be discovered or accepted without extensive system studies and years of argument – perhaps more years than are available. The changes in pollution generation

and natural resource usage may be easier to understand and to achieve. The severe reduction in worldwide birth rate is the most doubtful. Even if technical and biological methods existed, the improved condition of the world might remove the incentive for sustaining the birth reduction emphasis and discipline.

Future policy issues

The dynamics of world behaviour bear directly on the future of the United States. American urbanization and industrialization are a major part of the world scene. The United States is setting a pattern that other parts of the world are trying to follow. That pattern is not sustainable. Our foreign policy and our overseas commercial activity seem to be running contrary to overwhelming forces that are developing in the world system. The following issues are raised by the preliminary investigations to date. They must, of course, be examined more deeply and confirmed

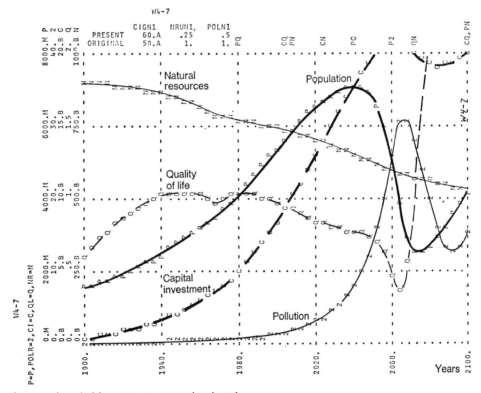

Figure 18.7 Increased capital investment rate and reduced natural resource usage from Fig. 18.6 are retained. In addition in 1970 the "normal" rate of pollution generation is reduced 50 per cent. The effect of pollution control is to allow population to grow 25 per cent further and to delay the pollution crisis by 20 years.

by more thorough research into the assumptions about structure and detail of the world system.

Industrialization may be a more fundamentally disturbing force in world ecology than is population. In fact, the population explosion is perhaps best viewed as a result of technology and industrialization. I include medicine and public health as a part of industrialization.

Within the next century, man may be facing choices from a four-pronged dilemma – suppression of modern industrial society by a natural resource shortage, collapse of world population from changes wrought by pollution, population control by war, disease, and social stresses caused by physical and psychological crowding.

We may now be living in a "golden age" where, in spite of the world-wide feeling of malaise, the quality of life is, on the average, higher than ever before in history and higher than the future offers.

Efforts for direct population control may be inherently self-defeating. If population control begins to result as hoped in higher per capita food supply and material standard of living, these very improvements can generate forces to trigger a resurgence of population growth.

The high standard of living of modern industrial societies seems to result from a production of food and material goods that has been able to outrun the rising population. But, as agriculture reaches a space limit, as industrialization reaches a natural-resource limit, and as both reach a pollution limit, population tends to catch up. Population then grows until the "quality of life" falls far enough to generate sufficiently large pressures to stabilize population.

There may be no realistic hope for the present underdeveloped countries reaching the standard of living demonstrated by the present industrialized nations. The pollution and natural resource load placed on the world environmental system by each person in an advanced country is probably 10 to 20 times greater than the load now generated by a person in an underdeveloped country. With four

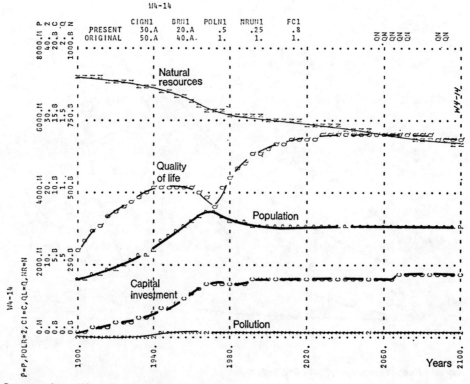

Figure 18.8 One set of conditions that establishes a world equilibrium. In 1970 capital investment rate is reduced 40 per cent, birth rate is reduced 50 per cent, pollution generation is reduced 50 per cent, natural resource usage rate is reduced 75 per cent, and food production is reduced 20 per cent.

times as much population in underdeveloped countries as in the present developed countries, their rising to the economic level of the United States could mean an increase of 10 times in the natural resource and pollution load on the world environment. Noting the destruction already occurring on land, in the air, and especially in the oceans, no capability appears to exist for handling such a rise in standard of living for the present total population of the world.

A society with a high level of industrialization may be nonsustainable. It may be self-extinguishing if it exhausts the natural resources on which it depends. Or, if unending substitution for declining natural resources is possible, the international strife over "pollution and environmental rights" may pull the average world-wide standard of living back to the level of a century ago.

From the long view of a hundred years hence, the present efforts of underdeveloped countries to industrialize along Western patterns may be unwise. They may now be closer to the ultimate equilibrium with the environment than are the industrialized nations. The present underdeveloped countries may be in a better condition for surviving the forthcoming world-wide environmental and economic pressures than are the advanced countries. When one of the several forces materializes that is strong enough to cause a collapse in world population, the advanced countries may suffer far more than their share of the decline.

A new frontier

It is now possible to take hypotheses about the separate parts of a social system, to combine them in a computer model, and to learn the consequences. The hypotheses may at first be no more correct than the ones we are using in our intuitive thinking. But the process of computer modelling and model testing requires these hypotheses to be stated more explicitly. The model comes out of the hazy realm of the mental model into an unambiguous model or statement to which all have access. Assumptions can then be checked against all available information and can be rapidly improved. The great uncertainty with mental models is the inability to anticipate the consequences of interactions between the parts of a system. This uncertainty is totally eliminated in computer models. Given a stated set of assumptions, the computer traces the resulting consequences without doubt or error. This is a powerful procedure for clarifying issues. It is not easy. Results will not be immediate.

We are on the threshold of a great new era in human pioneering. In the past there have been periods characterized by geographical exploration. Other periods have dealt with the formation of national governments. At other times the focus was on the creation of great literature. Most recently we have been through the pioneering frontier of science and technology. But science and technology are now a routine part of our life. Science is no longer a frontier. The process of scientific discovery is orderly and organized.

I suggest that the next frontier for human endeavour is to pioneer a better understanding of the nature of our social systems. The means are visible. The task will be no easier than the development of science and technology. For the next 30 years we can expect rapid advance in understanding the complex dynamics of our social systems. To do so will require research, the development of teaching methods and materials, and the creation of appropriate educational programmes. The research results of today will in one or two decades find their way into the secondary schools just as concepts of basic physics moved from research to general education over the past three decades.

What we do today fundamentally affects our future two or three decades hence. If we follow intuition, the trends of the past will continue into deepening difficulty. If we set up research and educational programmes, which are now possible but which have not yet been developed, we can expect a far sounder basis for action.

The nation's real alternatives

The record to date implies that our people accept the future growth of United States population as preordained, beyond the purview and influence of legislative control, and as a ground rule which determines the nation's task as finding cities in which the future population can live. But I have been describing the circular processes of our social systems in which there is no unidirectional cause and effect but instead a ring of actions and consequences that close back on themselves. One could say, incompletely, that the population will grow and that cities, space, and food must be provided. But one can likewise say, also incompletely, that the provision of cities, space, and food will cause the population to grow. Population generates pressure for urban growth, but urban pressures help to limit population.

Population grows until stresses rise far enough, which is to say that the quality of life falls far enough, to stop further increase. Everything we do to reduce those pressures causes the population to rise farther and faster and hastens the day when expediencies will no longer suffice. The United States is in the position of a wild animal running from its pursuers. We still have some space, natural resources, and agricultural land left. We can avoid the question of rising population as long as we can flee this bountiful reservoir that nature provided. But it is obvious that the reservoirs are limited. The wild animal usually flees until he is cornered, until he has no more space. Then he turns to fight, but he no longer has room to manoeuvre. He is less able to forestall disaster than if he had fought in the open while there was still room to yield and to dodge. The United States is running away from its long-term threats by trying to relieve social pressures as they arise. But if we persist in treating only the symptoms and not the causes, the result will be to increase the magnitude of the ultimate threat and reduce our capability to respond when we no longer have space to flee.

What does this mean? Instead of automatically accepting the need for new towns and the desirability of locating industry in rural areas, we should consider confining our cities. If it were possible to prohibit the encroachment by housing and industry onto even a single additional acre of farm and forest, the resulting social pressures would hasten the day when we stabilize population. Some European countries are closer to realizing the necessity of curtailing urban growth than are we. As I understand it, farm land surrounding Copenhagen cannot be used for either residence or industry until the severest of pressures forces the government to rezone small additional parcels. When land is rezoned, the corresponding rise in land price is heavily taxed to remove the incentive for land speculation. The waiting time for an empty apartment in Copenhagen may be years. Such pressures certainly cause the Danes to face the population problem more squarely than do we.

Our greatest challenge now is how to handle the transition from growth into equilibrium. Our society has behind it a thousand years of tradition that has encouraged and rewarded growth. The folklore and the success stories praise growth and expansion. But that is not the path of the future. Many of the present stresses in our society are from the pressures that always accompany the conversion from growth into equilibrium.

In our studies of social systems, we have made a number of investigations of life cycles that start with growth and merge into equilibrium. There are always severe stresses in the transition. Pressures must rise far enough to suppress the forces that produced growth. Not only do we face the pressure that will stop the population growth; we also encounter pressures that will stop the rise of industrialization and standard of living. The social stresses will rise.

The economic forces will be ·ones for which we have no precedent. The psychological forces will be beyond those for which we are prepared. Our studies of urban systems demonstrated how the pressures from shortage of land and rising unemployment accompany the usual transition from urban growth to equilibrium. But the pressures we have seen in our cities are minor compared to those which the nation is approaching. The population pressures and the economic forces in a city that was reaching equilibrium have in the past been able to escape to new land areas.

But that escape is becoming less possible. Until now we have had, in effect, an inexhaustible supply of farm land and food-growing potential. But now we are reaching the critical point where, all at the same time, population is over-running productive land, agricultural land is almost fully employed for the first time, the rise in population is putting more demand on the food supplies, and urbanization is pushing agriculture out of the fertile areas into the marginal lands. For the first time demand is rising into a condition where supply will begin to fall while need increases. The crossover from plenty to shortage can occur abruptly.

The fiscal and monetary system of the country is a complex social–economic–financial system of the kind we have been discussing. It is clear the country is not agreed on behaviour of the interactions between government policy, growth, unemployment, and inflation. An article by a writer for *Finance* magazine in July 1970, suggests that the approach I have been discussing be applied in fiscal and monetary policy and their relationships to the economy. I estimate that such a task would be only a few times more difficult than was the investigation of urban growth and stagnation. The need to accomplish it becomes more urgent as the economy begins to move for the first time from a history of growth into the turbulent pressures that will accompany the transition from growth to one of the many possible kinds of equilibrium. We need to choose the kind of equilibrium before we arrive.

In a hierarchy of systems, there is usually a conflict between the goals of a subsystem and the welfare of the broader system. We see this in the urban system. The goal of the city is to expand and to raise its quality of life. But this increases population, industrialization, pollution, and demands on food supply. The broader social system of the country and the world requires that the goals of the urban areas be curtailed and that the pressures of such curtailment become high enough to keep the urban areas and population within the bounds that are satisfactory to the larger system of which the city is a part. If this nation chooses to continue to work for some of the traditional urban goals, and if it succeeds, as it may well do, the result will be to deepen the distress of the country as a whole and eventually to deepen the crisis in the cities themselves. We may be at the point where higher pressures in the present are necessary if insurmountable pressures are to be avoided in the future.

I have tried to give you a glimpse of the nature of multi-loop feedback systems, a class to which our social systems belong. I have attempted to indicate how these systems mislead us because our intuition and judgment have been formed to expect behaviour different from that actually possessed by such systems. I believe that we are still pursuing national programmes that will be at least as frustrating and futile as many of the past. But there is hope. We can now begin to understand the dynamic behaviour of our social systems. Progress will be slow. There are many cross-currents in the social sciences which will cause confusion and delay. The approach that I have been describing is very different from the emphasis on data gathering and statistical analysis that occupies much of the time of social research. But there have been breakthroughs in several areas. If we proceed expeditiously but thoughtfully, there is a basis for optimism.

Suggested readings

Forrester, Jay W. (1961) *Industrial Dynamics*, The MIT Press, Cambridge, Mass.

Forrester, Jay W. (1968) *Principles of Systems*, Wright-Allen Press, Cambridge, Mass.

Forrester, Jay W. (1969) *World Dynamics*, The MIT Press, Cambridge, Mass.

Forrester, Jay W. (1971) *World Dynamics*, Wright-Allen Press, Cambridge, Mass.

Meadows, Dennis L. (1970) *Dynamics of Commodity Production Cycles*, Wright-Allen Press, Cambridge, Mass.

19 Towards a systems-based methodology for real-world problem solving

by P. B. Checkland

Introduction

The notions of "systems analysis" of complex problem situations and "a systems approach" to problem solving have become so modish that few are brave enough publicly to reject them and to argue for a reductionist rather than a holistic approach. One reason for this must be the sheer *generality* of claims made for using "a systems approach". The complex problems of organizations private and public, and the yet more difficult problems of society as a whole, are so obviously multi-faceted and contain so many connections that it is "obvious" that we must somehow embrace "the whole problem" in seeking to solve it, lest improvements in one area produce effects elsewhere which are inimical to the whole.

But constant lip service to "a systems approach", and exhortations to use it, do not hide the relative lack of determined persistent efforts both to define what a systems approach consists of and to use it in tackling real-world problems. It is not helpful to make claims for an approach unless it is possible to detail the concept sufficiently for interested persons to grasp it and use it in tackling problems of their own. A recent international symposium on "A Systems Approach to Management", for example, generated much useful discussion,[1] but absolutely absent from it was any account of how a systems approach to management might actually be made manifest in the management of an organization, let alone the "management" of society.

If "a systems approach" is to become more than an easily accepted but somewhat irritating concept, there is a need for expressions of it which eliminate any difference between what it is and how we may use it; the need is for accounts of systems-based *methodologies* which describe a systems approach as a way of analysing and hence trying to solve real-world problems.

In a previous paper[2] it has been suggested that the challenge facing those seeking to develop a systems approach is to develop methodologies appropriate across the spectrum from "the relatively 'hard' systems involving industrial plants characterized by easy-to-define objectives, clearly defined decision-taking procedures and quantitative measures of performance ... (to) ... 'soft' systems in which objectives are hard to define, decision-taking is uncertain, measures of performance are at best qualitative and human behaviour is irrational".

This paper is an attempt to begin to meet that challenge. It presents a general methodology which uses systems ideas to find a structure in apparently unstructured "soft" problems, and hence leads to action to eliminate, alleviate or solve the problem, or provides an orderly way of tackling "hard" problems. The methodology was evolved in the course of an action research programme of client-sponsored systems studies during the period 1969–1971, and refined in further projects in 1972 and 1973. It was derived from experience in real-world problem situations and "tested" in further problems. Tested ideas are rare, and although it is impossible in logic to establish accurately the worth or otherwise of a methodology such as this (a point discussed below), the users of it have found its guidelines helpful.

The methodology is expounded here by means of some account of projects which led to its formulation and reformulation. The aim is to hit a level between the merely anecdotal: "This happened ...", and the dubiously academic: "Questionnaires sent to 100 firms showed that ...".

Section 1 argues the need for ways of using systems ideas which are at once precise yet vague – precise in the sense that the ideas can actually be used to initiate and guide action, vague in the sense that the methodology must not be seen as, must not become, a technique. This section reviews the development of the systems movement and the strands of thinking within it which have led to previous expositions of systemic methodologies. Section 2 reviews the organizational context in which the present action research programme was carried out, and explains its methods; Section 3 describes some experiences which contributed directly to development of the methodology; Section 4 expounds the methodology itself; Section 5 describes further experience gained in attempting to use it subsequent to its initial formulation; and Section 6 discusses some of the problems and issues raised by the idea of a useable methodology for tackling real-world problems.

Busy, practical men with no time for nonsense might turn straight to Section 4 where they might think they have found a recipe. But that would be a pity, since the main aim of the paper is both to offer a methodology which is of practical use in real-world problems, and at the same time gain the reader's acceptance that the methodology is not a how-to-do-it handbook and cannot be applied in any automatic or mechanistic way.

1 The context of the work
The systems movement

The work described in this paper has been carried out within "the systems movement"; that is to say the author's conscious sense of location has been that his work has been a small part of the effort by workers in many different disciplines who are loosely united by the concept "system".

The systems *movement* (and any other word would imply a structure or unity of outlook which does not exist) is concerned ultimately with the concept of systemic wholeness, and the working out of the implications of the concept in any (or every) one of the arbitrary divisions of human knowledge which we presently know as "disciplines". There are systems thinking scientists, technologists, economists, managers, management scientists, psychologists, sociologists, anthropologists, geographers, political scientists, historians, philosophers, artists . . . and many more; and there is also a small group of people working in the area whose interest is in systems concepts as such.

The systems movement represents an attempt to be holistic, and to find out the consequences of being holistic, in any area of endeavour. The only unifying element is the notion "system", and this is the movement's paradigm, in Kuhn's sense,[3] that a paradigm in science is an achievement or set of achievements which a scientific community "acknowledges as supplying the foundation for its further practice", achievements which "attract an enduring group of adherents away from competing modes of scientific activity" and are "sufficiently open-ended to leave all sorts of problems for the redefined group of practitioners to resolve".

The systems movement believes that the concept "system" can provide a source of explanations of many different kinds of observed phenomena – which are beyond the reach of reductionist science. And there is no doubt that achievements so far are sufficiently open-ended to leave many problems to be resolved!

Although there is a long philosophical tradition of systems thinking, explicit statement of the systems stance as a conscious paradigm would seem to stem from Bertalanffy's work in the 1930's on biological organisms as open systems which creatively maintain a degree of organization by continuous exchange of energy, materials and information with their environment. Bertalanffy[4] went on to point out the relevance of his treatment to systems of many different kinds, and it is his exposition which has led to the systems movement having a conscious identity and at least a partial language, as well as organizations and publications.

Within this young tradition, the present work has been carried out. It is concerned with attempts to use the systems paradigm to analyse, elucidate and help to solve real-world problems, and is part of a wider attempt to understand and develop systems concepts by using them in this way.[5] The work is thus concerned with problems of "management", in the broad sense that much human activity involves planning, doing and monitoring, and that some aspects of what is seen as "a problem" are likely to be a mismatch between intention or expectation, and outcome. Thus while the work has nothing to contribute towards understanding of a human activity of the kind: falling in love, it is relevant to any human activity which is *purposeful*. (It need hardly be stated, one hopes, that it is not restricted to "management" interpreted in a class sense.)

Methodologies for using systems ideas

Within the systems movement defined above two main strands of thinking may be identified.

The first is that which derives from the work of Bertalanffy, and is formally identified in the phrase General System(s) Theory (G.S.T.).

The second is that which grew up around the development and subsequent widespread use of computers, and with the application of computers to problems in technology. Here the concern was both the engineering of large complex systems containing many different components brought together to achieve some explicit objective, and also the organization of all the different activities which must be successfully integrated if a technological project

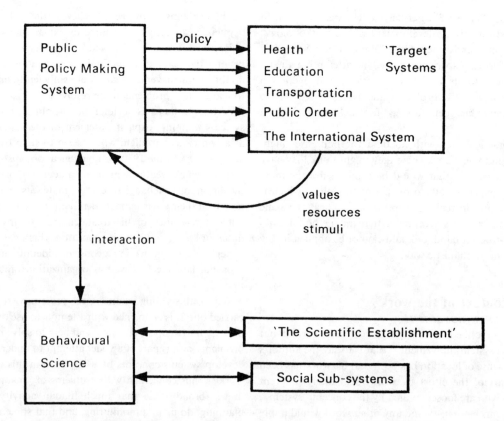

Figure 19.1 A picture version of Dror's GST model of policy making and behavioural science.

is to be efficiently accomplished; this we may identify as the Systems Analysis approach.

G.S.T. has not been much concerned with the development of tools for use in practical problems. Its concern has been mainly with obtaining an understanding of the fundamental nature of systems, broadly defined, and with tracing isomorphisms in systems whose content is at first sight very different. As Boulding describes it[6]

General Systems Theory is a name which has come to describe a level of theoretical model-building which lies somewhere between the highly generalized constructions of pure mathematics and the specific theories of the specialized disciplines.

When the concepts of G.S.T. are used to provide a methodological approach to a practical problem there is obviously an immense difficulty in building a bridge between the theory and the problem; usually the bridge collapses into the gap between the two. We may briefly illustrate the difficulties by considering an interesting paper

by Dror[7] ambitiously concerned with a General Systems approach to the problem of improving public policy-making by making use of the behavioural sciences. In some happy phrases which can make us all blush, Dror describes the present situation as a "mix-up between reliable factual knowledge, axiomatic assumptions, provisional theories, conceptual taxonomies, doubtful hypotheses and various types of value judgements . . .". He then goes on, "using a very simple version of systems theory", to suggest the model I have converted in outline into Figure 19.1. Something called the "Public Policy Making System" produces policies on a number of "Target Systems" such as Education, Health, Transportation, etc. and is itself affected by feedback from those areas in the form of values, resources and stimuli. The Policy Making System has interactions with the discipline "Behavioural Science", which itself also interacts with "The Scientific Establishment" and with many "social sub-systems". Consideration of this as a totality then leads to the beguiling, defensible, but very dangerous conclusion that "what is required is not some incremental change here or there, but fargoing redesign in the two relevant systems and their interchanges". "Illustrative redesign specifications" are then listed which include creation of new professional roles, major programmes of structural change within the policy-making and behavioural-science systems, new graduate teaching programmes, and significant changes in "research orientations, methods and subjects"!

Clearly there is a very large gap indeed between the present state of affairs and that state to which this G.S.T. analysis points, a gap likely to be unbridgeable. In fact the generality of G.S.T. is almost bound to lead to this kind of Utopianism; G.S.T. used methodologically is almost bound to lead to what Popper,[8] in his magisterial demolition of it, calls *Utopian engineering* – the idea that "rational action must have a certain aim", that "only when (the) ultimate aim is determined . . . only when we are in possession of something like a blueprint of a society at which we aim . . . can we . . . draw up a plan for practical action". Utopian engineering, which seeks the establishment of an ideal, has led only, Popper claims, to "the use of violence in the place of reason". He contrasts it with the more rational *piecemeal engineering* which searches for and fights against "the greatest and most urgent evils of society rather than searching for, and fighting for its greatest ultimate good". This approach is surely nearer the reality that, wherever we want society to go, we have no choice but to start from its present state, since we have no detailed knowledge for the large scale Utopian social experiments with which G.S.T. is likely to seduce us.

The second strand of systems thinking, the Systems Analysis strand, is more concerned with methodology, as it is bound to be given its base in engineering, the art of making things happen. Many methodologies for creating complex systems have been proposed, and some of them have been put to use during the last twenty years.

In the early 1960s A. D. Hall[9] described a methodology for translating scientific discoveries into realized applications which meet human needs, his account deriving from Bell Telephone Laboratories' experience. He envisages, and illustrates, the following sequence:

Problem Definition (essentially definition of a *need*)
↓
Choice of Objectives (a definition of physical needs and of the value system within which they must be met)
↓
Systems Synthesis (creation of possible alternative systems)
↓

Systems Analysis (analysis of the hypothetical systems in the light of objectives)
↓
System Selection (selection of the most promising alternative)
↓
System Development (up to the prototype stage)
↓
Current Engineering (system realization beyond prototype stage and including monitoring, modifying and feeding back information to design).

This methodology is conceived with hardware engineering in mind, and similar considerations have been expounded from a base in control engineering.[10]

An obvious extension of this kind of thinking is to systems beyond those which comprise the hardware itself, and this extension has been explored both in the military area and in the process industries. Optner,[11] as editor of a collection of papers concerned with the "systems analysis" strand of systems thinking, records that in the 1950s "Professionals with training in the social and physical sciences and management specialists with experience in weapons evaluation and procurement were agreed: the problems of defence after the Second World War required a more far-reaching problem-solving technology". And Hitch[12] in the first paper in this collection describes the essential elements as: an objective, alternative systems by which it may be accomplished, costs and resources of each alternative, a model (linking system, objectives, environment and resources), and a criterion for choosing the optimal alternative. These elements constantly recur as the components of the methodology developed within the RAND Corporation during the 1950s.

In the introduction to a book on the application of systems analysis to the planning of defence policy, edited by Quade and Boucher,[13] the RAND approach is summarized as follows:

One strives to look at the entire problem, as a whole, in context, and to compare alternative choices in the light of their possible outcomes. Three sorts of enquiry are required, any of which can modify the others as the work proceeds. There is a need, first of all, for a systematic investigation of the decision-makers objectives and of the relevant criteria for deciding among the alternatives that promise to achieve these objectives. Next, the alternatives need to be identified, examined for feasibility, and then compared in terms of their effectiveness and cost, taking time and risk into account. Finally an attempt must be made to design better alternatives and select other goals if those previously examined are found wanting.

Again there is emphasis on generating alternatives and comparing them using criteria relevant to the system objective or to the need the system is intended to fill. Obviously the lacuna here is the absence of guidance on how to generate alternatives. Even if alternatives are obvious, logically there is a blatant possibility that some unthought-of alternative would have given a better solution than any of those considered, and no amount of "brain-storming" or "lateral thinking" during an actual study can remove this defect.

One methodology within the "systems analysis" tradition has been described which avoids explicit steps of the kind: "generate alternative systems"; it is that described by Jenkins in the first issue of this Journal.[14]*

This methodology I interpret as follows. It starts from an organizational definition of system as a complex grouping of human beings and machines for which there is an overall objective. The procedure is then to select that system the engineering of which will solve the problem whose existence initiates the activity. The system is placed in a systems hierarchy, objectives and criteria of perform-mance are defined, and the chosen system is designed (via model building, simulation and optimization), imple-mented and reappraised in operation. Here the "generate alternatives" problem has to be solved by the initial examination of the problem and the choice of the system to be engineered. Logically, of course, what subsequently comes to be recognized as a wrong choice may be made; but the whole activity is conceived as a team activity aimed at helping a manager, so it is at least implicit that he will himself profoundly influence the choice of system to be engineered to solve his problem, even if that problem-solving task is itself conceived as a professional team activity.

As the methodology described below evolved during the action research programme, it diverged from those described above, and for interesting reasons which are discussed later. But the starting point was the methodology described by Jenkins, and the explicit aim was to explore the implications of trying to apply it to ill-structured, fuzzy, "soft" problem situations. What has finally emerged can be viewed as a general systems methodology which is perhaps nearer to the G.S.T. tradition than the Systems

* Reprinted as Article 8 in this book.

Analysis tradition, but which under special circumstances (those of a structured problem) can sharpen up into a version which would be at home in the latter tradition.

Before describing the work which led to formulation of the methodology it is useful briefly to examine some of the requirements of an ordered procedure for tackling ill-structured, or unstructured problems.

The requirements of a methodology for tackling unstructured problems

The common characteristic of the systems analysis methodologies described above is that they make use of the kind of thinking which is natural to design engineers, whose role is to provide an efficient means of meeting a defined need. The design engineer's situation is one in which *what* is required has been defined, and he must examine *how* it can be provided. His skill and flair are directed to providing ingenious possible answers to the question: How can it be done? The best design engineer is the man who generates the most efficient and ingenious alternatives, the man, for example, who first designs a bridge with arch and keystone where previous beam-based structures have required closely-spaced support pillars.

Much skill is called for in engineering design, and much resolution in converting design into realized artifact, but the relevant point here is that the design engineer's problem is essentially a *structured* one. Methodologies stemming from engineering thinking inevitably postulate a certain kind of structure in the situation in which the methodology will be used: either a need can be defined, or a system's objectives can be stated unequivocally, thus enabling the system to be engineered to achieve them. The need- and objective-defining are taken as given, in the sense that need-defining and objective-defining systems are not part of the problem situation.

Basically these methodologies derive from the model that sees human behaviour as goal-seeking. But this model, useful though it is in many situations, is inappropriate in many real-world problems which are seen as "problems" precisely because there is no agreement on needs, objectives, measures of performance, etc; and the lack of agreement may not be due simply to lack of understanding or lack of information – it may be fundamental, and for two different reasons. The lack may be due to incompatible ways of viewing the problem, incompatible weltanschauungen, or it may be that any goal-seeking model itself imposes false structure on the problem situation by seeing it as a matter of *ends* and *means* rather than ongoing relationships through time. Vickers[15] has argued most cogently against the dominance of "objectives" over "relationships" in our conscious thinking, and it is in the context of what he terms shared *appreciative systems* "carved out by our interests, structured by our expectations and evaluated by our standards of judgement" that any methods of using systems ideas to tackle real-world problems must be developed.

Vickers' insight is that our human experience develops within us "readinesses to notice particular aspects of our situation, to discriminate them in particular ways and to measure them against particular standards of comparison, which have been built up in similar ways". These *readinesses* are organized more or less coherently into "an appreciative system". New experience is conditioned by these readinesses and itself modifies them; such circular relations constitute the common facts of social life, but we fail to see this clearly because of our concentration on linear causal chains and on the notion of goal seeking.

I take this concept of an appreciative system to be the most useful description of the context of "problems" in the real-world, and one we must seek to use in spite of the greater simplicities of the goal-seeking model.

If we are to make progress, then, we must avoid both content-free methodologies derived in a flabby way from General Systems Theory, and over-precise goal-oriented formulations stemming from Systems Analysis. We need simultaneously to be precise enough to provide guidelines which can actually be used, and vague enough to remain problem-oriented, avoiding distorting the problem into a particular structure just because we would know how to tackle it if it came to us in that form.

Finally before describing the research and its outcome, it is necessary to make some general remarks about the need for methodology, since the idea that we need to develop systems-based methodology relevant to tackling real-world problems is not an everyday concept, and may seem a strange or unnecessary one. Scientists and engineers do not show much concern about methodology, why should we agonize about the importance of it in systems work?

A methodology I take to be an explicit, ordered, non-random way of carrying out an activity. As such it is independent of the *content* of the activity and can be considered separately from content, although in practice this is not easy to achieve: most people, asked to describe how they tackled a problem will quickly slip into describing the content of the problem itself. The reason is that methodology, once adopted, tends to become invisible;

it becomes, in both a logical and a behavioural sense, simply the way the activity is carried out, and is taken for granted. Most practising scientists and engineers show little interest in methodology because the pattern of their activity, both in its logic and its displayed behaviour has long been established. The four-year degree course in Chemistry I took at Oxford contained nothing at all about the methodology of science. Although I now find this astonishing I did not notice it at the time. The course was concerned with the content of chemistry; it was implicitly assumed that the research activity of the fourth year would be carried out in the same way as researches already described in the literature, with practical guidance gained by working alongside more senior researchers. The methodology of carrying out chemical research had become invisible.

In using a systems approach it is likely that methodology will eventually cease to be a major object of study, and the attention of most practitioners will be concentrated wholly on problem content. At present, while hopefully bringing about improvements in the problem situations themselves, it is more important to use groups of related studies to establish methodology itself.

2 The research method
Action research in systems at Lancaster
The research on which this paper is based was carried out as part of an on-going action research programme in the Department of Systems Engineering at Lancaster University, a programme which may well be unique in form and content. The programme is associated with Masters, Doctoral and Post-Doctoral work and involves carrying out mainly client-sponsored systems studies in real-world problem situations. In starting it in 1966, G. M. Jenkins' uniquely bold concept was that a fruitful way to explore systems concepts would be to tackle actual problem situations with a project team consisting of a faculty member, a full-time mature postgraduate student (for whom the project would be an exceptionally rich learning experience) and a member of the client organization which poses the problem.

More than a hundred such projects have now been carried out.

Systems ideas are the basis of project thinking, and the projects themselves, as well as seeking practical improvements in the problem situation, provide a growing body of experience which is a source both of insight into systems ideas and methodologies for using systems ideas. A methodology derived tentatively from a number of projects can hopefully be further tested and refined in subsequent projects: that is the pattern followed in this work.

Obviously there are problems which stem from the "action" nature of the research, and this point requires some discussion.*

The concept of action research arises first in the behavioural sciences. Forster[16] identifies Kurt Lewin as the father of the approach in the 1940's and the prime ideational source as Lewin's Gestaltist view of "the limitations of studying complex real social events in a laboratory, the artificiality of splitting out single behavioural elements from an integrated system". Forster arrives at a definition by augmenting that of Rapaport[17]. Forster's version is as follows:

A type of applied social research differing from other varieties in the immediacy of the researcher's involvement in the action process and the intention of the parties, although with different roles, to be involved in a change process of the system itself. It aims to contribute both to the practical concerns of people in an immediate problematic situation and to the goals of social science by joint collaboration within a mutually acceptable ethical framework.

This definition fits the Lancaster systems projects in that they are involved in "a change process in the system itself" as a means to both practical action and an experience relevant to the research aim of developing systems concepts. The problem with action research arises from the fact that it cannot be wholly directed. The essential nature of action research is revealed by asking the question: "What would action research in physics be like?" The impossibility of that concept shows that action research is a possibility only in a situation in which the elements are social interactions. (You cannot do action research on magnetism because there is no way in which you can intervene and affect or change the physical laws). The point is that, being concerned with intervention in purposeful systems, the action researcher, unlike the researcher in experimental science or technology can express his research aims as hopes but cannot with certainty design them into his "experiments". He is prepared to react to whatever happens in the research situation; he has to follow wherever the situation leads him

* I am grateful to my colleague Dr. T. R. Barnett for helping sharpen my ideas on action research.

or stop the research. In the present work an attempt was made to tackle ill-defined problems by using systems concepts, to explore the difficulties encountered and to propose and test ways in which the systems concepts were used. The problems, though very diverse in content were treated as a single group and lessons from the ones first tackled modified the approach used in later ones. In this situation the use of action research projects as the vehicle for the research is made legitimate because, and only because, the research aim is the very general one of developing a methodology for tackling "soft" ill-structured problems; hence *any* problems which meet that criterion are suitable for the purpose whatever other characteristics they may have.

3 Some systems projects
Three project experiences

Some aspects of three systems projects are now summarized. They were all characterized by having initial definitions of "the problem" which were vague and unstructured. The client organizations had no doubt that serious problems existed, but could not or (sensibly) would not define them in precise terms. Since a problem defined is a problem solved, in the sense that any precise formulation of a problem implies its solution, these projects were suitable ones for examining means of tackling "soft" problems.

The first project was in a textile firm having 1,000 employees. It had ceased to be profitable the year before the study and had newly recruited some senior managers with large-firm experience. One of them, the Marketing Director, initiated the systems project, probably, we felt, as a means of bringing pressure to bear on the Production side, whose planning and scheduling performance he regarded as inadequate. It was at once apparent that this was correct, but equally apparent was the fact that perfecting the production planning system would have a negligible effect on the Company's main aim, which was now nothing less than survival. There were at least a dozen significant candidates for the role of "the problem" including the inadequacy of financial information, the absence of any Company planning, poor production-marketing collaboration, inadequate control of nine regional stores, no quality control system, inadequate information flows to senior managers, and low staff morale. In the end progress was made by *choosing to view the Company in a particular way and working out the consequences of that view.* The Company was taken to be a system whose survival was threatened unless it could quickly – say within a year – improve its most basic short-term operation, namely winning customer orders and meeting them efficiently. The Company was therefore taken to be a system which generates and accepts customer orders and meets them sufficiently quickly and efficiently to ensure an increasing flow of them. The sequence of *decisions which recur* in such a system was isolated and a conceptual model was constructed by postulating a system component to take each decision. The sequence itself then led to a system structure, as has been described previously (Checkland and Griffin).[18] The concept led to the creation of two units for order processing, one customer-oriented, the other production-oriented, and to the engineering of the necessary information flows. Four subsequent projects then sought to bring the reality gradually nearer to the new concept.

The second project was in the engineering industry, in a large firm concerned with the design and construction of a small number of very large and very complex objects. A perspicacious director, concerned with the problems of integrating highly specialist expertise into the enterprise as as whole, set up the study with a remit which was deliberately, and usefully, vague: its theme was to be "information flow for decision making", and there was a specific suggestion from some of the specialist middle managers that the *interface* between Design and Production Planning should be examined as a particular problem area. Major elements in the overall problem situation were: an incredibly complex functional organization within which decision-taking was diffuse and which contained a number of project "task forces" which had lived on beyond the end of their intended life; a "project" organization which cut across the functional organization but which was purely a reporting, not a managing function; a senior management which (perhaps because of these characteristics) continually became involved in low-level day-to-day engineering problems; and a middle management remarkably dedicated to the success of the total enterprise, showing much more commitment to it, in fact, than is usually found in the process industries. Because of the middle management's dedication, unworkable procedures did actually work. Here again the thinking hinged on deciding the basic nature of the organization. It was decided to view it as a system to carry out a gigantic task – that of converting physical and abstract resources into the final complex object within a certain time, at a certain cost and while meeting various technical and safety constraints.

Within this frame of reference a conceptual model of the necessary system to carry out such a task was compared with the existing functional organization and project administration. General conclusions were drawn and these were then illustrated by examining a specific example. Specific illustration was centred not on the flow across the Design/Production Planning interface (which would have automatically assumed this to be a required part of the *structure* of the system) but on a comparison of how one specific part of the complex object *would have* been provided within the conceptualized system and *was actually* provided within the existing procedures. The illustration was apt in that it showed in microcosm the operation of the system as a whole.

The third project was in the publishing/printing industry, being specifically concerned with consumer and technical magazine publishing and printing. The work was sponsored by a small central group who were engaged in building a corporate planning system in a divisionalized Company; its audience was a committee chaired by the Managing Director and having as members the executive heads of the different divisions. The project problem was exemplified rather than posed. It was exemplified by the stated difficulty of answering questions of the kind "What is the appropriate mix of production facilities within a printing division over the next five years, given the rapidly changing market, the spread of printing contracts between our own and external printers, and the general overall need to improve Company profitability"? (The division structure was a typical "business area" organization, with each division encouraged to be autonomous. The management consultants who had suggested it said in their report that the divisional chief executives "can be held truly accountable for their own profit contribution or cost. However, they cannot be entirely free to take action . . . Before setting out on a major course of action . . . directors must seek approval and coordination from higher management". They did not, alas, say how that "coordination" should be provided. Asking: How can it be provided? is one way of stating the problem).

It did not seem useful to identify "the system" as "the corporate planning system"; instead, analysis of existing arrangements gradually moved over into consideration of the basic nature of the business and conceptualization of a system to carry it out. Here the basic business can be viewed as a system concerned with the provision of consecutive "images" to an audience which must be assessed continuously. The work of the system is carried out by two different groups whose technical interests are different (publishers and printers) and who constitute two very different social systems. In the end the conceptualization led to definition of a range of possible changes to the existing structure, the range covering different "amounts of change", and an assessment of the difficulty of implementing them.

An emerging methodology

What generalizations do these experiences illustrate?

All these projects included, as every systems study must, an *analysis* phase, a finding out of what exists at present in the problem situation. In methodologies appropriate to "hard" systems this analysis is "in systems terms", and the art of the analysis is to view the problem situation, without distorting it, as a hierarchy of systems, in order that "the system" (i.e. "the system to seek to engineer") can be selected. There is an implication here that the systems hierarchy will already exist in at least rudimentary form. This will certainly be the case in most "fairly hard" systems studies. If the study is concerned with, say, the management information needed to run a chlorine plant, we may be sure that there does exist at least a rudimentary version of such an information system – the plant simply could not run without it – just as there are bound to be existing versions of plant subsystems concerned with other necessary activities: production, costing, maintenance, industrial relations, etc.

But in softer systems it is much less obvious that the situation can be analyzed as an existing hierarchy of (albeit imperfect) systems. To pursue such an analysis may well distort the picture of the problem situation and may lead to a confused compromise between analysis and design in which the picture built up is neither an account of what exists nor a proposal concerning what should exist. This is difficult to avoid if existing arrangements fall short of being purpose-built systems – as most "existing arrangements" do.

Similarly any concentration on definition of objectives implies that an agreed definition of objectives for the systems in the hierarchy will not be too difficult to obtain, and will be useful once obtained; this is then the lead-in to systems design: the design is such that these objectives may be achieved. But in soft systems such definitions of objectives may be impossible to obtain and if obtained may not be useful. It may be that obtainable definitions are "public" ones which conceal the "real" objectives – perhaps even from the people who profess them; or it may be that objectives of a soft system are genuinely inexpressible; or it may be, remembering Vickers' distinction between goal-seeking and relationship-maintaining, that it

is simply inappropriate to try to define objectives, objectives being finite goals different in kind from the deeper underlying ongoing purposes of a soft system which, though it may be other things as well, will be a social system. And social systems are not usefully regarded as goal-seeking.

In soft systems like those of the three studies under discussion it was found most useful to make the analysis stage a building up of *the richest possible picture* of the situation being studied without pressing the analysis in systems terms. Such an analysis (guidelines for which are discussed below) enables selection to be made of a *viewpoint* from which to study further the problem situation, and enables some relevant systems (relevant, that is, to improving the problem situation) to be named tentatively.

In each of the three studies described above an early feeling of helplessness led to asking, not: What system needs to be engineered? but: *What is the fundamental nature of* (*notional*) *systems which from the analysis phase seem relevant to the problem?* In the textile firm the sheer multiplicity of problems forced the emergence of the view that the Company as a whole had to be encompassed, and that it had to be viewed as an order-processing system which needed to improve within a year in order to survive. In the engineering firm the useful lack of a precise problem definition and the suggestion that a particular organizational interface be examined led to a realization that the present position of such interfaces is arbitrary, and irrelevant to the nature of the enterprise, which is to use one of many possible organizational structures to accomplish a huge task. In the publishing/printing firm the analysis suggested that the problems were concerned centrally with the notionally autonomous divisions, different in activity and attitudes, which were nevertheless closely entwined in the overall activity of the enterprise. A view of the overall activity which brought this out was required.

In each of these projects (and a number of others) analysis led to this kind of *root definition* of relevant systems. From such definitions *conceptual models* of notional systems whose fundamental nature is embodied in the root definition were derived (relatively rigorous ways of doing this have since been developed and are discussed below). These models, which were not normative, but rather provided a means of organizing the systems thinking, then gave something which could be set alongside the actual situation in a *formal comparison* which enabled *definition of a range of possible changes*.

In the projects under discussion it so happened that structural, rather than procedural changes were debated, and in two cases, the textile firm and the publishing/printing firm, new organizational units were agreed as both desirable and feasible. (The engineering firm, whose historical pride was in the technical excellence of its functional groups, was not prepared to contemplate the possible changes which the comparison stage defined.)

It follows from the above that any *design* and *implementation* is, in general terms, the design and implementation of an agreed change rather than of a system. Design of a system emerges as a special case, appropriate when the problem definition is sufficiently sharp to enable objectives and measures of performance to be defined and hence to allow the thinking to be in terms of model building, simulating performance and optimizing.

Out of the three projects illustrated here and six similar ones, there emerged during 1969, 1970 and 1971 the outline of a methodology whose crux was the root definition and conceptualization of relevant systems. Attempts to use it (and understand it!) in subsequent projects since then have enabled it to be expressed in clearer terms and have enabled some of its implications to be revealed. It departed from "systems analysis" methodologies (as defined previously) firstly in a more open-ended analysis phase not carried out in systems terms, secondly in introducing the root definition/conceptualization stage, and thirdly in being forced to abandon the idea of *designing a system* except in the special circumstances of either a well-defined problem with explicit objectives and measures of performance, or a "green field" situation in which conceptualization can be used as the first phase of the design activity, a phase concerned with defining "what" before design itself gets down to defining "how".

The next section expounds the methodology and further illustrates it. Meanwhile we may summarize it in outline as in Figure 19.2.

4 The methodology
Introduction
The methodology assumes that we are concerned to tackle problems which arise in human activity systems. In a previous paper[2] it was argued that the basic proposition of a systems approach is that it is "reasonable and useful" to view the universe as a complex of interacting systems.

We may identify *natural* systems, from atoms to galaxies; and one of them, the human being, can create *designed* systems, whether abstract (a philosophy, for example) or concrete (a machine) which can be used in *human activity systems*. Quoting[2]: "Human activity systems comprise the area in which objectives can be originated"; in other words, they contain purposeful elements, and it is this which justifies the development of problem-solving methodology: the knowledge that there exists a will to understand and improve the situations we find ourselves in. The methodology now described can be viewed as a means of using systems ideas to structure problem situations in order that that will can be exercised.

Analysis
It has already been argued that the analysis phase should not be in systems terms unless the problem situation is a relatively structured one. If it is unstructured then seeking out "systems" at the start almost always leads to the identification of organizational groupings – departments or functions – as systems, which may or may not be appropriate. An organizational grouping is a particular "how"; the analysis needs to be in terms of "what".

Guidelines for analysis found adequate in a number of studies, including those described above, are illustrated in Figure 19.3.

The problem situation will exist within a number of environments and/or wider systems with which it will interact. Most of the environments will be what Emery and Trist call "turbulent fields".[19] The problem situation will itself be turbulent, but it will contain elements of "structure" which are relatively static, and elements of "process" which are dynamic, the former existing as the framework within which the latter operate. In the publishing/printing project the environments included an owner-company of which the publishing business was one business area, a particular information/entertainment market, a changing technology and two different social systems. "Structure" was present in the form of an organization broken down into subdivisions defined according to product type and functional activity. The "process" was the set of activities concerned with publishing and printing as a business activity and the activity of staying in that business in the long term.

Structure may be examined in terms of physical layout (which often has an effect on the "process" and on the relationship between the two, the "climate"), hierarchy, reporting structure and the pattern of communications both formal and informal. The *process* may, in any organizational context, be analyzed in terms of the basic activities: planning to do something, doing it, monitoring both

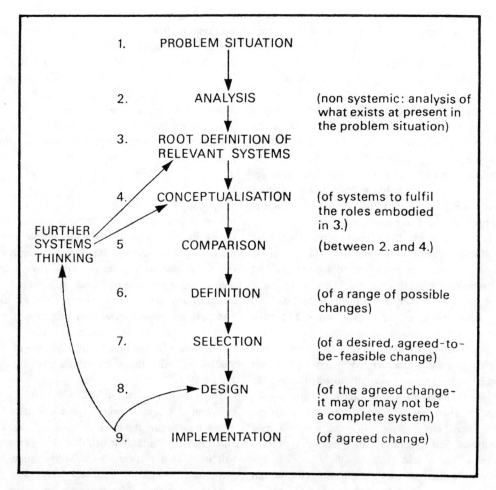

Figure 19.2 The emerging methodology.

how well it is done and its external effects, and taking action to correct deviations.

The relationship between structure and process, the "climate", is a core characteristic of any problem situation, and especially so if the problem is in an organization. In the engineering industry project a technology-based functional structure matched ill with the process operations of a task-system, but managed to survive (with ever-increasing complexity) because of the attitudes of those middle managers dedicated to the process. This was the core characteristic of this problem situation, the end point of the analysis.

It is difficult to know when to finish the analysis phase – even if only temporarily! But the analysis should not be regarded as complete until at least the following questions can be answered convincingly and in some depth.

Within and/or around the problem situation:

1. What *resources* are deployed in what *operational processes* under what *planning procedures* within what *structure*, in what *environments and wider systems, by whom?*

2. How is this resource deployment *monitored* and *controlled?*

Root definition of relevant systems

The analysis may be taken to be complete, at least on a first iteration, when it is possible to postulate a root definition of the basic nature of the system or systems thought to be relevant to the problem situation. This should be a condensed representation of the system(s) in

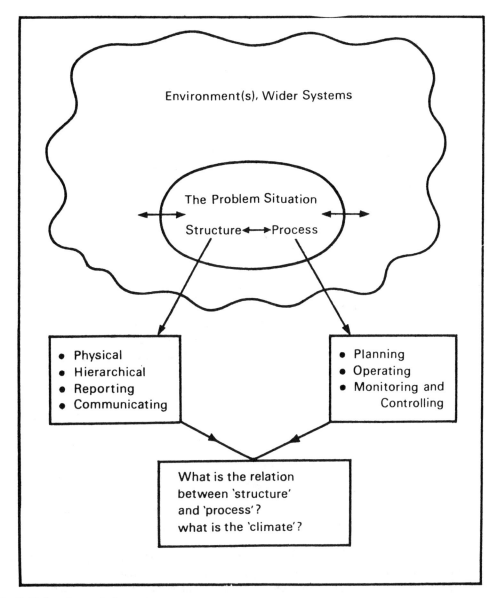

Figure 19.3 Guidelines for analysis.

its most fundamental form. Much will depend upon this definition and it needs to be pondered carefully; its aim is to capture insight.

In the case of the textile industry project the analysis revealed a firm whose crucial objective was survival. Hence the root definition of the relevant system was taken to be an order-generating and order-processing system, the aim being a quick improvement (within about a year) in the level of customer service.

In the publishing industry project the conclusion of the analysis was that the problems here were embedded in a rather more complicated system, one crucially concerned with assessing potential audiences, providing that audience with successive images, and ensuring that doing this as a business operations earned a surplus; Figure 19.4 summarizes the concept.

This root definition derived from the realization that the editorial activity and the printing activity were, in essence,

Figure 19.4 Root defintion of the publishing/printing project relevant system.

not the "marketing" and "production" activities of typical commercial enterprises but were the activities, valued for their own sake, of two different social systems in which business considerations were of low importance. ("I was spending all my time reading 'Management Today' instead of doing the editing I love" wrote a disgruntled magazine editor recently, complaining about the increasingly professional approach of her company). In such a system purely business considerations tend to be neglected, need to be built into the system, but are inappropriate to the kind of people involved in editing and printing.

For those who concocted it the "assess potential audiences' needs" and "provide regular images" elements in this root definition embodied the fact that a magazine editor genuinely feels a very close (almost mystical) rapport with his audience, and has to assess sensitively its changing attitudes. It is a fact that magazines for pubescent girls, for example, need to be edited by young women who can identify with teenagers and dream their dreams, rather than by cynical 50-year-old males. Such editors are

unlikely to treat magazine publishing primarily as a commercial enterprise: hence the form of the root definition.

There will of course never be a demonstrably "correct" root definition, only a range of possibilities, some glib and shallow, some full of insight. What is needed is a penetrating definition, derived from the richness of the analysis, which is revealing to those involved in the day-to-day workings of the systems concerned.

The nature of root definitions may be further illustrated by a few somewhat extreme examples.

We could formulate root definitions of a church around several different concepts: perhaps "a social welfare system", which downgrades the core of supernaturalism upon which most churches insist, or as "a ritual-organizing system", or as a "belief-maintenance system", or – building in a different weltanschauung – as a "system to provide support in the face of unanswerable questions". In an actual situation it might be profitable to explore the implications of several such root definitions, covering as these do both what a participant might want the system to be as well as what an outside observer might take it to be. A postgraduate student developed for the author a rich conceptual model of the Jewish church based on the root definition "a system to preserve ethnic identity".

A pop festival could be conceptualized as a purely commercial enterprise, but this would miss layers of meaning at a deeper level. Many thousands of young people do not travel to the Isle of Wight to live in fields in squalid conditions simply to be the customers of pop music sellers. A systems study of a "pop festival system" would have to begin with some such root definition as "a system to celebrate a life-style via the medium of pop music". Similarly if the systems approach were used to conceptualize an intended festival of contemporary jazz it would have to reach beyond commercial considerations to the politico-racial concerns of the current *avant garde*.

These are somewhat fanciful examples to illustrate the concept. A final example, less fanciful but highly insightful, comes from an industrial firm. A. B. Thompson, head of a department responsible for patents, trade marks and licence agreements in the Fibers Division of ICI, conceives his role as being concerned with the legal concept of intellectual property.[20] This is very important to a company operating on a world scale in a science-based business. Clearly a suitable root definition for the activity associated with this role is that it is "a system to *acquire, protect and exploit* intellectual property".

All of the above examples are necessarily general for illustrative purposes. In any particular systems project it is extremely important that the root definition should be specific to the particular situation of that project. To imagine that there can be once-and-for-all definitive root definitions applicable, say, to any distribution system, any marketing system, or any quality control system would be to make the same mistake as is made in those management science text-books which imagine that problems recur, and that they.can therefore deal with "the inventory problem", "the investment problem", "the depot location problem", etc. chapter by chapter.

Conceptualization

Conceptualization is the process of building conceptual models of the system or systems which are relevant to the problem situation and for which we have root definitions. The purpose is to create, in the light of the problem situation but in a mood of detachment from it, something which can be compared, formally and specifically, with the picture built up in the analysis phase. It is the part of the methodology in which systems thinking can be used in a rather formal way, and there should be a conscious break between analysis and conceptualization, marked by the postulation of root definitions.

Before describing the way in which conceptualization has been carried out in 20-odd systems studies, it is important to emphasize – in fact from experience so far impossible to over-emphasize – that the conceptual model is a picture, as objective as possible, of what is implied by the root definition. It is *not* a representation of the "ideal" which might be approached; it is absolutely *not* a representation of what "ought" to exist in the real situation. Although in a "green field" situation it has been possible to make use of conceptualization as a means of defining the basis of a design, conceptualization is *not* design, it is a means of structuring the thinking about fuzzy problem situations.

The two main problems of conceptualization concern finding a way to do it, and finding a way to validate the conceptual model which is its outcome. The present solution to the first problem is to assemble in correct sequence the *minimum* activities which are *necessary* in a human activity system described by the root definition. The second problem has been tackled by using systems concepts to assemble a generalized model of any human activity system, called a "formal system", which can be used, if not to validate the conceptualization, at least to ensure that it is not basically deficient.

Conceptualization starts from the root definition and asks: What would the activities have to be in a human activity system which meets the requirements of this definition? The aim is to include every activity implied by the definition, but no extra ones, on the principle of Occam's Razor. When a tentative sequence has been assembled it is useful to annotate it with major inputs and outputs. When this has been done we may ask of each activity: What decisions would have to be taken in carrying out this activity? And then at the next level of consideration: What information would the decision-taker require? Once these steps have been completed it is useful to consider the structure implied by the model so far: How might the activities be grouped? An example of this kind of activity is given in[18]. (It is of course possible that answering these questions may lead to reformulation of the root definition).

It is important in building the concept not to slip into describing what happens to exist in the real-world problem situation. The art of conceptualization lies in cleaving to the implications of the root definition while at the same time being not unaware of the reality; the art lies in finally achieving a bridgeable gap between the conceptual model and the problem situation.

The process may be illustrated by reference again to the publishing/printing project. The root definition (Figure 19.4) sees a relevant system as one concerned to:

assess a potential audience
provide it with successive images
ensure that the total operation earns a surplus.

It was decided to examine its implications in a system which begins with the "assess" activity, and produces a single consumer magazine.

The first activity (see Figure 19.5) is that of assessing the audience response to a sequence of issues. This is the crucial editorial activity of forecasting a kind of material which will serve to establish that editor-reader rapport which is the essence of this business and a prime value of the social system which the editor inhabits.

Given that assessment, material for the issues must now be selected or commissioned, as must advertising matter. This must also fit in with the assessment of the audience, and must be in sufficient quantity to meet those financial requirements which will have to be fed in from outside, from the Business Planning sub-system which the root definition implies.

Assembly and appraisal of a particular issue follows, and when satisfactory to the editor becomes "copy" which has now to be transformed into a form (plate or photographic image) which can be used for image duplication.

There will here be interaction between what the editor desires and what the printer's technologists can provide. Reappraisal may be necessary.

Printing follows agreement on satisfactory copy and from here the activity becomes technical: printing, collating, binding. Finally the magazine is distributed to the potential audience.

This operational sequence takes place with the production of each issue and involves the two activities of editing and printing. Logically the next activity to consider is of a different kind: the monitoring of the success of the operational activities by the other sub-system, that concerned with the operations as a business activity. This we may add to the operational diagram by representing it as an operation concerned with the whole of it, as in Figure 19.6.

The "monitor" activity itself will consist of appraising resources, making a plan to use those resources, comparing performance with plan and replanning. This sequence can

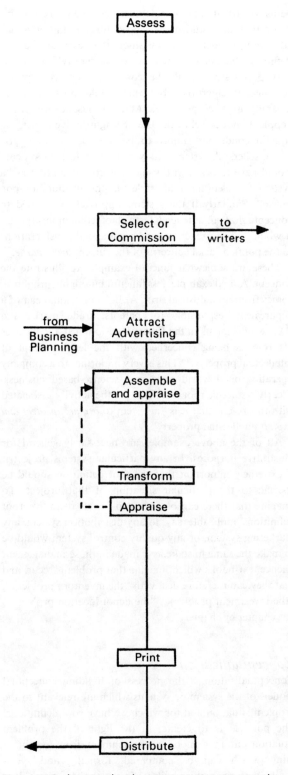

Figure 19.5 An operational system to create one magazine.

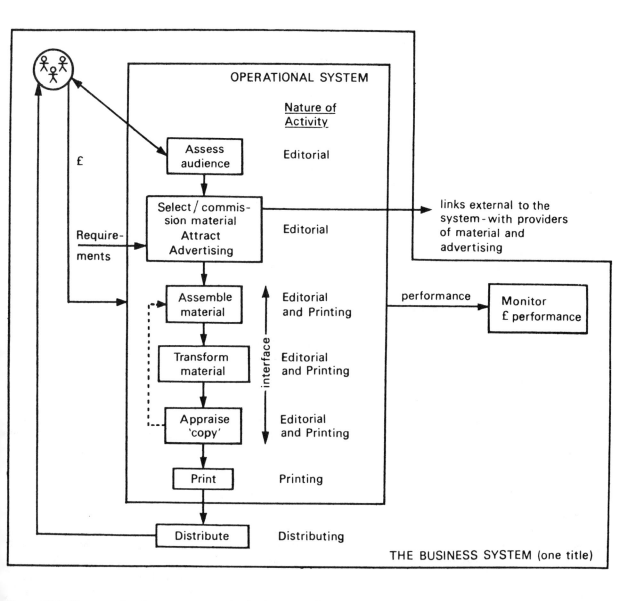

Figure 19.6 The operational system as part of a business system.

usefully replace the box "Monitor £ performance" in Figure 19.6, the right-hand side of which now becomes as shown in Figure 19.7.

The next consideration is that the resources which are the subject of this (single title) plan must be provided by a wider system whose concern is the use of resources covering other titles as well as this one. This wider system will be concerned with:

(a) providing resources for this title, or not providing them, depending upon its assessment of the total resources available,

(b) the relative merits (subjectively and/or quantitatively assessed) of different plans, and

(c) other more general considerations which in this business might be of the kind "In spite of its profitability we will not publish pornography".

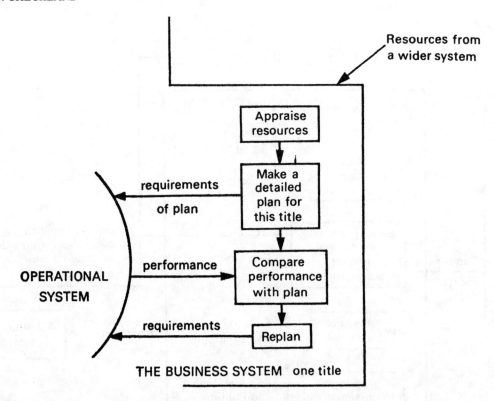

Figure 19.7 Expansion of the "Monitor" activity.

The conceptualization may now proceed in two directions.

At a more detailed level it is now possible to examine each activity in the diagrams above and answer the questions:

What information is needed to take this action?
What is its source?
Where is it received?
When is it sent? With what frequency? In what form?

The chart containing the answers to these questions and the diagrams above could then be used to draw up diagrams of

(a) operational and business system structures, and
(b) the information flows within those structures.

At a higher level, attention now turns to the wider system whose existence was a necessary postulate when considering the "monitor" activity of the business system for one title. This system will be concerned with appraising the *total* resources available, collecting information relevant

to overall plans, making individual-title outline plans, appraising whether these require extra resources not available within the company or leave resources unused, allocating resources to individual operational systems, monitoring performance and controlling via modifications to plans. In addition, a planning system at this level must also be concerned with long-term survival, and must contain a sub-system concerned with long-term appraisal of changes both internal and external. Internal changes will include investment in other resources, or divestment, and external changes will include changes in the nature of the market for successive "images", in the entertainment/education business. All this may be represented as in Figure 19.8.

In the event, the crux of this analysis turned out to be the central box of Figure 19.8, in which a central body can take decisions concerning particular titles – especially how and where to print them – in the light of overall knowledge of the total use of resources. It was this aspect which was highlighted in the "Compare" phase.

The activity described above consists of the first stages of conceptualization of a "formal" system for publishing

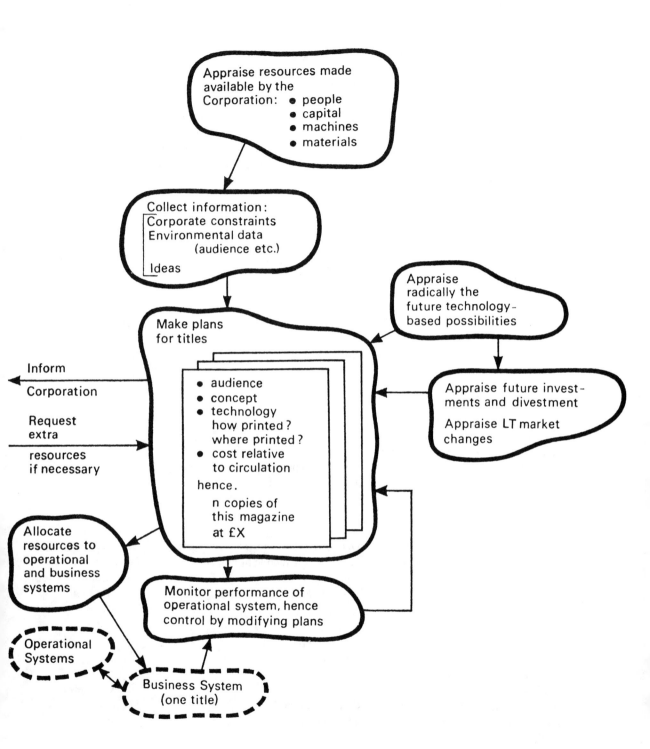

Figure 19.8   The overall business system.

magazines as a business activity. How can we have any certainty that it is "valid"? In absolute terms we cannot achieve that certainty, but it has been found useful to develop a simple general model of a purposeful human activity system and to use it as a means of ensuring that as the conceptualization proceeds the conceptual model does not lack some vital aspect or component. The emphasis has been on usability rather than sophistication, but obviously anyone may guide and validate a conceptualization by means of whatever systems concepts he finds helpful – I am thinking of material like Ackoff's compendium of systems concepts[21] or Beer's cybernetic model of an organization based on analogy with the central nervous system.[22]

In the present work it has been found useful to use a simple model which is a compilation of components which have to be present if an (open) human activity system is to be capable of purposeful activity, the latter defined to cover "maintaining relationships" as well as "achieving objectives". The model extends Jenkins' earlier "summary of properties of systems"[14] and follows Churchman's "Anatomy of System Teleology".[23]

The model, and two illustrations of it are as follows. Figure 19.9 is a picture-summary.

S is a "formal system" if, and only if:	Examples	
	Industrial Firm	University
(i) S has an objective, a mission, a definition of a final desirable state, or an ongoing purposes.	Exploitation of particular technological skills in a particular market? Social responsibilities? Survival?	Discovery, preservation and transfer of knowledge?
(ii) S has a measure of performance.	Financial performance? Profit? Employee relations? Public image?	Class hours? Public image? Publications? Ability to attract students and staff?
(iii) S has sub-components which are themselves systems (with objectives, measures of performance, sub-systems, etc.)	Divisions? Departments? Projects? (because Departments often are not related to mission) Functions? (e.g. Manpower Planning)	Academic departments? Functions? "Schools"? Individuals?
(iv) S has sub-components which interact, which show a degree of *connectivity* such that effects and actions can be transmitted through the system.	Divisions, Departments, Projects, Functions interacting by flows of money? materials? energy? information? decisions? instructions?	Academic departments, Functions, interacting by flows of money? information? opinions? advice?
(v) S exists in wider systems and/or environments with which it interacts (inputs and outputs). Boundaries are defined by the area within which the decision takers (vii) can cause action to be taken.	The economy? Government policy? The market (consumer preferences)?	U.G.C. policy? D.E.S. policy? Public opinion? Student opinion? Future employers?

		Examples	
		Industrial Firm	**University**
(vi)	S has resources, both physical and, through the human components, abstract.	Money? Men? Materials? Machines?	Money? Men? Materials? Machines?
(vii)	S contains a decision taker and a decision taking process. (Action is caused to be taken – which requires information flows via (iv)).	Various levels of management? Unions? Employees at all levels?	Council? Senate? H.O.D's? Staff? Students?
(viii)	S has some guarantee of continuity, is not ephemeral, will recover stability after disturbance ('long-run stability').	Government subsidies? Society's basic need for the products?	Society's commitment to enlightenment? Immunity from political attack? Shared beliefs?

Use of the model consists of asking, of the conceptual model, questions based on it, for example: What are the definable sub-systems and are the influences on them of their environments taken into account in the activities of the system?

Comparison and definition of possible changes

Judgement must be exercised as to when to finish a conceptualization and move to an explicit comparison of it with what exists in the problem situation. In the publishing/printing project the nature and level of the problems was such that the conceptual model was not pressed as far as the detailed examination of information flows implied by the activities in the model. In the textile company on the other hand the conceptualization included a detailed specification of the required information flows including their source, content, recipient, frequency and form. Similarly the comparison may be in general terms: how does the mode of operation and structure of the conceptual model compare with what exists in the real world as it emerged from the analysis? Or it may be highly specific; in a later stage of work in the textile company, when attention turned to the distribution system, a conceptualization was used to define a written set of detailed specific questions which were then answered by reference to present arrangements.

At whatever level to detail it is carried out, the comparison is done in order to reveal possible changes which could "improve" the problem situation.

In the publishing/printing company the comparison revealed about half a dozen major areas in which it was useful to debate the differences between the model and the reality. For example major implications of the model were:

– that important decisions concerning environment forecasts, magazine specification, resource acquisition and allocation, control of the business in the light of developments affecting many titles, and the decision where to print were taken within one system which itself assembled information relevant to those decisions

– that the summation of individual plans would be related to total resources available within the group.

– that the printer's activity was explicitly linked to his role in the magazine publishing system, and was not an autonomous profit generator.

– that individual printing contracts would not be negotiated individually.

– that an 'R and D' activity is concerned with the future of the business not just of the technology.

Discussion of all these, and comparison with present arrangements led to insight into the reasons for present arrangements being what they were, and enabled formulation of seven possible significant changes which could

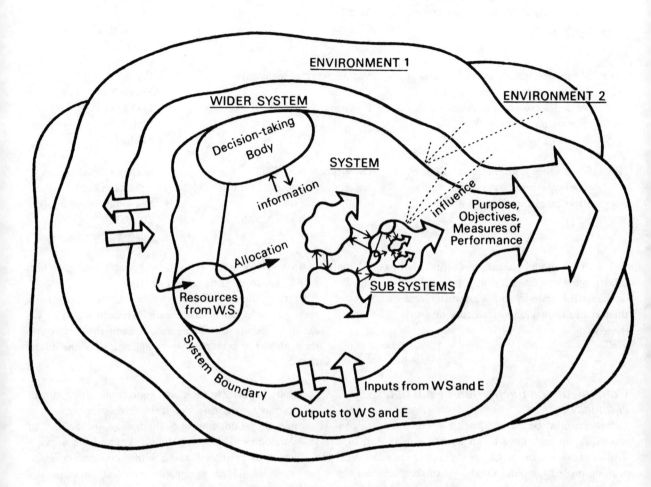

Figure 19.9 A simple model of a purposeful human activity system—a "formal system".

hopefully improve the problem, which, interestingly, had still never been stated in any precise way. "Changes" ranged from major structural changes in the organization and its management to the appointment of "title managers" at printers with the specific task of liaison with the publishing and editorial groups concerned with a particular magazine or group of magazines. Each potential change was assessed in terms of the *kind* of change involved (structural, procedural, attitudinal, or a change in the environment) and the subjectively assessed *amount* of change, and estimates were made of whether the changes would be acceptable to middle managers given the atti-

tudes revealed during the interviews of the analysis phase.

In the event the managing director's committee accepted from the central planning group, with whom we were working, a proposal for a new organizational unit concerned with the "where to print?" decision.

Two points should be reiterated. Firstly, in the Comparison stage of the study the conceptual model is there to help tackle the problem solving in a structured way, not to prescribe what "ought" to exist. Conceptual models tend to be ahistoric, unless the root definition can capture something of the previous history of the situation – which is difficult – and in any case such models have an antiseptic inhuman air. Implemented conceptual models would require inhuman beings to operate them. Secondly, the Comparison stage consists of a debate in which only those who live in the problem situation can select a change to be implemented. The systems analyst may state and defend a particular suggestion but the decision for action can only be made by the actors, not the analyst.

Design and implementation

In work in hard systems the assumption of the appropriate methodologies is that "design" is "design of the system to be engineered", and versions of the codified methods of engineering design, involving modelling, simulation and optimization can be used.

The author's experience in softer studies was that this concept had to be abandoned; "design" becomes design of a "change" selected as a result of the root definition/conceptualization/comparison process. Design here is not the creation of something which will perform in some specified people-proof way to achieve some defined objective, it is the creation of some modification to which purposeful individuals are prepared to give their commitment.

It is not easy to generalize about this stage because the "design" activity is intended to be specific to a particular situation at a particular time, involving particular people and a particular history. The most useful generalization which emerges from experience is that when faced with a significant task of implementation it can be useful to treat *it* as "the problem situation" and apply the methodology!

A systems project in 1972 in a manufacturing company was concerned with the implementation of the use of a rather sophisticated management tool (related to production planning and product assembly) which had been developed in previous studies. It was found helpful to view "implementation" as an activity system of limited life in which the decision-taking body would at first be those who developed the management tool and later would gradually become the managers who would make day-to-day use of it; as soon as these managers became the decision takers in a system which makes use of the tool the temporary "implementation" system would cease to exist and the developers of the tool could leave the stage. Progress was made by viewing implementation in this way and then using the conceptualization process as described above, in the light of existing management modes, to plan the introduction of the management tool.

Appraisal and reiteration

Including an Appraisal stage in the methodology is a dignified way of saying "Start again". It is included not only as a reminder that any of the stages might cause reiteration of earlier stages – either because, for example, the analysis is revealed as too shallow or the root definition lacking in insight (or too radical) – but also because the whole bias of the methodology is against the notion of once-and-for-all finite tasks and in favour of on-going purposeful maintenance of relationships. By the time implementation is accomplished the initial "problem situation" may well have changed. Changing attitudes and new experiences will make new root definitions relevant; more sophisticated notions of a formal system may require the conceptualization to be changed; and so on.

The methodology is a methodology for problem-solving only in the sense that "problem solving" is a way of describing normal human activity.

Finally we may briefly summarize the methodology as a sequence of stages, as shown in Figure 19.10, while remembering that in any real-life study they will tend ·to merge, and that iteration will almost certainly be necessary as developments in stages 3 to 6 cast doubt on the validity of the original analysis and conceptualization.

5 Further experience of using the methodology
Some general lessons

The methodology described in Section 4 derived from the author's inability to use "systems analysis" methodologies, with their concentration on explicit definition of objectives and "optimization" of "designs" on problems which were so woolly and unstructured that considering them in those terms rapidly caused the onset of a state described by Wittgenstein's phrase: "The methods pass the problems by". Attempts to remain at grips with the problems and yet draw out generalizations from a number of experiences led to the first formulation of the new methodology during nine systems studies carried out in 1969, 1970 and 1971. Increasingly precise formulation of it since then has enabled the author and colleagues to try to use it in more than twenty further studies. Some of the lessons learnt are summarized in this section.

The main lesson is that believing one has understood this way of tackling ill-structured problems is much easier than actually using it. There is a holding back involved in it, a refusal to entertain possible solutions until the analysis

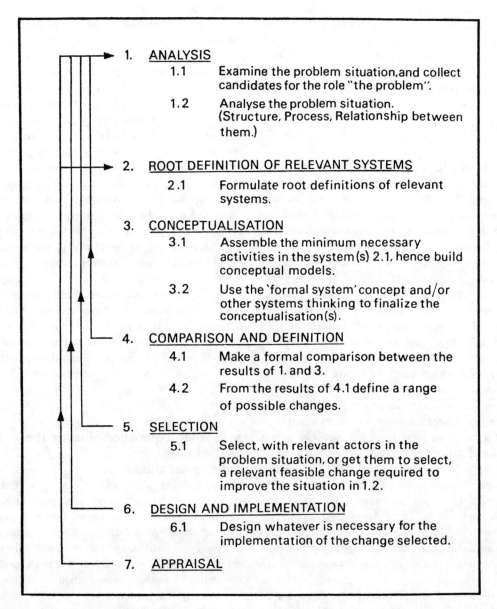

Figure 19.10   A summary of the methodology.

and the hard thinking which follows it have been completed, which accords ill with the most popular form of problem solving, namely to find some element in the problem situation which is striking, and to leap from that to possible solutions, subsequently, perhaps, taking into account a few of the interactions which obtrude. A management consultant visiting one of the companies in which we were working expressed amazement at the thoroughgoing nature of the analysis phase. "We try to start implementing something in the first week", he said, "in order to convince the client we are active". This outlook, commercially understandable in a consultant, unfortunately applies frequently to people trying to solve their own problems. Taking some kind of action is undoubtedly easier than thinking, and there is a common temperament, action rather than insight-oriented, which finds application of the methodology very difficult indeed. (It is not at all surprising that when Descartes' friends found him in bed at eleven o'clock in the morning, and he said he was "Thinking", they were furious.)

In fact there is nothing in the methodology which links its phases to a time scale: implementation might start within a week. If only one hour is available for conceptualization then the conceptual model will be the best which can be produced within an hour. In a short successful project in 1972 analysis took a week or two and the root definition, conceptualization and comparison stages were then all completed within one day; whereas in a major study currently underway the analysis phase is to occupy three months and the subsequent root definition of relevant systems may occupy some considerable time and involve wide debate.

Other general lessons concern the stages of the methodology itself. In the analysis phase it is often difficult for anyone with any systems training to avoid an analysis in systems terms, the most common error being to assume that internal organizational boundaries are system boundaries. This confusion has more than once led to conceptualization being a tidied-up description of what exists, rather than a rigorous-as-possible building up of what must follow from the root definition.

Formulation of root definitions is obviously not easy, but experience shows that it is better to accept one temporarily and return to refine it later, than to agonize over the initial formulation, since logically there can be no way of knowing that the definition is in any sense "correct". There are as many potential root definitions as there are ways of choosing to view a situation; the aim should be to choose one specific to the particular problem situation of the study. The best systems projects have been those with root definitions unique to the particular situation, defining not "a corporate planning system", perhaps, but "a strategic planning system (responsible to the Chief Executive) whose implemented plans will enable the organization to decide within two years whether or not it would be advantageous to move from marketing product W in market X, to marketing a service Y which involves the use of W, in market Z".

The greatest difficulty with conceptualization, apart from the intrinsic difficulties of deciding logically what activities in what sequence are necessary and sufficient to meet the implications of the root definition, lies in the temptation to regard it as a means of defining "the ideal". This is a temptation also for whoever it is who wants a solution to the problem, and it is worth special efforts to ensure that the Conceptualization and Compare stages are accepted by the client only as a way of viewing the problem situation in a structured way.

This difficulty is probably related to the "what/how" problem. Root definitions and conceptualizations are concerned with the "what" of problem situations; what elements do they contain, *what is their nature?* These are matters susceptible to relatively objective analysis. They enable the powerful weapon of logical thought to be used. Definition of feasible changes, and selection of a change to make in the actual situation, however, are concerned with "how" a particular client reacts to the problem situation; the "how" can accommodate all kinds of constraints, all kinds of deference to history, ignorance, prejudice or plain irrationality. Experience with the methodology so far suggests that many "problems" *are* problems because those who face them tenaciously cling to a "how" as if it were a "what". For example, consider a company which, given its particular business, has a need to produce technical innovations (that is a "what" in their situation). They might have a particular way of coping with that requirement which consists of having a Research Department, a Design Department and a Sales Department (that is their "how"). But that is only one particular "how" out of innumberable possibilities. Conceptualization of "an innovation system" and comparison with present arrangements would bring out the importance of "what" and the relative unimportance of any particular "how". The point being made is that this distinction is not an easy one to elucidate in real situations, and more work is needed on this aspect of the methodology.

Further project experiences

Some aspects of several of the projects which since 1971 have helped to enrich the methodology are now described.

(i) A project in an industrial company which manufactures synthetic fibres illustrated the value of the notion in the "formal system" model (see Section 4) that a system boundary is defined by the area within which a decision-taking body can exercise authority.

The problem situation was one in which the fibre manufacturer made a yarn which was sold to the textile trade for further processing; the processed yarn was bought by weavers or knitters and finally reached the consumer in a garment. Complaints at the garment stage or earlier obviously tended to be passed back down the processing chain and ultimately lodged with the fibre manufacturer.

Given the nature of this total yarn-to-garment system it is clear that it is logical for the management of the fibre manufacturer to be the decision-taker of a smaller system whose boundary coincides with the organizational boundary between himself and the yarn processor *only* if there exists a test which can be made on the original yarn which will indicate predictively that the yarn will be satisfactory at all stages through to the final garment. Such a test ensures that the yarn which passes it will make an acceptable garment as long as the yarn processing, knitting and garment making are done properly. Equally, if the yarn passes the test, faulty goods subsequently must be due to mistakes outside the fibre manufacturer's system. Unfortunately *no such test exists*; so that unless the market is extremely buoyant, there is an inherent weakness in the fibre manufacturer's position. The obvious solution, from a systems point of view, is for the fibre manufacturer to make himself the decision-taker of a system which includes the steps beyond yarn manufacture. Those who know this industry will be aware that this has been happening in recent years.

(ii) A rather unusual use of the methodology occurred in a project in which a remarkably open-minded professional consultant asked for a systems analysis of one of his completed assignments which both he and his client felt had had an unsatisfactory outcome.

Here the analysis was historical, involving interviews with both consultant and client, and the root definition and conceptualization stages consisted of an examination of what would have happened if consultant and client had consciously and mutually engineered a (temporary) system to tackle the client's problem. This was different from what had actually happened, and the differences suggested ways in which the consultant should change his mode of operation.

(iii) Most of the early projects were carried out in user-supported organizations (using Vickers' distinction between user-supported and public-supported,[15b] which is more insightful than the more usual "private sector" and "public sector"). Here there will be relatively easy-to-define aims for the organization and identifiable decision-taking bodies. Some of the more recent work has been in public-supported organizations where aims, decision-taking and control are more diffuse. Here it is more likely that the outcome of the systems work will be a structure for a debate.

Work in a hospital, for example, was concerned with an ill-defined problem connected with "the use of resources consequent upon medical decisions". Two groups are primarily concerned: doctors who would like to be able to take medical decisions as if the resources were infinite, and administrators who are primarily concerned with the limited nature of the resources and the fact that they are allocated to the hospital at certain time intervals.

Here the methodology was used to initiate and structure discussion between medical staff and administrators on the problems of resource allocation. Agreed experiments on resource-use planning came out of these discussions.

(iv) Beyond the diffuse problems of public-supported organizations are the yet more diffuse social problems which are not confined within organization boundaries. If you are a member of a government "think tank" you are likely to be given the problem of "the future of the National Health Service", or "juvenile delinquency", problems with societal rather than organizational boundaries. Can the methodology help?

Tentative findings are that it can be useful to tease out and formulate root definitions *as if* they could be made manifest in an organization. For example, if we were to examine the question of the future of the N.H.S. in the United Kingdom in these terms one useful strand in the examination might well be to recognize that what we have at present can be viewed as a National Ill-health Service, concerned with treating those who have become ill. A root definition of a *Health* Service might be more concerned with defining the possible state of health of a population, given the state of medical knowledge, measuring the present state of health, and formulating plans to bring the latter nearer to what is possible. The World Health Organization is actually doing some work on these lines.[24]

The approach might be a useful part of an appraisal of the N.H.S., but this is speculation: the project has not been done! One non-organization-based project which has been started is to consider the problem of the use of the Northern Uplands of England and Southern Scotland. This is an area which is of interest to many different groups for different reasons: farmers, local authorities, national Government, land owners, commercial interests, the military, amenity interests, etc. The problem is being examined by conceptualizing a *notional* "system to manage the uses of the Northern Uplands". Such a system will never be embodied in an organization but conceptualizing it does provide a way into the analysis which enables the different aspects of the problem to be marshalled in a hopefully neutral manner. The outcome is as yet uncertain, but this kind of approach will be vindicated if it achieves the modest aim of a survey which is "better than piecemeal".

6 Conclusion

The idea of a methodology for problem solving in the real world is a curious one. The nature and status of such a methodology is not obvious, as may be illustrated by considering what it is not.

It is not a technique. A technique is a procedure which if applied correctly in a suitable situation will with certainty produce a known result: there are *techniques* for making a cricket ball swing, for launching space rockets, for handling queueing problems mathematically, and for myriad other activities. The methodology does not have that kind of certainty.

It is not a science. A science is characterized in practice by paradigms which define meaningful experiments,[3] and by the repeatability of experimental results; and in logic by the progress which can be made by the refutation of hypotheses, as Popper establishes.[25] The methodology does not measure up to this prescription. Although it is based on the systems paradigm, we cannot obtain or expect repeatable results in purposeful systems, and the idea of making progress via refutation is equally inapplicable. Thus if a reader tells the author "I have used your methodology and it works", the author will have to reply "How do you know that better results might not have been obtained by an *ad hoc* approach?" If the assertion is: "The methodology does not work" the author may reply, ungraciously but with logic, "How do you know the poor results were not due simply to your incompetence in using the methodology?"

If the methodology is not a technique and is not a science, what then is it? Some further negative statements are helpful:

It is not optimum-seeking; it seeks what are agreed by concerned people to be "improvements". The powerful but unreasonable hunger for "optimum" solutions in human activity systems will remain unsatisfied, happily, just because those systems are purposeful, that is to say, human.

It is not utopian; it does not *require* any definition of ultimate goal or objective, only an elucidation of ongoing purpose.

It is hence not a methodology of system design, only of conceptualization, and design of changes.

In summary: the methodology tries to face the fact that problem solving is dependent upon problem structuring. It provides through systems ideas a way of seeing diffuse, ill-structured problems in a patterned way, and tries to do so without distorting the problems in the way that application of techniques usually does. It seeks not to be reductionist but to provide a conceptual framework within which many different aspects of problem situations can be accommodated. It enables those who have a concern for a problem to make decisions – incremental or radical – aimed at solving, alleviating or eliminating it.

The methodology has been found to be helpful in a wide range of problems of many different types; but given the nature of it even that is an assertion which cannot be *proved*.

Acknowledgements

The author is extremely grateful to all of those people, colleagues, students and managers, with whom he has discussed the methodology as it has evolved.

Firstly I am grateful to my colleague Gwilym Jenkins who with boldness and drive conceived and established the action research programme which was the vehicle for this work.

I am also especially grateful to those who struggled with me on the systems studies which are the source of this paper: R. H. Anderton, T. R. Barnett, D. H. Brown, J. H. Collins, C. H. Pogson, L. Watson, I. Woodburn, D. G. W. Allen, D. J. Brown, R. Griffin, G. R. Hewitt, N. G. Jarman, R. W. Keen, G. L. Moss, W. P. Murray, D. C. Nevin, D. J. Scott, G. Severn, A. R. Thomas, D. I. Thomas, A. M. Waugh.

Finally I am grateful to Ross Barnett for his constructive criticisms of the first version of the paper, which enabled a number of improvements to be made.

References

1 Checkland, P. B., "A Systems Approach to Management: a discussion of the St. Gallen Symposium", *J. Sys. Eng.*, **3**, No. 1, 1972.

2 Checkland, P. B., "A Systems Map of the Universe", *J. Sys. Eng.*, **2**, No. 2, 1971.

3 Kuhn, T. S., "The Structure of Scientific Revolutions", University of Chicago Press, 1962,

4 Bertalanffy, L. von, "General System Theory", Braziller, 1968.

5 (a) Jenkins, G. M., "Systems and their Optimisation", Inaugural Lecture, University of Lancaster, 1967.

   (b) Checkland, P. B., "Systems and Science, Industry and Innovation", Inaugural Lecture, University of Lancaster, 1969, and *J. Sys. Eng.*, 1, No. 2, 1970.

6 Boulding, K. E., "General Systems Theory – the Skeleton of Science", *Management Science*, 2, No. 3, 1956.

7 Dror, Y., "A General Systems Approach to Uses of Behavioural Sciences for better Policymaking", Rand Paper P. 4091.

8 Popper, K. R., "The Open Society and its Enemies", Routledge, 1945.

9 Hall, A. D., "A Methodology for Systems Engineering", Van Nostrand, 1962.

10 Chestnut, H., "Systems Engineering Methods", Wiley, 1967.

11 Optner, S. L. (Ed.), "Systems Analysis", Penguin Books, 1973.

12 Hitch, C., "An Appreciation of Systems Analysis", Rand Corporation, 1955.

13 Quade, E. S. and Boucher, W. I. (Eds.), "Systems Analysis and Policy Planning: Applications in Defence", Elsevier, 1968.

14 Jenkins, G. M., "The Systems Approach", *J. Sys. Eng.*, 1, No. 1, 1969. (Article 8).

15 (a) Vickers, G., "Value Systems and Social Process", Tavistock, 1968.

   (b) Vickers, G., "Freedom in a Rocking Boat", Allen Lane, the Penguin Press, 1970.

16 Forster, M., "An Introduction to the Theory and Practice of Action Research in Work Organisations", *Human Relations*, 25, No. 6.

17 Rapaport, R. N., "Three Dilemmas in Action Research", *Human Relations*, 23, No. 6.

18 Checkland, P. B. and Griffin, R., "Management Information Systems: A Systems View", *J. Sys. Eng.*, 1, No. 2, 1970.

19 Emery, F. E. and Trist, E. L., "The Causal Texture of Organisational Environments", *Human Relations*, 18, No. 1, 1965.

20 Thompson, A. B., Lecture at Lancaster University, 1971.

21 Ackoff, R. L., "Towards a System of System Concepts", *Management Science*, 17, No. 11, 1971.

22 Beer, S., "Brain of the Firm", Allen Lane, The Penguin Press, 1972.

23 Churchman, C. W., "The Design of Inquiring Systems", Basic Books, 1971.

24 Litsios, S., "General Introduction to Organisation and Strategy of Health Services Research". Paper to a meeting of the Scientific Group on Research in Epidemiology and Communications Science; WHO, Geneva, October, 1970.

25 (a) Popper, K. R., "The Logic of Scientific Discovery", Hutchinson, 1959.

   (b) Popper, K. R., "Conjectures and Refutations", Routledge, 1963.

Reprinted from Checkland, P. B. (1972) "Towards a system-based methodology for real-world problem solving" *Journal of Systems Engineering*, 3, 2.

20 Engineers as analysts of social systems: A critical enquiry
by Ida R. Hoos

Semantics of systems analysis

Not since M. Jourdain, the untutored tradesman in Molière's play, *Le Bourgeois Gentilhomme,* made the happy discovery that prose was what he had been talking all his life, has there appeared so ubiquitous and so handy a talent as "systems capability". In its common and current usage, this term denotes the ability to study, design, devise, revise and/or analyze systems. And here we encounter the first booby trap, created by the loose lexicology of the word *system*. Resort to Webster's Dictionary confuses rather than clarifies, with a generous offering of some seventeen definitions from which to choose. There are many more. Every writer on the subject seeks to achieve refinement of conceptualization through verbalization, a not uncommon ploy in the realm of the written word. Generally accepted ingredients of a working definition may be found in the following: "a set of interrelated components working together to accomplish a certain objective".* Not a bad statement, this. But not very useful, either, for it can be applied with equal appropriateness to my toaster and to TWA. Herein lies the making of another booby trap, that of fallacious analogy, for to impute verisimilitude where only superficial similarity exists leads to nonsensical conclusions about everything, including skill transfer. In this instance, to the fixit man who tinkers with my toaster will be attributed the capability of coping with TWA, its fleet of aircraft, its worldwide ticketing procedures, its luggage transfer and tracing mechanisms, its pilot and personnel training practices and whatever of these singularly or collectively may come under the heading of *system*.

Not intended as mere pedantry, this example typifies the slippery semantic basis on which the "systems approach" has been rationalized as the panacea for society's ailments, past and future. Here at long last, we are led to believe, is the end of the by-guess-and-by-gorry era; horse-and-buggy methods are passé. We have the systems approach to win

* Borrowed from C. West Churchman.

wars, design strategies for peace, curb crime, devise transportation, improve managerial efficiency in public and private sector alike, and guarantee a braver new world for the future. In our era of advanced technology, we have "space-age techniques", as those associated with and derived from the systems approach are often called. Much like *jinn* (defined by Webster as "rational, but intangible beings"), these are the tools presumably appropriate to our every task and ready to serve our purposes.

Development of engineering as a profession

That the engineering community should condone, let alone encourage, so amorphous a state of conceptualization as that which exists with respect to both the techniques and their application is an anomaly, particularly when one reviews the historical development of engineering. Ever since the Middle Ages, when engineering was regarded as a kind of "craft mystery" – a combination of artistry, intuition, and trial and error – there has been a discernible trend towards differentiation and specialization. During the Renaissance, the making of engines for battle (hence the word *engineer*), the draining of mines and building of roads and bridges called for specific skills. Associations and societies reflected and strengthened the push towards greater differentiation. In recent years, professionalization and specialization have advanced in tandem relationship, with proliferation of fields within fields occurring; thus, the advent of nuclear engineering and computer technology since World War II. Each classification has generated its own body of theory, its own analytical descriptions and idealized models. To judge from the meticulous articulation of requirements for academic degrees in each, "crossover" or "passing" has been virtually impossible. In practice, the electrical engineer does not presume to design bridges; the nuclear engineer does not concern himself with sewage treatment; the computer specialist constructs no dams. But, in the present popular proclivity for *social* systems work, the demarcations again become blurred. Engineers *en masse* are exhorted by the deans of their colleges to turn their talents to solving the amorphous mess known as social problems – to become "public technologists", "civil science experts" and to tackle health, education and welfare as their social duty.

With heritage couched in the military so cosily that a special term, *civil engineering*, had to be coined to describe activities in the civilian sphere, perhaps engineering may be suffering from a case of what psychiatrists call "collective unconscious guilt". Psychologists have identified conscious guilt among workers in munitions factories, and engineers employed in the California experiment, to be discussed later, expressed the desire to be able to tell the wife and kids what they did at work. Perhaps, on the other hand, the quest for social service is a manifestation of the current striving for relevance.

With commencement exercises exhorting greater social commitment and professors urging a deeper dedication to social values, even to the extent of their taking a kind of Hippocratic oath (*New York Times,* 1973), engineers are being pushed willy-nilly into new roles.

They are caught between the Scylla of "doing their own thing well", which, in its pathological extreme, has earned the label of "Eichmannism", and the Charybdis of abandoning their specialized capabilities in favour of a generalized doing of the public good. If the proposed code of ethics is to serve a useful purpose, its details must be spelled out. Otherwise, the implication would be allowed to stand that engineers have within their power the capacity, that the state-of-the-art has advanced to the point, and that all that is needed is a moral commitment, for them to solve social problems. Perhaps ethical dedication could more properly take the form of more mundane and less esoteric matters. Here is a random list of activities for engineers seeking "social relevance": medical electronics not so faulty that they deliver death while monitoring (London, 1971), overpasses that do not cave in, television sets not hazardous for electric shock potential, cars that perform safely even without the vigilance of Nader's crusaders.

Redundantly but inexorably, the breaking down of time-honoured boundaries has come about through abdication of the very specificity and precision that formerly made for professionality. Through the conduit of "systems" which, variously defined, are the stock-in-trade of all branches of engineering, a kind of amalgamation has occurred. They all deal with systems; hence, they produce "systems experts". And with systems loosely defined to fit everything from the afore-mentioned toasters to TWA, the circular semantic syllogism is complete.

Systems analysis as panacea

It behoves us to ascertain how this came about and where it is likely to lead. As to the first question, the phenomenon of receptivity towards systems techniques as a nostrum for all of society's ailments is not pure happenstance. Since, as historiographers inform us, ours is the computer age, the scientific civilization or the space age, then consistent with our *Zeitgeist** is the notion that technological solutions are the ones best suited to solving our problems, the more so, it is argued, because a preponderance of these problems can be attributed to or are associated with technological causes. And since enormous and growing complexity is an outstanding characteristic of our web and tangle of social problems, only systems analysis, with its capacity to embrace the whole, order the parts and achieve "rational" goals with mathematical precision, is adequate to the task at hand.

But systems analysis has more than a temporal relationship with the space age; systems analysis epitomizes the space age. When the overworked cliché, "A nation that can put a man on the moon can . . .", is evoked to prove technical prowess, reference is being made, wittingly or unwittingly, directly or indirectly, to the systems methods used with singular success in space exploration and, previously, under the name of *operations research,* in the Battle of Britain. Adding to the aura of invincibility was the US Secretary of Defence McNamara's astute use of the techniques in convincing Congress that war was too big business for the generals. With the whiz kids and the Rand Corporation to bedazzle and bemuse an unsophisticated Congress, the "scientific management" of procurement and strategy was added as a triumphant chapter to the saga of systems analysis. That the wizardry was short-lived, that subsequent Congressional investigations revealed fatal weaknesses in the techniques as management tools for the business of war are facts that have been cavalierly overlooked. A legend once born, a mythology was in the making. And those who could have penetrated the miasma swathing the high priests chose instead to take personal advantage of it. McNamara's band spun out to all branches of government and, in their endeavours, were joined by a heterogeny of professionals, paraprofessionals and pseudo-professionals – all bent on solving society's problems "scientifically and rationally". No one elected to keep

---

* Spirit of the times.

the emperor honestly naked. And so systems analysis and its counterparts and components, management information systems, cost/benefit measures, programme budgeting, performance and production evaluations, and the like have pursued a chameleon-like course, appearing in one guise or another in every branch and at every level of government. And, at every stage of this numbers game, there are "expert technicians", eager to desert their wonted fields for greener pastures. Engineers may not always be in the vanguard but their tools are!

In its journey from strictly engineering tasks and texts to the realm of the military and outer space, systems analysis has undergone considerable transformation. Lost is the methodological rigour sought in its original state; what remains are the empty forms, devoid of content. Jingo and jargon substitute for precision, the more so as systems analysis becomes the stock-in-trade of the motley assemblage of practitioners now claiming expertness. Besides the many kinds of engineers, there are economists, urban planners, policy analysts, operations researchers, management scientists, econometricians and even sociologists. Engineering firms, computer manufacturers and assorted research institutes and "think tanks" are all busy peddling what has come to be known as "knowledge technology".

Perpetration and perpetuation of a hoax need not, however, be inferred as the reasons for the continuing bastardization of what were respectable and legitimate concepts in their own discipline. Systems analysis has come to represent the "dominant paradigm", to use Kuhn's (1971) term, of our time. (Kuhn describes the concept as a fundamental way of perceiving, thinking and doing, consistent with a particular vision of reality.) Acceptance of the paradigm which, says Kuhn, gains status if it has been demonstrated to solve *some* kinds of urgent problems, affords it a kind of legitimacy. It becomes a kind of language. Systems analysis can therefore be considered the dominant paradigm of our era. The prevailing mental set is such that approaches with technical trappings, that feature quantitative measures and which sound "scientific", enjoy a hospitable environment. So welcome was the transplant of the tools from technical to social matters that the California experiment, conspicuous for its pioneering in this respect, became an historic landmark, criticism of which smacked of unpatriotic, perhaps even subversive, opposition to "scientific progress".

The California experiment

The original four contracts won plaudits without proving anything more decisive than the power of politics and salesmanship. Systems analysis was the vehicle designated by then Governor Brown to convey space-age techniques to the public arena, where he wanted them utilized to design systems of criminal justice, information handling, waste management and mass transportation. Brown stressed growing magnitude and complexity of such public concerns as the factors rendering them amenable to systems analytic treatment. Improved governance was not his only objective. There was also the hope that the public sector would provide employment opportunity and avenues for diversification for skilled manpower threatened with job loss due to retrenchment in California's aerospace and defence industries. Although committees reviewing the proposals, submitted by an array of accounting firms, research institutes, computer manufacturers and aerospace companies, insisted that the sole criterion was merit, selection of the latter for the four original contracts may not have been due to pure chance, nor to undisputed superiority over all other contenders. The fact that Lockheed, North American Aviation, Aerojet General and Space General were chosen lent initial credence and impetus to their subsequent campaign to dominate a market that was not yet displaying its full potential for bullishness.

Enquiry as to the qualifications of the engineers assigned to carry out the systems analysis of crime, transportation, etc., discloses a paradox. Many of them were chosen, not because of their demonstrated engineering capability but because of a college minor in Business Administration or a course in Sociology. With only a few exceptions, they were probably not the companies' most valued engineers but, perhaps, the most expendable. The tendency to use "public technology" as a dumping ground for surplus engineers has become even more apparent as traditional jobs in industry have dried up. Public concern has been aroused over this new kind of unemployment; in recent years, increasing joblessness among mid-career engineers in their middle years and in middle-income brackets has begun to cause uneasiness not only over the obvious economic consequences but about the more subtle possibility that long-cherished American myths would be undermined. Confidence in higher education as a guarantor of careers is shaking. Threatened are the neat correlations between unemployment and poor education, lack of skill and paucity of experience. To counteract a situation not statistically significant in total labour force numbers but unsettling as a sociological phenomenon, the League of Cities, the US Department of Labour and other agencies jointly sponsored programmes to facilitate the "reorientation" of aerospace engineers. These were built on the assumptions that *here* was a reservoir of "systems capability" and that *there* was an accumulation of ailing "social systems" and that all that was needed were the will and way to make a match.

All three were in error. To begin with, many of the displaced engineers had not been in systems work. In fact, national statistics show that only a minute proportion have. In the second place, although public management problems abound, labelling them "civil systems" or "public service systems" does not render them readily amenable to the engineer's treatment. In the third place, despite the will, which sometimes displayed the force of a juggernaut, and the way, which manifested itself in federal funds under the Public Employment Programme (PEP), the marriage did not last. The honeymoon was of short duration.

The engineers soon discovered the seriousness of the first booby trap mentioned earlier, i.e., the vagueness of the word *system*. For them a system was a thing; its working was governed by certain laws; its actions were controllable and predictable. In the realm of social affairs, the system is an *idea*; it is a construct. In the words of a political scientist, "all systems are human artifacts designed to facilitate choices . . . They are overwhelmingly dependent on the hierarchy of values in the mind of the system's architect . . . To adopt such systems as 'real' implies a belief in the 'naturalness' of an imperfect heuristic device" (Haas and Ruggle, 1975). Only the least important of a system's workings are subject to immutable laws; if its actions are controllable and predictable in the short run, long-run behaviour is all the more likely to defy precise calculation. Face to face in a real-life situation, the engineers did not know what to do and the public agencies did not know what to do with them. For the engineer accustomed to explicit tasks performed in a highly structured situation, the amorphous situation was unsettling. For the public official, the specification of managerial objectives was tantamount to the demand for a quantified *apologia pro sua vita*, and in many cases he was not able to provide it. Many of the positions created under PEP petered out when the funds were exhausted.

The case of public welfare

Let us consider, as a case in point, public welfare, so often chosen as a target for systems treatment. How does one define a "public welfare system"? Welfare is mainly a philosophy, a social commitment of concern for the less fortunate. It is a set of activities. It is a complex of history and laws that varies as to geographical location and

bureaucratic level. It is a tangle of relationships – between people, between conflicting and overlapping agencies, between intangible forces. It is a political whipping-boy, the brunt of blatant manipulation by officials who use its pliable statistics to suit their purposes. What are its objectives? The requests for proposals for systems studies stress "reduction of dependency". This would imply that welfare systems should be designed to get people off them. But one wonders whether that objective should not more properly be the responsibility of *other* systems in the society. If the education system supplied sufficient skills for success in jobs; if the labour market system behaved so as to provide adequate employment opportunities and pay; if there were a system of child care that would enable women to work; if public health systems operated in such fashion that illness would not be financially catastrophic; if public housing systems functioned so that people could live safely and decently even on low incomes – would not these be more socially desirable and more efficacious than a public welfare system "to reduce dependency"?

The engineers, faced with the frustration of reducing to a simplistic model the complexities of social welfare, resorted to the busy work of information gathering. Observation of innumerable systems studies indicates that this step, indicated as part of the larger analysis, often engulfs the whole effort. As a result, a systems analysis of any given system becomes preoccupied with its information as though that were an end in itself. For the engineers working on public welfare, development of an information system provided an activity which they found *gemütlich*. And, with their *Weltanschauung,* the objective of such a system was to save money by screening out all the bad guys, bums, free loaders and welfare cheats that they assumed must be the cause of the rising costs. What they designed was a system so expensive that its operations would have constituted a severe and permanent drain on the State, probably far exceeding the cost of maintaining the fraudulent cases that exist and never coming close to the big abuses countenanced by the political aspects of public welfare, nor to the realities involved in welfare costs.

The engineer soon discovers that crime, welfare and the like are not one system, but many systems, not one problem but many problems, only some of which fall within any disciplinary or "scientific" scope. Indeed, for most social problems, there is no technical or methodical "solution". Their very definition depends on the point of view of the analysis; his value system is imbedded in the way he designates the objectives, identifies pertinent variables and assigns costs and benefits. And in all these crucial matters, his schooling and experience as an engineer may hinder rather than help him. Thanks to the process of "trained incapacity" he, probably more than any other professional, purposefully rivets attention on certain types of problems or aspects of them and does well what he does, with careful disregard for those matters which he considers outside his purview.

Socialization of the engineer

With no pejorative intent, the point must be made that engineers, probably to a greater degree than any other group, are caught in the dilemma of social responsibility. Ethical issues have been considered by their professional associations only insofar as they have affected the relations of individual engineers with their colleagues and employers but rarely with the complex and diffuse questions relating to the society at large (National Society of Professional Engineers, 1962). Professor William M. Evans (1969), who has conducted authoritative research into this matter, offers the following theory:

> One reason for the widespread neglect on the part of engineers of the problem of social responsibility for technological change is the difficulty of accepting responsibility for events *over which they exercise no control*. As salaried employees performing in the main a staff function, engineers are rarely in a position of making policy decisions concerning the wisdom of developing or not developing a new engineering product, or concerning what, if any, action might be taken to counteract its potential or actual negative social effects. This is particularly true for the overwhelming proportion of engineers engaged in production or in development research, where the norms governing their conduct are neither *service* – typical of the professional-client relationship – nor *autonomy*, typical of the scientist-employer or in the science-patron relationship, but obedience, typical of the employee in the employer-employee relationship.

From C. P. Snow (1954) to Seymour Lipset (1972) with Smithers (1969) in between, we can, in addition, trace a pattern of career preferences, political perspectives and private aspirations that characterize engineers as possessed with "a basic lack of sociability" and a strong incidence of "low people-orientation".

Engineers, like all other forayers into unwonted places, demonstrate the validity of Abraham Maslow's (1966) sage maxim: "If the only tool you have is a hammer, you tend to treat everything as if it were a nail". With the systems approach the prevailing paradigm of our time, the tendency is to construe all of society's ailments as though they were malfunctioning "systems"; and in applying the hammer treatment, engineers, for reasons historical, political and economic, constitute the core of latter-day social saviours. They have been designated the standard-bearers to "bring science and engineering, through technology, to bear more effectively on societal problems". In all fairness, therefore, we must take care lest we kill the messenger who brings bad tidings. Perhaps it is not the engineers who should be criticized for behaving true to form, in only doing what is asked of them. Perhaps we should look farther and direct our criticism to government agencies which should know better but which still perform the rites of the Cargo Cult.* This is the current activity of the prestigious and respected National Science Foundation and the General Accounting Office. The former, in a remarkable report, noteworthy for its ignorance of the performance of "the highly promising, sophisticated new methods . . . particularly systems analysis, computerization and the mathematical simulation in 'models' of the dynamics of complex problems" (National Science Foundation, 1972), is called upon to "formalize the participation of scientists or engineers" in "seeking solutions to the major problems confronting our people". Specifically, under terms of HR 15789 (July 1972) introduced by Rep. John Davis, a member of the House Committee on Science and Astronautics, there would be established a "Civil Science Systems Administration", with $25 million for 1973, $20 million for 1974 and $10 million for 1975. The descending scale presumably indicates that the national problems, pinpointed as "health care, poverty, public safety, pollution, unemployment, housing, education, transportation, nutrition, communications and energy resources", responded over time to the treatment! Out of this legislation there emerged "Public Technology, Inc.", developer of "Urban Technology System" and dedicated presumably to carrying out the Presidential mandate, high-minded and totally unworkable, used as a preface for the NSF report (Nixon, 1971):

> My colleagues in the Congress, America can be her true self only when she is engaged in a great enterprise.
>
> To build a full generation of peace is a great enterprise.

* The Cargo Cult is a tribal custom practised in the Melanesian Islands by natives who, having seen "silver birds" laden with treasure (cargo) materialize out of the sky after US Navy "Sea Bees" cleared the jungle for runways during World War II, still hack out the jungle and expect the "silver birds" to return.

To help the poor and feed the hungry, to provide better health and housing and education, to clean up the environment, to bring new dignity and security to the aging, to guarantee equal opportunity for every American – all these are great enterprises.

To build the strong economy that makes all these possible – to meet the new challenges of peace, to move to a new prosperity without war and without inflation – this truly is a great enterprise, worthy of our sacrifice, worthy of our cooperation and worthy of the greatness of a great people.

With disregard for the flaws of the systems approach in the management of the military establishment, its own home territory, the General Accounting Office furthered the cause of "great enterprises" by generating a report to Congress on "Means for Increasing the Use of Defense Technology for Urgent Public Problems" (Comptroller-General, 1972). Parroting the popular verbiage, instead of providing the critical inquiry more typical of its public service, the GAO explains why the inquiry has been undertaken:

The Congress and the President have expressed concern that greater application be made of the vast scientific and technological resources of the Federal Government – until now directed in large part to defense and space problems – to help solve massive sociological problems facing the United States.

Designated as target areas in *this* context are transportation, law enforcement, environmental protection, education, housing and urban development. The wishful thought embodied here is that this effort will yield the following benefits: "nondefense markets should evolve and the conversion could have a favourable impact on employment, the domestic economy, and the international trade balance" (Comptroller-General, 1972)!

The roster of problems grows in length and in complexity. Does the state-of-the-art advance commensurately? I think not. Even the cliché that caused so much of the cult has now been called into question. The nation that could put a man on the moon could ensure the technical performance of the hardware but created havoc in personal lives and emotional upheaval beyond repair. Life stories of astronauts subsequent to their return to terrestrial pursuits attest to the damage, recondite but real, incalculable but important, caused by these exploits (Aldrin, 1973). Mathematical precocity has saddled us with outrageously costly programmes that assure neither peace nor prosperity; technical virtuosity continues to bedazzle the uninitiated and to subvert social planning. We have been hoisted on our own petard. We welcomed technical solutions because ours is a technological era, because we interpreted our problems as being technological, and because we imputed to technology the capability of solving them.

Systems analysis as technique for solving social problems

If we had examined the techniques divested of all the rationalizations, we might have recognized earlier that they simply were not appropriate to the myriad of social tasks to which they were being assigned. In order for the desired technological transfer to take place, certain conditions had to be met and certain assumptions about systems made explicit. In engineering, the application of systems analysis to a problem is predicated on knowledge of a family of parameters that describe and define that system in precise terms. Built in here is explicit recognition of a set of values of those parameters at which the system performs optimally (Silver, 1969). In social planning, there exist neither undisputed parameters nor uncontrovertible criteria. Quite the contrary. These lie only in the eye of the beholder, and thus are subject to the most biased interpretations and manipulation. The evidence indicates that the "new utopia" (Boguslaw, 1965) created by engineers may not be the best of all possible worlds.

Moreover, some of the piles on which the case for technology transfer has depended have been systematically demolished by careful and methodical analysis. Professor L. A. Zadeh of the Electronics Research Laboratory of the University of California's College of Engineering contends that the capacity for dealing with complexity, the main selling point for systems analysis as practised in engineering, just does not exist. Instead, as the complexity of a system increases, "our ability to make precise and yet significant statements about its behaviour diminishes until a threshold is reached beyond which precision and significance (or relevance) become almost *mutually exclusive characteristics* (emphasis added). It is in this sense that precise quantitative analyses of the behaviour of humanistic systems are not likely to have much relevance to the real-world societal, political, economic and other types of problems which involve humans whether as individuals or in groups" (Zadeh, 1972). From his observations, Zadeh has developed what he calls the *principle of incompatibility*, to describe the intrinsic unsuitability of the conventional quantitative techniques of systems analysis for dealing with complex real-life social problems.

The incompatibilities are underscored by Robert A. Frosch (then Assistant Secretary of the US Navy) in a series of antitheses that "pit the systems world against some aspects of the real world" (Frosch, 1969). In so doing, Dr Frosch disencumbers the loaded argument that the *approach* is good and that only the uses are faulty.

> To the charge that I am writing about bad systems engineering, I can only say that I am taking a pragmatic view. The thing is defined by what is done, not what is said; and if what I am describing is bad systems engineering, I can only say that I seldom see any other kind.

He demonstrates that these techniques are proving to be

> a poor substitute for real science and engineering. They are at the least, not doing what they are advertised as doing, if they are not *making things worse*. It could be that things would be even worse without these new techniques, but I would like to ask some questions and suggest some reasons for believing that systems engineering, systems analysis, and management, as practised, are likely to be part of the problem, and indeed causative agents.

We consider ourselves to be a rational people. We are comfortable with the simplistic simulations of the first step in systems analysis and choose to ignore the implications of Zadeh's and Frosch's contributions. Our technologically bemused society might do well, in this regard, to heed Banquo's observations on the witches' performance:

> And often times, to win us to our harm
> The instruments of darkness tell us truths,
> Win us with honest trifles, to betray us in deepest
> consequence. (*Macbeth*, Act I, Sc. IV.)

References

Aldrin, E. E. (1973) *Return to Earth,* Random House, New York.

Boguslaw, R. (1965) *The New Utopians,* Prentice-Hall, Englewood Cliffs, NJ.

Comptroller-General of the United States (1972) *Means for Increasing the Use of Defense Technology for Urgent Public Problems,* General Accounting Office, B-175132, 29th December.

Evans, W. M. (1976) "The engineering profession: a cross-cultural analysis", from a chapter in Perrucci, R. and Gerstl, J. (eds.), *The Engineer and the Social System*, John Wiley, New York.

Frosch, R. A. (1969) "A new look at systems engineering", *I.E.E.E. Spectrum,* September 1969, 24–28.

Haas, E. B. and Ruggie, J. G. (1975) "International technology and international action: who, how and why", *International Organization* **29** (3), Summer 1975.

Kuhn, T. S. (1971) *The Structure of Scientific Revolution,* 3rd impression, University of Chicago Press, Chicago.

Lipset, S. M. and Ladd, E. C. (1972) "Politics of academic natural scientists and engineers", *Science* **176,** 9th June, 1972.

London, M. P. (1971) "Defects in medical electronics draw heavy fire from hospitals", *Electronic Design,* 28th October, 1971, 22–26.

Maslow, A. (1966) *The Psychology of Science: A Reconnaissance,* Harper & Row, New York.

National Science Foundation (1972) Report of the National Science Board, *The Role of Engineers and Scientists in a National Policy for Technology,* National Science Foundation, Washington D.C., p. 5.

National Society of Professional Engineers (1962) *Ethics for Engineers: Canons of Ethics, Creed & Rules of Professional Conduct,* National Society of Professional Engineers, Washington D.C.

New York Times (1973) "Professor urges oath for engineers", 9th October, 1973.

Nixon, President Richard M. (1971) Speaking before a joint session of Congress, 9th September, 1971.

Silver, S. (1969) "Science and technology", *Science Journal* **5A**(4), October 1969, 39–44.

Smithers, A. (1969) "Occupational values of students", *Nature* **222,** 24th May, 1969.

Snow, C. P. (1954) *The New Men,* Macmillan, London.

Zadeh, L. A. (1972) "Outline of a new approach to the analysis of complex systems and decision processes", Memorandum no. ERL-M342, University of California, College of Engineering, Berkeley, Calif.

Reprinted from I. R. Hoos, "Engineers as analysts of social systems – a critical enquiry", *Journal of Systems Engineering* (1976) vol. 4, no. 2.

Glossary of technical terms

Allometry The relative growth of a part in relation to an entire organism; the measure and study of such growth.

Anabolism (see *Metabolism*) The reassembly (of the results of catabolism) into complex molecules.

Autotroph An organism which is independent of outside sources of organic substances for the provision of its own organic constituents. It can manufacture its own organic substances from inorganic material. Normally used to refer to an organism which obtains its energy supply directly from the sun by means of photosynthesis.

Biomass The living mass of an animal or plant population.

Catabolism (see *Metabolism*) The breaking down of food materials into simple molecules.

Determinism The doctrine that all things, including the will, are determined by causes.

Deterministic Having a specific outcome or where outcomes must follow from specific courses of action or inputs (cf. stochastic).

Empirical Gained from experience and not based on theory.

Entropy A form of energy represented by the degree of order in which matter is arranged. The entropy of a system is a measure of its degree of *dis*order. To reduce entropy requires an input of energy. The natural tendency of all matter is for its entropy to increase.

Epistemology The theory of knowledge.

Ergonomics The study of tasks in relation to the environment in which they are performed and the personnel who perform them, and the application of scientific knowledge to the improvement of efficiency.

Ethology The study of animal behaviour, usually with particular reference to observation of the natural behaviour.

Field theory Method of analysis in behavioural science that describes actions or events as the resultant of dynamic interplay among sociocultural, biomechanical and motivational forces.

Fiscal Pertaining to the public treasury.

Functionalism (1) Doctrine or practice which emphasizes practical utility or functional relations. (2) Theory of culture which analyzes the interrelatedness and interdependence of patterns and institutions within a cultural complex or social system and emphasizes the interaction of these forms in the maintenance of sociocultural unity.

Gemütlich Good-natured, genial, easy-going.

Gestalt Organized whole. Gestalt psychology – a type of psychology which contends that mental processes and behaviour cannot be analyzed into elementary units since wholeness and organization are features of such processes.

Heterotroph An organism requiring a supply of organic material (food) from its environment from which to make most of its own organic constituents. Depends ultimately on synthetic activities of autotrophic (q.v.) organisms. All animals and fungi, most bacteria and a few plants are heterotrophs.

Heuristic Serving to guide, discover or reveal. Used of a method which is unproved or incapable of proof; trial and error.

Hill climbing A method of finding the highest or lowest values of a function of many variables, by changing individual variables and noting the effect.

Idiograph A private mark, trademark.

Isomorphism Similarity or identity in form.

Iteration Repeated application of a procedure or method.

Metabolism The sum total of the chemical and physical changes constantly taking place in living matter.

Morphology   The (study of the) structure and form of organisms.

Nomothetic   Relating to the formulation of laws.

Non-parametric statistics   A class of statistical methods applicable to a large set of probability distributions used to test for correlation, independence, etc.

Ontogenesis   The history of the development of an individual organism.

Operations research (Operational research)   The application of the methods of science to complex problems arising in the management of large systems of men, machines, materials and money in industry, business, government and defence.

Optimization   Finding the "best" solution or situation in terms of some stated criteria; devising a means of meeting the largest possible combination of ranked goals.

Paradigm   An intellectual framework.

Parameter   A variable in terms of which it is convenient to express other variables, which may then be regarded as being dependent on that parameter.

Phylogenesis   The evolutionary development of any organic type, species or race.

Physiognomy   The characteristic appearance of a plant community, by which it can often be recognized at a distance. Also applied to the arrangement of facial features.

Phytosociology   Branch of botany comprising ecology (relationship between organism and its surroundings), chorology (biogeography) and genetics (hereditary and variation) of plant associations.

Poikilothermic   Cold-blooded, i.e., having a body temperature which is dependent on the environmental temperature.

Positivism   The doctrine that man can have no knowledge of anything but what he sees and that what he infers from observation is opinion and not knowledge.

Recursive   A procedure which includes itself within the procedure; (of a definition) consisting of rules which allow values or meaning to be determined with certainty.

Reductionism   A doctrine in which explanations are sought in terms of events that operate at a "lower" level, e.g., the behaviour of a cell is sought in terms of the properties and behaviour of cell constituents and so on down to subatomic level.

Relaxation-oscillation   An oscillation that consists of a build-up of displacement followed by a sudden release of the displaced system.

Simulation   An operational model of a system which should be able to reproduce many aspects of the actual behaviour of the real system.

Skinner box   A box from which an animal cannot escape, provided with objects whose manipulation by the animal is followed, often automatically, by a reward.

Somatic   Pertaining to the body.

S–R   Stimulus–response.

Stochastic   Having a *probability* attached to it. A stochastic process is one where the next event is probabilistically related to previous events.

Suboptimization   From Jenkins: optimization of a subsystem. Used more loosely to describe a less-than-best solution.

Teleological   The doctrine of final causes or of adaptation to a definite purpose. Loosely, the idea that future states or goals can affect current behaviour.

Time constant   The time required for a physical quantity, which varies exponentially with time, to rise from zero to $1-1/e$ (i.e., 63%) of its final steady value. More loosely, the time required for a system output to reach a given percentage of its final value after a change in an input is made.

Transfer function   A mathematical expression relating the output of a closed-loop system or subsystem to its input.

Tropism   Orientation in response to stimulus.

Veridical   Truth-telling.

Vitalism   The doctrine that there is a principle that gives life to all nature, a non-physical inner force called "vital force".

Index